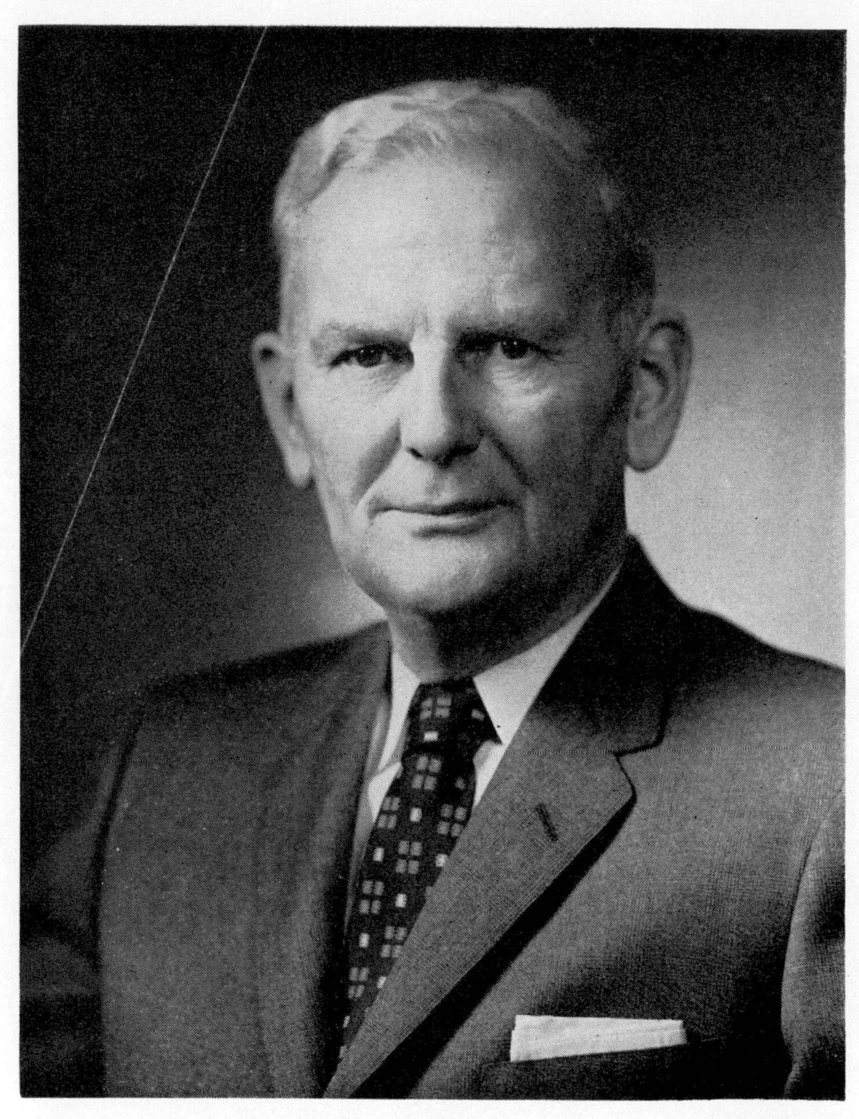

Fabian Bachrach

Benjamin H. Willier

A Symposium on

THE CHEMICAL BASIS OF DEVELOPMENT

Sponsored by

THE
McCOLLUM-PRATT INSTITUTE
OF
THE JOHNS HOPKINS UNIVERSITY
with support from
THE NATIONAL SCIENCE FOUNDATION

Edited by

WILLIAM D. McELROY AND BENTLEY GLASS

BALTIMORE
THE JOHNS HOPKINS PRESS
1958

PREVIOUS SYMPOSIA OF THE McCOLLUM-PRATT INSTITUTE

Copper Metabolism—A Symposium on Animal, Plant and Soil Relationships.

Phosphorus Metabolism—A Symposium on the Role of Phosphorus in the Metabolism of Plants and Animals, Vol. I.

Phosphorus Metabolism—A Symposium on the Role of Phosphorus in the Metabolism of Plants and Animals, Vol. II.

The Mechanism of Enzyme Action.

Amino Acid Metabolism.

Inorganic Nitrogen Metabolism.

The Chemical Basis of Heredity.

Distributed in Great Britain by: Oxford University Press, London. Printed in the United States of America by The Colonial Press Inc., Clinton, Mass.

The Library of Congress catalog entry for this book appears at the end of the text.

PREFACE

A Symposium on the Chemical Basis of Development was held at The Johns Hopkins University under the sponsorship of the McCollum-Pratt Institute on March 24–27, 1958. This volume consists of the papers and informal discussions presented during the Symposium.

The present volume is in many ways a logical sequel to the preceding volume on the Chemical Basis of Heredity which was the published account of the Symposium held in 1956. Developmental biology encompasses a wide range of problems dealing with both the initiation and the progression of sequences of events that lead to the emergence of adult characteristics. The genes, at the focus of studies in heredity, partake directly or indirectly in all these events involved in development. Thus the chemical basis of development can be viewed as an elaboration or expression of the chemical basis of heredity.

In the planning of the present Symposium we attempted to bring together those biologists and biochemists who had made observations which might help in explaining some of the chemical aspects of growth and differentiation. By facilitating an exchange of information among the various disciplines represented at the Symposium we can surely expect to increase the rate of progress in this important area of biology.

I should like to acknowledge the active participation of the members of the McCollum-Pratt Institute and of the Biology Department in the planning of the Symposium in honor of Professor B. H. Willier for his distinguished contributions as teacher and investigator in developmental biology. It is also a pleasure to acknowledge the valuable contributions of the following moderators: Dr. Jean Brachet, Dr. Johannes Holtfreter, Dr. Elmer Butler, Dr. Louis Flexner and Dr. Viktor Hamburger. We also wish to thank Dr. Paul Weiss for his summation and evaluation of the contributions as well as of the role of the Symposium in furthering progress in the science of developmental biology.

Through the generous aid of the National Science Foundation it was possible to support a number of foreign investigators as participants in the Symposium. Unfortunately, there were many that we were unable to

invite because of inadequate funds. We hope, however, that the published book will be of value to all who are interested in developmental biology and in particular to those who were unable to attend the Symposium.

W. D. McElroy
Director of McCollum-Pratt Institute

CONTENTS

Part I

DEVELOPMENTAL CYTOLOGY

CHEMICAL CONCEPTS OF CELLULAR DIFFERENTIATION

Clement L. Markert

Department of Biology
Johns Hopkins University

In a symposium devoted to the chemical basis of development, it is perhaps appropriate that the first report should make a general assessment of the significance of our topic. Biological phenomena, though closely interrelated, are for purposes of study and investigation assignable to one or more of the major disciplines of biology, each concerned with a significant attribute of living systems: their structure, function, ecological relationships, evolutionary history, heredity, and development. Of these, the field of development has been relatively slighted despite the tremendous importance of developmental processes in characterizing living organisms. No doubt part of the lack of attention stems from the manifest difficulty inherent in any analysis of development. The nature of this problem was stated very well by Ross G. Harrison (16) more than 30 years ago in his presidential address to the American Society of Zoologists. He said:

"The living embryo changes continually; its form, its mechanisms and its functions change; its parts function while changing. These transformations are themselves functions. We have, then, superposed on the ordinary functions of nutrition, respiration, protoplasmic and nervous transmission, action of internal secretions circulating in the internal medium, etc., a whole system of developmental functions, which, as far as we have been able to find out, are totally different from the former. The embryologist has, therefore, a problem of a higher order of complexity—a superproblem—to contend with than has he who directs his attention to the study of the structure or function of the finished organism.

"This is usually overlooked. Embryology, from its close relation to comparative anatomy and from the employment of schemata to represent its processes, came to bear the reproach of physiologists that it was a morphological science and on that account dealt with statics and not kinetics. A moment's consideration shows this view to be altogether erroneous. The

organism never reaches a state of rest until it has run its course or is securely preserved in a bottle. The physiologist accepts the finished organism as given and endeavors to find out how it works. The embryologist, on the other hand, attempts to show the origin of the mechanisms which the physiologist is content to accept ready made for study. May not the embryologist, then, return the reproach and say that the physiologist is merely looking for something easy to do?"

These words of Harrison properly emphasize the difficulties inherent in embryological investigations, but they do not make clear the indispensable role of physiologists and biochemists in providing the essential tools and information with which to analyze development in chemical terms.

Since the development of the organism is dependent upon the organization and development of its parts, it is possible to study development and differentiation on several levels of physical and chemical organization. These levels of organization are reflected in the titles of the reports to be delivered here. We may not forget, however, that no description of structure or function, however sophisticated it may be, is truly developmental biology, for development is primarily concerned with the transformation of one condition into another. Although the structural and functional characteristics of each successive embryonic state are inseparable from the mechanisms that transform them, it is the vectorial qualities of embryonic states on which developmental biologists must focus attention. It is doubtful that transformations at these various levels of organization can be comprehended within a single mechanism, and the relationships that must exist between changes on the simpler levels of organization—on a molecular level, for example—and developmental processes at the more complex levels of organization of cells, tissues, and organs, are at present completely obscure.

Nevertheless, there is a strong desire to interpret complex developmental events in terms of simpler antecedent events and eventually in terms of molecular changes (41, 42). The closely allied field of genetics affords us hope in aspiring to make such interpretations because identified genetic characters (like those concerned in development) range through all levels of physical and chemical organization, from the entire organism to cytoplasmic inclusions and chromosome morphology. Furthermore, in developmental genetics we have been able on occasion to trace gross effects back to simpler morphological and/or chemical events. Some genetic characters may be traced to the synthesis of, or to the failure to synthesize, specific protein molecules, and thence to the gene. Genetically controlled complex characters are attributed to antecedent interactions at lower levels

of organization, and therefore analysis involves the unravelling of these patterns of interaction which depend upon such variables as effective concentrations of substances, relative rates of reactions, and the timing or programming of events. Although the problems of interpretation may prove extraordinarily complicated in physiological genetics, no serious conceptual difficulties appear to exist. Granted initial qualitative differences at the gene and molecular levels, subsequent variations follow logically.

We may note that the analysis of such patterns of interaction involve two distinct aspects which may be as applicable to development as to genetics: (1) the characteristics of individual genes and the initial elementary events for which they are responsible, and (2) the interactions of products of genic activity which yield the wide array of metabolic patterns characterizing the specialized cells and tissues of the emerging adult organism. In physiological genetics the initial gene changes are the raw materials that make the science possible, but in the study of normal development no such simple, causal, fundamental event can yet be discerned. However, an effort has been made to overcome this difficulty, conceptually at least, by making the activity of genes during development dependent upon the physical and chemical environment in the cell—an environment for which the genes themselves are largely responsible. A sort of cyclical feedback is visualized between the genome and its ever-changing chemical environment so that the changing interactions between gene and environment provide the motive power for driving embryonic cells along their diverse paths of differentiation (48). Although this way of viewing embryonic development seems logically sound, it is not very informative and reduces studies of embryonic change to problems in metabolic complexity. Even so, there are numerous points of observational and experimental attack within such a conceptual framework.

Ontogeny of Metabolic Patterns

The characteristic metabolic pattern of cells and tissues at any stage of differentiation may be analyzed in terms of the substances present at any given time (8) or in terms of the substances produced during a defined period of development (24). A wide variety of substances—simple and complex—have been identified and measured in various parts of embryos in an effort to provide a biochemical description of development. Enzymes have been prime objects of study (10, 15, 27, 34) because of their decisive position in the metabolic machinery of the cell, but the products of enzymatic activity have also been studied both for their own significance and as indicators of enzyme activity. To a substantial degree the state of

differentiation of a cell is a reflection of the pattern of its enzymatic composition (35), and the progress of differentiation depends upon mechanisms for changing effective enzyme concentrations in cells. Two problems appear here: (1) the origin of enzymatic activity; and (2) the regulation of the amount of activity. These two problems may relate to different aspects of a single mechanism, but at present this seems unlikely.

Adaptive Enzyme Synthesis in Embryos

One notion commonly advanced to account for the effective origin of new enzymatic activity is that of adaptive enzyme synthesis (7, 26). This notion is attractive because it makes simple variations in the chemical environment of cells adequate to account for their changing enzymatic content and therefore for their differentiation. Unfortunately, there is very little direct experimental evidence from embryos to support this notion (11, 12, 19, 20). Its general significance in embryos is severely limited by the fact that embryonic cells of different types do not develop the same additional enzyme even when placed in identical chemical or tissue environments. Thus, though mechanisms for enzyme induction may exist in embryos, such mechanisms do not account for the diverse capacities of cells to respond. The origin of these divergent capacities for enzyme synthesis is the more fundamental problem in development, with the elicitation of response of secondary significance.

Embryonic Induction

The origin of metabolic capacities is in part due to that interaction between tissues in development commonly known as embryonic induction. This type of interaction probably involves the passage of specific substances from inducing to reacting tissues (14, 29), but more than simple chemical exchange may be required, at least in some types of induction (13, 44). The inductive stimuli are of limited duration and are exerted over short distances by specific tissues at specific periods in their development. Only particular tissues at receptive stages in their development are competent to react to a given stimulus. Other tissues remain indifferent. The transmitted substances involved in some types of induction appear to be proteins, as shown by the work of Toivonen (39), Kuusi (22, 23), Niu (28, 29), Yamada (49), and others. Although embryonic induction may result in the synthesis of new enzymes, the mechanism of embryonic induction does not seem equivalent to that of enzyme induction.

Role of the Chemical Environment in Differentiation and Maintenance

Leaving aside the specific problem of adaptive enzyme synthesis, there is little doubt that the chemical environment of differentiating and already differentiated cells is of great importance in the development and maintenance of specific characters. Embryonic cells explained to cultures in vitro do not readily continue their differentiation, and mature cells cultivated in vitro (45) commonly lose much of their specialized metabolic machinery. Furthermore, the nutritional requirements and synthetic activities of cells in vitro are to some extent dependent upon the structure of the population of which they are a part (33)—thus indicating the importance of mutual interaction in regulating the chemical environment for developing cells in vivo. The interaction of cells is to a substantial degree mediated through surface contact and is dependent upon the specific properties of the cell surface (41, 42, 43, 44). These surface specificities are reflections of the metabolic pattern of the cell and are responsible for defining the structure of the cell population of any tissue and for regulating the relationships between tissues. The particular association into which any cell enters of course limits the type of cellular (and chemical) environment to which it will be exposed; the changing chemical properties of the environment then further modify cellular metabolism to alter surface specificities which compel the regrouping of cells into new associations.

This sensitivity of the metabolic pattern in cells to the chemical environment has stimulated extensive research on the developmental effects of a wide variety of chemical substances—nutrients, antimetabolites, enzyme inhibitors, antibodies, tissue extracts, etc. These substances are generally used to produce a kind of metabolic deletion or addition experiment. If development is significantly altered by such chemical intervention, then one may hope to identify chemical events that are decisive for the type of development studied. The rationale for this type of investigation assumes that the metabolic pattern of the cell is a steady state that may be shifted to alternate steady states by enhancing or repressing strategically placed reactions. Although mechanisms for transforming steady states have been presented in plausible form by several investigators, none of these model mechanisms has been demonstrated to operate in developing embryos. However, several biochemical mechanisms have been described that help to maintain a metabolic steady state (48). Specifically, metabolic stability may be achieved by feedback controls involving products and enzymes within a single chain of reactions (40) and by similar, though more com-

plex, interactions between different chains of reactions. Such mechanisms offer exciting prospects for analyzing chemical processes in developing embryos, although the four-dimensional web of events that constitutes embryonic development is far more complex than the metabolic patterns studied so successfully in microorganisms.

Genetic Control of Development

Let us turn now to the primary material of physiological genetics mentioned previously—that is, the genome of the cell. Just as adult characters are gene-controlled, so also of necessity are the developmental steps which produced them (37). A goal in developmental genetics is the identification of the primary effect of a gene change that leads to an alteration in development. Enough progress has been made to demonstrate the multifarious consequences in development of changing the initial activity of a gene (36), but the primary or even derived chemical consequences of gene function still escape detection in almost every case. All stages of development at various levels of organization and all major components of an interacting system, as well as the identified mechanisms of their interaction, have been shown to depend upon genic activity. The capacity of cells to respond or to elaborate inductive stimuli, or to synthesize a given enzyme and carry out a biochemical reaction, or even to acquire particular asymmetries of organization, have all been related to single gene changes. Does not the truly impressive data of developmental genetics enable us to assume that integrated developmental events are no more than the expression of a corresponding integrated pattern of primary genic activity (48)? If so, developmental phenomena will ultimately be analyzed in terms of mechanisms controlling genic activity. All else would then be mere derivative superstructure. An alternative and still tenable view is that developmental phenomena are superimposed upon a foundation of uniform primary genic activity in all cells. The effectiveness of a given gene would then depend upon the characteristics of its chemical environment rather than upon the gene itself. This view receives some support from the precision of mitotic phenomena that seem to guarantee each metazoan cell an identical genetic endowment from the fertilized egg. That is, all the cells of an organism, through this mechanism, should have the same genes.

Gene Function

The concept that all potential genes in every cell function continuously or even intermittently seems very doubtful, since numerous cellular functions known to be genetically controlled are apparently restricted to only

certain specialized cells and cannot be detected in most cells of an organism. The gene controlling the ability to synthesize the enzyme tyrosinase will serve as an example. Animals with mutant, inactive forms of this gene cannot synthesize tyrosinase, therefore make no melanin pigment, and consequently become albinos. However, in a normal animal only the melanin-synthesizing cells give any evidence of possessing a gene for tyrosinase synthesis. The remaining cells are indistinguishable from the corresponding cells of an albino animal. If geneticists had only mammalian eggs to work with, it is doubtful that they ever would have recognized the gene for tyrosinase synthesis. This points up the fact that apparent gene function is dependent upon the state of differentiation of the cell and in its turn the state of differentiation at any time is dependent upon the integrated pattern of previous gene activity.

An illustration of this reciprocal relationship is provided by the genes for pink eye in the house mouse (25). When genes for pink eye are present in the pigment-forming cells of the mouse (that is, in the migratory melanoblasts that produce melanin pigment when the cell resides in an appropriate cellular environment), the melanin granules formed have an abnormal structure. Thus these genes control the characteristic expression, pigment granule synthesis, of this type of cellular differentiation. More important, however, is the fact that these same genes prevent the harderian gland of the mouse from providing its usual favorable environment for melanoblast differentiation. In all other respects the harderian gland appears normal, but no pigment cells are able to reach maturity within this gland of pink-eye mice. Other tissues of these mice, despite the presence of genes for pink eye, do retain the capacity to elicit melanoblast differentiation—the cells of the hair papilla, for example. These observations indicate that the effect of a gene on a particular step in differentiation is dependent upon the metabolic pattern of the cell (its state of differentiation)—a pattern which in its turn is dependent upon all the previous effective influences exerted upon the cell both from within and without. The role of genes in melanoblast differentiation and in the formation of pigment patterns has previously been clearly analyzed and demonstrated also in the domestic fowl (46, 47).

In mice, we do not know the initial function of the genes for pink eye, but this function, whatever it may be, ultimately affects quite different steps in the differentiation of a variety of cell types. On the other hand, the gene for tyrosinase synthesis (and this may be its primary function) affects only a terminal step in differentiation of a single cell type. No other effect of this gene has been observed, and the simplest interpretation

is that this gene does not function in other cell types. In this example we have been relating a functional gene to the production of a specific molecule—specifically, a protein enzyme. A vast amount of genetic data supports this gene–enzyme relationship (17). And a growing body of data now relates the enzymatic content of embryonic cells to their state of differentiation (27, 34). We will hear more of this later in the symposium, but I should like briefly to present the results of one such investigation on the esterases of developing mouse tissues.

Ontogeny of Esterases

The esterases investigated are concerned with the hydrolysis of carboxylic acid esters of phenols. There is a large number of such esterases, perhaps twenty, that together constitute a family of enzymes of overlapping specificities. These esterases may readily be separated from one another by electrophoresis in starch gels and individually identified by their electrophoretic mobility, and their substrate and inhibition specificities (18). Each adult tissue exhibits its own distinctive repertory of these esterases arranged in characteristic relative concentrations. During embryonic and early post-natal development the esterases appear one after another as the tissue reaches new stages of differentiation, until finally the repertory is completed at the time the tissue reaches maturity. Furthermore, electrophoretically homologous esterases from different tissues are alike in their substrate and inhibition specificities. If each of these esterases represents the primary activity of a different gene, then the characteristic esterase pattern of different tissues reflects the particular array of esterase genes activated in that tissue during the course of differentiation. Since the relative and absolute concentration of any particular esterase varies in different tissues, the specific effects of the esterase genes must be subject to quantitative modification by metabolic activities of the tissue.

Biophysical Aspects of Development

Before concluding this discussion of the genic control of the chemical basis of development we should note another important aspect of developing organisms—an aspect more properly classified under biophysics than under biochemistry. This aspect relates to the movement and organization of organs, tissues, cells, subcellular entities, and intercellular materials. This changing physical organization of developing embryos and their parts cannot at present be explained in chemical terms, nor have we even elucidated the primary physical factors involved. One need only recall our inability to explain the movement of chromosomes, or of migratory cells,

despite extensive investigation, in order to emphasize both the importance and the difficulty of analyzing the physical changes in differentiating cells and tissues. But even in this biophysical area of development the genes have indicated their masterful role. The organization of the eggs of the snail, *Lymnaea,* is such that cleavage is asymmetrical, the spindle being tilted to one side. As the egg divides, the planes of cleavage are alternately tilted in opposite directions to produce a spiral organization of the resulting blastomeres. This cleavage pattern is reflected in the direction of spiral in the shell of the resulting adult snail and may be either left-handed or right-handed. The potential direction of spiral is fixed in the egg organization by the maternal organism in accord with her own genotype. Only a single gene appears to be involved (5, 9, 38). This example, though it tells us nothing about primary gene activity, indicates gene control of basic cell structure, perhaps of course through controlling elementary chemical reactions.

Differential Gene Activation in Differentiation

To return now to the general relationship between genes and developmental events, the preferred viewpoint in this presentation has pictured a cell, when subjected to differentiating stimuli, as responding through the activation of a gene which then initiates a new reaction. Perhaps, on occasion, genes are also deactivated. At least differentiated cells, when explanted to tissue culture, after repeated multiplication in this disorganized environment lose some of their enzymes (31). This loss may be interpreted as a failure to maintain the responsible genes in an activated state during repeated cell divisions. An adequate description of differentiation must account not only for the origin of differences among cells but also for the persistence of these differences through many cell generations. Although relatively persistent, the characteristics of differentiated cells are not uniformly stable. When put to the test by growth in abnormal tissue culture environments some properties are readily lost while others persist, perhaps in conformity with the new pattern of stimuli from the culture environment. However, it should be noted that even after prolonged culture for many months in identical media, originally distinct cell types remain distinct from one another. The cell is not just a reflection of the current attributes of the environment, whatever they may be, but rather the cell reacts to changed conditions in a distinctive fashion determined by its own characteristics. In the absence of cell division the differentiated properties of cells are more stable and this is not surprising if genic activation is fundamental to cellular differentiation, for the replication of genes

would pose additional problems in the retention and replication of the activated state of the gene as contrasted with the inactive state.

A more serious problem in making genic activation fundamental is the mutual exclusiveness of diverging paths of differentiation. The acquisition of one character commonly excludes an alternative. On the level of genes it is difficult to visualize a simple mechanism by which the activation of one gene would preclude the activation of another. Perhaps there are also mechanisms for specifically inhibiting genes so as to render them inaccessible to activating mechanisms.

If differential genic activation does occur during cellular differentiation, then this should be reflected in a gradual differentiation of the chromosomes. Such a mechanism of differentiation should be most welcome, since it would provide developmental biologists with a simple elementary event —genic activation—with which to work in analyzing development. Part of the great success of genetics and biochemistry must surely stem from the fact that these disciplines are able to focus on elementary events—gene changes or biochemical reactions—and are not bemused by the complexities flowing from these elementary events.

Chromosomal Differentiation

But do we have any evidence for believing that genic activation or chromosomal differentiation does in fact occur? Later reports will deal specifically with differentiation at subcellular levels, and no extended comments of mine would be in order now. However, at least three lines of evidence can be brought to bear on this issue, and I should like to describe them briefly. First, the recent work of King and Briggs (21) on nuclear transplantation lends strong support to the view that the nucleus (and inferentially the chromosomes) differentiate during development. These investigators transplanted nuclei from frog embryonic cells at various stages of differentiation into enucleated frog eggs. The subsequent development of these eggs measures the capacities of the transplanted nuclei. Nuclei from cells in early stages of development proved equivalent in developmental capacity to an egg nucleus—that is, normal animals developed from eggs containing such transplanted nuclei. However, nuclei from progressively later stages of development gave rise to an increasing proportion of abnormal embryos. Most significantly, the nature of these abnormalities was correlated with the state of differentiation of the cell furnishing the donor nucleus. Upon serial retransplantation of nuclei from these abnormal embryos the same pattern of abnormal development was

observed in the succeeding generations. Thus differentiated nuclear characteristics had become fixed and transmissible through repeated nuclear division. It seems likely that non-replicating parts of the nucleus would have been diluted out during these many divisions, leaving the chromosomes as most probably the bearers of the fixed, differentiated characteristics of the nucleus.

The second line of evidence stems from the observations of Pavan (6, 30) and of Beermann (4) on the chromosomes in the larval tissues of certain insects. These chromosomes display an intricate and characteristic banding pattern. During development this banding pattern is modified by the temporary appearance along the chromosome of greatly enlarged areas known as Balbiani rings. The occurrence and distribution of these rings along the chromosomes is specific for both the tissue and its stage of development. Probably these rings indicate areas of more active chromosomal function, but in any event, the chromosome morphology varies, and in a fashion that is characteristic of the stage of cellular differentiation. We may thus conclude that these chromosomes are themselves differentiated.

The third line of evidence is based upon direct chemical analysis of nuclei and chromosomes from various differentiated cells or tissues (1, 2, 3). These analyses reveal four principal constituents in chromosomes: (1) deoxyribonucleic acid, (2) ribonucleic acid, (3) histones, and (4) residual protein. The DNA remains constant, as would be expected, but the RNA varies considerably in amount not only between different tissues but also within the same tissue at different levels of physiological activity. Analysis of histones reveals no striking differences (except in gametes); but residual protein does vary in different tissues. Taken together, these analyses strongly suggest that chromosomes undergo chemical differentiation in accord with the functional requirements of the differentiating cell (32).

Hypothesis of Development

This sketchy survey of various aspects of the chemical basis of development, with particular emphasis on the role of the genes, may be concluded with the presentation of a working hypothesis that compounds old and new speculation to explain the changing sequence of metabolic patterns that characterizes cellular differentiation. The hypothesis may be described in four parts:

(1) The newly fertilized egg contains chromosomes that are undifferentiated with reference to those functions that will later distinguish and

characterize differentiated cells. The egg is endowed at the outset with an unstable pattern of metabolic activities that begins to change in distinctive ways in different regions of the egg.

(2) As cleavage proceeds, the chromosomes in various regions of the embryo are subjected to different chemical environments. By some still obscure mechanisms specific metabolic patterns in the cell impose correspondingly specific proteins on the DNA of the chromosomes. The coupling of these proteins to specific regions of the DNA produces a functional nucleoprotein or activated gene. Previously this portion of the DNA was non-functional because of the absence of an essential protein complement.

(3) The creation of a functional gene during development would be reflected in a specific synthesis—an enzyme, for example. This new synthetic activity would change the metabolic pattern of the cell and would result in the activation of additional genes in the same cell or in adjacent cells. This cyclic interaction would stabilize when the metabolic pattern of the cell ceased to change or when the chromosomes were completely differentiated.

(4) Functional genes would display varying degrees of stability. Under conditions of artificially induced rapid proliferation, as in tissue culture, the maintenance of the differentiated structure of the chromosome through numerous replications would not always occur, and the cell would appear to dedifferentiate, to become simpler in the variety and specializations of its syntheses. In non-dividing adult cells a high order of stability would easily be maintained even in the face of chemical provocation to the cell, because the activated genes would remain unchanged by nonspecific variations in their chemical environment.

The observations and conclusions that I have discussed do not of course critically test this hypothesis. Perhaps pertinent evidence will be forthcoming in later papers, and in any event, if we are stimulated to take a closer look at chromosomes during development the hypothesis will have served a useful purpose. Speculation has frequently proved valuable, and we may confidently agree with Darwin when he said in a letter to Wallace, "I am a firm believer that without speculation there is no good or original observation."

REFERENCES

1. Allfrey, V. G., Mirsky, A. E., and Stern, H., *Advances in Enzymol.*, **16**, 411-500 (1955).
2. Allfrey, V., Mirsky, A. E., and Osawa, S., in *The Chemical Basis of Heredity* (McElroy, W. D., and B. Glass, eds.), p. 200-231, The Johns Hopkins Press, Baltimore (1956).

3. Allfrey, V., in *The Chemical Basis of Heredity* (McElroy, W. D., and B. Glass, eds.) p. 186-194, The Johns Hopkins Press, Baltimore (1956).
4. Beermann, W., *Cold Spring Harbor Symposia Quant. Biol.,* **21,** 217-232 (1956).
5. Boycott, A. E., and Diver, C., *Proc. Roy. Soc. (London), B,* **95,** 207-213 (1923).
6. Breuer, M. E., and Pavan, C., *Chromosoma,* **7,** 371-386 (1955).
7. Cohn, M., *Bacteriol. Revs.,* **21,** 140-168 (1957).
8. Deuchar, E. M., *J. Embryol. Exptl. Morphol.* **4,** 327-346 (1956).
9. Diver, C., Boycott, A. E., and Garstang, S., *J. Genet.,* **15,** 113-200 (1925).
10. Ephrussi, B., in *Enzymes: Units of Biological Structure and Function* (Gaebler, O. H., ed.), p. 29-40, Academic Press, New York (1956).
11. Gordon, M. W., in *Neurochemistry* (Korey, S. R., and Nurnberger, J. I., eds.), p. 83-100, Hoeber-Harper, New York (1956).
12. Gordon, M., and Roder, M., *J. Biol. Chem.,* **200,** 859-866 (1953).
13. Grobstein, C., *Advances in Cancer Research,* **4,** 187-236 (1956).
14. ———, and Dalton, A. J., *J. Exptl. Zool.,* **135,** 57-74 (1957).
15. Gustafson, T., *Intern. Rev. Cytol.,* **3,** 277-327 (1954).
16. Harrison, R. G., *Science,* **85,** 369-374 (1937).
17. Horowitz, N. H., *Federation Proc.,* **15,** 818-822 (1956).
18. Hunter, R. L., and Markert, C. L., *Science,* **125,** 1294-1295 (1957).
19. Jones, M., Featherstone, R. M., and Bonting, S. L., *J. Pharmacol. Exptl. Therap.,* **116,** 114-118 (1956).
20. Kato, Y., and Moog, F., *Science,* **127,** 812-813 (1958).
21. King, T. J., and Briggs, R., *Cold Spring Harbor Symposia Quant. Biol.,* **21,** 271-290 (1956).
22. Kuusi, T., *Ann. Zool. Soc. Zool. Botan. Fennicae Vanamo,* **14,** 1-98 (1951).
23. ———, *Arch. Soc. Zool. Botan. Fennicae Vanamo,* **12,** 73-93 (1957).
24. Markert, C. L., *Cold Spring Harbor Symposia Quant. Biol.,* **21,** 339-348 (1956).
25. ———, and Silvers, W. K., *Genetics,* **41,** 429-450 (1956).
26. Monod, J., in *Enzymes: Units of Biological Structure and Function* (Gaebler, O. H., ed.), p. 7-28, Academic Press, New York (1956).
27. Moog, F., *Ann. N. Y. Acad. Sci.,* **55,** 57-66 (1952).
28. Niu, M. C., *Anat. Record,* **122,** 420 (1955).
29. ———, in *Cellular Mechanisms of Differentiation and Growth* (Rudnick, D., ed.), p. 155-172, Princeton U. Press (1956).
30. Pavan, C., and Breuer, M. E., *Symposium on Cell Secretion* (G. Schreiber, ed.), p. 90-99, Univ. Minas Geraes, Belo Horizonte (1955).
31. Perske, W. F., Parks, Jr., R. E., and Walker, D. L., *Science,* **125,** 1290-1291 (1957).
32. Ris, H., in *The Chemical Basis of Heredity* (McElroy, W. D., and B. Glass, eds.), p. 23-62, Johns Hopkins Press, Baltimore (1956).
33. Sato, G., Fisher, H. W., and Puck, T. T., *Science,* **126,** 961-964 (1957).
34. Shen, S. C., in *Biological Specificity and Growth* (Butler, E. G., ed.), p. 73-92, Princeton Univ. Press (1955).
35. Spiegelman, S., *Symposia Soc. Exptl. Biol.,* **2,** 286-325 (1948).
36. Stern, C., *Am. Scientist,* **42,** 213-247 (1954).
37. ———, in *Analysis of Development* (Willier, B. H., Weiss, P., and Hamburger, V., eds.), p. 151-169, W. B. Saunders Co., Philadelphia (1955).
38. Sturtevant, A. H., *Science,* **58,** 269-270 (1923).
39. Toivonen, S., *J. Embryol. Exptl. Morphol.,* **2,** 239-244 (1954).
40. Vogel, H. J., in *The Chemical Basis of Heredity* (McElroy, W. D., and B. Glass, eds.), p. 276-289, The Johns Hopkins Press, Baltimore (1957).
41. Weiss, P., *Yale J. Biol. and Med.,* **19,** 235-278 (1947).
42. ———, in *The Chemistry and Physiology of Growth* (Parpart, A. K., ed.), p. 135-186, Princeton Univ. Press (1949).

43. ———, *Quart. Rev. Biol.,* **25,** 177-198 (1950).
44. ———, *J. Embryol. Exptl. Morphol.* **1,** 181-211 (1953).
45. White, P. R. (ed.), Decennial Review Conference on Tissue Culture, *J. Natl. Cancer Inst.,* **19,** 467-843 (1957).
46. Willier, B. H., and Rawles, M. E., *Genetics,* **29,** 309-330 (1944).
47. ———, and ———, *Yale J. Biol. and Med.,* **17,** 319-340 (1944).
48. Wright, S., *Am. Naturalist,* **79,** 289-303 (1945).
49. Yamada, T., and Takato, K., *Embryologia,* **3,** 69-79 (1956).

THE INITIATION OF DEVELOPMENT

R. D. Allen

Department of Biology
Princeton University

Although the general title of this paper would indicate a comprehensive coverage of fertilization, and of artificial and natural parthenogenesis, only certain limited aspects of these fields will be considered. In the last decade a number of reviews have appeared on the role of interacting substances in fertilization (116, 163, 202), the acrosome reaction (31, 46), cortical changes and the physiology of activation in the sea urchin (12, 174, 175, 177, 178, 181, 182) and in fish (222), and the block against polyspermy (63b, 162). The recent book, *Fertilization,* by Lord Rothschild (163), contains a wealth of information on many aspects of the initiation of development. The present account will cut across many of the subjects listed above in an effort to bring into focus some relationships between two of the central groups of processes leading to development: those events and processes leading toward syngamy, and those leading toward activation.

The present state of knowledge regarding fertilization and activation is such that the vast majority of papers deal with echinoderms. Only the barest beginnings have been made on investigation of other forms, except for fish (cf. 222 for references). For this reason, the present account will deal principally with the work done on sea urchins. However, an effort has been made to include considerable comparative material where promising leads may provide a stimulus to further research. In addition to sections on syngamy and activation, material has been included on the structure and chemistry of the surface layers of the egg, since this is basic to a discussion of surface changes preceding activation.

I. Processes Leading to Syngamy

1. The Acrosome Reaction

Although there have been scattered accounts of filamentous connections between the egg and spermatozoon prior to contact of the gametes at fertilization (22-24, 53), it was J. C. Dan who in a series of studies on a variety of echinoderms, mollusks, and annelids showed unequivocally that the acrosome region of the mature sperm could give rise to an acrosome filament (42-48, 215). Excellent reviews have appeared recently by Dan (46) and by Colwin and Colwin (31) in which the morphological details of acrosomal changes are discussed, along with information on some of the physiological conditions which elicit an acrosome reaction. No attempt will be made here to duplicate either the historical treatment or the descriptive accounts presented in these reviews. Rather, the present aim will be to summarize the principal features of the acrosome reaction which may have a direct bearing on the processes leading to syngamy and activation of the egg. Particular attention will be given to work which has appeared since the last reviews.

The main features of the acrosome reaction (46) are: (1) formation of a fibril from the acrosome region of the spermatozoon; (2) the release of some substance which immediately disperses; and (3) the lateral displacement of the middle-piece. Ultrathin sections viewed in the electron microscope have shown that the acrosome consists of two parts, an apical globule of electron-dense material, and a basal stalk which extends into an invagination of the nucleus (1; also 43, p. 58). During the acrosome reaction, two separate events seem to occur: (1) discharge of the substance of the apical globule; and (2) formation of the filament from the body of the acrosomal stalk (Afzelius et al., 3, 4). A similar conclusion was reached regarding the dual nature of the acrosome region in *Hydroides* by Colwin, Colwin, and Philpott (32, 33), who found a peripheral component which collapsed during the acrosome reaction, and a central component involved in the formation of the filament. In sections of heavily inseminated eggs, Afzelius and Murray (4) observed that all of the attached spermatozoa had undergone at least a partial reaction, with the acrosomal globule expelled; more often a complete reaction had occurred, including filament formation. The mechanism of the acrosome reaction is still unknown, but it is now certain from measurements of the nuclear invagination that the latter is not everted during the acrosome reaction (4).

The physiological conditions which call forth or are necessary for the

acrosome reaction have been listed in the review of Dan (46); they are summarized here with newer information added.

1. *Physiological maturity of the spermatozoa* seems to be an essential prerequisite for the acrosome reaction, as ascertained by studies of *Mytilus,* in which the time of natural spawning could be determined (48).

2. *The presence of calcium* in the medium is required for echinoderm sperm to exhibit an acrosome reaction; however, the sperm agglutinates if jelly is added. Agglutinated sperm did not show reduced fertilizing capacity, an observation suggesting that the normal action of the jelly was due not to "muzzling" of sperm by fertilizin, but to premature response of the acrosome (4, 45). Yanagimachi (223) has observed that sea urchin spermatozoa do not attach radially at the surface of eggs in the absence of calcium. This is probably a consequence of the failure of the acrosomes to react under these conditions. The importance of calcium is further shown by the fact that the acrosome reaction can be elicited by excess calcium alone in *Mytilus* (215).

3. *The presence of species egg water* can evoke an acrosome reaction, especially in the echinoderms studied by Dan (43, 44, 46). This effect has also been shown quantitatively with living *Thyone* sperm (37). Similar results have been reported for *Asterias* and *Nereis* (117). However, Rothschild and Tyler did not find convincing evidence for a stimulating action of egg water on sperm of *Strongylocentrotus purpuratus* (168), and Afzelius and Murray are of the opinion that in several species of European sea urchins the effect of egg water was more injurious than specifically stimulating (4). In contrast to the situation in echinoderms, spermatozoa of gastropods and of the oyster (which has no jelly layer) are comparatively insensitive to egg water treatment (46).

4. *Alkaline sea water* (*p*H 9 or over) causes breakdown of the acrosome in sea urchins (43, 46), in the holothurian *Thyone briareus* (37), and in various mollusks (46, 48, 202). According to Dan, the action of alkaline sea water has physiological significance, since it can act favorably on fertilization as well as on the acrosome reaction (46).

5. *Contact of a non-specific nature,* such as to glass or collodion, sometimes elicits an acrosome reaction in *Hemicentrotus* (43), but not in *Echinocardium cordatum* (169). Oyster sperm respond readily to contact with glass, as when stirred with a glass rod (46, 48). From the fact that sperm sometimes attach to, penetrate, and even activate heterologous eggs, it could be inferred that non-specific contacts of this sort might elicit an acrosome response.

6. *Contact with one of the surface layers of the egg* can result in an

acrosome response. A distinction should be made between those species in which the sperm normally swim only to the outer border of the jelly and those in which it can penetrate the jelly to the vitelline membrane. In the first group, which includes the starfish and holothurian eggs, the acrosome reaction can be seen to have occurred at the outer border of the jelly [cf. especially Chambers' observations (22-24) when reinterpreted (29, 31, 35-37)]. However, in the second group, for which the sea urchin, the worm *Hydroides,* and various mollusks will serve as examples, the attached sperm nearly always exhibit at least a partial reaction at the egg surface proper (3, 4, 33, 48, 214).

It is perhaps too early to draw conclusions regarding the relative importance in various species of dissolved jelly, intact jelly, or the egg surface proper in initiating the acrosome reaction. However, the fact that sea urchin eggs show an increased rate of fertilization following *careful* removal of the jelly by mechanical means or at a *p*H no lower than 5.5 (59, 63a, 67), would seem to indicate the absence of an essential role for the jelly, either intact or in solution, for the acrosome reaction. The fact that the jelly can in high concentration induce an acrosome reaction might be attributed to certain chemical similarities between the jelly and mucopolysaccharide substances believed to be present in the cortex (84, 125, 174, 179, 183).

2. The Mechanism of Sperm Entry

There is at present no quantitative information regarding the relative contributions of the egg surface and of the sperm itself in sperm entry. Differences of opinion in the older literature are exemplified by the term "perforatorium" applied to the acrosomes of certain species, on the one hand, and on the other by the analogy sometimes drawn between sperm "engulfment" on the part of the egg and phagocytosis. In Dan's recent study of sperm entry in various echinoderms (41), it was shown that while sperm movements occurred before attachment, and even during and after penetration in some species, in others (especially starfish) movements of the spermatozoon either stop during entry or clearly play no role (cf. 22-24). In sea urchins, the spermatozoa often continue moving while attached. The sperm head appears to twist, but it is not known whether this is rotation (182) or yawing (57); probably it is the latter, since attachment by the acrosome would probably impede rotatory movements. Yanagimachi (223) has studied these so-called "boring movements" of sea urchin sperm at the egg surface, and has shown that under conditions of calcium deficiency the sperm do not "bore" or orient themselves radially, although

they maintain motility. This is probably explained by the more recent discovery of the necessity of calcium for the acrosome reaction (45). In spite of the interesting relationship which Yanagimachi found between the degree of successful cross-fertilization and the ability of the fertilizing spermatozoa to exhibit "boring movements," there is no evidence that the movements themselves play any role in sperm entry. In certain mollusks, the sperm head is held fast by its attachment point so that neither rotatory nor yawing movements could occur (214).

The initial phase of sperm entry is passage through the vitelline membrane of the egg. In some mollusks, this membrane is exceedingly thick and tough. It was shown several years ago by Tyler (199) that an egg-membrane lysin could be extracted from spermatozoa of *Megathura* and *Haliotis* which dissolved membranes of the same species. Since then, Wada, Collier, and Dan have demonstrated the presence of a similar egg-membrane lysin in *Mytilus edulis* sperm, and have shown its probable localization in the acrosome (215). It is released during the acrosome reaction and causes localized dissolution of the egg membrane at the point of sperm entry. Although egg-surface lysins have been described for sea urchins (191), there is so far no evidence for dissolution of the vitelline membrane in the neighborhood of sperm attachment in thin sections viewed with the electron microscope (4).

In those species in which a prominent fertilization cone forms, it is apparent that this reaction on the part of the egg is a response to attachment of the acrosome filament (29, 30, 31, 35-37). In oocytes, especially those of the sea urchin and sand dollar, it is well known that several exaggerated fertilization cones form, often in response to almost every spermatozoon which attaches to the egg surface (81, 167, 219). During the time that a block against polyspermy is gradually established, the number of reception cones which appear on insemination decreases (187). At the same time, the size of the reception cone becomes reduced.

In the most complete and detailed observations on sperm entrance to date, Colwin and Colwin have shown in *Holothuria, Asterias,* and *Thyone* that the fertilization cone, or a projection thereof, creeps up the attached acrosome filament at the same time that the sperm sinks into the egg. Once within the egg, the sperm (complete with tail) moves deeper into the egg cytoplasm through the conspicuous hyaline fertilization cone and funnel (29, 30, 31, 35-37) (Fig. 1). The hyaline funnel was recognized by cytologists because of its staining properties (cf. 219, 221). Three questions are raised by the above observations on sperm entry: (1) what elicits fertilization cone formation; (2) why the membrane of the fertilization

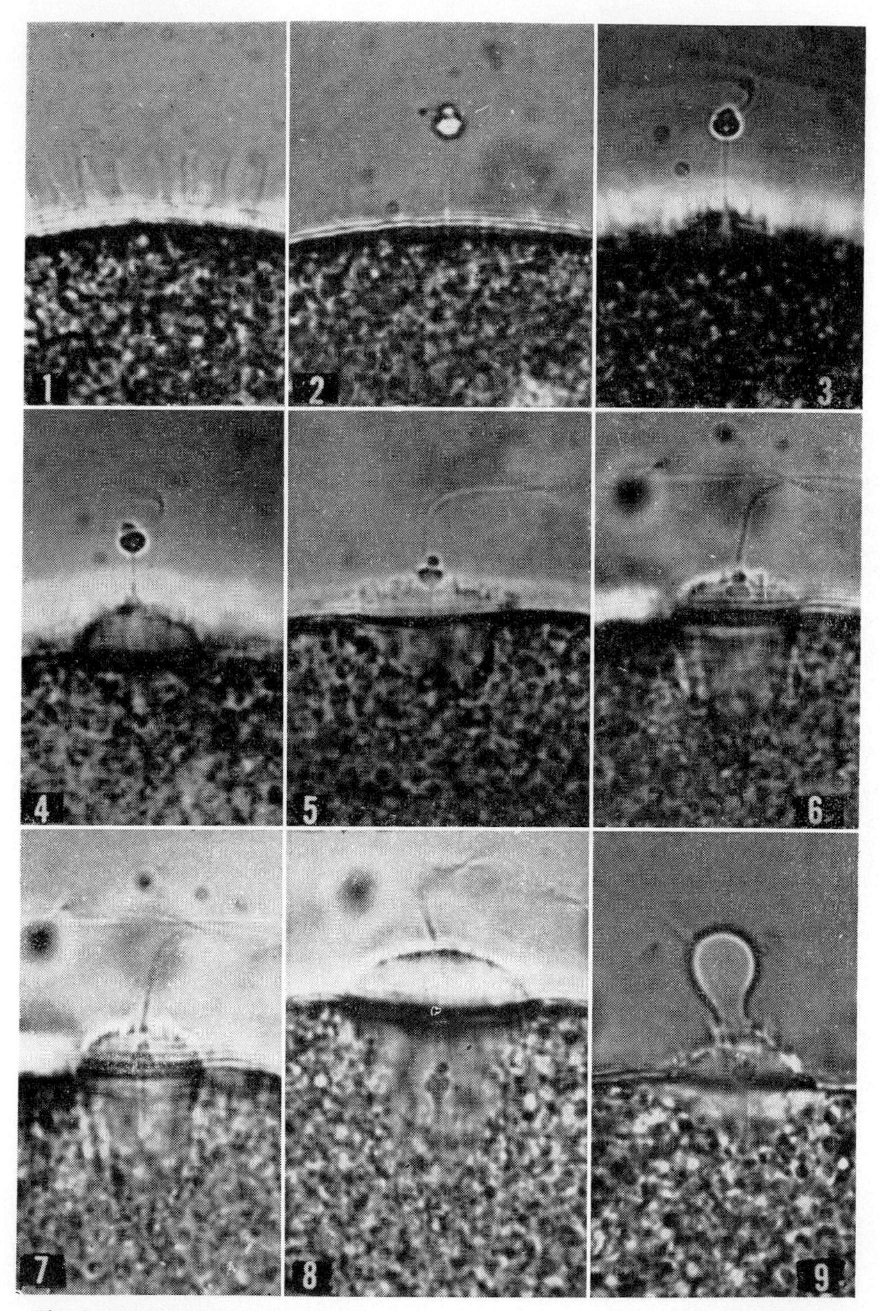

Fig. 1. Unretouched photographs of sperm entry in living *Holothuria atra* (From Colwin and Colwin, 29, 31). Frame 1 shows filamentous radiations from the egg surface extending into the jelly layer. Frame 2 shows a spermatozoon with its acrosome filament extending to the egg surface; no cone formed and the sperm did not enter. Frames 3-8 show successive stages of sperm entry in different eggs. Frame 9 shows a cone with an exudate from a ruptured region. The spermatozoon appeared unaffected.

cone "creeps" up the acrosomal filament to engulf the spermatozoon; and (3) what force pulls the sperm through the hyaline "funnel" region of the cone into the endoplasm. Since the fertilization cone forms but once except in material destined to become polyspermic, it is reasonable to suppose that it represents a specific egg response to some chemical or mechanical action of the acrosome of the fertilizing spermatozoon. Monroy (128) has speculated from his observations on the action of various enzymes on the surface of *Pomotoceros* eggs that a protease from the sperm might elicit cone formation. The fact that the cone forms as an external projection which grows in volume during sperm entry suggests that it could be formed either by an influx of water or by expulsion of fluid from the egg interior. Either might result from the weakening (by the action of local enzymes or surface-active agents) of the membrane in the region of the cone. It is perhaps most noteworthy that the granular material nearest to the attached acrosome recedes, leaving the hyaline funnel through which the sperm enters. If the cytoplasm in the funnel and surrounding the bordering granules were fluid, the funnel would rapidly fill up again with granules by Brownian movement. Since this does not occur, it is likely that the cytoplasm either of the funnel or surrounding the funnel is gelated. If the latter were true, the acrosome might prove to be anchored at the region of the cytoplasm which later became the apex of the funnel, and be pulled down as the cytoplasm in that region contracted away from the surface (Fig. 1). An anchorage at the apex of the funnel is suggested by the following observation: ". . . in a few cases it was found that if enough pressure were applied to the cover-slip to cause the cone to rupture and form an exudate, the spermatozoon within the cone was not expelled" (31, p. 163). One of the other possible mechanisms of sperm penetration that has been suggested (169), namely, that the acrosome might contract and pull the sperm in, appears to be incorrect, for the length of the acrosome remains constant during entry (31). In *Mytilus edulis,* Wada has described what appears to be a dynamic system within the egg for pulling in the fertilizing spermatozoon while rejecting supernumerary ones; he believes this is a morphological representation of the block against polyspermy (214). The sperm possess a 12-micron acrosome filament which apparently pierces the egg on attachment; at least this occurs when sperm attach to isolated "vitelline membrane and vitelline layer preparations" (214). Available evidence so far suggests the acrosome filament may function as a "handle" by which the sperm is drawn into the egg.

3. Early History of the Spermatozoon Inside the Egg

Until recently, the events taking place with respect to the spermatozoon immediately following its penetration into the egg were largely unknown except for observations on fixed material (e.g. 219-221). Much information has been provided by the observations of J. C. Dan with the phase contrast microscope on the Japanese echinoderm eggs, some of which are noted for their extraordinary transparency. Among the species studied, variation was found in the activity of the sperm tail during entrance; in *Asterina pectinifera,* for example, the tail was motionless, while in *Pseudocentrotus* vigorous writhing movements were observed. In all species she studied, Dan found that the entire spermatozoon entered, including the tail (41). Older observations (cited by Wilson, 221) were not in agreement as to whether the sperm tail entered, in sea urchins as well as in other animals. It is interesting to note that Dan's observations have been confirmed for *Thyone* and *Holothuria* (29, 31), and for *Paracentrotus* (165). In *Clypeaster* and *Mespilia,* the sperm tail does not cease its movements, for Dan has seen corresponding movements of the head and tail, along with a centripetally directed flow of cytoplasm, combining to bring about early translatory movements of the sperm head from the point of sperm entry (41). These movements came to a halt as the sperm tail was completely drawn into the cytoplasm; formation of the sperm aster soon followed (41).

Classical accounts of the fate of the sperm head within the egg stress the rather puzzling rotation of the sperm head which either precedes or coincides with formation of the aster. The observations of Dan with regard to autonomous movements of the sperm head soon after entry suggest a possible mechanism of rotation. If the sperm tail, on being drawn into the egg, were freer to move in the cytoplasm than the sperm head, the former would be expected to bend into a broad loop (see Wilson, 221, p. 445, Fig. 207), which would rotate the sperm head by as much as 180 degrees. This was suggested by the otherwise perplexing observation that, in spite of the length of the sperm tails (40-55 microns), in no case did a sperm head move more than 20 microns from its entrance point before aster formation (41, p. 409). E. Chambers (21) and R. Chambers (24) have also noted that the site of sperm aster formation was frequently laterally displaced from the position of the fertilization cone remnant.

Rothschild (164) has recently published a remarkable electron micrograph showing a sperm three minutes after penetration into an egg, and lying only a micron or two beneath the cortex. This picture revealed: (1)

the dissolution of the nuclear membrane except in the region of the centriole; (2) the double nature of the centriole; (3) that the sperm tail is clearly visible in the cytoplasm of the egg; and (4) that changes have already occurred in the middle-piece structure. Within four or five minutes after entry, the sperm becomes invisible in living sea urchin eggs, but reappears again as a hyaline "pronucleus" which is led by the growing sperm aster to the center of the cell. The disappearance of the sperm nucleus is caused by its swelling, during which it changes from a phase-retarding to a phase-advancing object when viewed in the cytoplasm.

4. The Migration of the Sperm Nucleus

In 1925, Wilson (221) summarized the evidence then available on the mechanism of migration of the sperm head within the egg cytoplasm and pointed to two components, the penetration path, which is nearly radial, and the copulation path, in which the sperm nucleus veers toward the egg nucleus. E. Chambers reexamined the problem, with the added precaution of avoiding compression of the eggs under observation (21). Under these conditions, only one component was found in *Lytechinus* eggs, the radially directed penetration path which is independent of the presence of the egg nucleus, since it occurs in enucleate egg fragments. When a sperm penetrates a flattened egg surface, it penetrates perpendicularly to that surface (21). In eggs made cylindrical by confining them in glass capillaries, the depth of penetration of the sperm is roughly equal to the radius of the capillary (6). These facts have suggested that the growth of the sperm aster might propel the sperm head toward the egg center, particularly since the rays of the aster extend to the cortex (21). Such an astral mechanism for migration is also suggested by observations made by A. Brachet (20) and Allen (6) on sperm movements in dispermic eggs, in which the sperm nuclei push one another apart by growth of their asters.

It has been suggested that the formation of the sperm aster and sperm migration both depend on some kind of interaction between the sperm and the mature cortex (6, 185, 186). In oocytes which are unable to exhibit a cortical response other than exaggerated fertilization cones, the spermatozoa which cause these cones enter, but neither rotate nor migrate to the center (219). In the oocyte this could also be due to cytoplasmic unripeness (51); however, in mature sea urchin gametes, sperm which penetrate a region of egg surface which is injured so that it lacks cortical granules will not form an aster (6, p. 409), whether or not a cortical response is initiated. Sperm passing through the cortex of eggs treated with redox dyes sometimes also fail to form an aster (180). As will be shown in

Section III 7, the occurrence of a cortical reaction is a prerequisite for normal nuclear movements preparatory to syngamy.

In spite of the inferences which can be drawn from the sea urchin work regarding the role of the sperm aster in the migration of the sperm nucleus, it is quite possible that other mechanisms play some part. For example, Dan's observation of centripetally directed cytoplasmic streaming suggests that similar processes might occur later during the astral growth period and should be looked for. Probably time-lapse cinematography of sperm nucleus migration in sufficiently transparent eggs could permit a decision between possible astral growth and cytoplasmic streaming mechanisms. None of the studies carried out so far have had this end in view. It is interesting to note that in the medusan, *Spirocodon,* the sperm characteristically enters so near the egg nucleus that no astral mechanism is employed to bring about syngamy (42). The same has been reported to occur in the eggs of *Mespilia* when the sperm enters near an eccentrically situated egg nucleus (41).

5. *Migration of the Egg Nucleus*

Movement of the egg nucleus to its point of fusion or association with the sperm nucleus seems to be more complicated than the migration of the sperm nucleus. Even in artificially activated eggs a "centering" of the egg nucleus occurs (134), showing that such movements can occur independently of the presence of the sperm nucleus. However, in artificially activated eggs, centering may possibly be mediated by growth of a "monaster." In fertilized eggs, the egg nucleus typically migrates without the formation of any conspicuous astral rays. Chambers (21) concluded from his analysis of 36 camera lucida records in which both the nuclei were in the same focal plane that the egg nucleus is carried to the "astral lake" (centrosome) by a current of centripetally directed cytoplasm. Although Chambers found that the adjacent granules accompanied the nucleus, it would be desirable to have cinematographic records of the behavior of a considerable portion of surrounding cytoplasm before deciding on cytoplasmic streaming as the sole mechanism for movement of the egg nucleus. The need for such a study is emphasized by the fact that A. R. Moore decided on the basis of observations quite similar to those of Chambers that the egg nucleus of *Temnopleurus* and of *Dendraster* moved without disturbing the surrounding granules and therefore must be pulled by fibrillar connections (134).

The present skepticism regarding cytoplasmic streaming as a sole basis for movement of the egg nucleus stems from observations of *Psammechi-*

nus eggs fertilized in glass capillaries (6). When an egg is taken in so that the capillary approaches the egg symmetrically with respect to the position of the egg nucleus, the latter remains stationary in the cylindrically shaped cell. However, if the egg is rotated so that the capillary approaches it asymmetrically, its nucleus later "creeps" to another position, as if it were satisfying unequal tensions between hypothetical stretched fibers holding the nucleus from all sides. This should not be taken to mean that the nucleus is held by fibers, for other mechanisms could undoubtedly account for this behavior. Following fertilization, the egg nucleus, irrespective of its distance from the point of sperm entry, seeks the axis of the capillary and elongates in this axis before it begins to migrate. Its migration is accompanied by a bulging out in the direction of the sperm nucleus. This was also noted by Chambers, but only just before syngamy (21). In spherical eggs, Chambers noted that the rate of nuclear migration was slow at its beginning and speeded up to a maximum in the middle of its journey. Progress was again slow during entrance into the "astral lake." In cylindrical eggs, the rate of nuclear migration is more or less constant, irrespective of the distance between the nuclei (6) (Fig. 2). Besides rendering eggs cylindrical in capillaries, other devices have been used in order to alter experimentally the distance over which the nuclei must migrate. Chambers (21) obtained his fastest migration when the egg nucleus passed through the rather wide neck of a flask-shaped cell, one lobe of which was an exovate in which the egg nucleus was originally situated. On the other hand, E. B. Harvey found that centrifugation caused a separation of the nuclei by throwing the sperm nucleus to the heavy pole and the egg nucleus to the light pole (72); under these conditions nuclear fusion was delayed by as much as an hour, but it is likely that the effects of centrifugal force were due not only to separation of the nuclei, but to disruptive effects on cytoplasmic structure as well.

Besides nuclear migration, other changes occur at the same time which lead to syngamy and cleavage. One of these is the swelling of the nuclei, which is especially exaggerated if syngamy is delayed (72); the sperm nucleus may even come to exceed the egg nucleus in size before they eventually fuse. If fusion fails to occur, the nuclei may "break down" (i.e., lose their limiting membranes). In this case, the sperm nucleus often forms the center of a mitotic division, while the egg nucleus develops a monaster (72). Sometimes in cases of delayed fusion the sperm aster divides to form the amphiaster before the nuclei have come together; this occurs particularly in etherized eggs (220) and following centrifugation (72). The ability of the sperm centriole to divide and to give rise to an

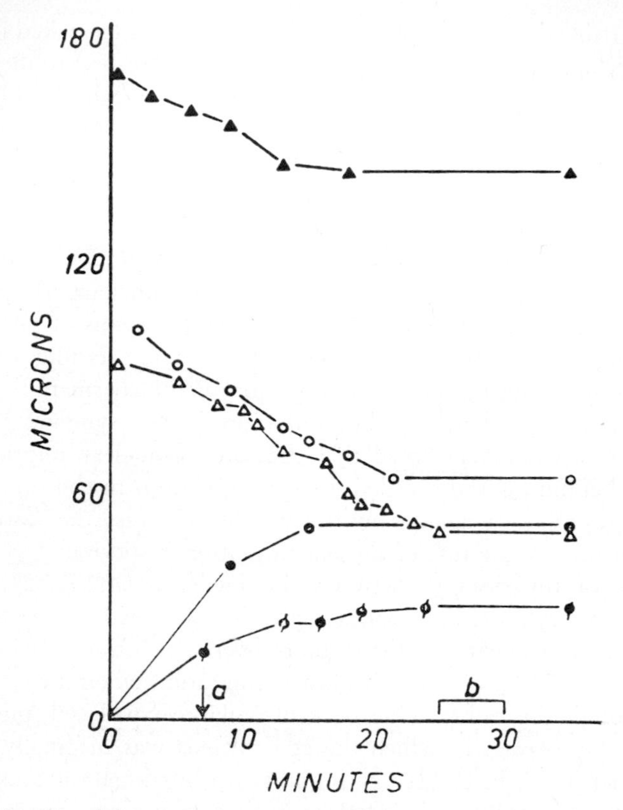

Fig. 2. Migration of the egg nucleus toward, and the sperm nucleus away from the point of sperm entrance (O on the ordinate). *a* is the approximate time of elongation of the egg nucleus, and *b* is the approximate time when the sperm aster disappears. Black circles represent the migration of a sperm nucleus in an egg contained in a wide capillary; black circles barred represent a parallel experiment in a much narrower capillary. Each curve represents a different experiment (Allen, 6).

amphiaster probably explains the fact that when eggs are divided mechanically by a cotton fiber following fertilization, in such a way as to separate the sperm and egg nuclei into different cell fragments, the piece with the sperm nucleus divides, but the other fragment containing the egg nucleus does not (224). The same is true of eggs divided by centrifugal force, except for an interesting case noted by E. B. Harvey (72): in *Paracentrotus lividus,* when eggs were divided by centrifugal force 15 minutes after insemination, the amphiaster associated, as usual, with the sperm nucleus. However, at 17 minutes after insemination the amphiaster remained with the egg nucleus in some, but not all, eggs. By 19 minutes,

the nuclei could not be separated. It would appear that the division center, which has apparently been attached physically to the sperm nucleus, acquires, just prior to syngamy, a firm attachment with the egg nucleus. This mechanical association may be important in the last stages of nuclear fusion.

II. Structure and Chemistry of the Egg Surface

1. The Jelly Layer

a. The sea urchin egg. The jelly layer of the sea urchin egg is initially rather compact, but swells on hydration to form a loose coat separated from the egg surface by 3-5 microns (67). Several observers have noted that protozoa can swim in the space between the jelly and the egg surface proper (67, 212). This is true not only in the European species *Psammechinus miliaris,* but also in *Strongylocentrotus purpuratus* from California (Mrs. J. Laties, pers. commun.). Due to its low refractive index, the jelly cannot be seen even with the interference microscope, a fact indicating that its concentration is less than about 0.005% organic material (124). The jelly can be visualized, however, (1) after staining with Janus green, (2) when outlined by squid or India ink, or (3) as an invisible barrier separating crowded eggs (73). The jelly does not ordinarily reveal any molecular structure in the polarizing microscope, but when vitally stained with Janus green B, it becomes intensely birefringent due to the lining up of the dye molecules tangentially to the egg surface (123) (Fig. 3). Similar birefringence has been seen in the jelly after treatment with sperm extracts (188). At present, insufficient information is available concerning the site of attachment of the dye or extract molecules to make any interpretation in terms of molecular structure of the jelly. In the starfish egg, Chambers (24) and Fol (53) saw evidence of radial structure in the jelly, to judge by the alignment of ink particles which entered.

The jelly layer undoubtedly provides the egg cell with considerable protection against mechanical injury, for eggs without jelly are sticky and fragile (185, 188). The jelly slowly dissolves in sea water to form "egg water" or "fertilizin," which in sufficient concentration has the power to agglutinate homologous (and sometimes heterologous) sperm (63, 116, 175, 200, 202). As was first shown by Kupelwieser (97), the jelly layer can be removed with acid sea water. At first it appeared that the jelly was essential for fertilization, since jelly-less eggs were difficult to fertilize unless large numbers of sperm were present (200). However, more recently Hagström et al. have shown that jelly removal by more careful means

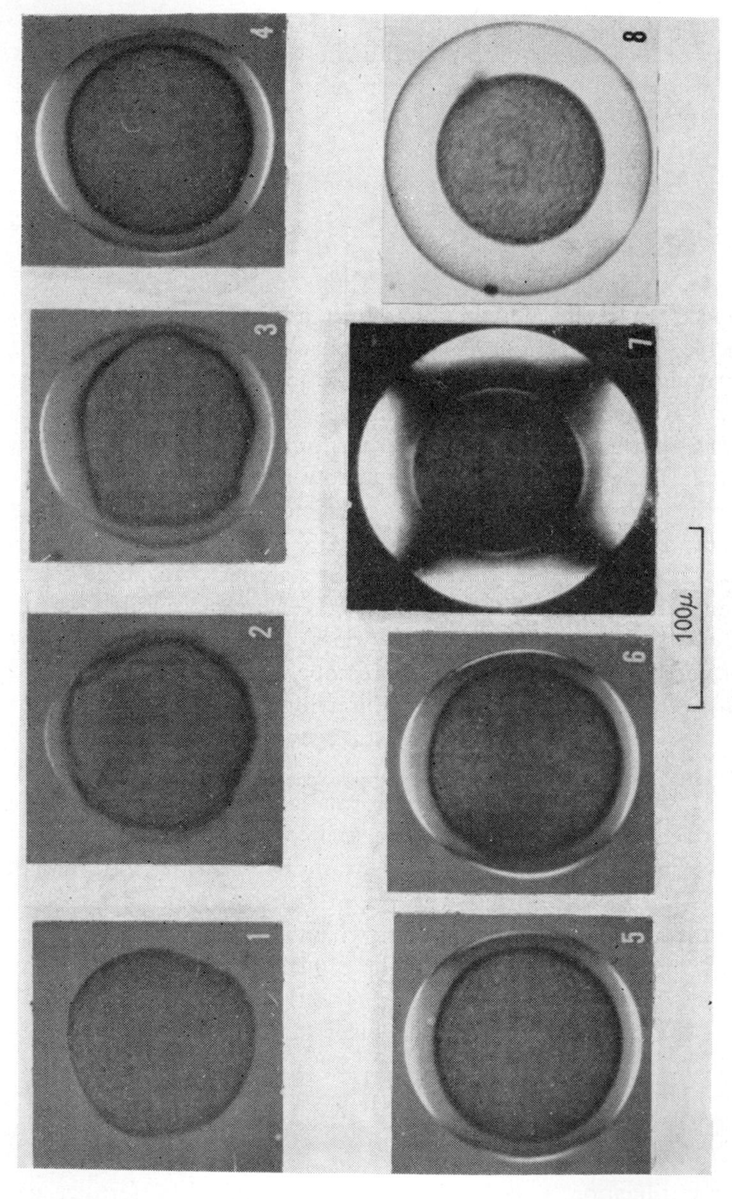

Fig. 3. Frames 1-6 show successive stages in the elevation of the fertilization membrane in *Paracentrotus lividus* photographed at 1 min. intervals in polarized light (compensated). Frame 7 shows the polarization cross in the jelly of an egg vitally stained with Janus green (uncompensated polarized light). Frame 8 shows the same in ordinary light (Mithison and Swann, 123).

actually enhances fertilization (see Fig. 4) and decreases the number of sperm necessary to obtain either fertilization or polyspermy (59, 62, 63a, 67). Previous difficulties were due to injury to the egg surface by sea water of a too acid *p*H. This was shown by the fact that "cytofertilizin" (60) and one of the proteolytic enzymes (EII) (108-110) of the egg leak out on acid treatment. Although it might seem that the presence of a small amount

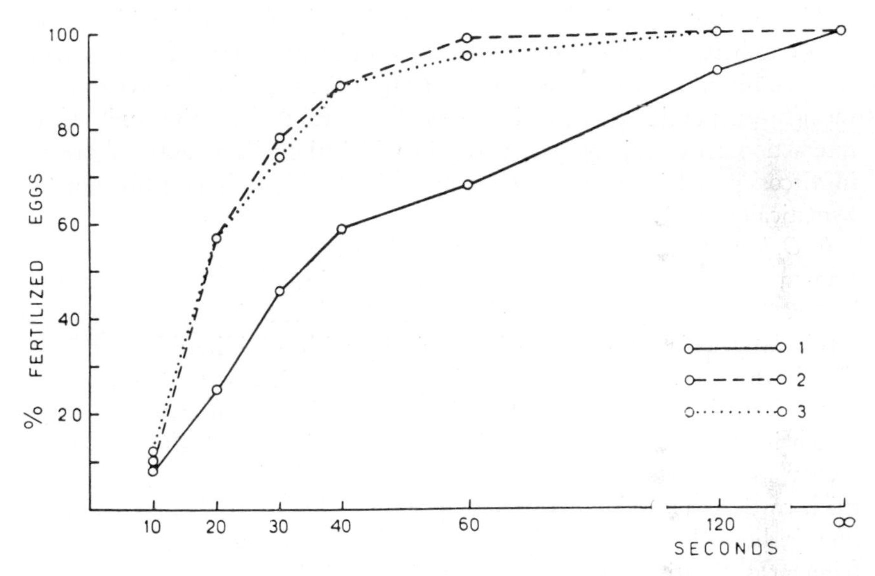

Fig. 4. Acceleration of the fertilization rate by jelly removal in eggs of *Psammechinus microtuberalatus*. 1, Control eggs with intact jelly. 2, Eggs deprived of their jelly coats by treatment with acid sea water at *p*H 5.8. 3, Eggs deprived mechanically of their jelly coats. Points represent counts of about 250 eggs (Hagström and Markman, 67).

of jelly on the surface could be essential, this is rendered improbable by the fact that substances which destroy or precipitate the jelly (periodate, and jelly-precipitating-factor or "antifertilizin") do not inhibit fertilization under these conditions (63a).

Due largely to the studies of Vasseur (209-213) and Tyler (cf. 205 for references), there is considerable information regarding the chemical nature of the dissolved sea urchin egg jelly. In solution, this material has a molecular weight of 280,000-300,000 with an axial ratio of 28:1 in *Arbacia* (205), and it behaves as an electrophoretically homogeneous acid substance migrating to the anode even at *p*H 2 (192). However, Messina and Monroy have separated *A. lixula* jelly into two components, one precipitable

with protamine sulfate and containing all the fucose and some galactose, whereas the remaining fraction contains only galactose and is devoid of agglutinating ability (115).

On hydrolysis the jelly yields various different monosaccharides, depending on the species (210, cf. 212 for references), sulfate, and amino acids. It appears that the jelly is a highly sulfonated glycoprotein free of hexosamine and glucuronic acid. Except for the lack of the latter two substances, the jelly, or at least its carbohydrate moiety, bears considerable resemblance to heparin, both in its high content of sulfate esters of monosaccharides and in its anticoagulant activity (82). Like heparin, dissolved jelly is metachromatic; this property has proved a useful tool for the study of the interaction between jelly and sperm, in which the jelly material decreases in viscosity and is apparently depolymerized, although possibly not enzymatically (114).

b. Other invertebrate eggs. Compared to the sea urchin, very little is known about the structure and composition of the jelly of other invertebrates. To cite a few examples, the egg of the clam *Spisula solidissima* has a thin jelly which stains metachromatically with toluidine blue (9, 198). *Chaetopterus* eggs likewise have a jelly layer, but it is not metachromatic in toluidine blue (90). An interesting case is the egg of *Nereis limbata,* which is free of external jelly prior to fertilization; soon after successful sperm attachment, the jelly is extruded from precursor granules in the thick cortical layer at all points except where the sperm has attached. In *Nereis,* both the formed jelly layer and its precursor granules are birefringent, suggesting crystalline orientation of their molecules (85). What information is available suggests chemical properties not too different from those of the sea urchin egg (39). *Sabellaria vulgaris* eggs are also free of external jelly when shed, but extrusion of the jelly accompanies spontaneous breakdown of the germinal vesicle in this species, and fertilization may occur at any time with respect to the events of jelly extrusion (150).

c. Amphibian egg jelly. Frog egg jelly seems to have chemical properties somewhat similar to that of the sea urchin, at least in its content of mucopolysaccharide and amino acid residues. However, according to the study of Folkes, Grant, and Jones, 90 per cent of the sulfate of frog jelly is accounted for by cystine and methionine, a proportion suggestion that most of the carbohydrate is not esterified with sulfate (54). Minganti (120) has also shown the presence of various monosaccharides which show the same kind of species differences noted in echinoderm jellies. The presence of hexosamines and the absence of acid-hydrolyzable sulfate were confirmed.

It is interesting to note that sperm-agglutinating activity has been found in frog egg jelly (18).

For interesting comparisons of the layers the spermatozoa must penetrate before reaching the eggs of other chordates, see the paper of Leghissa (101) for ascidians, and the review of Austin and Bishop (16) for mammals.

2. *The Cortex of the Mature Egg*

Many eggs, in common with a number of other cells, possess an outer differentiated layer or "cortex." Although this layer is difficult to observe microscopically under ordinary conditions, especially in pigmented or yolky eggs, it can be made plainly visible by centrifugation (74, 136). In the eggs in which fertilization has been most commonly studied, three main types of cortex have been described: (1) the "labile" cortex which undergoes profound reorganization or breakdown at fertilization or maturation, and is characteristic of most echinoderms, several chordates, and some members of other groups; (2) the "stable" cortex which contains the same morphological features as occur in the first type, yet remains visibly unaltered at fertilization; and (3) those showing no clearly differentiated cortical layer of appreciable thickness or granular structure such as is to be seen in sea urchins. Ascidian eggs may belong to this type (101).

a. The sea urchin egg. The cortical layer of the sea urchin egg was first observed by Harvey following centrifugation, which exposed the single layer of distinctive cortical granules distributed somewhat unevenly over the surface (74) (see Fig. 5). In tangential view, there appears to be a clear layer outside the cortical granules. This clear layer is bounded on the exterior by a fine line which has been assumed to mark the position of the vitelline membrane. Although the cortex is difficult to see in tangential optical section, it can be better visualized by raising the refractive index of the observation medium, as was shown photographically by Motomura (140). The clear layer so well demonstrated by this method corresponds in apparent thickness and location to the light-scattering layer described originally by Runnström (170, cf. also 12, 58). For this reason, the clear layer has been referred to as the "luminous hyaline layer," not to be confused with the hyaline (ectoplasmic) layer which appears on the surface some time after fertilization.

Recently, Mitchison and Swann (123) and Mitchison (121, 122) have raised the question of the reality of some of these surface layers "observed" with the light microscope. Mitchison, for example, has failed to

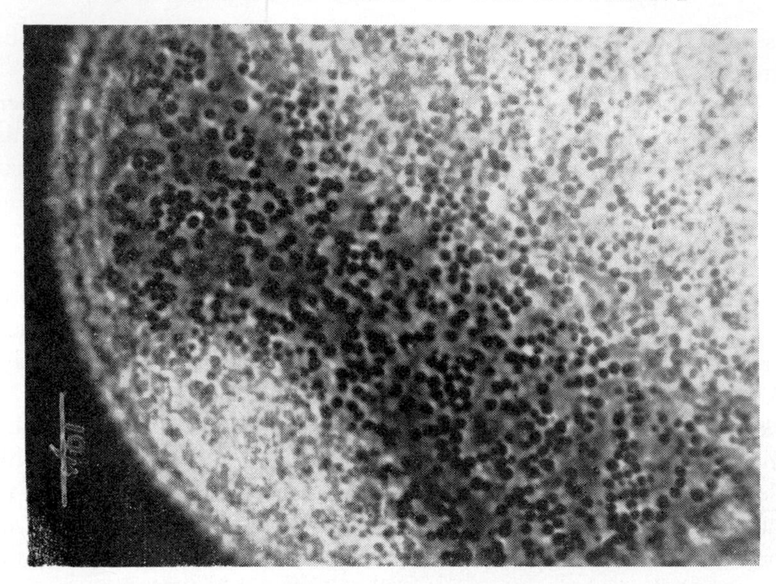

Fig. 5. An unfertilized egg of *Strongylocentrotus purpuratus* photographed in phase contrast after centrifugation (Allen, 8).

demonstrate the vitelline membrane, luminous hyaline layer, or cortical granules in fixed material, but was apparently unaware that the fixation of some of these structures had been successfully achieved by earlier workers. The cortical granules were first described in fixed material by Hendee (76) and later photographed elegantly by Motomura (140) after fixation in Champy's fluid, treatment with 0.5 *N* NaOH, and staining in Janus green. Cortical structure has also been preserved by Runnström, Monné, and Wicklund (190), and by Monné and Hårde (125) for cytochemical work. Although it is not certain, it seems probable from his photographs that Motomura did, as he believed, demonstrate the vitelline membrane or its precursor in the unfertilized egg of *Strongylocentrotus* (*Hemicentrotus*) *pulcherrimus*. Mitchison's failure to demonstrate some of these surface layers in fixed material was due probably not only to his choice of fixatives, but also to choice of material, as *Paracentrotus* and *Arbacia* are distinctly inferior objects for cortical studies compared to *Psammechinus,* which is also available in Naples. The other aspect of the skepticism regarding the surface layers is, however, quite legitimate; there certainly are optical difficulties involved in observing the surfaces of eggs, especially at low working apertures, because of the diffraction rings produced by the

complex light-scattering surface of the egg. It is therefore fortunate that other lines of evidence are now available with which to test the reality and fine structure of the egg surface.

Nearly all eggs have been regarded as having some kind of *primary membrane* (i.e., one formed by the egg), which, when closely applied to the egg surface, has been called a *vitelline membrane* (221). Although there was much dispute a generation ago as to whether sea urchin eggs possess a vitelline membrane, more recent evidence has been taken to mean that it does (for references to the early controversies, see 26, 136, 140; also 175, 178, 182). Present interest centers around the question of whether the fine line situated at the outer border of the luminous hyaline layer is actually a membrane which elevates at fertilization, or whether the fertilization membrane is formed de novo at fertilization (see also Section III 3). Mitchison is quite correct in stating that the evidence from microdissection experiments for the presence of a membrane proves only that such a membrane can be formed from the surface, and not that one existed there before treatment (121). One approach to the problem has been the use of enzymes. Runnström et al. (172, 181, 187, 188), Minganti (118), and Monroy and Runnström (132) have shown that pretreatment with trypsin results in subsequent failure of the fertilization membrane to elevate. Once formed, the fertilization membrane is resistant to trypsin, but not to the hatching enzyme (94, 132). These results have been interpreted as showing not only the presence of a vitelline membrane on the unfertilized egg surface, but also its protein nature. Recently, Tyler and Spiegel have shown that the proteolytic enzyme papain does not destroy the vitelline membrane, since the latter deflates after elevation in the enzyme solution and merges again with the egg surface. They conclude on the basis of the available evidence that the question of the existence of a vitelline membrane on the unfertilized egg is still open (208). The matter seems now to have been solved by the electron micrographs of Afzelius, in which the vitelline membrane has been distinguished as a continuous bordering structure 100 Å thick (2). The same structure has been observed as the outer component of the fertilization membrane, thus confirming the role of the vitelline membrane in the "dual origin of the fertilization membrane" (cf. 140, 171-173, 175, 187-190). The question of whether the vitelline membrane dissolves when treated with proteolytic enzymes appears also to have been solved by the observation of Afzelius and Minganti (reported in 181) that the vitelline membrane is still present in electron micrographs after trypsin pretreatment before fixation. Apparently trypsin, like

low temperature (12), weakens the structure of the membrane so that the cortical granules can be expelled through it (181), causing "fenestrated membranes" (119).

The chemistry and physiology of the vitelline membrane remain somewhat obscure. Because of its low thickness and irregular contour, it is inaccessible to the polarizing microscope until after membrane elevation, when it becomes altered (see Section III 3). Lipid content would be suggested by its osmophilia in electron micrographs, and protein content by its sensitivity to trypsin and chymotrypsin. Although this membrane has generally been assumed to play no significant part in the permeability of the cell, it is worthy of note that trypsin treatment increases the permeability of *Psammechinus* eggs to water (119).

The cortical granules of the sea urchin egg are of particular interest because of the role that they play in the cortical reaction and membrane elevation (see also Section III, 3 and 4). Their structure has been described in *Arbacia* by McCulloch (113) and Lansing, Hillier, and Rosenthal (100), and in several species of European sea urchins by Afzelius (2). Typically, these granules appear to be lamellar, with what appear to be peripheral inclusions, and are surrounded by a double membrane 75-90 Å thick. The number and thickness of the lamellae are characteristically different for each species studied, although the size range is fairly constant (0.5-1.0 microns) (see Fig. 6). The chief limitation of electron microscopy seems to be fixation; although Afzelius has tried an impressive array of fixatives, and has found essentially the same internal structure for the cortical granules in all, it must nevertheless be kept in mind that the cortical granules are extremely labile, and it is possible that the peripheral inclusions might represent the beginnings of abortive granule breakdown due to injurious effects of the fixatives.

The chemistry of the cortical granules is a subject to which an increasing number of workers will turn for an explanation of fertilization in chemical terms. The investigation of the chemical properties of small cell inclusions is limited to two main types of approach, cytochemical staining techniques and chemical examination of isolated material. Both approaches have been applied with limited yet promising results. With cytochemical techniques, Monné and Hårde (125), Immers (84), and Runnström and Immers (183) have found evidence for mucopolysaccharide in the cortex and probably the cortical granules and interesting changes in staining properties at fertilization. Several attempts have been made to isolate cortical material from living or fixed eggs. Some of Moser's observations on the stability of oxalate-treated eggs have suggested the possibility of obtaining cortical

material (138). Motomura (146) has reported isolated fragments obtained by rupturing acid-fixed eggs; the method is open to obvious disadvantages, and apparently no chemical work on this material has been published at the time of this writing. Nakano and Ohashi have collected and analyzed the carbohydrate present in the "cortical granular material" after the latter

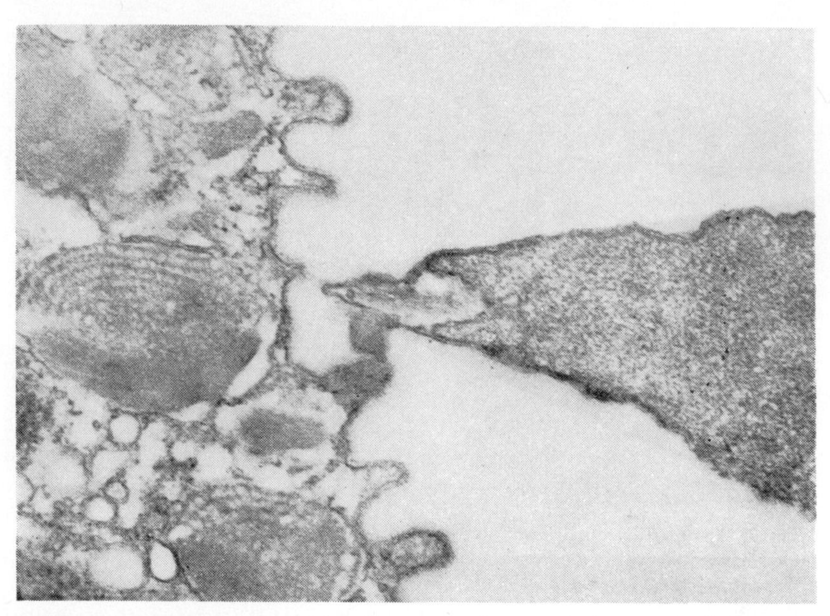

Fig. 6. An electron micrograph of a thin section of an attached sperm (probably a supernumerary one) at the surface of an egg of *Strongylocentrotus droebachiensis*. The acrosome globule has been expelled; part of the filament can be seen in contact with the egg. Note the lamellar structure of the cortical granules. (Courtesy of Dr. B. Afzelius.)

had been expelled from the cortex by urea treatment (149). Their results are of interest, as they find only fucose in the carbohydrate component released, but as a means for studying the chemical composition of the cortical granules the method is not ideal, for it may cause release of other substances as well (as, for example, the vitelline membrane material, 140). A more promising approach was suggested by the fact that strips of cortex can be torn from mature, jelly-free eggs of *Psammechinus* by virtue of their adhesiveness to glass surfaces (7) (see Fig. 7). Later it proved possible to isolate strips or even hulls of cortical material from living eggs by high centrifugal forces (8). This method worked satisfactorily on eggs of *Strongylocentrotus purpuratus* but was not applicable to *Arbacia* because the pigment, which had a similar high density, could not be separated from

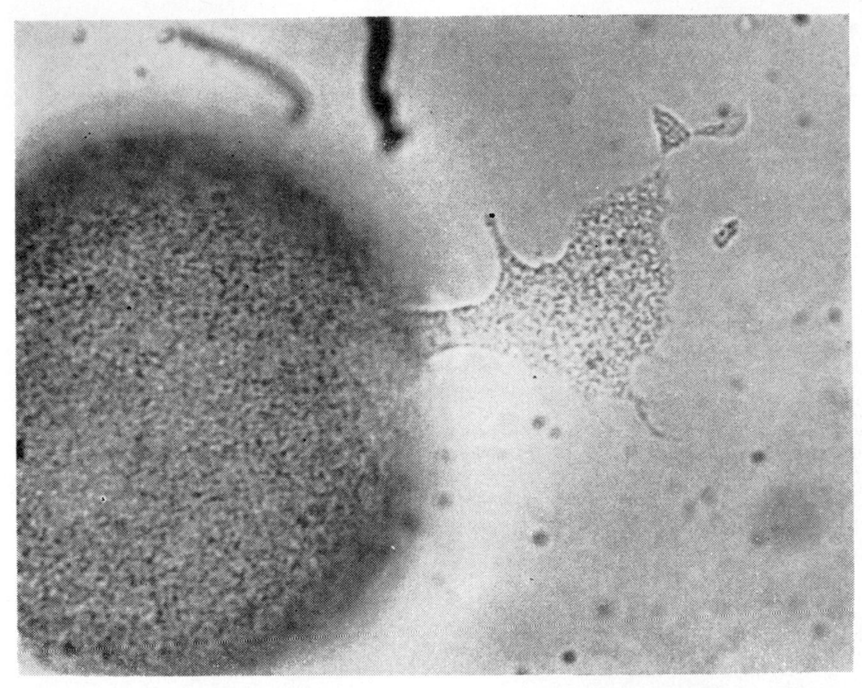

Fig. 7. An unfertilized jelly-free egg of *Psammechinus miliaris* which had been rolled after having adhered to a cover-slip. Note the strip of cortex partly pulled off the egg.

the cortical material. Although the centrifugation method for the removal of cortical material will require further refinement before it can be most profitably applied to chemical studies of the cortex, certain information was gained during the development of the method. The fact that the cortical material could be removed without dispersing the endoplasm added weight to the hypothesis of a subcortical membrane (7, 8, 156). At forces close to 170,000 × gravity, the cortical material itself separated into "membranes" (presumed to be natural or altered vitelline membranes) and "carpets" of cortical gel (Fig. 8).

The physical nature of the cortical gel in which the cortical granules are embedded has attracted much interest because of the changes undergone in this region during fertilization or artificial activation. Several attempts have been made to approach its molecular structure with the polarizing microscope. There is general agreement that the cortex of the sea urchin exhibits positive radial birefringence before fertilization, and that this disappears at fertilization (49, 122, 123, 126, 127, 130, 131, 175,

188-190). Interpretations, however, vary. Runnström et al. (reviewed in 175), and Monroy et al. (122-131) have conceived of the cortex as consisting of a primarily lipoid or lipoprotein structure similar to a liquid crystal. On the other hand, Mitchison has proposed a looped protein structure (cf. 122 for discussion and references), and Dan and Okazaki have clearly shown that at least part of the cortical birefringence behaves like strain birefringence because it is increased by stretching and is diminished by compression. The arguments in favor of a lipid structure are not supported by the electron microscope, which should be capable of detecting any significant amount of oriented lipid material by its osmophilia. Electron micrographs have, moreover, added another complication: the egg surface has been found to be covered by submicroscopic "microvilli" (or a brush border) which would render interpretations of data from the polarizing microscope very uncertain at the present time (cf. 2, 27, 100). In the future it will probably prove most profitable to combine studies of the sea urchin cortex in the polarizing microscope with parallel observations with the electron microscope under various experimental conditions. At present too little is known about the specificity of agents which have been thought to remove either proteins or lipids selectively.

The "luminous hyaline layer" is a part of the egg surface about which little is known, but it merits some attention because of the striking changes

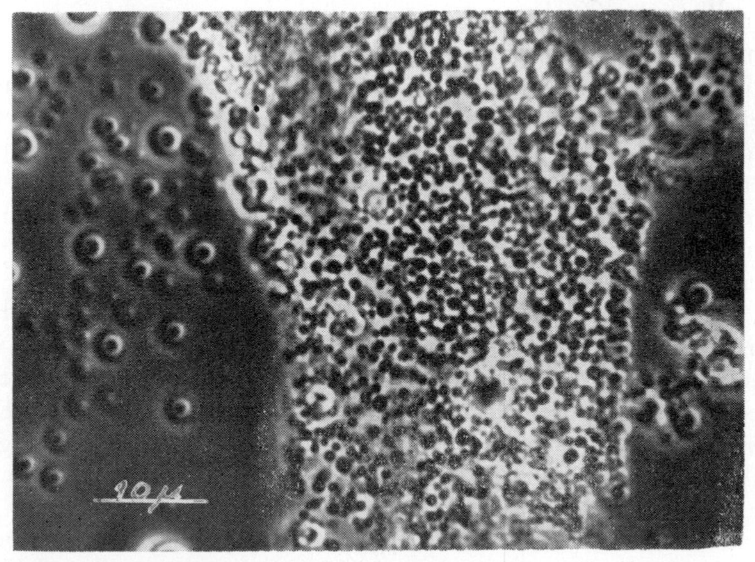

Fig. 8. Cortical material isolated from *S. purpuratus* eggs by ultracentrifugation (8).

in light-scattering it undergoes at fertilization (12, 58, 170). This layer may well be an undifferentiated part of the cortical gel lying outside the borders of the cortical granules; such a zone certainly can be seen in electron micrographs (2) (see Fig. 6). Under normal conditions, the color of this layer changes only when the cortical granules are discharged (see Section III 3), a fact suggesting that the light might be scattered from the outer surfaces of the cortical granules (136). This appears not to be the case, however, since Hagström (58) has found treatments which influence the light-scattering layer without visibly affecting the cortical granules.

Until recently, it was assumed that the permeability barrier of the mature egg lay beneath the vitelline membrane and outside the cortical granules. Two independent lines of evidence suggest a subcortical permeability barrier, however: (1) Parpart and Laris (156) have shown that the cortex is apparently permeable to certain non-electrolytes which do not enter deeper into the cell: and (2) cortical material can be stripped from living eggs without dispersing the endoplasm (7, 8). The above evidence is somewhat weakened by the fact that some non-electrolytes are activating agents for *Arbacia* eggs (138), and it is not yet known whether this is because of their penetration (156) or because they initiate a propagated wave of activation (cf. 195, 196). There is also little information on how rapidly a torn sea urchin egg can reform its outer surface. The electron microscope has not proven as decisive in settling the location of the plasma membrane as might have been anticipated. One of the published electron micrographs of Afzelius (2, Fig. 2) and several unpublished micrographs of Parpart (pers. commun.) show what might be interpreted as a subcortical membrane of wavy outline, but the matter cannot be decided on the basis of present evidence. It would not be surprising if a delicate membrane of the order of thickness of 50-60 Å might be very difficult to detect in sea urchin eggs, where the distance for fixatives to penetrate is great, and where shrinkage would be likely to disrupt delicate structures.

b. Other eggs with a "labile" cortex. A similar cortical layer has been seen in the eggs of other echinoderms besides the sea urchin. Just, who thoroughly investigated the cortical reaction in a number of marine eggs, failed to see the cortical granules in any of the species. However, in *Echinarachnius* (the sand dollar) he observed their products, the cortical globules in the perivitelline space during membrane elevation (87, cf. also 26). The presence of cortical granules in this species has been confirmed (9). Eggs of the starfish *Asterina pectinifera* also contain labile cortical granules (140), as do those of the American starfish *Asterias forbesii,* and of the

Japanese crinoid *Comanthus japonicus* (47). Little is known regarding the chemistry, physiology, and ultrastructure of the cortical layers in these forms.

Cortical changes remarkably similar to, but on a larger scale than, those in sea urchin eggs have been reported in a number of fish. Okkelberg (155) was apparently the first to describe such changes in the egg of the brook lamprey, *Entosphenus wilderi,* where the disappearance of cortical alveoli precedes the formation of the perivitelline space. More recently, the physiology of cortical conduction has been studied intensively, especially by Yamamoto, whose most recent paper gives many useful references (222). The organization of the cortical region of the fish egg is somewhat different from that in the smaller invertebrate eggs. In the first place, the cortical alveoli are much larger than cortical granules (4–25 microns compared to 0.5–1.0), and alveoli can be dislodged by moderate centrifugation (99). However, like the sea urchin granules, the fish alveoli discharge their contents (mucopolysaccharides) into the perivitelline space, and the alveolar membrane apparently becomes part of the new cell surface (93, 99). According to Kemp (93), no characteristic ultrastructure appears in electron micrographs of fish cortical alveoli; evidently they form from the primitive "yolk vesicles" during oogenesis and migrate outward.

Frog eggs show an entirely different cortical structure, including a layer two or three deep of cortical granules which disappear at fertilization (91, 92, 143) (Fig. 9). These are also lacking in distinctive ultrastructure; they apparently form either in the cortical layer or just below it during oogenesis (93). A labile cortex containing cortical granules has also been described for the hamster egg (15).

A labile cortex is also found in *Nereis limbata* eggs; however, it is of a different kind. Instead of being thin, with a single layer of granules, as in sea urchins, it is thick and tightly packed with jelly-precursor granules. Costello (40) believes that jelly extrusion at fertilization is basically similar to the cortical reaction in echinoderms.

c. Eggs with an apparently "stable" cortex. It has been noted in studies with various annelid or mollusk eggs that although a differentiated cortex was present, no striking changes of the type noted in sea urchin or fish eggs occurred on fertilization. This was first noticed in *Spisula* eggs (5). According to Rebhun (159), the cortical granules of *Spisula* are formed in situ early in oogenesis and differ only slightly in appearance in electron micrographs from yolk (Fig. 10). The rigidity of this cortex is sufficiently great that the granules remain in place even after 10 minutes at 200,000 $\times$

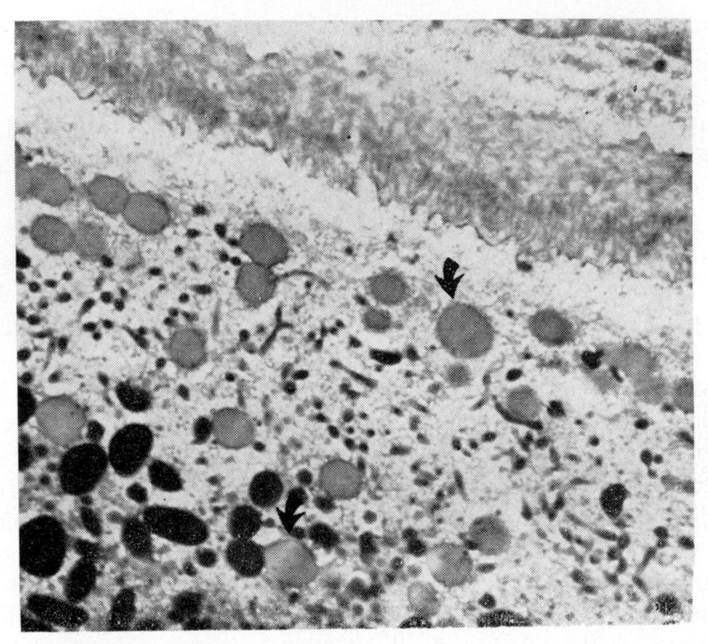

Fig. 9. Electron micrograph of a thin section of the cortex of the maturing egg of the frog *Rana pipiens,* showing the cortical granules (arrow). Exterior to the cortex is the zona radiata, showing microvilli. Courtesy of Dr. Norman E. Kemp (cf. 92).

gravity (9); strips of cortex can be peeled away in this species in the same manner as in the sea urchin (7).

Chaetopterus eggs also exhibit cortical granules which can be seen upon centrifugation (Fig. 11). These are stable on fertilization. It would probably be of great value to examine in detail with combined electron and polarization microscopy the alterations in ultrastructure which occur during fertilization in eggs with a stable cortex; in this way some change common both to the eggs with labile and with stable cortices might be found. Preoccupation with the sea urchin egg has led to a failure so far to separate the structural events involved in membrane elevation from those attending activation. The latter may well be masked in labile cortices.

III. Processes Leading to Activation

1. The Activating Function of the Acrosome

The starting point for a discussion of the processes leading to activation should perhaps be a consideration of the possible activating function of the

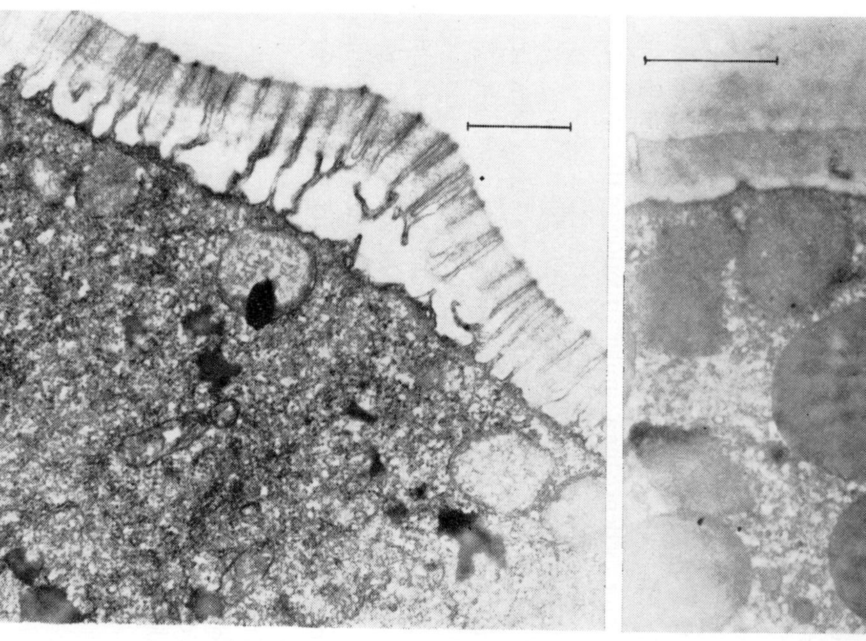

Fig. 10. Electron micrograph of a thin section of a *Spisula* egg 29 minutes after fertilization, showing the presence of cortical granules which differ somewhat from the yolk granules seen in the endoplasm. Note the thick vitelline membrane or layer into which run microvilli. Courtesy of Dr. L. I. Rebhun.

Fig. 11. Electron micrograph of a thin section of a *Chaetopterus* egg showing the continued presence of cortical granules 51 minutes after fertilization. Note here, as in the case of *Spisula,* the thick vitelline membrane or layer and the microvilli. Courtesy of Dr. L. I. Rebhun.

acrosome (see Section I 1). Although there have been no experimental studies pointed in this direction since the discovery of the acrosome reaction, there is ample evidence in the descriptive literature on fertilization to suggest such a function. In *Nereis,* it is well known that jelly extrusion and initiation of maturation, manifestations of activation in this species, occur while the sperm is attached only by its acrosomal region. Although Lillie (103) was the first to remove the attached sperm and show that egg development proceeded as well as in artificial parthenogenesis, it was Goodrich (56) who showed by careful micromanipulation experiments that *Nereis* sperm could be pulled away from their attachment at the egg surface as early as two minutes after insemination, and yet activation (but no cleavage) followed.

If some of the observations of R. Chambers (23, 24, 25) on the starfish *Asterias* are reinterpreted in the light of the findings of J. C. Dan and of Colwin and Colwin (28-37, 43-48), it becomes almost certain that the cortical reaction and membrane elevation are initiated while the sperm is attached only by its long acrosome filament. In fact, some of Chambers' line drawings show the fertilizing spermatozoon about to pass through the already-formed fertilization membrane. As will be shown in the next section, there is some evidence for a similar situation in the sea urchin.

2. *The Latent Period Before the Cortical Reaction*

A number of observers have recognized that there was a delay between insemination and membrane elevation of about 30-35 seconds (e.g., Just, 88). Moser (136), who was the first to make detailed observations on the disappearance of the cortical granules at fertilization, recognized that this process took from 10 to 20 seconds to begin. However, the time of insemination does not permit a reliable estimate of when the attachment of the fertilizing spermatozoon took place. Several years ago, Hagström and Hagström (64) introduced the lauryl-sulfate interruption method for determining the time of successful sperm attachment in eggs of a population by instantaneously inactivating free swimming spermatozoa in aliquots of fertilizing gametes at different times after insemination. With this method, it is possible to determine with considerable accuracy from fertilization rate curves (cf. Figs. 4, 12) the time at which 50 per cent of the eggs had been fertilized. By combining this method with a second interruption of the same batch of fertilizing gametes in 4 per cent formalin, which kills the eggs immediately and arrests cortical propagation but not membrane elevation over areas already covered by the cortical reaction, it was possible

to establish the time at which 50 per cent of the same eggs had begun to show cortical granule breakdown (Fig. 12). The period between sperm attachment and the beginning of the visible cortical changes has been designated the *latent period* (10).

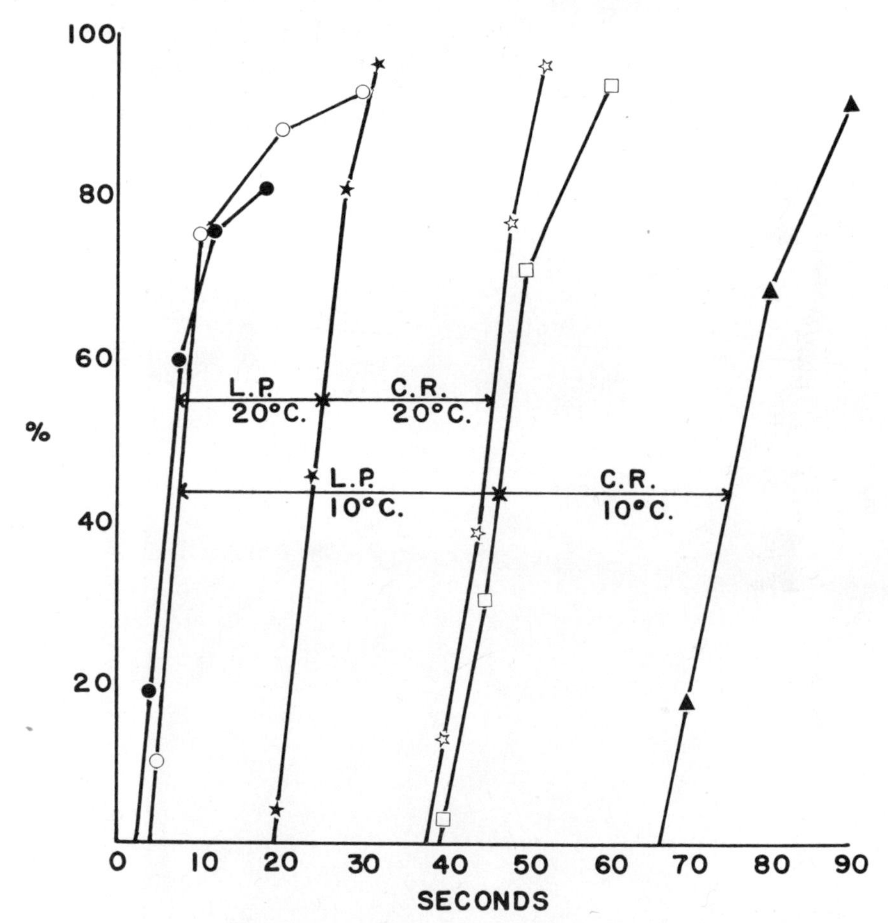

Fig. 12. Graphed data from which the duration of the latent period and of the cortical reaction were determined (explanation in the text). The two left-hand curves show the time of attachment of the successful spermatozoa at 10 (open circles) and 20 (black circles) degrees. The middle curves (marked with open squares or black stars) show the time of initiation of cortical granule breakdown at these respective temperatures. The right-hand curves (black triangles and open stars) represent the completion of the cortical reaction (Allen and Griffin, 10).

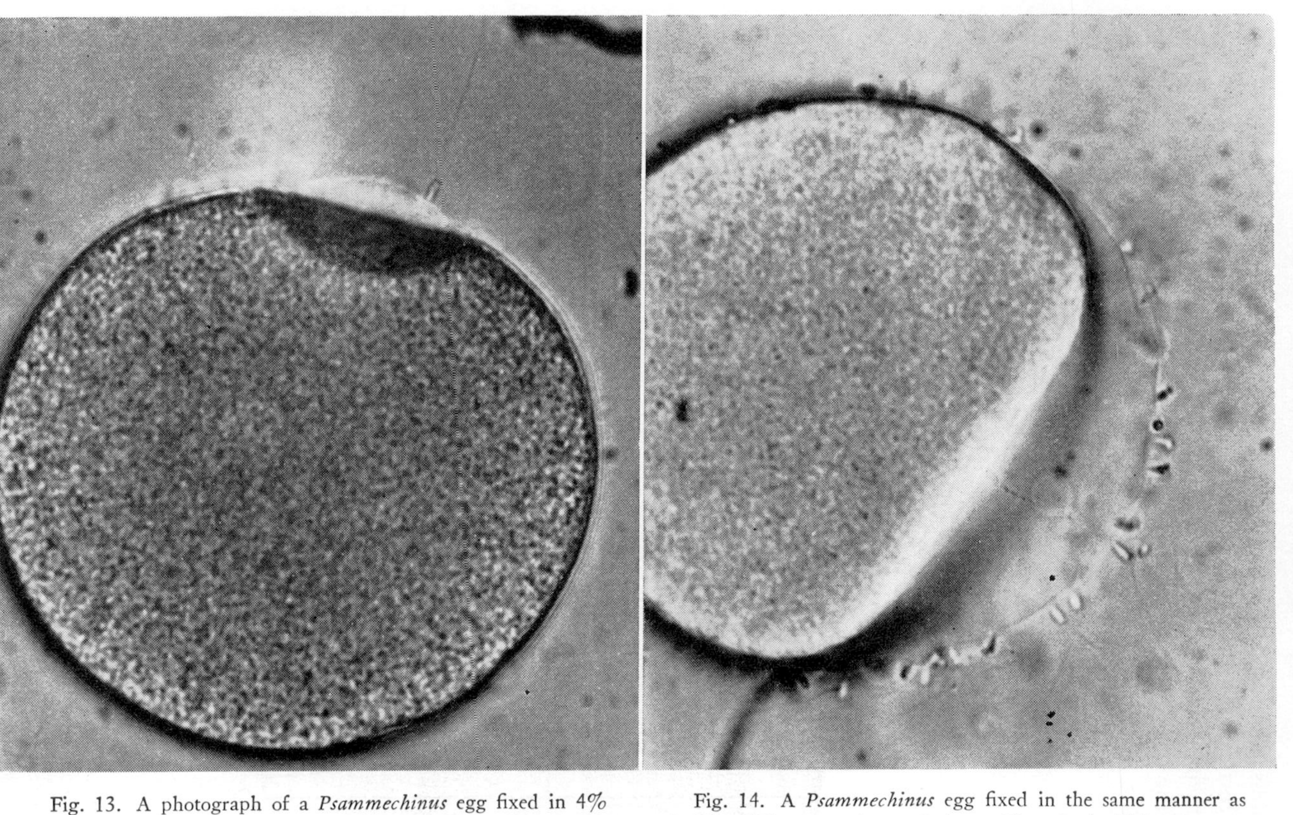

Fig. 13. A photograph of a *Psammechinus* egg fixed in 4% formalin within a few seconds after the beginning of the cortical reaction. Note that the fertilizing spermatozoon has been pulled from the cortex by post-fixation membrane elevation (Allen and Griffin, 10).

Fig. 14. A *Psammechinus* egg fixed in the same manner as in Fig. 13 but several seconds later. Note the fertilizing spermatozoon now embedded in the cortex (Allen and Griffin, 10).

different sperm is an exceedingly rare occurrence, as has been determined by observation of several thousand eggs fixed in formalin at various times after insemination (9). This must be due to some resistance on the part of the egg, for after pretreatment with nicotine, many of these attached sperm do enter (63b, 161, 162, 168). It seems necessary then to agree tentatively with Rothschild and Swann that there exists some kind of "fast block" against polyspermy, if not to exclude supernumerary sperm directly, then to prevent more than one sperm from initiating a cortical response. There is evidence that as the sea urchin passes through maturation from the oocyte stage, it changes from a multiple-response pattern to the production of one fertilization cone of considerably reduced size (187). This acquisition of a "selecting mechanism" on the part of the egg can be reversed by the sulfhydryl inhibitor N-ethylmaleimide. This agent returns the egg to the condition in which it responds to many attached sperm by the production of multiple fertilization cones, so that it becomes polyspermic (68).

3. *The Role of the Cortical Reaction in Membrane Elevation*

It is now generally recognized that activation in the sea urchin involves dramatic changes in the surface layers of the egg, changes which have been referred to as the *cortical reaction.* Loeb (106) was the first to grasp the potential importance of these changes when he proposed his "superficial cytolysis" theory of activation. The nature of this process was first revealed in an observation of E. N. Harvey, who commented in a footnote on the presence in *Arbacia* eggs of ". . . numerous minute stained granules, quite unmoved by the centrifuge. At the time of fertilization, these disappear, apparently going to form the substance which passes out of the egg and hardens to a fertilization membrane" (74). The "minute . . . granules," later called the cortical granules, were rediscovered independently three times (76, 105, 136). Moser (136) was the first to demonstrate the wave-like nature of cortical granule breakdown in the sea urchin egg (although similar changes had been described in fish (155; for references cf. 99, 221)), and to show that it coincided with the wave of surface "roughening" observed by earlier authors; he also compared this wave with the wave-like dark-field color change discovered by Runnström (170) and concluded that the latter was an expression of the disappearance of the cortical granules, which he believed reflected the light in dark-field. Hagström (58) later showed, however, that the two phenomena could be experimentally separated. Moser also showed that granule breakdown,

although not always propagating, resulted from a wide variety of chemical and physical stimuli (saponin, toluol, pricking, ultraviolet light, direct current, urea, glycerol, and thiourea) (137, 138). Because none of these agents were effective in breaking down cortical granules in oxalated eggs, he interpreted his results as indicating the primary necessity of calcium in the light of the "calcium-release theory" (cf. 75 for discussion). It has not been shown, however, that oxalate (or citrate) selectively binds calcium without side effects on cells. Moser suggested that membrane elevation might come about by the formation of vesicles or vacuoles at the surface which might fuse at the outer border to form the fertilization membrane and at the inner border to form the new cell surface.

Prior to 1940, there had been two opposing views with respect to the origin of the fertilization membrane (cf. 136 for references): (1) that the membrane was "formed" de novo from a precursor at the time of fertilization; or (2) that a membrane preexisted on the egg surface and became elevated. These opposing views were beautifully reconciled by the work of Motomura (140), who showed that the cortical granules, which could be followed by their staining with Janus Green, merged with the vitelline membrane of the egg, thus establishing the dual origin of the fertilization membrane. The view of Motomura concerning the fate of the cortical granules, as shown in Fig. 17, is essentially that held today, except for a few modifications. It is probable that some of the material from the cortical granules contributes colloids to the perivitelline space and hyaline layer (157, 158). The dual origin of the fertilization membrane provides an explanation for the fact that centrifuged *Asterias* (38) and *Arbacia* (71) eggs give rise to fertilization membranes which are thicker and more widely separated from the egg surface at the centrifugal pole. The "membrane precursor" substance which had been displaced centrifugally was the cortical granular material, which was at that time unknown (cf. 8).

Through the work of Runnström et al. (171-173, 188-190) and of Endo (52), we have a rather complete and detailed account of the morphological events in the development of the fertilization membrane. The wave of cortical granule breakdown which precedes membrane elevation occurs randomly in a zone which spreads over the surface (6, 52). Endo observed swelling of the cortical granules before expulsion, but this was not observed in parallel observations with *Psammechinus* eggs, possibly because the process proceeds too rapidly (6). Runnström observed globular and rod-shaped particles in trypsin-treated and underripe eggs, and has recorded the details of the delayed merging of some of this material with the vitelline membrane. Endo has confirmed these observations in general and has illus-

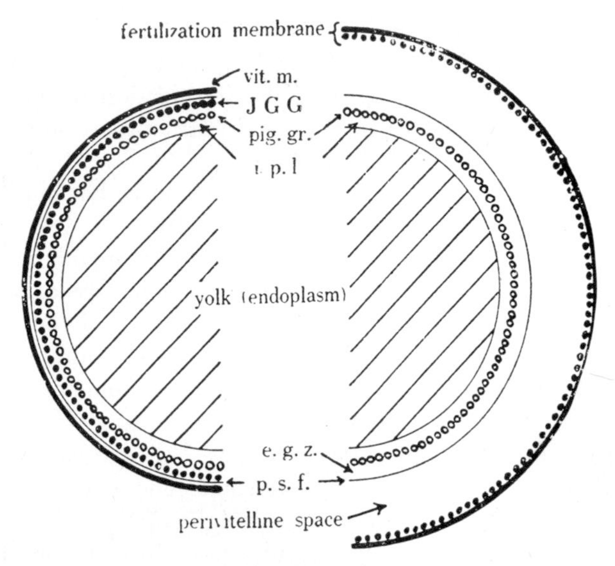

Fig. 17. A diagram showing the disposition of cortical granular material before (left half) and after (right half) fertilization. e.g.z., extragranular zone; i.p.l., inner protoplasmic layer; J.G.G., Janus green granules (cortical granules); pig. gr., pigment granules; p.s.f., protoplasmic surface film; vit. m., vitelline membrane (Motomura, 140).

trated his paper with remarkable photographs showing the steps involved in the merging of the granular material with the vitelline membrane. During this process, the membrane begins to thicken, harden, and become resistant to enzymes except for the hatching enzyme (see Section II 2). The hardening has been shown to be due to the release from the cortex of a "third [hardening] factor" which can be isolated by extraction of living eggs with acid sea water (142). (The hardening factor is not the jelly.) Extracted eggs exhibit fragile fertilization membranes which can be hardened by adding back the neutralized acid extract. Recently Motomura has succeeded in isolating and probably localizing (just beneath the cortex) the substance involved. He has called this substance "colleterin," but it is probably identical with "antifertilizin."

Endo (52) studied the birefringent rods which Runnström discovered in the perivitelline space and showed that they probably consist of the substance that hardens the fertilization membrane, for both substances are attacked by the hatching enzyme but not by trypsin, and are precipitated by calcium. Furthermore, the sign of birefringence is the same with respect to the axis of crystalline or membrane orientation. As the membrane elevates, its birefringence increases, presumably due to the ad-

dition of oriented material from the inside (123, 187) (cf. Fig. 3). However, the suggestion of Dan and Okazaki (49) that this may be partly strain birefringence is plausible, since the fertilization membrane is undoubtedly stretched somewhat by the colloid osmotic pressure of material in the perivitelline space (78, 79, 80, 107).

The origin of the colloids of the perivitelline space has not been established; it is probable that this material comes from or with the cortical granules (157). Its concentration is about 0.07% dry organic matter (124), and it very likely contains a mucoprotein or mucopolysaccharide precipitable by calcium (158, 183). The fact that the volume of the perivitelline space can be experimentally altered by the *p*H of the medium (81) or can be doubled or tripled by non-electrolytes which simultaneously interfere with the hardening of the membrane (135, 138) suggests that the materials which come out of the cortex can serve either to harden the membrane or to provide colloid osmotic pressure. The results of Dean and Moore (50) suggest that the molecular weight of the colloidal particles must exceed 10,000, for smaller molecules pass through the fertilization membranes of *Dendraster* eggs.

In addition to the hyaline (ectoplasmic) layer, Hiramoto has recently shown the existence of a new gel layer in the perivitelline space of *Hemicentrotus* and *Clypeaster* eggs. Since the same methods were used by Chambers (25) to demonstrate the absence of gel in the perivitelline space of other echinoderm ova, we must conclude that species differences exist. Hiramoto's gel layer (78, 79) apparently does not exist in the eggs of *Psammechinus,* for these slide back and forth inside their fertilization membrane when held in a capillary (6).

4. *The Function of the New Surface Layers of the Fertilized Egg*

Although it would seem at first sight that the fertilization membrane would most likely serve as a mechanical barrier to the entrance of supernumerary sperm, it has been shown repeatedly that eggs with their membranes mechanically removed could not be refertilized (cf. 194 for references). Sugiyama (194) has confirmed these results and has demonstrated that the sperm barrier beneath the fertilization membrane is broken down to permit refertilization in sea water lacking divalent ions. Hagström and Hagström (65) confirmed and extended these results and demonstrated a high degree of coincidence between refertilizability and damage to the hyaline layer. Since the hyaline layer is a product of the cortical reaction and the only apparent physical barrier to the sperm beneath the fertilization membrane, it seems justified to accept Hagström's view that the hyaline

layer can function as a barrier to the entrance of supernumerary sperm in the absence of a fertilization membrane. Nakano (148) has held a similar view on the function of the hyaline layer from experiments on the fertilization of activated eggs following treatment with sea water lacking divalent ions. Recently, however, Tyler, Monroy, and Metz (207) have reported the possibility of refertilizing mechanically demembranated eggs of two species of *Lytechinus*. Although, as the authors point out, these results are probably partly explained by the thinness of the hyaline layer in this species and by the slowness with which this layer arises, it is quite likely that the hyaline layer was not completely formed at the time the membranes were removed. There are indications that the hyaline layer is formed, at least in part, from materials precipitated from the perivitelline space (52, 133, 157, 158). In the case of membrane removal before hyaline layer formation, these materials may be permanently lost, resulting in underdeveloped hyaline layers. Hagström and Hagström (65) have shown that basic substances such as lysozyme and clupein cause polyspermy, probably by precipitating the acid mucopolysaccharides in the cortical granules, and preventing this material from taking part in the formation of the hyaline layer. Since the formation of the hyaline layer proceeds at different rates in different species, it would have been of interest to test the refertilizability of *Lytechinus* eggs which had been demembranated after full growth of the hyaline layer. It is interesting to note that mechanical as well as chemical means can be employed to remove the hyaline layer; E. B. Harvey showed that the hyaline material could be peeled off the egg by centrifugation (72). So far, there have been no published attempts at refertilizing eggs with mechanically removed hyaline layers. Aside from the sperm-barrier role of the hyaline layer, this structure is well known to hold the blastomeres together during cleavage, although it is not necessary for cleavage itself (77).

5. *The Nature of the Propagated "Fertilization-Impulse"*

The literature contains a great many reports on treatments which will cause membrane elevation (cf. 73, 201 for references); however, relatively few of these cause further developmental changes. Sugiyama (195-197) has made a very significant advance by showing that various agents which he tried could be divided into two groups: (1) those which acted directly on the cortical granules to bring about their localized breakdown (including saponin, "monogen," wasp-venom, and "lipon"); and (2) those which initiate a propagating wave of cortical granule breakdown in what is presumably the same manner as the sperm (distilled water, urea, and

butyric acid). The different action of these groups of agents was revealed by ingenious experiments in which the surfaces of eggs were exposed only partially to the reagent. It would have been very valuable, particularly in experiments using capillary tubes, if the rates of propagation of the "fertilization-wave" or "impulse" had been measured under the stimulating action of the different substances to determine whether their effect was actually similar to that of the sperm.

There have been a few attempts to approach the nature of the propagating wave by study of its kinetics. Rothschild and Swann (167) analyzed cinematographic records of a light-scattering change propagated around the largest optical section of *Psammechinus miliaris* eggs. Because only equatorially fertilized eggs exhibit the true rate of propagation, only a few of many records taken could be used. Two hypotheses were dealt with, namely, that the sperm might release a substance which diffused either through the interior or through the cortex to cause the observed surface changes. Kacser (89) later reanalyzed and replotted the same record and decided that the curve did not indicate either diffusion mechanism, but rather was compatible with an autocatalytic mechanism. This suggestion is more in accord with the results of Sugiyama (197) and of Allen (6) indicating that the egg has the ability to exhibit a self-propagating impulse in response to artificial activating agents which presumably do not diffuse through the cell to cause their effect. A later attempt to extend the cinematographic data on cortical propagation (9) revealed one new fact: if the rates of propagation were plotted for the two hemispheres of the egg cut by the penetration path of the sperm, they were found not to be equal, but sometimes half as rapid on the surface nearest to the egg nucleus as on the opposite side. This may have some relation to the fact noted by Allen, Lundberg, and Runnström (13) that the part of the egg surface nearest to the egg nucleus had the highest threshold to electrical stimulation (see Fig. 16). It is doubtful whether the nucleus itself exerted any effect, as the opposite results were obtained with respect to the nucleus in centrifuged eggs. It is not known whether the threshold effect and the differential rates of propagation were related to egg polarity or to the distribution of some endoplasmic constituent. Moser noted an influence of the distribution of endoplasmic materials on the cortical response to artificial agents (138). It is apparent that much more work is needed to clarify some of the extraneous factors affecting the kinetics of cortical conduction; such work should be carried out on an egg such as *Echinocardium,* which has a clearly marked polarity and an easily followed dark-field change. It is worth mentioning that differential rates of cortical conduc-

tion at different parts of the egg surface have been noted in fish (222).

An attempt to study the kinetics of propagation in cylindrically shaped eggs in capillaries yielded unexpected and puzzling results (6). The rate of propagation was initially similar to that in spherical eggs (Fig. 18), but it soon decreased and often died out entirely, particularly in the more

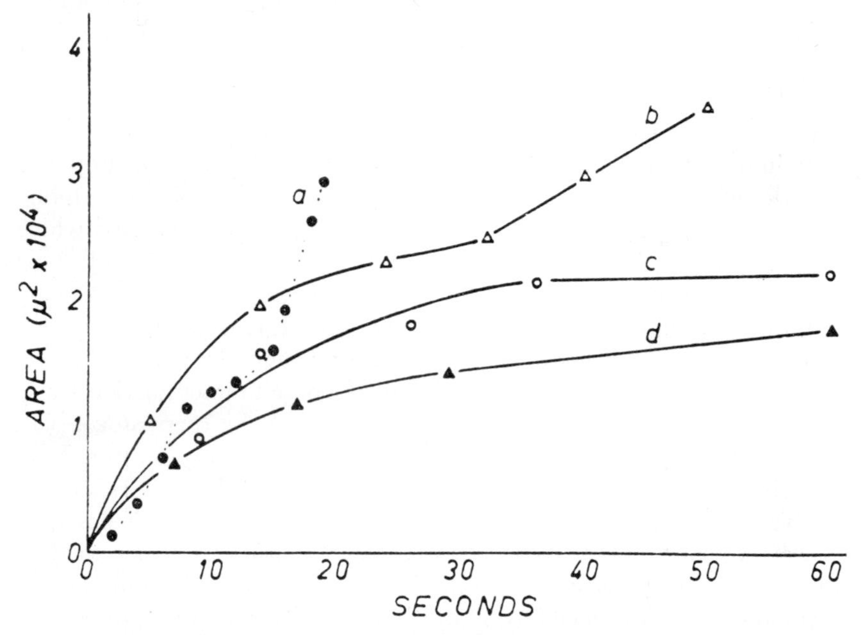

Fig. 18. The rate of propagation of the fertilization impulse as studied *a* by the dark field change in spherical eggs (data replotted from Rothschild and Swann, 167) and *b, c,* and *d* by the breakdown of cortical granules in cylindrical eggs in capillaries. Egg *b* was treated with ATP, length 188 μ; egg *c* was a dispermic egg (length 423 μ); and egg *d* was monospermic (Allen, 6; see also 12).

stretched eggs. Temperature coefficients for propagation rates in cylindrical eggs were between 2 and 3, except for impulses initiated by parthenogenetic concentrations of periodate, for which the temperature coefficient dropped to nearly 1 (12). This fact suggested that a chemical component of the wave had been short-cut by periodate treatment, which is believed to free the egg from the influence of a natural mucopolysaccharide inhibitor believed to be present in the cortex (174, 175, 181-183). More recently, approximate temperature coefficients have been measured for the durations of the latent period and of the cortical reaction as 2.3 and 1.4 respectively. The latter value is characteristic for a diffusion process in spherical eggs,

yet conduction in cylindrical eggs showed a Q_{10} characteristic of chemical processes. It is possible that the capillary had the effect of slowing whatever chemical component of the cortical reaction would normally occur during the latent period, with the result that this would then act as a rate-limiting process in the later visible phase of cortical granule breakdown. This suggestion is put forth tentatively and may require modification as more data become available. The kinetic approach to the fertilization impulse has so far been disappointing; this is largely due to the technical difficulties in obtaining sufficient data.

Aside from somewhat unsatisfactory information on its kinetics, the other information available about the propagated "fertilization impulse" concerns what will initiate it, favor its conduction, or block it. Among chemically defined initiating substances are those previously listed which Sugiyama has studied; to these should be added periodate (6, 12). One would be tempted to believe from this list that the egg is poised to respond by some autocatalytic mechanism to any sort of non-specific "trigger." However, this appears not to be the case, for not only do many activating agents fail to pull the trigger (cf. 195), but response to insemination seems to depend on the origin and physiological state of the spermatozoa (61, 175, 204). We must conclude, therefore, that the spermatozoon introduces a certain "charge" of activating substance which, depending on its amount or composition, can initiate qualitatively different impulses. It has been shown that some eggs in a population show marked differences in their ability to conduct a fertilization impulse (6, p. 416, Tables I and II).

Among the experimental conditions which favor propagation of the fertilization wave are reduced temperature, glycine, adenosine triphosphate (ATP), and periodate pretreatment; at least this is the case for eggs fertilized in capillaries. Among the agents which tend to block the fertilization impulse are elevated temperature, either alone or in combination with other conditions, the non-specific poison nicotine, and either deformation, stretching, or extensive contact with glass surfaces involved in the capillary experiments. However, in spite of reports to the contrary (185), there is no evidence that contact or even attachment to glass can inhibit the passage of the cortical reaction (cf. 7). Okazaki has recently reported blocking the cortical reaction with the uncoupling agents dinitrophenol and azide, but these acted only at elevated temperatures and were not antagonized by ATP. It seems reasonable to suppose that the effect Okazaki found (154) was due primarily to elevated temperature (cf. 11) in synergism with some effect of the chemical agents which need not necessarily have been that of uncoupling phosphorylation from oxidative processes. The sensitivity of

the fertilization impulse to elevated temperature is not unlike heat narcosis in nerve, for it is effective only during conduction and causes no injury when applied before or after conduction (11, 12). Inhibition by deformation, as would be suggested from the capillary experiments, is also reminiscent of nerve. For this reason it is of great interest that Tyler, Monroy, Kao, and Grundfest (206) have succeeded in demonstrating a change in membrane potential within a half minute after insemination. Sugiyama (197) has recently demonstrated two properties of the activation process in sea urchin eggs that are characteristic of irritable processes in general: (1) the ability of an egg to conduct a fertilization wave is blocked on narcosis with urethane; and (2) summation of two subthreshold stimuli will produce a fertilization wave if given within a few minutes of one another. The latter suggests the build-up of some substance within the egg which would trigger the fertilization wave or impulse.

6. *Chemical Theories of Activation*

The early chemical theories of activation are not very useful in interpreting the mechanism of the fertilization impulse and its role in activating the egg. The earliest, F. R. Lillie's "fertilizin" theory, cannot be reconciled with most of the information available at present (for a discussion of the fertilizin theory in the light of recent findings, see 63a).

Prof. J. Runnström, his students and collaborators have approached the physiology of activation in a systematic manner by studying the action of various substances which enhance or inhibit various aspects of the fertilization process. Among the inhibitors found have been various mucopolysaccharides, including heparin, blood group substances, an extract of *Fucus,* and even the dissolved jelly of the egg (63a, 69, 70, 95, 176, 179, 181, 182, 216-218). Periodate ions were found capable of removing the inhibiting action of these substances, and in addition caused certain changes in the eggs indicative of incipient activation, or "preactivation," which was accompanied by a lowered threshold to artificial activation (96, 184). In sufficient concentration, periodate was effective in causing artificial activation. For this reason, it was of particular interest when Lundblad detected the successive activation of three proteolytic enzymes at the time of fertilization (108-110). The first of these to be activated, E II, was found on isolation to be capable of being activated by periodate, a fact suggesting that it occurred naturally in combination with a mucopolysaccharide inhibitor, perhaps the same one which seemed to act in an inhibitory manner on fertilization, especially in under-ripe eggs (see especially 175, 179).

On the basis of these and other results, Runnström has proposed a

"kinase theory" of activation based on available facts. It is proposed that the kinase is originally bound to a natural inhibitor, and perhaps also to ATP and Mg^{++} ions (174, 175, 179). The introduction of a substance from the spermatozoon (originally suggested to be antifertilizin) would bind the inhibitor and release the kinase, which would in turn activate various proenzymes in the cell. In the past, R. S. Lillie also proposed the involvement of an enzyme (protease) in the early stages of activation (104). Lundblad's proteolytic enzyme E II has been proposed to act as the kinase by virtue of its original binding with a carbohydrate inhibitor. It might turn out that the inhibitor was identical with "cytofertilizin," since there is evidence that both this material and E II may be localized in the cortex, since they can apparently "leak out": E II during jelly removal in acid sea water below *p*H 5.5 (109, 110), and cytofertilizin upon aging (58). It is possible that we have only begun to find enzymes at the surface which might participate in the process of activation. For example, Numanoi (151-153) has suggested a role for sulfatases in fertilization and activation. It will be interesting to follow the future of work on such enzymes, for they might provide a direct enzymatic means for destruction of the proposed natural carbohydrate inhibitor within the egg. In order to interpret the available evidence on the conduction of the fertilization impulse in terms of the kinase theory, it is necessary to assume a two-step process, in which first an enzymatically controlled change spreads over or through the egg on stimulation from the sperm; this would lower the threshold of the surface for the second phase, presumably a diffusion process involving a small molecule over a short distance. The value of such speculations as these is only in planning experiments, for there are many questions left unanswered, such as the nature of the stimulating substance from the sperm, the chain of enzymes, inhibitors, etc., which are involved, and the time sequence of their action in relation to visible events.

A somewhat simpler theoretical approach to the chemical mechanism of activation has been undertaken by Monroy, who has assumed from observations with the polarizing microscope (see Section II 2 b) that the sea urchin egg cortex is a lipoprotein system with the properties of a liquid crystal (126, 127, 129), which undergoes structural changes due mostly to changes in the lipids themselves. Accordingly, he has designed interesting model experiments on the interaction between living sea urchin sperm and a lipoprotein extracted from hens' eggs. His results show that sperm can cause the release of free phospholipids which later break down into substances with hemolytic activity. Monroy has supposed that something like this sequence of events takes place during activation of the egg by the

sperm, and possibly in the propagation of the surface changes. These interesting experiments may lead to a better understanding of some of the metabolic pathways of phospholipid utilization, since these materials constitute a major endogenous source of substrate for sperm cells (166). For a number of reasons, however, the theoretical basis of these experiments is at present not very attractive. Although there is no question that the unfertilized egg is birefringent, and that this birefringence disappears dramatically at fertilization, there has been much disagreement as to the significance of this observation. There seems to be, at the present time, no clear evidence for the localization in the cortex, below the vitelline membrane, of oriented lipid layers; otherwise these would show in the electron micrographs. Therefore, interpretation of the cortical changes in terms of changes in lipid molecules may be premature. Furthermore, in view of the fact that wasp-venom, saponin, and various detergents, which attack lipoid and lipoprotein structures, exert only a localized effect on the egg surface (195, 197), it seems unlikely that a lipoprotein-splitting process could be the basis of propagation of the fertilization impulse. However, lipoprotein-splitting processes could certainly be important in the passage of the sperm through the vitelline membrane.

7. *The Significance of the Cortical Reaction in Relation to the Processes Leading to Syngamy*

The discovery of methods to block the passage of the fertilization impulse has provided the possibility of weighing the relative significance of the entrance of the sperm and the passage of the fertilization impulse for later development (6, 11, 63b). Eggs with a blocked fertilization impulse have been designated "partially fertilized" because a portion of their surface remains unaltered and susceptible to refertilization. Not only are the surfaces of the fertilized and unfertilized parts different in these eggs, but the endoplasm is different as well. In partially fertilized eggs obtained by the capillary method (Fig. 19), the light-scattering properties of the endoplasm underlying the fertilized surface showed the same decrease as upon fertilization in spherical eggs, and the division between unfertilized and fertilized endoplasm could be seen to persist (6). However, when spherical eggs were made partially fertilized by blocking the fertilization impulse with heat, the initial differences between unfertilized and fertilized endoplasm did not always remain, suggesting that a mixing had occurred. The following nuclear changes occurring in partially fertilized eggs represent deviations from the normal: (1) growth of the sperm aster and migration of the sperm nucleus were restricted to fertilized cytoplasm; (2) the egg

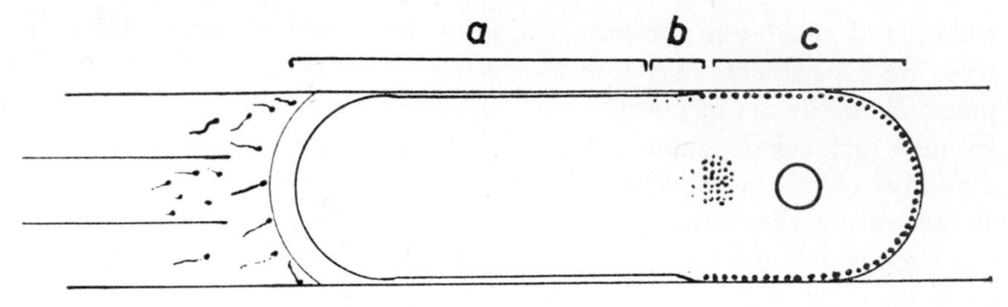

Fig. 19. Diagram of a partially fertilized egg in a capillary. *a,* fertilized portion; *b,* intermediate zone; and *c,* unfertilized portion (Allen, 6).

nucleus migrated only if originally located in fertilized cytoplasm; however, it was able to undergo swelling or even break down in unfertilized cytoplasm; and (3) sometimes nuclear fusion failed to occur; when it did take place, cleavage was delayed, and often the cleavage furrow did not pass entirely through the cell (Fig. 20).

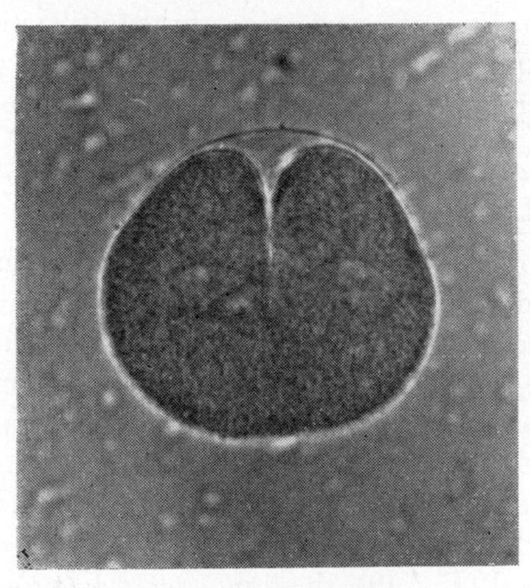

Fig. 20. A partially fertilized *Psammechinus* egg showing an incomplete cleavage furrow. The fertilization impulse was blocked by elevated temperature (Allen and Hagström, 11).

The observations on partially fertilized eggs have raised a new and important problem: what is the action of fertilized cortex on its underlying endoplasm? Some observations which bear on this point, but do not answer the question, have been made in the *Arbacia punctulata* egg, where fertilization is followed in about 10 minutes by a mass migration of nearly all of the echinochrome pigment granules (chromatophores) to the surface (112). In partially fertilized eggs the pigment granules migrate only to

fertilized parts of the cortical layer, to produce a red patch at the point of sperm entry (14). In experiments with eggs in capillaries, it was shown that fertilized cortex could "induce" pigment granule migration from a distance of about 26 microns within unfertilized cytoplasm (Fig. 21). The

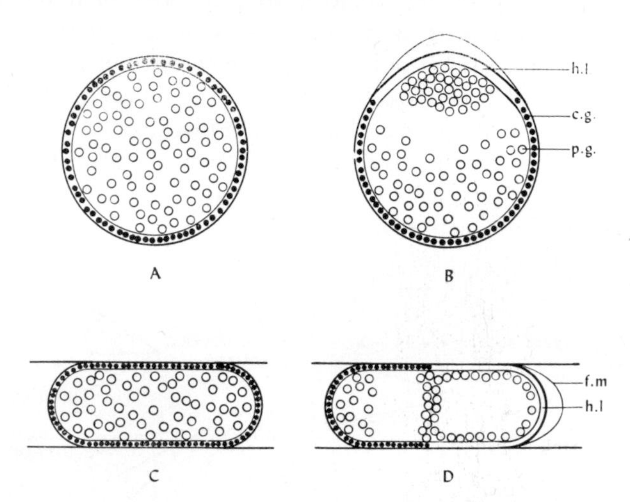

Fig. 21. A highly schematic representation of the behavior of pigment granules in *Arbacia* eggs when the fertilization impulse is blocked, leaving the eggs partially fertilized. A and B are spherical eggs, unfertilized and 10 minutes after partial fertilization; C and D are cylindrical eggs, unfertilized and after partial fertilization. c.g., cortical granules; f.m., fertilization membrane; h.l., hyaline layer; p.g., pigment granules (cf. Allen and Rowe, 14).

mechanism of the interaction between fertilized cortex and the pigment granules is unknown, but it provides a visible manifestation of endoplasmic activation as a result of influences emanating from the cortical layer after fertilization.

The results presented so far in this section leave us with at least two possible interpretations: either the presence of cortical granules in the cortex imposes some kind of inhibition on developmental processes from which the egg must be "released" in order to develop, or else the fertilization impulse or wave is itself an activating influence and the disappearance of cortical granules is incidental to activation. Fortunately, there is evidence on this point in observations made long ago by Motomura (139, 140). Optimal exposure to butyric acid, followed by return to sea water, results in membrane elevation and endoplasmic activation. However, prolonged exposure to butyric acid stabilizes the cortical granules so that on subsequent return to sea water and fertilization the granules remain

intact through cleavage, indicating that they are not in themselves deterrents to cleavage. Motomura has also shown more recently that it is possible to activate eggs by other means without disturbing the cortical granules (143, 145). We can conclude tentatively from these observations that the event of primary importance in the initiation of development, at least in echinoderm eggs, is the fertilization wave, which evidently transmits a state of excitation not only around the cortex, but presumably into the endoplasm as well. The cortical granules might seem at first to lose some of their former importance, but it should be stressed that their most essential role seems to be in establishing the new surface layers after fertilization. They also serve quite importantly as the only markers we have for the progress of the fertilization impulse.

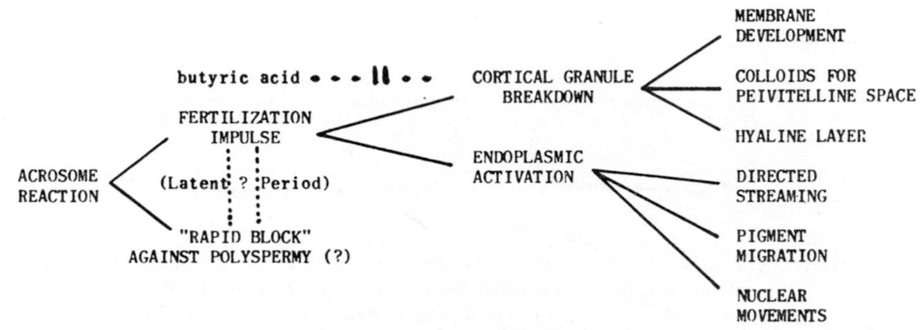

Fig. 22. Explanation in the text.

In Fig. 22, which is based on the work discussed above, of many authors, an attempt has been made to point out what now appear to be some of the causal relationships in the early events in the initiation of development in the sea urchin. On examination of this scheme, it will be seen that although the processes involved in syngamy, on the one hand, and activation, on the other, can be separated experimentally by artificial activation, nonetheless, under normal conditions of fertilization, the two sets of processes undoubtedly interact, as shown by the failure of the nuclei to migrate and fuse if the fertilization impulse is blocked. There are many problems in the physiology and biochemistry of activation which still await solution, although promising leads have been uncovered in many directions. It is hoped that in the future more attention will be directed toward fertilization in eggs with a stable cortex, for in these it may be easier to distinguish the processes which are involved in activation without the interference of the membrane elevation mechanism.

I wish to express my appreciation to the following individuals for kindly contributing illustrations for this article: Drs. B. Afzelius, A. and L. Colwin, N. E. Kemp, J. M. Mitchison, and L. I. Rebhun. I am also grateful to Prof. John Runnström for allowing me to read his manuscript, *Fertilization,* which will be published in *The Cell* (182).

REFERENCES

1. Afzelius, B., *Z. Zellforsch. u. mikroskop. Anat.,* **42,** 134-148 (1955).
2. ———, *Exptl. Cell Research,* **10,** 257-285 (1956).
3. ———, in *Electron Microscopy, Proceedings of the Stockholm Conference, September 1956* (F. S. Sjöstrand and J. Rhodin, eds.), p. 167-169, Academic Press, New York (1957).
4. Afzelius, B. A., and Murray, A., *Exptl. Cell Research,* **12,** 325-337 (1957).
5. Allen, R. D., *Biol. Bull.,* **105,** 213-239 (1953).
6. ———, *Exptl. Cell Research,* **6,** 403-422 (1954).
7. ———, *Exptl. Cell Research,* **8,** 397-399 (1955).
8. ———, *J. Cell. Comp. Physiol.,* **49,** 379-394 (1957).
9. ———, unpub.
10. Allen, R. D., and Griffin, J. L., *Exptl. Cell Research* (in press).
11. Allen, R. D., and Hagström, B., *Exptl. Cell Research,* **9,** 156-167 (1955).
12. ———, and ———, *Exptl. Cell Research,* **Suppl. 3,** 1-15 (1955).
13. Allen, R. D., Lundberg, A., and Runnström, J., *Exptl. Cell Research,* **9,** 174-180 (1955).
14. Allen, R. D., and Rowe, E. C., *Biol. Bull.* (in press).
15. Austin, C. R., *Exptl. Cell Research,* **10,** 533-540 (1956).
16. Austin, C. R., and Bishop, M. W. H., in *Beginnings of Embryonic Development* (A. Tyler, R. C. von Borstel, and C. B. Metz, eds.), p. 71-107, A.A.A.S., Washington, D. C. (1957).
17. Bataillon, E., *Arch. Zool. exptl. et gén.,* **46,** 101-135 (1910).
18. Bernstein, G. S., *Biol. Bull.,* **103,** 285 (1952).
19. Bowen, R. H., *Anat. Rec.,* **28,** 1-13 (1924).
20. Brachet, A., *Wilhelm Roux' Arch. Entwicklungsmech. Organ.,* **30,** 261-303 (1910).
21. Chambers, E. L., *J. Exptl. Biol.,* **16,** 409-424 (1939).
22. Chambers, R., *J. Gen. Physiol.,* **5,** 821-829 (1923).
23. ———, *Biol. Bull.,* **58,** 344-369 (1930).
24. ———, *J. Exptl. Biol.* **10,** 130-141 (1933).
25. ———, *J. Cell. Comp. Physiol.,* **19,** 145-150 (1942).
26. Chase, H. Y., *Biol. Bull.,* **69,** 159-184 (1935).
27. Cheney, R. H., and Lansing, A. I., *Exptl. Cell Research,* **8,** 173-180 (1955).
28. Colwin, A. L., and Colwin, L. H., *Biol. Bull.,* **109,** 357 (1955).
29. ———, and ———, *J. Morphol.,* **97,** 543-568 (1955).
30. ———, and ———, *Biol. Bull.,* **109,** 357-358 (1955).
31. ———. and ———, in *Beginnings of Embryonic Development* (A. Tyler, R. C. von Borstel, and C. B. Metz, eds.), p. 135-168. A.A.A.S., Washington, D. C. (1957).
32. Colwin, A. L., Colwin, L. H., and Philpott, D. E., *Biol. Bull.,* **111,** 289 (1956).
33. ———, ———, and ———, *J. Biophys. Biochem. Cytol.,* **3,** 489-510 (1957).
34. Colwin, L. H., and Colwin, A. L., *J. Morphol.,* **95,** 351-372 (1954).
35. ———, and ———, *Biol. Bull.,* **109,** 357-358 (1955).
36. ———, and ———, *Biol. Bull.,* **109,** 357 (1955).
37. ———, and ———, *Biol. Bull.,* **110,** 243-257 (1956).
38. Costello, D. P., *Physiol. Zool.,* **8,** 65-72 (1935).
39. ———, *J. Gen. Physiol.,* **32,** 351-366 (1949).

40. ———, *Biol. Bull.*, **113**, 341-342 (1957).
41. Dan, J. C., *Biol. Bull.*, **99**, 399-411 (1950).
42. ———, *Biol. Bull.*, **99**, 412-415 (1950).
43. ———, *Biol. Bull.*, **103**, 54-56 (1952).
44. ———, *Biol. Bull.*, **107**, 203-218 (1954).
45. ———, *Biol. Bull.*, **107**, 335-349 (1954).
46. ———, *Intern. Rev. Cytol.*, **5**, 365-393 (1956).
47. Dan, J. C., and Dan, K., *Jap. J. Zool.*, **9**, 565-573 (1941).
48. Dan, J. C., and Wada, S. K., *Biol. Bull.*, **109**, 40-55 (1955).
49. Dan, K., and Okasaki, K., *J. Cellular Comp. Physiol.*, **38**, 427-435 (1951).
50. Dean, R. B., and Moore, A. R., *Biodynamica*, **6**, 159-163 (1947).
51. Delage, Y., *Arch. zool. exptl. et gén.*, **29**, 285-326 (1901).
52. Endo, Y., *Exptl. Cell Research*, **3**, 406-418 (1952).
53. Fol, H., *Arch. zool. exptl. et gén.*, **6**, 145-169 (1877).
54. Folkes, B. F., Grant, R. A., and Jones, J. K. N., *J. Chem. Soc.*, **440**, 2136-2140 (1950).
55. Godlewski, E., *Wilhelm Roux' Arch. Entwicklungsmech. Organ.*, **33**, 196-254 (1912).
56. Goodrich, H. B., *Biol. Bull.*, **38**, 196-201 (1920).
57. Gray, J., *J. Exptl. Biol.*, **32**, 775-802 (1955).
58. Hagström, B. E., *Exptl. Cell Research*, **9**, 407-413 (1955).
59. ———, *Exptl. Cell Research*, **10**, 24-28 (1956).
60. ———, *Exptl. Cell Research*, **11**, 160-168 (1956).
61. ———, *Exptl. Cell Research*, **11**, 507-510 (1956).
62. ———, *Arkiv Zool.*, **10**, 307-315 (1956).
63a. ———, The role of the jelly coat and the block to polyspermy in the fertilization of sea urchins (thesis). Uppsala (1956).
63b. Hagström, B. E., and Allen, R. D., *Exptl. Cell Research*, **10**, 14-23 (1956).
64. Hagström, B., and Hagström, Britt, *Exptl. Cell Research*, **6**, 479-484 (1954).
65. ———, and ———, *Exptl. Cell Research*, **6**, 491-496 (1954).
66. ———, and ———, *Exptl. Cell Research*, **6**, 532-534 (1954).
67. Hagström, B., and Markman, B., *Acta Zool.*, **38**, 219-222 (1958).
68. Hagström, B., and Runnström, J., *Protoplasma*, **44**, 154-164 (1954).
69. Harding, C. V., *Exptl. Cell Research*, **2**, 403-415 (1951).
70. Harding, C. V., and Harding, D., *Arkiv Zool.*, **3**, 357-361 (1952).
71. Harvey, E. B., *Biol. Bull.*, **65**, 389-396 (1933).
72. ———, *Biol. Bull.*, **66**, 228-245 (1934).
73. ———, *The American Arbacia and Other Sea Urchins*. Princeton Univ. Press, Princeton (1956).
74. Harvey, E. N., *J. Exptl. Zool.*, **10**, 507-556 (1911).
75. Heilbrunn, L. V., *An Outline of General Physiology*. W. B. Saunders Co., Philadelphia (1952).
76. Hendee, E. C., *Papers Tortugas Lab. Carnegie Inst. Wash. Publ.*, **27**, 101 (1931).
77. Herbst, K., *Wilhelm Roux' Arch. Entwicklungsmech. Organ.*, **9**, 424-463 (1900).
78. Hiramoto, Y., *Jap. J. Zool.*, **11**, 227-243 (1954).
79. ———, *Jap. J. Zool.*, **11**, 333-344 (1954).
80. ———, *Annot. Zool. Jap.*, **28**, 183-192 (1955).
81. Hobson, A. D., *Proc. Roy. Soc. Edinburgh*, **47**, 94-117 (1927).
82. Immers, J., *Arkiv Zool.*, **42A**, 1-9 (1949).
83. ———, *Arkiv Zool.*, **3**, 367-371 (1952).
84. ———, *Arkiv Zool.*, **9**, 367-375 (1956).
85. Inoué, S., *Biol. Bull.*, **97**, 258 (1949).
86. James, S. B., *Biochem. J. (London)*, **49**, liv (1951) (abstract).
87. Just, E. E., *Biol. Bull.*, **36**, 1-10 (1919).
88. ———, *The Biology of the Cell Surface*. Blakiston, Philadelphia (1939).

89. Kacser, H., *J. Exptl. Biol.*, **32**, 451-467 (1955).
90. Kelly, J. W., *Protoplasma*, **39**, 386-388 (1950).
91. Kemp, N. E., *J. Biophys. Biochem. Cytol.*, **2**, 281-292 (1956).
92. ———, *J. Biophys. Biochem. Cytol.*, **2** (Suppl.), 187-191 (1956).
93. ———, pers. commun.
94. Kopac, M. J., *J. Cellular Comp. Physiol.*, **18**, 215-220 (1941).
95. Kriszat, G., *Exptl. Cell Research*, **7**, 103-110 (1954).
96. Kriszat, G., and Runnström, J., *Exptl. Cell Research*, **3**, 597-604 (1952).
97. Kupelwieser, H., *Wilhelm Roux' Arch. Entwicklungsmech. Organ.*, **27**, 434-462 (1909).
98. Kusa, M., *Annot. Zool. Jap.*, **24**, 22-28 (1950).
99. ———, *Embryologia*, **3**, 105-129 (1956).
100. Lansing, A., Hillier, J., and Rosenthal, T. B., *Biol. Bull.*, **103**, 294 (1952).
101. Leghissa, S., *Riv. biol. (Perugia)*, **43**, 187-197 (1951).
102. Lillie, F. R., *Problems of Fertilization*, Univ. Chicago Press, Chicago (1919).
103. ———, *J. Morphol.*, **22**, 362-390 (1911).
104. Lillie, R. S., *Biol. Bull.*, **32**, 131-158 (1917).
105. Lindahl, P. E., *Protoplasma*, **16**, 378-386 (1932).
106. Loeb, J., *Proc. Soc. Exptl. Biol. and Med.*, **7**, 120-121 (1910).
107. ———, *Wilhelm Roux' Arch. Entwicklungsmech. Organ.*, **26**, 82-88 (1908).
108. Lundblad, G., *Arkiv Zool.*, **6**, 387-415 (1953).
109. ———, *Arkiv Kemi*, **7**, 127-157 (1954).
110. ———, Proteolytic activity in sea urchin gametes (Thesis). Uppsala (1954).
111. Mazia, D., *J. Cellular Comp. Physiol.*, **10**, 291-303 (1937).
112. McClendon, J. F., *Science*, **30**, 454-455 (1909).
113. McCulloch, D., *Exptl. Cell Research*, **3**, 605-607 (1952).
114. Messina, L., *Pubbl. staz. zool. Napoli*, **25**, 454-458 (1954).
115. Messina, L., and Monroy, A., *Pubbl. staz. zool. Napoli*, **28**, 266-268 (1956).
116. Metz, C. B., Specific egg and sperm substances and activation of the egg, in *Beginnings of Embryonic Development* (A. Tyler, R. C. von Borstel, and C. B. Metz, eds.), p. 23-69, A.A.A.S., Washington, D. C. (1957).
117. Metz, C. B., and Morrill, J. B., Jr., *Biol. Bull.*, **109**, 349 (1955).
118. Minganti, A., *Exptl. Cell Research*, **5**, 492-499 (1953).
119. ———, *Exptl. Cell Research*, **7**, 1-14 (1954).
120. ———, *Exptl. Cell Research*, **Suppl. 3**, 248-251 (1955).
121. Mitchison, J. M., *Quart. J. Micr. Sci.*, **97**, 109-121 (1956).
122. ———, *Exptl. Cell Research*, **10**, 309-315 (1956).
123. Mitchison, J. M., and Swann. M. M., *J. Exptl. Biol.*, **29**, 357-362 (1952).
124. ———, and ———, *Quart J. Microscop. Sci.*, **95**, 381-389 (1953).
125. Monné, L., and Hårde, S., *Arkiv Zool.*, **1**, 487-497 (1951).
126. Monroy, A., *Experientia*, **1**, 335-336 (1945).
127. ———, *J. Cellular Comp. Physiol.*, **30**, 105-110 (1947).
128. ———, *Arkiv Zool.*, **40A**, 1-7 (1948).
129. ———, *Exptl. Cell Research*, **10**, 320-323 (1956).
130. Monroy, A., and Monroy-Oddo, A., *Pubbl. staz. zool. Napoli*, **20**, 46-60 (1946).
131. Monroy, A., and Montalenti, G., *Biol. Bull.*, **92**, 151-161 (1947).
132. Monroy, A., and Runnström, J., *Arkiv Zool.*, **40A**, 1-6 (1948).
133. Moore, A. R., *Protoplasma*, **3**, 524-530 (1928).
134. ———, *Protoplasma*, **27**, 544-551 (1937).
135. ———, *Scientia*, **86**, 195-199 (1951).
136. Moser, F., *J. Exptl. Zool.*, **80**, 423-440 (1939).
137. ———, *J. Exptl. Zool.*, **80**, 447-464 (1939).
138. ———, *Biol. Bull.*, **78**, 68-79 (1940).
139. Motomura, I., *Science Repts. Tôhoku Univ., Fourth Ser.*, **9**, 33-45 (1934).

140. ———, *Science Repts. Tôhoku Univ. Fourth Ser.*, **16**, 345-364 (1941).
141. ———, *Science Repts. Tôhoku Univ., Fourth Ser.*, **18**, 554-560 (1950).
142. ———, *Science Repts. Tôhoku Univ., Fourth Ser.*, **18**, 561-570 (1950).
143. ———, *Science Repts. Tôhoku Univ., Fourth Ser.*, **19**, 203-206 (1952).
144. ———, *Annot. Zool. Jap.*, **25**, 238 (1952).
145. ———, *Science Repts. Tôhoku Univ., Fourth Ser.*, **20**, 213-217 (1954).
146. ———, *Science Repts. Tôhoku Univ., Fourth Ser.*, **20**, 318-321 (1954).
147. ———, *Science Repts. Tôhoku Univ., Fourth Ser.*, **23**, 167-181 (1957).
148. Nakano, E., *Jap. J. Zool.*, **11**, 245-251 (1954).
149. Nakano, E., and Ohashi, S., *Embryologia*, **2**, 81-85 (1954).
150. Novikoff, A. B., *J. Exptl. Zool.*, **82**, 217-237 (1939).
151. Numanoi, H., *Sci. Papers Coll. Gen. Educ., Univ. Tokyo*, **3**, 55-66 (1953).
152. ———, *Sci. Papers Coll. Gen. Educ., Univ. Tokyo*, **3**, 67-70 (1953).
153. ———, *Sci. Papers Coll. Gen. Educ., Univ. Tokyo*, **3**, 71-80 (1953).
154. Okazaki, R., *Exptl. Cell Research*, **10**, 476-504 (1956).
155. Okkelberg, P., *Biol. Bull.*, **26**, 92-99 (1914).
156. Parpart, A. K., and Laris, P. C., *Biol. Bull.*, **107**, 301 (1954).
157. ———, and ———, *Biol. Bull.*, **109**, 350 (1955).
158. Parpart, A. K. and Cagle, J., *Biol. Bull.*, **113**, 331 (1957).
159. Rebhun, L. I., pers. commun.
160. Reverberi, G., *Pubbl. staz. zool. Napoli*, **15**, 175-193 (1935).
161. Rothschild, Lord, *J. Exptl. Biol.*, **30**, 57-67 (1953).
162. ———, *Quart. Rev. Biol.*, **29**, 332-342 (1954).
163. ———, *Fertilization*. Methuen & Co., London (1956).
164. ———, *Discovery*, **18**, (2), (1956).
165. ———, *Endeavour*, **25**, 79-86 (1956).
166. Rothschild, Lord, and Cleland, K. W., *J. Exptl. Biol.*, **29**, 66-71 (1952).
167. Rothschild, Lord, and Swann, M. M., *J. Exptl. Biol.*, **26**, 164-176 (1949).
168. ———, and ———, *J. Exptl. Biol.*, **27**, 400-406 (1950).
169. Rothschild, Lord, and Tyler, A., *Exptl. Cell Research*, **Suppl. 3**, 304-311 (1955).
170. Runnström, J., *Acta Zool.*, **4**, 285-311 (1923).
171. ———, *Arkiv Zool.*, **40A**, 1 (1947).
172. ———, *Arkiv Zool.*, **40A**, (17), 1-16 (1948).
173. ———, *Arkiv Zool.*, **40A**, (19), 1-6 (1948).
174. ———, *Pubbl. staz. zool. Napoli*, **21** (Suppl.), 9-21 (1949).
175. ———, *Advances in Enzymol.*, **9**, 241-328 (1949).
176. ———, *Exptl. Cell Research*, **1**, 304-308 (1950).
177. ———, *Symposia Soc. Exptl. Biol.*, **6**, 39-88 (1952).
178. ———, *Harvey Lectures*, **46**, 116-152 (1952).
179. ———, *Zool. Anz.* **156**, 91-101 (1956).
180. ———, *Exptl. Cell Research*, **12**, 374-394 (1957).
181. ———, in *Festschrift Arthur Stoll*, 850-868, Sandoz A. G., Basel (1957).
182. ———, Fertilization, in *The Cell* (in press).
183. Runnström, J., and Immers, J., *Exptl. Cell Research*, **10**, 254-263 (1956).
184. Runnström, J., and Kriszat, G., *Exptl. Cell Research*, **1**, 335-340 (1950).
185. ———, and ———, *Exptl. Cell Research*, **3**, 419-426 (1952).
186. ———, and ———, *Exptl. Cell Research*, **12**, 526-536 (1957).
187. Runnström, J., and Monné, L., *Arkiv Zool.*, **36A** (18), 1-25 (1945).
188. Runnström, J., Monné, L., and Broman, L., *Arkiv Zool.*, **35A** (3), 1-32 (1944).
189. Runnström, J., Monné, L., and Wicklund, E., *Nature*, **153**, 313-314 (1944).
190. ———, ———, and ———, *J. Colloid Sci.*, **1**, 421-452 (1946).
191. Runnström, J., Tiselius, A., and Lindvall, S., *Arkiv Zool.*, **36A** (22), 1-25 (1945).

192. Runnström, J., Tiselius, A., and Vasseur, E., *Arkiv Kemi Mineral. Geol.*, **15A** (16) (1942).
193. Seifritz, W., *Protoplasma*, **1**, 1-14 (1926).
194. Sugiyama, M., *Biol. Bull.*, **101**, 335-344 (1951).
195. ———, *Biol. Bull.*, **104**, 210-215 (1953).
196. ———, *Biol. Bull.*, **104**, 216-223 (1953).
197. ———, *Exptl. Cell Research*, **10**, 364-376 (1956).
198. Thomas, L. J., *Biol. Bull.*, **106**, 124-138 (1954).
199. Tyler, A., *Proc. Natl. Acad. Sci. U. S.*, **25**, 317-323 (1939).
200. ———, *Biol. Bull.*, **81**, 190-204 (1941).
201. ———, *Biol. Revs.*, **16**, 291-336 (1941).
202. ———, *Physiol. Revs.*, **28**, 180-219 (1948).
203. ———, *Am. Naturalist*, **85**, 195-219 (1949).
204. ———, *Biol. Bull.*, **99**, 324 (1950).
205. ———, *Exptl. Cell Research*, **10**, 377-386 (1956).
206. Tyler, A., Monroy, A., Kao, C. Y., and Grundfest, H., *Biol. Bull.*, **111**, 153-177 (1956).
207. Tyler, A., Monroy, A., and Metz, C. B., *Biol. Bull.*, **110**, 184-195 (1956).
208. Tyler, A., and Spiegel, M., *Biol. Bull.*, **110**, 196-200 (1956).
209. Vasseur, E., *Arkiv Kemi Mineral. Geol.*, **25** (6) (1947).
210. ———, *Acta Chem. Scand.*, **2**, 900-913 (1948).
211. ———, *Acta Chem. Scand.*, **6**, 376-384 (1952).
212. ———, Chemistry and physiology of the jelly coat of the sea urchin egg (Thesis), Stockholm (1952).
213. Vasseur, E., and Immers, J., *Arkiv Kemi*, **1**, 39-41 (1949).
214. Wada, S. K., *Mem. Fac. Fisheries, Kagoshima Univ.*, **4**, 105-112 (1955).
215. Wada, S. K., Collier, J. R., and Dan, J. C., *Exptl. Cell Research*, **10**, 168-180 (1956).
216. Wicklund, E., *Arkiv Zool.*, **6**, 485-501 (1954).
217. ———, Improving and inhibiting agents action on the gametes and on their interaction at fertilization in sea urchins (Thesis), Uppsala (1954).
218. Wicklund, E., Kriszat, G., and Runnström, J., *J. Embryol. Exptl. Morphol.*, **1**, 319-325 (1953).
219. Wilson, E. B., *An Atlas of the Fertilization and Karyokinesis of the Ovum*, Macmillan, New York (1895).
220. ———, *Wilhelm Roux' Arch. Entwicklungsmech. Organ.*, **12**, 529-596 (1901).
221. ———, *The Cell in Development and Heredity*, Macmillan, New York (1925).
222. Yamamoto, T., *Exptl. Cell Research*, **10** (2), 387-393 (1956).
223. Yanagimachi, R., *Dobusugaki Zasshi* (*Zool. Mag.*), **62**, 220-224 (1953).
224. Ziegler, H. E., *Wilhelm Roux' Arch. Entwicklungsmech. Organ.*, **6**, 249-293 (1898).

DISCUSSION

Dr. Novikoff. I would like to put a conceptual question to Dr. Markert, and a specific one to Dr. Allen.

I wonder, Dr. Markert, if two levels of organization, cell and tissue, were distinguished sufficiently in your presentation of the esterase story. When you follow different esterases in homogenates of the whole embryo, to what extent are you describing shifting cell populations and to what extent enzymatic differentiation within the individual cells?

To the degree that specific staining methods reveal the true levels of enzyme activities, it may be said that different cell types of a tissue almost invariably

show marked quantitative differences. And even among the parenchymatous liver cells, a more homogeneous tissue than most, such quantitative enzyme differences are always found. Non-specific esterase and lipase are more active in the centrolobular cells than in the cells near the lobule periphery. The same is true for DPNH-diaphorase activity; with succinic dehydrogenase, however, the situation is reversed: its activity is high in the peripheral cells and low in the centrolobular cells.

Have you used such staining methods on your material?

My question to Dr. Allen concerns the possibility that in some eggs the egg filaments described by earlier embryologists may also play an important role in sperm entry. Does the egg play a more significant role where it possesses conspicuous filaments, as in *Sabellaria* and *Nereis?*

Dr. Allen: As far as I know, there are no reports of filaments from the egg which could be confused with the type of sperm filament which I have discussed this morning. There have been reports, however, especially the work by Colwin and Colwin in *Holothuria,* of egg filaments as well as sperm filaments. However, the sperm filaments can always be distinguished from the others. Monroy showed many years ago in *Pomatocerus* that there were many filaments emanating out of the egg. However, this was before the acrosome reaction had been clearly described. He did mention, I believe, that the filament from the sperm did look different from those of the egg. Possibly Dr. Colwin would like to comment on this problem.

Dr. Colwin: I think I agree with you. There is really a difference between the filaments from the egg and the sperm. In some species the acrosome filament of the spermatozoon can be produced even when no eggs are present so that obviously it cannot come from the egg. The egg filaments are probably akin to microvilli. With regard to *Sabellaria,* which I know you have studied a good deal, Dr. Novikoff, I believe that the filaments you saw were certainly egg filaments. But in our studies of *Sabellaria* we found that there were acrosome filaments as well—the situation was *fundamentally* the same as in the other species we have studied.

Dr. Markert: I should like to ask Dr. Allen a question but first perhaps I should comment on Dr. Novikoff's question. In studying the development of enzymes it is necessary, as Dr. Novikoff suggests, to correlate information from homogenates with data from intact or sectioned tissues. Particularly in complex tissues where more than one type of cell contains esterase and where homogenate analyses reveal several distinct esterases, it is quite possible that the various esterases are distributed non-uniformly among the active cells. The duodenum, in fact, provides such an example. The cells of the villi are strongly positive when alpha naphthyl butyrate is used as substrate in tissue sections, and only faintly positive when naphthyl AS acetate is used as substrate. Just the reverse is true for the Brunner's glands in the wall of the duodenum. By applying these two substrates to electrophoretically resolved esterases in

starch gels it is apparent that three esterases, designated A, G, and H, show the greatest specificity for naphthyl AS acetate while the remaining esterases are relatively more specific for alpha naphthyl butyrate. Thus the Brunner's glands probably contribute relatively more of the A, G, and H esterases and the cells of the villi more of the remaining esterases to homogenates of the duodenum. From this type of data we can identify the successive addition of new esterases by particular cell types during differentiation. I don't believe that the evidence can be interpreted merely on the basis of shifts in cell populations.

And now I should like to address a question to Dr. Allen. Dr. Allen, you raised the question of whether the cortical reaction was an autocatalytic one or not, or whether it might be possible also that the acrosome reaction was a consequence of something provided by the sperm cell itself. It wasn't clear to me how variations in the physiology of the sperm could be reconciled with the idea of an autocatalytic reaction.

Dr. Allen: The answer to this question is not very clear to me either, Dr. Markert. One possibility is that the sperm has to inject a particular quantity of some "initiating substance" into the egg. This amount injected might be greater in some cases, and the fertilization wave would then proceed at a more rapid rate and stand less chance of dying out. We do know that the fertilization wave can proceed at different rates under different physiological conditions. This suggests that different sperm might introduce a different quantity or quality of substance into the egg cortex. There is really not much basic information pertinent to this point.

Dr. Willier: I would like to ask you a question about Just's old observation on the sand dollar, *Echinarachnius*. He felt that in this form there was a wave of negativity spreading over the egg surface.

Dr. Allen: Just made some interesting observations on *Echinarachnius*. His observations, in fact, first suggested that there might be a latent period. He remarked that after sperm attachment there seemed to be a period when nothing happened. Then, he observed a wave of "turbidity" which he commented on in other papers as a "wave of negativity." The turbidity was probably the same as the "roughening" that Libby Hyman saw and the change in surface color that Runnström observed coincident with the breakdown of cortical granules. The term "negativity" is not very meaningful today. I think that Just himself probably wasn't too clear on what he observed.

Dr. Weiss: I would like to make some remarks on the very important question raised by Dr. Novikoff. In general, one must check experiments with homogenates against more intact preparations. Any change in an organ such as the liver which appears later must have come about by changes either in the admixture of immigrant cells or from a change in the native cell population itself. Immigrant cells in this particular case, except for the case of blood cells, are ruled out, and so I think the evidence is clear that we are dealing with a progressive change in the enzyme pattern of the local liver cell line. Perhaps

the problem will be a little easier if we raise our sights from the cell individual and the enzymes of the individual cell and begin to look at the continuum of cell generations or the cell line. I think when we look at it from this point of view the evidence seems quite conclusive.

I would like, however, to ask a question of Dr. Markert. Dr. Markert ruled out the very attractive hypothesis of the differentiation of extrachromosomal material. He argued that at each step during the differentiation of the cell when it divided, if the extrachromosomal material were differentiated, it would be diluted out as the nuclear content merges with the cytoplasm. However, this can be looked at in exactly the opposite way. When the nucleus is reconstituted after division, it reacquires a part of the cytoplasm which lies around it. So, the nucleus could, so to speak, bite off a part of the cytoplasm to which it had previously contributed some of its own products. I would be a little cautious about concentrating solely on the chromosomes.

Dr. Markert: Your point is well taken. It really is quite difficult to distinguish between the two possibilities. I probably just prefer the chromosomes due to my own genetic background.

Dr. Brachet: I would like to ask Dr. Allen if there is any known correlation between increases in enzymatic activity and the breakdown of cortical granules. We might have a situation comparable to that of the lysosomes in the liver, in which there is a great concentration of hydrolytic enzymes. If that would be true, and if there would be a release of these enzymes when fertilization occurred, it would make a very nice and complete picture.

Dr. Allen: Yes, I think we are coming back to some of Loeb's old ideas about "superficial cytolysis" in newer terms. However, it is extremely difficult to assign to one enzyme or to many enzymes the responsibility for the events in fertilization which we see. This is because the time scale is so very short. Of course, it would be very nice to show that some enzyme is activated at this time, but I am not sure how best to approach this problem. In the few seconds in which fertilization occurs the application of histological or biochemical techniques to detect these changes may well in themselves lead to activation, so the problem has technical difficulties of considerable magnitude. The information which we have on this is the work of Lundblad showing that a proteolytic enzyme, E II, becomes active "at fertilization." However, he did not define precisely what he meant on the time axis by "at fertilization." As you know, a difference between the exact time of sperm attachment and a minute or so later might make a considerable difference. I think we are just getting some idea now as to what the temporal sequence of events is. The important changes for the cortical reaction and for a number of other events taking place at this time may lie within the latent period. These important events may well be all over by the time we actually see the cortical reaction.

Dr. Harris: Dr. Markert made a very interesting observation in discussing the esterases, namely that cells cultured in vitro tend to lose these enzymes to some extent. I am wondering whether this may be in part an adaptive phe-

nomenon. With respect to cholinesterase, Burkhatter, Jones, and Featherstone have shown a direct relationship between the amount of acetylcholine in culture and the level of this particular enzyme. I would like to know if Dr. Markert has tried to reverse the loss of esterases in culture by the addition of appropriate substrates. If it were possible to restore the level of certain of these enzymes, we might then have a means of contrasting adaptive and constitutive enzymes in these cells. It would be an example of modulation in the sense that Weiss and others have used this term. If, on the other hand, the loss is irreversible, it might have to do then with the loss of certain genes or a change in their action during the evolution of cell strains.

Dr. Markert: No, I haven't tried to restore esterase activity by the addition of substrates for these enzymes, partly because the substrates used in testing for these esterases are not normal constituents of the cell, and I doubt that these substrates would act as inducers. Nevertheless, the experiment you suggest should be performed.

Dr. Pasteels: I was quite interested in Dr. Allen's observations on the fertilization reaction in mollusks. I should like to ask him a question regarding mollusk eggs. In the case of a mollusk such as *Barnea,* or *Gryphaea,* there is no visible elevation of the fertilization membrane, yet there are large cortical granules containing mucopolysaccharides. These granules remain intact after fertilization just as in the marine anellid *Chaetopterus.* It would be interesting to know what happens in the absence of the elevation of the fertilization membrane.

Dr. Allen: Yes, I think observations with the electron microscope would be interesting in this regard. Last summer Dr. Rebhun started to look at this in the *Spisula* egg. We have high hopes that he might find something of interest on this.

Dr. Ebert: I note that Dr. Allen emphasized fertilization, not simply egg activation, and that he advanced arguments for the possible role of the sperm. Yet we know of many cases of artificial activation; does one need to argue that the sperm contributes anything at all in the activation process? Do the cortical granules disappear in parthenogenesis?

Dr. Allen: It was shown in the early days of the century that agents which cause parthenogenesis by and large cause membrane elevation. At that time cortical granules were not generally known about. The reverse situation, however, seems not to be true; it is apparently possible to get membrane elevation without complete activation of the egg. Part of this might be due to failure of the egg centrosome to function in cell division. There is evidence that Sugiyama's "fertilization impulse" must be initiated for complete activation. As he showed, many "membrane-elevating" substances by-pass this process. Also, some activating agents undoubtedly injure the egg. Much of the work in parthenogenesis should be done over now that we know a little more about the cortical reaction.

Dr. Bodian: It seems to me that sometimes negative evidence can be as

intriguing as the beautiful positive data that you have presented. When Dr. Brachet brought up the question of the existence of lytic enzymes, possibly in the granules, I was reminded of the fact that you passed very quickly over your difficulties in handling separated cortical granules. Would it be too embarrassing for you to tell us what the difficulties were?

DR. ALLEN: Not at all. I had three weeks in which to go to Dr. Daniel Mazia's lab where he had both a preparative ultracentrifuge and unpigmented sea urchin eggs. In ten days I succeeded in getting a method to isolate cortical granules, and then spent the rest of the time in bed with the flu. The method has not been published and I hope perhaps Dr. Immers in Sweden may take this up.

DR. P. P. COHEN: Are there any extracts of sperm which simulate the effect of the fertilization process?

DR. ALLEN: Many such extracts have been described. The first attempt was probably that of Just who boiled sperm in oxalate and showed that he could get activation. Since then, a number of reports have appeared, and I think probably most of these are due to basic proteins such as protamines which probably precipitate some of the acid mucopolysaccharides in the cortex. This is somewhat suggested by the fact that eggs agglutinate very strongly at the same time that they become activated. Dr. Wicklund in Sweden has studied the effect of protamines on the activation of sea urchin eggs; I have some doubt as to whether this is initiation of the fertilization wave as is caused by sperm and butyric acid. More likely, it is an interference in some other reaction that attends fertilization, for the breakdown of cortical granules in protamine is extremely gradual and takes place in a manner which is quite different from that in the cortical reaction attending fertilization.

DR. GRANT: The fact that you have species of eggs which have cortical granules that do not participate in the formation of the fertilization membrane suggests that these cortical granules must have some other function during development. Now, is there any breakdown of cortical granules in these eggs in later stages of development that is correlated with any morphogenetic event?

DR. ALLEN: My studies of embryology usually stop after the membrane is elevated so I am afraid I cannot answer your question. I don't know anything about the role of these things. I have, however, just learned from Dr. Afzelius that he once in a while finds cortical granules in quite late stages, blastulae or later.

PHASES OF DEPENDENT AND AUTONOMOUS MORPHOGENESIS IN THE SO-CALLED MOSAIC-EGG OF TUBIFEX

Fritz E. Lehmann

Zoology Department, University of Berne, Switzerland

The Transformation of Oocyte Organization into the Architecture of the Embryo as a Principal of Embryology

In the days of Roux, Driesch, Morgan and Spemann (see Seidel, 38) it seemed fully justified to distinguish two categories of development: regulative and mosaic-like morphogenesis. With the method of isolation of fragments of embryos or eggs only one main problem was accessible: the question, namely, whether fragments are capable of developing into whole embryos, as in the case of the sea-urchin, or into mosaic-like half embryos, as in the case of the ascidian egg. This original question lost much of its alternative character during the subsequent periods of embryological research in which Spemann and Hörstadius (see Seidel, 38) started to work with refined transplantation methods. It has become evident that different regions of one and the same embryonic system show different degrees of regulative or mosaic-like development. Independent and self-organizing regions coexist with more or less dependent areas which are governed by the dominant regions. In addition to this it has been recognized that the various egg types differ in their characteristic patterns of organization. However, the morphodynamic organization of any embryonic system cannot be unraveled by direct light microscopical examination, but is as a rule only indirectly deduced from the various results of experimental data. The organization of an egg appears as a carrier of different action and reaction systems which are released in the moment of activation of the egg. From this time on local processes of independent self-organization, chemical induction of dependent regions by distant or contact actions, and topogenetic activities are interlinked in a very complex manner. The later formative processes of development depend very much upon the egg organi-

zation. Therefore it is possible to deduce from anormogenetic developmental types typical features of the egg organization.

At present the morphodynamic organization of the echinoderm egg, some spirally cleaving eggs of molluscs and annelids, several ascidian eggs and the amphibian egg is rather well known. All these eggs possess two structurally distinct regions: the egg cortex, the structure of which appears to be very stable in centrifuged eggs; and a complex endoplasm with several particulate inclusions. The experimental results have disclosed the fact that in the morphogenetic organization of the various eggs cortex and endoplasm are involved in a very different manner.

The organization of the spirally cleaving egg of *Tubifex* is intermediate between that of the echinoderm and that of the amphibian type. There is a cortex with polar fields the action of which determines the localization of the polar plasms, and there is an endoplasm consisting of two sorts of cytoplasm, the polar plasm and the yolk-containing cytoplasm. From the polar plasms there originates the cytoplasm later forming the germ bands. The yolk-containing endoplasm is the precursor of the intestine.

Let us consider here two extremely differing egg types. The echinoderm egg possesses a cortex which carries a double system of antagonistic gradient fields (Runnström and Hörstadius). The endoplasm contains only traces of a morphogenetic pattern. Before the formation of the gray crescent, the amphibian egg is devoid of a clearly demonstrable cortical pattern, but shows different endoplasmic regions with characteristic morphogenetic potentialities: an animal-marginal zone which later forms ectoderm and mesoderm, and a vegetative zone which gives rise to the intestine.

From this brief sketch it can be seen that animal eggs are characterized by cytoplasmic patterns the parts of which carry different morphogenetic functions. In the following section we have to discuss how the intricate cooperation of dependent and independent germinal regions contributes to the formation of the embryonic architecture, especially in the development of *Tubifex*.

From Self-Organizing and Inducing Cellular Areas to Mosaic-like Patterns in the Tubifex Embryo[1]

The Epigenetic Formation of the Cytoplasmic Pattern During Maturation and Cleavage

Shortly before the formation of the first cleavage spindle the cytoplasmic pattern of the *Tubifex* egg is completed. Both poles of the egg carry a well-

[1] For illustrations the reader is referred to Lehmann (17) and Lehmann and Mancuso (19).

delimited condensation of polar plasm rich in mitochondria and giving a positive Nadi-reaction. The egg center contains a large cytoplasmic area with the mitotic apparatus, which is surrounded by the large mass of endoplasm carrying yolk. Thus the final cytoplasmic pattern of the egg is formed relatively late. This is to be observed not only in *Tubifex* but also in eggs of several molluscs, annelids, ascidians, and even amphibians. In these different egg types analogous processes are seen in the segregation of several sorts of cytoplasm. These phenomena have rightly been called by Costello "ooplasmic segregation" (5).

As far as *Tubifex* is concerned these delimited cytoplasmic areas are not at all uniform gels containing but a single sort of macromolecule or even "formative stuffs" (E. B. Wilson, 40, p. 1065). The main regions of the *Tubifex* zygote (plasmalemma, polar plasms, yolk-containing endoplasm, nuclear apparatus) consist of very *characteristic populations of particulates.* This is revealed by electron microscopy of ultrathin sections (Weber, 42; Lehmann and Mancuso, 19). Some of the particulates mentioned are to be considered as the carriers of vital phenomena, namely, mitochondria, and the various components of the hyaloplasm (microsomes of vesicular or granular type and cytoplasmic fibrils). We have designated these "vital particulates" as "biosomes" (14) because presumably they possess a vital property, namely, *structural and biochemical continuity.* In the oocyte of *Tubifex* there occurs another category of particulates, "nutrient particulates," such as lipid droplets and yolk spheres. As all these "nutrient particulates" carry cytoplasmic membranes, they may play also an important role in metabolism and eventually in morphogenesis. Vital and nutrient particulates constitute the *important particulate level of living embryonic cells.* This level is distinguished by a typical structural differentiation closely connected with specific cellular activities (7, 19). The polar plasms possess numerous mitochondria and basophilic bodies of the form and size of chromidia or larger microsomes. The endoplasm is poor in endoplasmic reticulum and mitochondria, rich in lipid and yolk spheres, all of which are coated by a delicate cytoplasmic membrane. The plasmalemma or cortex is not yet too well known as regards its fine structure.

Our centrifuging experiments have allowed us to concentrate the particulate components of the two polar plasms in one single layer. If the living eggs are centrifuged in a well-stabilized position, accumulation of one large polar plasm at one pole can be brought about. We have observed the development of eggs with one polar plasm at the animal pole. These eggs cleaved normally and developed later on into embryos with normal germ bands. Eggs with a single polar plasm at the vegetative pole pro-

duced a smaller percentage of embryos because in this experiment cleavage proved to be disturbed more frequently. It is remarkable that the mass of polar plasm concentrated at one pole does not show any tendency to move to the other pole devoid of polar plasm. Polar plasm concentrated in the equatorial region of the egg behaves very differently. Immediately after centrifugation, the condensed polar plasm spreads along the cortex in two opposite directions and begins to reach the original animal and vegetative poles. The cortex of the animal and vegetative poles probably contains fields which possess a specific attraction for polar plasm.

Selective adhesion between different cell types plays an important role in the morphogenesis of amphibians, as Townes and Holtfreter (39) have shown. In our case, however, we deal with a case of *intracellular* and not intercellular *adhesiveness between different cytoplasmic regions*. In fact, the segregation and concentration of polar plasms which takes place during the maturation divisions shows some analogies to the movement and the changing selective adhesiveness of whole embryonic blastemas. Before the meiotic divisions begin, the polar plasm material is spread out in nearly the whole of the subcortical area of the egg. At the period of visible polar plasms it is totally concentrated in two regions and has considerably augmented its mass.

This can be demonstrated by centrifuging and stratifying the various meiotic stages. Especially during the phase of the second meiotic lobulations, the concentration of polar plasms seems to proceed rapidly. The more the polar plasms are concentrated underneath the polar cortex, the more they are delimited from the neighboring yolk-containing cytoplasm. The quinones of naphthalene and phenanthrene interfere strongly with the interaction of polar plasms and polar cortex. Treatment of young maturation stages inhibits the concentration of polar plasms at the poles, with the result that there remain irregular subcortical sheets of polar plasm in wide areas of the egg surface. At the same time the formation of regular and conspicuous meiotic lobulations is inhibited and distorted (37).

Our experiments demonstrate that the development of the cytoplasmic pattern of the *Tubifex* zygote represents a kind of "ooplasmic segregation" which is brought about by complex interactions between egg cytoplasmic particulates and egg cortex. The egg endoplasm segregates during meiosis into two separate cytoplasmic territories, the polar plasm with its population of many mitochondria and chromidia, and an endoplasm rich in nutrient particulates. *The particles* of these territories must be endowed with a *characteristic adhesiveness* which keeps them together even after treatment with the centrifuge. But this ooplasmic segregation leads to the

typical final pattern only if the condensation of the polar plasm is governed by the action of the polar cortical fields.

The morphodynamic processes during meiosis of the *Tubifex* egg obviously show features of interdependent development and not an independent behavior of the egg parts. This conclusion is corroborated by the fact that the two-cell stage of *Tubifex* can still give rise to double embryos. Another feature is also in favor of our interpretation. As we have shown, it is possible to fuse the whole mass of the polar plasms either at the animal or the vegetative poles. In both cases the zygote with a fused polar plasm can give rise to a normal embryo. All these facts mean that the organization of the one-cell stage does not represent a mosaic-like pattern, the parts of which are fully determined.

The Role of Early Cleavage in the Differential Distribution of the Polar Plasms

As mentioned above, the segregation of the polar plasms in the zygote does not determine definitely the pattern of embryo formation. This is only the case after the large somatoblasts *2d* and *4d*, containing two main portions of the polar plasms, have been formed. These seem to be the principal blastomeres necessary for embryo formation. Immediately after the first cleavage the two separate polar plasms fuse in the blastomere *CD* into one large, well-delimited territory. This is transferred partly to the ectoblast *2d*, and partly to the mesoblast *4d*. As soon as the somatoblasts are segregated, they show, according to Penners' experiments, separate and mosaic-like potencies (25-29). *2d* is only capable of producing the ectodermal germ bands, and *4d* only gives rise to the mesodermal germ bands. The fused mass of polar plasm present in the cell *CD* must have undergone in the following cleavage steps a segregation into two different types of cytoplasm, an "ectodermal" and a "mesodermal" plasm.

In the past there was much discussion about "organ-forming stuffs" (40), which might be responsible for the different potencies of the somatoblasts. But the possibility was not considered that the two somatoblasts might develop differences not on the molecular but on the particulate or bisomatic level. It has been possible to prove for the embryo of *Tubifex* (see Table 1) that in fact striking cytoplasmic differences of ultrastructure are present in the two somatoblasts (19). In the ectoblast *2d* there occurs a dense cytoplasmic reticulum with many fibrous and vesicular elements, and with rather few mitochondria, fat droplets, and yolk spheres. The mesoblast shows a looser cytoplasmic reticulum but a very rich population of mitochondria and a considerable territory with numerous lipid droplets and

yolk spheres. In the somatoblasts of *Ilyanassa* a similar differential distribution of particulates has been observed (Clement and Lehmann, 3). The cell *2d* is rich in mitochondria, but poor in lipid droplets and devoid of yolk spheres. In contrast to this, *4d* not only possesses mitochondria, but has many lipid droplets and some yolk globules.

TABLE 1

DIFFERENCES IN THE PARTICULATE POPULATION OF THREE MAIN BLASTOMERES OF THE 21-CELL EMBRYO OF *Tubifex*

(Lehmann and Mancuso, 1957)

	Somatoblast *2d* Telectoblast	Somatoblast *4d* Mesoblast	Entoblast *4D*
Hyaloplasmic Reticulum	+++	++	+
Mitochondria	Nadi reaction positive ++	Nadi reaction positive +++	Nadi reaction negative; only perinuclear +
Lipid droplets	+	+++	++
Yolk spheres	+	++ Only in vegetative part of *4d*	++++

In both these cases of spiralian eggs we find rather striking quantitative differences in the distribution of particulates. In the better investigated case of *Tubifex* the differential distribution of the basophilic reticulum and the mitochondria is especially remarkable. This certainly indicates differences in metabolic pattern, because metabolic activities of the reticular (microsomal) and the mitochondrial particulates are probably very different. Some other morphodynamic processes which finally differ qualitatively are first determined by systems of factors which only show quantitative differences (genetic determination of sex, determination of properties of the lateral mesoderm in amphibians by quantitative factors, gradients of sea urchin). From these cases the assumption may be derived for the somatoblasts of *Tubifex* that the differences of the two somatoblasts may primarily reside in different proportions of the respective populations of particulates. This may induce secondarily a divergent protein metabolism (Weber, 43) and bring about development of qualitative morphogenetic differences.

Inhibition of Somatoblastic Differentiation by Abnormal Distribution of the Polar Plasms

If the idea is correct that definite proportions of particulates within a given cell determine the final metabolism and by this means the morphogenetic character of the somatoblasts, it is to be expected that disturbances in the distribution of polar plasm to single cleavage cells may bring about anormogenetic development of the embryo. In the case of *Tubifex* this expectation was easy to realize, because cleavage can be distorted by several factors. Centrifuging, as well as different chemical treatments, disturbs the cleavage pattern seriously. In many cases abnormally cleaving cells form several medium-sized cells instead of the large somatoblasts *2d* and *4d*. These abnormal cells contain polar plasm, as can be shown by a positive Nadi reaction. But they are unable to form germ bands. They live nearly as many days as the controls require to reach the stage of hatching. But the abnormal germs possess only entoderm cells and several small groups of undifferentiated ectoderm cells. Differentiated and segmented organs are completely lacking. In these cases obviously the embryo did not lose embryonic material. But some processes must have been suppressed which are necessary for the determination of the ectodermal and mesodermal germ bands. This break in the sequence of the normal developmental processes is presumably produced by the abnormal cleavage. The normally occurring condensation of the polar plasms in the large somatoblasts is not possible because of the formation of several smaller cells. Concomitantly, the differential distribution of the various cytoplasmic constituents is made impossible and the mosaic pattern of somatoblasts cannot appear.

It seems a very remarkable feature in the development of a spiralian egg that a simple disturbance in the distribution of polar plasm can bring about such a far-reaching effect upon embryonic differentiation. Here the early cleavage of *Tubifex* displays characteristic epigenetic features which are not in accord with the general concept of mosaic development. This statement might sound surprising if we consider the many results in embryological literature which seem to be mostly in favor of a pronounced mosaic-like character of spiralian development, especially in marine forms. But the marine spiralians are distinguished from *Tubifex* by two principal features: they possess a remarkable mechanical resistance, and very often they develop planktonic larvae.

The difference in mechanical resistance is very striking. Marine eggs like those of *Ilyanassa* can be stratified by strong centrifugation, but the

stratification disappears rapidly afterwards. On the contrary, the eggs of *Tubifex* are easily stratified and keep the induced order of layers for longer periods. Therefore the dislocation experiments in *Tubifex,* leading to a changed cytoplasmic pattern, are impossible in other spiralian eggs because of the instability of the experimentally induced layers.

Planktonic larvae of marine spiralians possess larval organs which show very strong mosaic characters already during early cleavage. As larval organs are lacking in *Tubifex,* we are mainly dealing with cells responsible for the later embryonic pattern. Therefore in the development of the somatoblasts epigenetic factors seem to remain active during early cleavage. Apparently they have not yet been investigated in detail in other spiralians with well-developed larval forms.

The development of specific somatoblastic cytoplasms appears as a central problem of spiralian development. Especially the isolation of the whole mass of ectoderm and mesoderm plasms in an early period is a peculiarity which does not occur in echinoderms or amphibians. The fact of a transitory separation of the ectoderm-forming and mesoderm-forming cytoplasms from all other neighboring cells might be plausibly explained by our assumption (above). This postulates that the proportions of the various particulates in the two somatoblasts determine finally the morphogenetic character of the somatoblasts. During the period of isolation of these organ-forming cytoplasms the necessary stabilization of the divergent morphogenetic characters of the somatoblasts takes place. And it is only during this short period of the isolated somatoblasts that the development of *Tubifex* shows characteristic mosaic-like features, as proven by *Penners'* radiation experiments.

Hence we distinguish two principal periods in the development of *Tubifex.* A first period lasts from the first maturation division till the formation of the two somatoblasts. This period is characterized by numerous epigenetic activities which are closely interlinked. The second period begins with the embryo possessing the two somatoblasts and lasts till the formation of germ bands. In this period development depends in a mosaic-like mode on the somatoblasts.

The Interaction of Several Factors in Determining the Decisive Cleavage Pattern of Tubifex

As we have seen, the cleavage of the *Tubifex* egg is to a high degree responsible for the sorting out and the determination of the different cytoplasms of the somatoblasts. Some centrifugation experiments on *Tubifex*

eggs indicate the kind of interaction of cortex, endoplasm, and cleavage spindle which are responsible for the cleavage pattern. During meiosis, size and position of the minute polar bodies are determined by the position of the meiotic spindle in the cortex. Location of the spindle on either pole produces a radially symmetrical pattern of lobulations. Attachment of the translocated spindle in the equatorial cortex induces a bilaterally symmetrical pattern of lobulation. Similar patterns can be produced by translocating the first cleavage spindle to different regions of the cortex of the zygote.

The cleavage rhythm itself, i.e., the rhythmical sequence of interphasic state of nucleus and cytoplasm and cytoplasmic motility connected with mitotic nuclear activity, seems to be mainly located in the cytoplasm. Analogous rhythmical changes of interphase state and motility occur even in enucleated parts of cells (isolated polar lobes of *Ilyanassa*) and in cells of *Tubifex* chemically deprived of the nuclear apparatus (Woker, 41). This change between interphase and mitotic state of the embryonic system is best illustrated by Pasteels' observations on activated but not cleaving eggs of *Chaetopterus* (24). These eggs differentiate after activation without cytoplasmic divisions. The nuclear apparatus produces a characteristic monastral cycle. The cortex of the monastral embryos continues with the same formative activities as the normally cleaving control embryos. During the phases of micromere formation there appear small and numerous lobulations in the activated eggs. In the period of the formation of the somatoblasts the experimental eggs developed large lobe-like protrusions. These changes of form indicate for the egg of *Chaetopterus* a sequence of tendencies, first to form smaller micromere-like lobulations, and then to produce larger somatoblast-like lobes.

The spiralian egg seems to contain a metabolic system developing in a characteristic rhythm of interphase and mitotic states. A progressive change of the fine structure seems to condition a sequence of small and large lobulations. The large mitotic apparatus of the spiralian embryo determines by its final position and the production of anaphasic action substances the positions of the furrows.

This complex interaction of cleavage factors is responsible for the formation of the somatoblasts. Whereas abnormalities of cleavage do not seriously interfere with development, either in amphibian or in sea-urchin eggs, disturbance of cleavage in *Tubifex* may suppress somatoblast formation. This means that in *Tubifex* cleavage plays an important role as an epigenetic factor of embryo formation.

Autonomous versus Dependent Development or Intracellular versus Blastematic Morphodynamics

[See Table 2]

The original aim of this review was to contrast the autonomous differentiation of spiralian eggs with the dependent differentiation occurring in sea urchin and vertebrate development. But a closer analysis of *Tubifex* development has shown conclusively that the organization of the egg-pattern as well as the formation of somatoblasts is governed by groups of interacting epigenetic factors. Only the final stage of the somatoblast embryo represents a period of mosaic-like behavior of the somatoblasts. The power of regulation and the interaction between blastomeres seem to be extremely low. Autonomy of single blastomeres is in this phase very conspicuous and has been known for a considerable time.

TABLE 2

Morphogenetic Reaction Systems During Embryogenesis

1. *Intracellular reaction patterns*	
Spiralians:	a) Ooplasmic segregation
	b) Intrablastomeric segregation of cytoplasm during spiral cleavage, and separation of autonomous organ-forming cell types
Vertebrates:	Ooplasmic segregation
2. *Intrablastematic reaction patterns*	
Spiralians:	Segmentation of mesodermal germ bands in *Tubifex*
Vertebrates:	Self-organization of chordamesoderm and entoderm, and separation of autonomous organ-forming blastematic areas
3. *Interblastematic reaction systems*	
Spiralians:	Pattern formation in ectodermal germ bands induced by mesodermal germ bands
Vertebrates:	Induction of neural plate by the roof of archenteron

But the whole of the processes leading to the mosaic-like architecture has remained obscure for a long time. This may be explained by the peculiar fact that in mosaic types processes of segregation and determination are of a purely intracellular character and therefore rather difficult to attack experimentally. In contrast to this, morphodynamic events in sea urchins and vertebrates are generally blastematic and hence accessible to the classical transplantation methods.

In this period of developing histochemistry and electron microscopy the intracellular type of morphodynamics becomes especially attractive to the biologist. The stepwise sorting out of specific cytoplasms within cells is often accompanied by histochemical events and changes in the particulate populations. At the moment these well-delimited organ-forming cyto-

plasms are easier to investigate than the gradient fields of amphibians and sea urchins. So it might be expected that the analysis of the intracellular mode of differentiation may furnish new facts and ideas for the research of the intercellular or blastematic type of morphogenesis.

REFERENCES

1. Boell, E. J., and Weber, R., Cytochrome oxidase activity in mitochondria during amphibian development. *Exptl. Cell Research,* **9,** 559-567 (1955).
2. Bretschneider, L. H., and Raven, C. P., Structural and topochemical changes in the egg cells of *Limnaea stagnalis* during oogenesis. *Arch. néerl. zool.,* **10,** 1-31 (1951).
3. Clement, A. C., and Lehmann, F. E., Ueber das Verteilungsmuster von Mitochondrien und Lipoidtropfen während der Furchung von *Ilyanassa obsoleta* (Mollusca, Prosobranchia). *Naturwiss.,* **43,** 578-79 (1956).
4. Costello, D. P., Experimental studies of germinal localization in *Nereis.* I. The development of isolated blastomeres. *J. Exptl. Zool.,* **100,** 19-66 (1945).
5. ———, Segregation of ooplasmic constituents, *J. Elisha Mitchell Sci. Soc.,* **61,** 277-289 (1945).
6. Dalcq, A., Etude micrographique et quantitative de la mérogonie double chez *Ascidiella scabra. Arch. biol.* (*Liége*), **49,** 397-568 (1938).
7. Eakin, R. M., and Lehmann, F. E., An electron microscopic study of developing amphibian ectoderm. *Wilhelm Roux' Arch. Entwicklungsmech. Organ.,* **150,** 177-198 (1957).
8. Huber, W., Ueber die antimitotische Wirkung von Naphthochinon und Phenanthrenchinon auf die Furchung von Tubifex. *Rev. suisse zool.,* **54,** 61-154 (1947).
9. Krause, G., Induktionssysteme in der Embryonalentwicklung von Insekten. *Ergeb. Biol.,* **20,** 159-198 (1957).
10. Lehmann, F. E., Polarität und Reifungsteilungen bei zentrifugierten Tubifex-Eiern. *Rev. suisse zool.,* **47,** 177-182 (1940).
11. ———, Die Indophenolreaktion der Polplasmen von Tubifex. *Naturwiss.,* **29,** 101 (1941).
12. ———, Die Zucht von Tubifex für Laboratoriumszwecke. *Rev. suisse zool.,* **48,** 559-561 (1941).
13. ———, Mitoseablauf und Bewegungsvorgänge der Zellrinde bei zentrifugierten Keimen von Tubifex. *Rev. suisse zool.,* **53,** 475-480 (1946).
14. ———, Ueber die plasmatische Organisation tierischer Eizellen und die Rolle vitaler Strukturelemente der Biosomen. *Rev. suisse zool.,* **54,** 246-251 (1947).
15. ———, Chemische Beeinflussung der Zellteilung. *Experientia,* **3,** 223-232 (1947).
16. ———, Zur Entwicklungsphysiologie der Polplasmen des Eies von Tubifex. *Rev. suisse zool.,* **55,** 1-43 (1948).
17. ———, Plasmatische Eiorganisation und Entwicklungsleistung beim Keim von Tubifex. *Naturwiss.,* **13,** 289-296 (1956).
18. ———, and Hadorn, H., Vergleichende Wirkungsanalyse von zwei antimitotischen Stoffen, Colchicin und Benzochinon, am Tubifex-Ei. *Helv. Physiol. et Pharmacol. Acta,* **4,** 11-42 (1946).
19. ———, and Mancuso, V., Verschiedenheiten in der submikroskopischen Struktur der Somatoblasten des Embryos von Tubifex. *Arch. Julius Klaus-Stift. Vererbungsforsch. Sozialanthropol. u. Rassenhyg.,* **32.**
20. ———, and Wahli, H. R., Histochemische und elektronenmikroskopische Unterschiede im Cytoplasma der beiden Somatoblasten des Tubifexkeimes. *Z. Zellforsch. u. mikroskop. Anat.,* **39,** 618-629 (1954).

21. Meyer, A., Die Entwicklung der Nephridien und Gonoblasten bei *Tubifex rivulorum* Lam., nebst einigen Bemerkungen zum natürlichen System der Oligochaeten. *Z. wiss. Zool.,* **133,** 517-562 (1929).
22. Novikoff, A., Morphogenetic substances or organizers in annelid development. *J. Exptl. Zool.,* **85,** 127-155 (1940).
23. Novikoff, A. B., Embryonic determination in the Annelid, *Sabellaria vulgaris.* I. The differentiation of ectoderm and endoderm when separated through induced exogastrulation. II. Transplantation of polar lobes. *Biol. Bull.,* **74,** 198-234 (1938).
24. Pasteels, J., Recherches sur la morphogénèse et le déterminisme des segmentations inégales chez les Spiralia. *Arch. anat. microscop.,* **30,** 161-197 (1934).
25. Penners, A., Experimentelle Untersuchungen zum Determinationsproblem am Keim von *Tubifex rivulorum* Lam. *Arch. mikroskop. Anat. u. Entwicklungsmech.,* **102,** 51-100 (1924).
26. ———, Experimentelle Untersuchungen zum Determinationsproblem am Keim von *Tubifex rivulorum* Lam. II. Die Entwicklung teilweise abgetöteter Keime. *Z. wiss. Zool.,* **127,** 1-137 (1926).
27. ———, Experimentelle Untersuchungen zum Determinationsproblem am Keim von *Tubifex rivulorum* Lam. III. Abtötung der Teloblasten auf verschiedenen Entwicklungsstadien des Keimstreifs. *Z. wiss. Zool.,* **145,** 220-260 (1934).
28. ———, Regulation am Keim von *Tubifex rivulorum* Lam. nach Ausschaltung des ektodermalen Keimstreifs. *Z. wiss. Zool.,* **149,** 86-130 (1936).
29. ———, Abhängigkeit der Formbildung vom Mesoderm im Tubifex-Embryo. *Z. wiss. Zool.,* **150,** 305-357 (1938).
30. Raven, Chr. P., The development of the egg of *Limnaea stagnalis* L. from the first cleavage till the trochophore stage, with special reference to its "Chemical Embryology." *Arch. néerl. zool.,* **7,** 496-506 (1946).
31. ———, Morphogenesis in *Limnaea stagnalis* and its disturbance by lithium. *J. Exptl. Zool.,* **121,** 1-78 (1952).
32. ———, and Bretschneider, L. H., The effect of centrifugal force upon the eggs of *Limnaea stagnalis* L. *Arch. néerl. zool.,* **6,** 255-278 (1942).
33. Reverberi, G., The mitochondrial pattern in the development of the ascidian egg. *Experientia,* **12,** 55-56 (1956).
34. ———, and Pitotti, M., Ricerche sulla distribuzione delle ossidase e perossidasi, il "cellineage" di uova a mosaico. *Pubbl. staz. zool. Napoli,* **18,** 250-263 (1940).
35. Ries, E., Histochemische Untersuchungen über frühembryonale Sonderungsprozesse in zentrifugierten Eiern von Aplysia. *Biodynamica,* **40,** 1-8 (1938).
36. ———, Versuche über die Bedeutung des Substanzmosaiks für die embryonale Gewebedifferenzierung bei Ascidien. *Arch. exptl. Zellforsch. Gewebezücht.,* **23,** 95-121 (1939).
37. Roetheli, A., Chemische Beeinflussung plasmatischer Vorgänge bei der Meiose des Tubifex-Eies. *Z. Zellforsch. u. mikroskop. Anat.,* **35,** 62-109 (1950).
38. Seidel, F., Geschichtliche Linien und Problematik der Entwicklungsphysiologie. *Naturwiss.,* **42,** 275-286 (1955).
39. Townes, P., and Holtfreter, J., Directed movements and selective adhesion of embryonic amphibian cells. *J. Exptl. Zool.,* **128,** 53-119 (1955).
40. Wilson, E. B., *The Cell in Development and Heredity.* Macmillan, New York (1925).
41. Woker, H., Die Wirkungen des Colchicins auf Furchungsmitosen und Entwicklungsleistungen des Tubifex-Eies. *Rev. suisse zool.,* **51,** 109-172 (1944).
42. Weber, R., Zur Verteilung der Mitochondrien in frühen Entwicklungsstadien von Tubifex. *Rev. suisse zool.,* **63,** 277-288 (1956).
43. ———, Ueber die submikroskopische Organisation und die biochemische Kennzeichnung embryonaler Entwicklungsstadien von Tubifex. *Wilhelm Roux' Arch. Entwicklungsmech. Organ.* (in press).

DISCUSSION

DR. PASTEELS: I am not convinced by the arguments of Dr. Lehmann about the differences in developmental mechanism of the *Tubifex* egg and other forms. It is true that centrifugation affects severely the development of the unsegmented egg of *Tubifex* and demonstrates an interaction of "plasms"; but I have myself shown that the same holds true for the egg of amphibians.

DR. LEHMANN: Yes, I admit that in some of your experiments there occurred in amphibian embryos inhibition of differentiation. For the case of *Tubifex* I was surprised that the block of differentiation occurred without loss of important materials of the egg cell. The cleavage just runs the wrong way and there results consequently a wrong distribution of cytoplasm to the cells. Finally the differentiation cannot proceed further. I should expect this also in the case of some insects. The eggs of *Diptera,* for instance, show a very high degree of cytoplasmic pattern in the egg cell. If it would be possible to disturb the genesis of this pattern, distorted differentiation might be predicted.

DR. CLEMENT: I should like to ask Dr. Lehmann to what extent he thinks visible segregation patterns may be symptomatic of differentiation rather than themselves being the primary factor. Also would you attach more significance to one species of particulate things than to another. I am thinking of the centrifuge experiments of E. B. Wilson on *Chaetopterus,* for example, where the eggs were fragmented, and from small hyaline or nearly hyaline fragments normal or fairly normal differentiation could be obtained. I have seen similar things myself in the eggs of a mollusk, *Physa,* where most of the yolk and lipid can be thrown out and still normal differentiation occurs.

DR. LEHMANN: This question cannot be answered entirely. Let's talk about the reticulum and the mitochondria. It can be said today that these two elements are carriers of different types of metabolism and we could not exchange mitochondria with reticulum or vice versa. We believe that they are biochemically very different things. If one were really able to change the proportions of these materials, it might have great consequences. In regard to your other point, it has been known for a long time that if you take out yolk or lipid it doesn't seem to disturb the development on the average; however, we cannot totally disregard these granules. Since we have seen that these yolk granules have membranes and that digestion is going on, these granules cannot be metabolically inert. The same is, of course, true for the lipid droplets. I personally believe that these elements are in their behavior especially important. Another point is this. Marine eggs are especially well constructed and their resistance to mechanical damage is great. The *Tubifex* egg is buried in the sand and is by no means resistant to mechanical damage. If one centrifuges an *Ilyanassa* egg, for example, after a very short time the original cytoplasmic pattern is restored. In contrast, after centrifugation the cytoplasm of the *Tubifex* egg cannot restore itself to its original pattern, and this makes it easy to obtain an abnormal distribution in the cells. My question would be to the other people

interested in mosaic eggs, whether it would be possible to alleviate the abnormal cleavage by chemical treatment.

DR. WILLIER: Would you care to comment on Penners' observations that twinning can be produced in *Tubifex* eggs by increased temperatures or anaerobiosis?

DR. LEHMANN: Yes, I have observed this readily when the pole-plasm is equally divided at the first cleavage. When this happens, the two cells can go on to form a whole sequence of somatoblasts and finally two little worms.

DR. MARKERT: I believe Dr. Lehmann pointed out that one of the important mechanisms of differentiation involves the movement of particles within the cell. I wonder if you would care to comment on the possible mechanisms by which the particles can be moved?

DR. LEHMANN: I asked Dr. Allen the same question just a few days ago and he told me he didn't know anything. Too bad!

DR. NOVIKOFF: I would like to return to the question raised by Dr. Clement. As Dr. Lehmann indicated, things like gradients are more difficult to study than mitochondria and endoplasmic reticulum. Might it be that morphogenetic determinants exist in the pole-plasm which cannot yet be visualized in the electron microscope? Obviously the mitochondria are of great metabolic importance, and it would be of much interest if an egg fragment could be freed of *all* cortical mitochondria and still develop normally. The endoplasmic reticulum and ribonucleoprotein granules, too, must be important in cell metabolism. But is there any evidence yet that any of these organelles are the primary morphogenetic determinants?

DR. LEHMANN: May I just answer to this point. We have also taken into account the possibility that mass proportions of the various particulates may be one factor, of course the cortex is another one and the third one may be that from the interreaction also results a different protein metabolism which is not so obvious. We must never forget that the proteins are specific and this we cannot visualize in the electron microscope.

DR. WILLIER: Are you implying, Dr. Novikoff, that the mitochondria might be a causal factor in differentiation?

DR. NOVIKOFF: They might be. I was trying to emphasize another possibility, that a morphogenetic material might exist in the pole-plasm whose distribution was not disturbed by centrifugation and whose structure has not yet been described. Perhaps there is an aspect of "hyaloplasm" still not resolved in the electron micrographs of today.

DR. COHEN: Is the centrifugal effect a reversible one? If you were to spin these cells in the direction which has already given you abnormal effects and were then to rotate them 180° and spin again, would these effects be reversed?

DR. LEHMANN: No, we didn't do such experiments but that would be possible, I think.

DR. WEBER: Observations of *Tubifex* eggs by electron microscopy show that it is very difficult to get rid of cortical mitochondria by centrifugation. These

stick very firmly to the cortex and perhaps are of physiological importance for the cleavage pattern. In this connection I would like to ask Professor Lehmann what his idea is as to what fixes the cleavage pattern, for this seems to be very important for the arrangement of cytoplasmic structures in different cleavage cells.

Dr. Lehmann: Well, that goes beyond my knowledge, but I mentioned earlier in my paper that the cortex can be varied somewhat and it is certain that local variations exist within the cortex. Then there is another point: namely, from the centrifugation of the mitotic apparatus, which is very large, we can conclude, as some English workers have done, that the mitotic apparatus is giving off at these poles substances which have influence here on the surface. And then we have a surface "bubbling" which Pasteels has worked out in the other paper I quoted. During the whole cleavage there is a sort of change in the physiological state of these structural materials which brings about either large lobulations or small lobulations; that is a causative factor, and we have no idea where it is localized. But in general I came to the conclusion that many factors are localized in the cytoplasm and rather few in the nucleus concerning these conditions.

Dr. Willier: Is it true, Dr. Lehmann, that in the first division cleavage is unequal?

Dr. Lehmann: Yes.

Dr. Willier: Since it is true that the first two blastomeres of the *Tubifex* egg are unequal in size and are anterior and posterior, features that are said to be due to the organization of the cytoplasm, the organization of the cytoplasm determines the position of the spindle and this in turn determines the position of the first cleavage plane which results in an unequal first division. We still talk about the organization of the egg, Dr. Lehmann, but precisely what do we mean by that term?

Dr. Lehmann: We mean by organization of the egg the characteristic pattern of some cytoplasmic regions: the cortex with two invisible fields on the vegetative and animal poles, the polar plasms with many mitochondrial and microsomal particulates suspended in a hyaloplasmic reticulum, the endoplasm containing many yolk spheres and little cytoplasmic reticulum which has to be considered as the main part of the cytoplasmic ground-substance, besides the interstitial fluid and the nuclear region with nucleus, perinuclear cytoplasm and centrospheres.

The cleavage pattern of the *Tubifex* egg might be determined by an unalterable fine structural pattern of the cellular cortex, for which we have some factual evidence. But this structural factor of the cortex requires the synergistic activities of the oriented mitotic apparatus and a rhythmically changing activity of the hyaloplasmic reticulum which is at the same time an important carrier of contractile properties of the embryonic cell.

Dr. Ebert: I am surprised to hear Novikoff's statement indicating that he retains a vestige of the "mysticism" of the embryologist, despite the fact that he

has been working in biochemistry for several years. I can't see any need for invoking hyaloplasm or other "formative stuffs" until we have examined carefully the role of the microsome fraction, the endoplasmic reticulum. Perhaps, we will have to search beyond current concepts of cytoplasmic organization, but I see no real need to look for mysterious "stuffs" in eggs at this time.

DR. NOVIKOFF: I am sorry if I left the impression that the determinants of which I spoke were mystical. Even the gradient concept or others of more classical embryology need not be viewed as mystical. I was simply cautioning against permitting the concreteness and brilliance of biochemical analyses and of electron micrographs to hide from us the important gaps in our knowledge. I expect that neither the lists of biochemical properties found in mitochondria, microsomes and other subcellular particles nor the details of their fine structure revealed by electron microscopy exhaust all important phenomena in the cell. These are neither mystical forces nor entelechies; rather, they are aspects of concrete reality still to be described.

DR. COWDEN: Have you attempted to study the distribution of ribose nucleic acid in the developing mosaic embryo of *Tubifex* and *Ilyanassa?*

DR. LEHMANN: No, we haven't tried that. I can only tell you that we can visualize this cytoplasmic reticulum, and this is strongly basophilic. I might remark in addition about these things which Dr. Novikoff felt might be in the cell but which we had not yet visualized. I have recently talked to Dr. Allen about the amoeba. He told me the cytoplasmic reticulum of these particular cells is a biphasic system. There is the true reticular material and an interstitial material. This fluid interstitial material may be centrifuged off and presumably is composed of low molecular weight compounds.

DR. SPRATT: I think it might not be remiss to point out a possible danger. This has been pointed out by others before with regard to interpreting results of centrifugation experiments on eggs. I think it is necessary to have a whole spectrum of centrifugal forces in order to make a safe interpretation of the data. For, under certain centrifugal forces certain materials will be moved and, of course, others will not be moved. This will have an important bearing on the interpretation. I also have another question which refers to a matter already suggested by one of you. I refer to the return to the normal condition following centrifugation. If the egg is left alone, you get a normal redistribution of the egg components under normal gravity forces, and thus the interval of time between the end of the centrifugation and the onset of cleavage plays an important role in this respect.

DR. LEHMANN: The experiments Dr. Spratt is proposing were already published in 1948 (*Revue Suisse de Zool.* **55,** 1-43). We have applied graded series of centrifugal forces and different stages of ovocytes have been subjected to centrifuging. Here I only referred to centrifugation of meiotic stages with strong centrifugal forces. Under these conditions the whole mass of presumptive pole-plasm can be concentrated irreversibly on one pole, and on the other

pole there is no polar plasm formed later on. Certainly a few mitochondria may stick to the cortex devoid of polar plasm but that does not seem to have any effect on reformation of polar plasm. These results are most easily explained to be a question of the movement of particulate and partly coherent cytoplasmic materials and not of molecular materials.

DR. YAMADA: Dr. Lehmann, in your recently published electron micrographs of amphibian embryos and also those we have obtained at Nagoya we could assume that the segregation of amphibian germ layers is accompanied by the appearance of different populations of mitochondria. We find a high concentration of active mitochondria in and about the organizer and apparently there occurs an increase of concentration of mitochondria here than in the ectoderm. Do you think there is an activation of mitochondria in different regions of the ectoderm during their differentiation? This might be the case in so-called regulative eggs. Now in the case of the so-called mosaic eggs according to your results there are quite different mechanisms by which these differences in mitochondrial populations are brought about; that is, segregation is established before cleavage. But I don't think that the mitochondria are the only particles alone responsible for segregation.

DR. WEISS: I don't think I would like to let this occasion pass by and let the discussion between Dr. Novikoff and Dr. Ebert go unresolved. We have developed in our history and approach as ideate animals in which seeing is believing. First, we believed only in the things which we saw in the microscope and now we believe only in things which we see in the electron microscope and which we denied in fact at times when we couldn't see them. Now, as a matter of fact, we believe in things under the electron microscope that may not even have been in there in the living animal so long as we can create and make some something visible. I think Dr. Novikoff made a very good point. I don't think that we are at the stage where we should monopolize a particular thing just because it is visible and then say that this is the seat of the ghosts to which we then allocate all of the various properties. I think the system is a multiphasic system and I think all its components may be equally important; our task is to identify just what role and function each one of them plays. I think we are sterilizing our future if we deny simply *per primam* that they don't exist. Now, I make this comment because we may not come back to this spiralian egg, and it has some properties which are unique to it, and that is the property Dr. Lehmann alluded to. Namely, the cleavage is very well regulated. It has been shown that this regulation after the four-cell stage alternates so that the spindles turn one way in one division and then turn around the other way in the next division, and this alternation of the slant of the spindles is characteristic of these eggs. In some experiments and observations by Schachs in the old days he indicated that this can be somehow referred to some asymmetric spiral organization in the cytoplasm. This is what Dr. Willier referred to in his question. I don't think anyone has seen any substratum for that spiraling

orientation in the electron microscope or in any other way. Now, if it is present, the next question is, is it significant? And I think the significance of this asymmetric organization in the cytoplasm is evidenced by the fact that Crampton and others, by reversing that orientation by pressure and other means, were able to turn the whole symmetry of the developing snail around. Thus, a left-turning snail became a right-turning snail just by the simple trick of altering the first cleavage plane. Now, we have at present I would say no conceptual approach to this type of crystalline arrangement in the cytoplasm. We don't see any morphological expression of it. We have to take these signals such as we get from these observations. I think this question ought to be kept in mind because it links up with the question that Dr. Markert asked: what directs currents or streams of substance? They are oriented, they are organized, they are not random diffusions. We have no conceptual foundation for assuming what orients them, or what directs them, and so I think the future is wide open along this line. I think we are just clouding our views if we think that only the things which we can see in the electron microscope, such as the granules, the microsomes, even only the ones that contain RNA, should be taken into consideration.

Dr. Nace: Miss Laurel Glass and I have some information which may help to remove some of the mysticism about materials below the resolution of the electron microscope and which may have some bearing on the organization of the oocyte (Laurel Glass, Ph.D. Thesis, Duke University, 1958).

Antisera against adult female frog sera (*Rana pipiens*) were produced in rabbits, conjugated with fluorescein and used as immunohistochemical reagents on eggs collected throughout the growth phase of frog oogenesis. The procedures were similar to those described elsewhere in this volume (Nace and Clarke).

During the stages of pre-vitellogenesis oocytes smaller than 15 μ did not take the stain. But, as shown in the accompanying diagram, the cytoplasm of later stages stained with this reagent, whereas the nuclei and follicle-theca layers did not. The cytoplasmic fluorescence became greater as growth continued and was particularly intense in oocytes of about 100 μ diameter. In the last phases of pre-vitellogenesis the fluorescence gradually localized to a cytoplasmic rim corresponding to the cortex of the 200 μ oocytes.

During the period of vitellogenesis the distribution of staining changed. In the Y_1 oocyte, defined by Kemp as the stage in which yolk granules begin to appear below the cortex of the egg, low intensity fluorescence was visible in the follicle-theca complex. The cortical layer became negative and the cytoplasm stained little if at all. The yolk platelets did not stain. However, between the nucleus and cell membrane marked staining was seen in structures which may correspond to the so-called yolk nuclei.

In the Y_2 and Y_3 stages of vitellogenesis, during which the band of yolk granules gradually extends from the cortex toward the nucleus, the follicle-theca complex fluoresced at about the same intensity as in the Y_1. Irregular patches

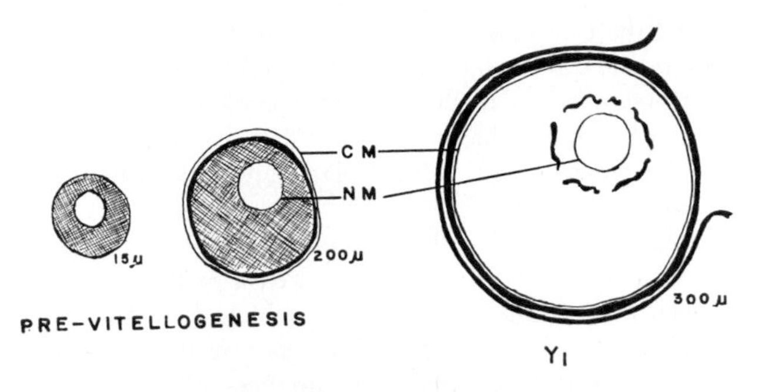

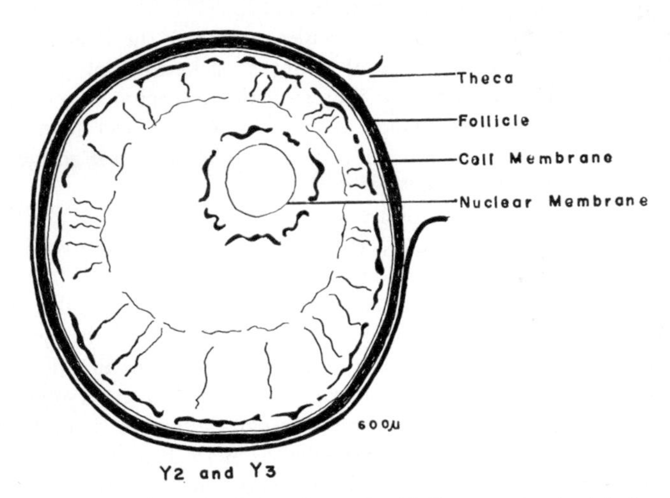

Diagrammatic representation of staining observed with fluorescent anti-adult frog sera at various stages of frog oogenesis. Except for the lines representing the nuclear membrane and the cell membrane, all lines and shadings represent fluorescence. Stage designations according to Kemp.

of fluorescence were seen in the egg cortex. The cytoplasm showed positive staining between the yolk platelets and appeared as "streamers" of fluorescence extending from the cortically-located fluorescent patches toward the inner periphery of the band of yolk platelets. At this stage, a thin band of fluorescence appeared in the cytoplasm just inside the band of yolk platelets. It retained this position as the band of yolk platelets widened to fill the area between the cell membrane and the nucleus and was distinct from the heavily-fluorescing structures closer to the nucleus which seemed to correspond to the "yolk nuclei." Nuclear staining was not seen.

In Y_4 eggs the pattern of Y_3 staining continued. The cortical patches fluo-

resced intensely and the cytoplasmic "streamers" of fluorescence between yolk platelets extended to the advancing edge of the yolk platelet band. Some of the smaller yolk platelets began to fluoresce independently of the cytoplasmic matrix in which they were imbedded. The follicle-theca complex stained more intensely than in the previous stage. Nucleolar staining was first seen at this stage.

In the mature ovarian oocyte, Y_5, the follicle-theca complex did not stain as heavily as in the Y_4. The cortex of the egg showed a peripheral region which did not stain and an inner granule-filled region which did stain. The surface of large yolk platelets stained intensely, perhaps as a result of the inability of the antibody to penetrate the platelets. The smaller yolk platelets also fluoresced. At this stage nearly all nucleoli stained with these fluorescent antisera. Very prominent fluorescent sites were seen as large, or in some cases, dispersed, patches lying against the nuclear membrane.

Thus, it would seem that macromolecules possessing the serological specificity of adult frog serum assume typical patterns of localization in the growing oocyte and that these patterns are characteristic of specific stages. If the situation in the amphibian corresponds to that found by Schechtman *et al.* in the bird and Telfer in the insect, it might be supposed that these antigenic reactive groups are of maternal origin.

There was some indication of an asymmetric distribution of the fluorescence in the oocyte, although this is uncertain as yet. In connection with this discussion it would be of interest to show that this material was not associated with EM-visible structures but rather constituted part of the so-called hyaloplasm.

Dr. Clement: Professor Lehmann has pointed out that the egg of *Tubifex* does not fit the classical conception of a mosaic system. In this connection I would like to describe some recent experiments on the embryonic determination of the foot in the marine gastropod *Ilyanassa obsoleta.* They show that the egg of this form passes through a regulative phase before assuming the final determined state, and that intercellular dependencies are involved in the determination of the foot.

The foot in *Ilyanassa* appears to arise mainly from two third quartet micromeres, 3c and 3d, which are situated at first some distance apart on the posterior side of the egg. During gastrulation, and later, the descendants of these cells evidently converge to a position just behind the blastopore where the single, median foot, with its pair of statocysts, makes its appearance. If, at the 24-cell stage, the 3d micromere is surgically removed, the left half of the foot either fails to develop at all or is represented in the larva by only a trace; the right half of the foot and other larval structures develop well. Removal of the 3c micromere at the same stage results in absence or severe reduction of the right half of the foot. If both 3c and 3d are removed, the egg produces a footless larva. There are thus two determined primordia of the foot at the 24-cell stage; the egg cannot compensate for the loss of either of them, and is in this respect a mosaic.

The conditions are quite different at the 4-cell stage. At this time the D macromere is the prospective source of the cell (3d) which produces the left half of the foot, and the C macromere is the prospective source of the cell (3c) which produces the right half of the foot. However, if the C macromere is removed at the 4-cell stage, the remaining ABD combination will give rise to a larva with a complete foot; in the presence of the D macromere, the egg is able to undergo regulation and produce the right half of the foot from a source other than the missing 3c micromere. On the other hand, if the D macromere is removed at the 4-cell stage, the ABC combination never, so far as I have observed, produces foot structure at all. The ability of the C macromere to differentiate foot tissue appears to depend upon the presence of the D macromere.

Dr. Willier: The one concluding remark I would like to make is that we are still faced with the problem of how much of development is preformistic and how much of it is epigenetic.

THE ROLE OF THE CELL NUCLEUS IN DEVELOPMENT

A. E. Mirsky and Vincent Allfrey
The Rockefeller Institute,
New York, N. Y.

When the role of the cell nucleus in development is considered, a question which soon arises is whether all the genetic factors present in the chromosomes of the germ cells are present in all cell types of the organism. In discussing this question we should remember that the hereditary factors in the chromosomes are potentialities, and that the realization of these potentialities depends upon conditions both within the nucleus and in the surrounding cytoplasm. The problem of the role of the nucleus in development was stated in such terms as early as 1894 by Hans Driesch (14).[1] He took the position that although nuclear activity varies in different cells, nuclear potentialities remain unchanged.

Since Driesch's time there have been some observations that support the view that all the genetic factors are present in all cells. It is well known that the genetic loci of the germ cells of *Drosophila* are represented in the bands of the salivary chromosomes. An important component of the germinal material, deoxyribonucleic acid (DNA), is present in a constant amount for each set of chromosomes in germ cells and in the various somatic cells of many organisms (25, 10). Several of the histone proteins, which are attached to DNA in the chromosome, are remarkably similar, if not identical, in different somatic cells of an organism (11, 12). Interesting as these observations are, they are inconclusive in demonstrating that all chromosomal genetic factors are retained in the course of development.

Let us turn to the evidence that nuclear activity varies. Before doing so, however, an important condition for nuclear activity should be mentioned. Within the nucleus, the synthesis of both ribonucleic acids (RNA) and proteins requires a source of energy, and thus depends on the presence of phosphorylated nucleosides, such as adenosine triphosphate (ATP). These high-energy phosphates have been shown to be present in a wide variety

[1] We are indebted to Professor Viktor Hamburger for this reference.

of isolated nuclear types (27). Moreover, a study of isolated nuclei prepared from the thymus has shown that the nucleus has its own system for phosphorylation, and that the presence of DNA is essential for the aerobic synthesis of ATP. Nuclei deprived of their DNA by treatment with deoxyribonuclease fail to synthesize ATP, but if DNA is restored to them, ATP synthesis resumes (6). Thus one may consider the DNA of the nucleus to be a cofactor in this aerobic phosphorylating system, and one may conclude that an essential non-specific function of DNA is to mediate ATP synthesis. Much of the activity of the nucleus, including its capacity to synthesize RNA and protein, will depend upon the quantity of mononucleotides present in the nucleus and the extent to which these compounds are present as di- or as tri-phosphates. An active nucleus, such as that of a thymus lymphocyte, contains a much greater quantity of mononucleotides than does an inactive nucleus, such as that of an erythrocyte.

Variations in nuclear activity may be expected to depend upon changing conditions of the surrounding cytoplasm. An example of decisive cytoplasmic influence on the state of the nucleus is the observation by Karl Sax on the pollen grains of *Tradescantia* (28). Here, in the first pollen-grain mitosis, the orientation of the mitotic spindle places the daughter nuclei in different regions of the cytoplasm, and it is this difference that causes one daughter nucleus to be vegetative and the other generative. Similar examples of nuclear differentiation have been more recently observed in protozoa.

Biochemical studies of nuclear activity show how rapidly nuclei may respond to cytoplasmic changes (4). This has been shown in a study of protein synthesis in pancreatic acinar cell nuclei during the cycle of enzyme synthesis and secretion. After a prolonged fast, feeding produces intense secretory activity of the acinar cells. Due to discharge of stored digestive enzymes, the cells of the pancreas immediately begin to synthesize protein to replace the secreted material. This synthesis of digestive enzymes occurs in the cytoplasm, and within 30 minutes after feeding there is a marked increase in the uptake of isotopically labeled amino acids by the cytoplasmic proteins (3). At the same time, the cytoplasm influences the nucleus so that there occurs an increase in the amino acid uptake by histones and other proteins of the chromosomes. The response of the nucleus to changing conditions in the cytoplasm can also be demonstrated over longer intervals by first labeling the proteins of the nucleus and then comparing the rates of loss of nuclear isotope in fed and fasted animals. In such isotope retention experiments one finds that the rate of "turnover" of

chromosomal proteins is much higher when the animals are fed and protein synthesis in the cytoplasm is thereby accelerated (4).

The activity of chromosomes may be expected to depend upon the internal environment of the nucleus. The intranuclear environment has special characteristics which set it apart from the rest of the cell. An example of this is the role of sodium ions in nuclear processes. It was found recently that isolated thymus nuclei synthesize proteins rapidly only if they are present in a medium containing sodium ions; an equivalent concentration of potassium ions is ineffective (5). This observation suggests that although potassium ions preponderate in the cytoplasm, there may be a relatively high concentration of sodium ions in the nucleus. Direct support for this view is provided by autoradiographs made in 1949 by Abelson and Duryee, in which Na^{24} ions are seen to accumulate in the nuclei of living frog oocytes which are placed in a medium containing $Na^{24}Cl$ (1).

In addition to such characteristics as a high sodium ion concentration, which may be found in all nuclei, are there nuclear components that are restricted to nuclei of special cell types? Differentiation of a cell is recognized by presence in it of proteins not found in other cells. Hemoglobin, myoglobin, and myosin are examples of proteins which identify certain types of cells. Other proteins, enzymes especially, are notably more highly concentrated in certain cells than in others. Are there signs that in a similar way nuclei may be said to be differentiated? The most reliable data on the nuclear content of enzymes and other special proteins come from observations on nuclei prepared in non-aqueous media (2). The isolation procedures employed are modifications of the method introduced by Martin Behrens in 1932 (9). This is a scheme which prevents water-soluble materials from moving between nucleus and cytoplasm during the course of the isolation. Its success depends on a rapid freezing and removal of water from the tissue, which is then ground and fractionated in non-aqueous solvents (e.g. mixtures of cyclohexane and carbon tetrachloride). When the specific gravity of the nucleus differs sufficiently from that of other subcellular components it can be separated from them by centrifugation. This separation is facilitated by selecting a medium of density lower than the nuclear specific gravity and higher than that of possible cytoplasmic contaminants. The nuclei of many tissues were prepared in this way and were shown by chemical, immunological, and enzymatic tests to be essentially free of cytoplasmic contamination. Such nuclear preparations show that some enzymes which "differentiate" a cell type are absent from the cell nucleus, while others are present in the nucleus. In general it may be said that the nucleus itself is differentiated. An example is the

presence of hemoglobin in the avian erythrocyte nucleus (30, 2), indeed in the nucleus of an erythroblast (13); myoglobin, on the other hand, is absent from the nucleus of the heart muscle cell.

Nuclear differentiation has also been demonstrated in the superb nuclear transplantation experiments of Briggs and King (24). Nuclear differentiation as it occurs in the course of cell differentiation during development is recognizable in the work of these investigators because under the conditions of their experiments nuclear differentiation is not reversible. It is possible that reversal does not occur because in these experiments the necessary conditions are not realized. This should be said because the basic changes that bring about differentiation in nucleus and cytoplasm are not yet understood. If differentiation under all conditions studied is always found to be an irreversible process, such a summary of experience would lead to implications about the nature of the basic molecular changes involved in differentiation—for example, to implications about changes in the genetic material of the chromosomes. We should, therefore, consider in a broad way what is known of differentiation to see whether there are observations suggesting that under some conditions differentiation is reversible.

The best attested examples of reversal of differentiation in animal cells are those that come from experiments on the eyes of salamanders. There are two such examples: in one (the so-called Wolffian regeneration) removal of the lens causes iris cells to lose some of their differentiated characteristics and then develop into lens cells; in the other, removal of the retina causes retinal pigment cells to lose some of their special characteristics and then to become retinal nerve cells. These examples of what appear to be "dedifferentiation" and "redifferentation" are best described in the experiments of L. S. Stone (31, 32).

Such well-studied cases of what appears to be a reversal of differentiation are rare in animals. There are many examples in plants (16). Investigations of "dedifferentiation" cannot at present be said to have led to very definite conclusions. Enough, however, is known to show that the essential irreversibility of differentiation should be questioned. And this means that it cannot at present be said that differentiation implies changes in the genetic constitution of chromosomes, although there can be little doubt that differentiation is associated with changes in nuclear activity.

Nuclear activity is known to produce substances which have decisive influence on the cytoplasm. One such substance, diphosphopyridine nucleotide (DPN), is a coenzyme. An enzyme required for its synthesis is found only in the nucleus, at least in those cells so far studied (21, 26).

Since the quantity of this enzyme varies considerably in nuclei of different cells, there are probably variations in the quantity of DPN supplied to the cytoplasm. Such variations would cause changes in rates of metabolism and so modify the course of development.

A release of DPN to the cytoplasm represents a relatively non-specific way in which the nucleus can modify the course of cell development. Yet the nucleus exerts characteristically specific effects which determine the nature and activity of the cell, and the structure and composition of its proteins. This controlling role of the nucleus in the formation of cell proteins, now so well attested in the case of the hemoglobins (22, 23), is believed to be mediated by ribonucleic acids. There are several good reasons for this belief. The first is the clear requirement for ribonucleic acid in cytoplasmic protein synthesis (3, 20); the second is the demonstration that the ribonucleic acid of the tobacco mosaic virus determines what type of protein is made in virus infection (17, 18); the third is based on the repeated observation in tracer experiments that the rate of incorporation of precursors into ribonucleic acid of the nucleus far exceeds the corresponding rate for RNA in the cytoplasm. This naturally led to the speculation that all the RNA of the cell is made in the nucleus. What has been shown is that DNA participates in the synthesis of RNA in the nucleus, and that RNA synthesis proceeds most actively in the nucleolus (5, 7). Although there is no conclusive evidence that all the RNA of the cell is made in the nucleus—indeed, kinetic studies (8), and differences in composition (29) argue against too simple an hypothesis—there is good evidence suggesting that nuclear RNA can pass to the cytoplasm. The experiments of Goldstein and Plaut (19), in which nuclei bearing labeled RNA were transferred to unlabeled *Amoeba* and the isotope distribution subsequently determined by the radioautographic technique, show that nuclear RNA can, in some form, pass to the cytoplasm. Another very suggestive observation has recently been made by Edström and Eichner (15), who found a direct proportionality between nucleolar volume and the cell body content of ribonucleic acid in supraoptic neurons. Observations of this sort lead strongly to the conclusion that the specific aspects of development, such as the synthesis of special proteins characteristic of differentiation, are due in large measure to the kinds of RNA (or ribonucleoprotein) that come into the cytoplasm from the nucleus.

Biochemical investigation of how the nucleus acts upon the cytoplasm is now well started. Nuclear activity, we have seen, is much influenced by the state of the cytoplasm. Biochemical investigation of this aspect of

nuclear-cytoplasmic interaction, as yet hardly begun, will clarify much that is now obscure in differentiation and development.

REFERENCES

1. Abelson, P. H. and Duryee, W. R., *Biol. Bull.,* **96,** 205 (1949).
2. Allfrey, V. G., Stern, H., Mirsky, A. E. and Saetren, H., *J. Gen Physiol.,* **35,** 529 (1952).
3. ———, Daly, M. M. and Mirsky, A. E., *J. Gen. Physiol.,* **37,** 157 (1953).
4. ———, ——— and ———, *J. Gen. Physiol.,* **38,** 415 (1955).
5. ———, Mirsky, A. E. and Osawa, S., *Nature,* **176,** 1042 (1955).
6. ———, and ———, *Proc. Natl. Acad. Sci. U. S.,* **43,** 589 (1957).
7. ———, and ———, *Proc. Natl. Acad. Sci. U. S.,* **43,** 821 (1957).
8. Barnum, C. P., Huseby, R. A. and Vermund, H., *Cancer Research,* **13,** 880 (1953).
9. Behrens, M., *Hoppe-Seyler's Z. physiol. Chem.,* **209,** 59 (1932).
10. Boivin, A. R., Vendrely, R. and Vendrely, C., *Compt. rend. acad. sci.,* **226,** 1061 (1948).
11. Crampton, C. E., Stein, W. H. and Moore, S., *J. Biol. Chem.,* **225,** 363 (1957).
12. Davison, P. F., *Biochem. J. (London),* **66,** 703 (1957).
13. de Carvalho, S. and Wilkins, M. F. H., *Proc. 4th Intern. Congress Intern. Soc. Hematol.,* p. 119-120, Grune & Stratton, N. Y. (1954).
14. Driesch, H., *Analytische Theorie der organischen Entwicklung,* Leipzig (1894).
15. Edström, J. E. and Eichner, D., *Nature,* **181,** 619 (1958).
16. Esau, K., *Plant Anatomy,* John Wiley and Sons, N. Y. (1953).
17. Fraenkel-Conrat, H., *J. Am. Chem. Soc.,* **78,** 882 (1956).
18. Gierer, A. and Schramm, G., *Z. Naturforsch., Pt. b,* **11,** 138 (1956).
19. Goldstein, L. and Plaut, W., *Proc. Natl. Acad. Sci. U. S.,* **41,** 874 (1955).
20. Hoagland, M. B., Stephenson, M. L., Scott, J. F., Hecht, L. I. and Zamecnik, P. C., *J. Biol. Chem.,* **231,** 241 (1957).
21. Hogeboom, G. H. and Schneider, W. C., *J. Biol. Chem.,* **197,** 611 (1952).
22. Hunt, J. A. and Ingram, V. M., *Nature,* **181,** 1062 (1958).
23. Ingram, V. M., *Nature,* **180,** 326 (1957).
24. King, T. J. and Briggs, R., *Cold Spring Harbor Symposia Quant. Biol.,* **21,** 271 (1956).
25. Mirsky, A. E. and Ris, H., *Nature,* **163,** 666 (1949).
26. Morton, K. C., *Nature,* **181,** 540 (1958).
27. Osawa, S., Allfrey, V. G. and Mirsky, A. E., *J. Gen. Physiol.,* **40,** 491 (1957).
28. Sax, K., *J. Arnold Arbor.,* **16,** 301 (1935).
29. Smellie, R. M. S., McIndoe, W. M. and Davidson, J. N., *Biochim. et Biophys. Acta,* **11,** 559 (1953).
30. Stern, H., Allfrey, V. G., Mirsky, A. E. and Saetren, H., *J. Gen. Physiol.,* **35,** 559 (1952).
31. Stone, L. S., *Anat. Rec.,* **106,** 89 (1950).
32. ———, and Steinitz, H., *J. Exptl. Zool.,* **124,** 435 (1953).

DISCUSSION

Dr. Spiegelman: Dr. Mirsky, how specific is the restoration of nuclear RNA synthesis by DNA? Will any type of DNA do it?

Dr. Mirsky: Yes, DNA from many sources will do it. DNA from many sources and also synthetic polynucleotides are effective; however, dinucleotides

are ineffective. The question of specificity here is rather hard to answer. We do not know whether the same products are formed when a polynucleotide is substituted for the original DNA.

Dr. Markert: Dr. Mirsky, you spoke of the constancy of the DNA and histones in the nucleus. I wonder if you would care to extend your remarks to include the residual proteins and RNA?

Dr. Mirsky: The amount of RNA varies from one tissue to another, and it also varies in a single tissue under different physiological conditions. This variability is an interesting phenomenon which we, and of course many others, are studying. The subject is too broad and big to treat exhaustively in this discussion. An interesting aspect of this question is the relative significance of nucleolar and other nuclear RNA. As for the "residual protein," and by that I mean non-histone protein of the chromosomes, it is difficult to distinguish between "nuclear" and "chromosomal" protein. In the large nuclei of oocytes the distinction may be clear, but in nuclei of lymphocytes it is neither semantically nor physically clear what we mean by this distinction. In our system, once sucrose is removed from the medium, some proteins are immediately leached out of the nucleus. This protein is being actively synthesized and its synthesis depends upon the presence of DNA. It might therefore be associated with DNA and we are tempted at the moment to consider it to be part of the chromosome.

Dr. Hadorn: Dr. Mirsky, do you feel that all of these functional activities are directed by and under the control of so-called Mendelian genes?

Dr. Mirsky: Well, Dr. Hadorn, that is an extremely interesting question and I am not sure that I can answer it. I think that much of what happens during the interphase period of a cell's life is of nucleolar origin. For example the synthesis of DPN is a nuclear function, and yet it was found in Dr. Brachet's laboratory that most of the DPN-synthesizing enzyme is in the nucleolus. It is very difficult for us to answer your question because much of the biochemical activity of the interphase nucleus is located in the nucleolus; and so the answer to your question depends upon how the Mendelian genes function in formation of the nucleolus.

Dr. Lehmann: There are some indications that RNA-proteins inside and outside the nucleus are associated with saturated and especially with unsaturated lipids. Considerable changes of the level of different lipids may occur, when the physiological state of a tissue is changing for example from a well fed to a starving state. Do you know any facts about association of lipids with RNA-proteins and their change in different physiological states?

Dr. Mirsky: Yes, lipids are surely important. The lipids in all of these nuclear fractions should be investigated. You know the biochemist keeps something and throws away something else. We usually discard the lipid fraction and I agree that this in unfortunate.

Dr. P. Cohen: You refer to the fact that the arginase of the liver nucleus

is different from the arginase in the kidney nucleus. Do you have any experimental evidence that might support the idea that the arginase of the nucleus differs from that of the cytoplasm? I think there is some reason to believe that they might be different.

Dr. Mirsky: We have no information on that. I might say, however, that the hemoglobins found in the nucleus and cytoplasm seem to be the same. It would be interesting to know whether this is true of nuclear and cytoplasmic arginase.

Dr. McElroy: When you say that DNA is a cofactor for ATP synthesis by the nucleus, what do you mean?

Dr. Allfrey: Well, Dr. McElroy, we have used the term "cofactor" in a very broad sense. Experimentally, one finds that under the proper conditions a thymus nucleus will make ATP, and that if you remove the DNA from the nucleus it can no longer phosphorylate its AMP to make ATP. Now, if to a DNAase-treated nucleus, you restore thymus DNA or other DNAs, RNAs, or even polyadenylic acid, ATP synthesis is restored. All of the polynucleotides we have tested have this capacity to somehow serve as "cofactors" for ATP synthesis. Mononucleotides, however, and adenylic acid dinucleotides, do not have this capacity, so we can say that there is a size restriction on polynucleotide structure which somehow determines their capacity to serve in ATP synthesis by the nucleus.

Dr. McElroy: Is this a catalytic function or could it be serving as a substrate for ATP synthesis?

Dr. Allfrey: Well, we cannot eliminate the possibility that the DNA might be a substrate but the reason we feel that it has a catalytic function is because ATP synthesis in the nucleus is aerobic. Now if DNA or other polynucleotides were breaking down in some way, supplying through their hydrolysis or phosphorolysis the energy needed for ATP synthesis, one would expect this to also go on in a nitrogen atmosphere. But one actually finds that there is an absolute requirement for oxygen.

Dr. Mirsky: DNA is acting as a cofactor for ATP synthesis in the nucleus. From a biological point of view it should be emphasized that this is an important function of DNA.

Dr. Swift: Since you raised the question of the constancy of DNA, I wonder if you would care to comment on the localized increase in DNA found in salivary gland chromosome puffs by Pavan and Ficq, and also by Rudkin and Stich. Also, I wonder how you feel about the decrease in DNA after cold treatment found in specific chromosome regions of *Trillium* and some other plants by LaCour and others.

Dr. Mirsky: I think the work of LaCour is in one category and that Pavan's is in an entirely different one. At this time there are so many examples of the constancy of DNA that apparent exceptions should be examined critically. In the experiments of LaCour and his colleagues the DNA per cell, as measured

by the Feulgen procedure, diminishes in plants during cold treatment and then returns to its original value when the temperature is restored. From the present experiments it cannot be said whether the DNA actually decreases or whether some of it is depolymerized sufficiently to be lost in the Feulgen procedure. If DNA is lost, then new DNA is synthesized when the temperature is restored. This could be recognized by uptake of labeled thymidine.

As for the work of Pavan and his coworkers, I think it is interesting in many respects. Professor Pavan showed me his preparations several years ago. It was clear that Feulgen staining showed marked increases in DNA in some bands of the chromosomes and not in others. In a paper published soon thereafter I remarked that this was an exception to the rule of DNA constancy. Pavan thought at first that polytenization had stopped in these chromosomes. In fact the recent experiments by Ficq and Pavan show that polytenization is going on very rapidly. We have here a cell that is very highly polytenized, which is continuing to increase in polyteny and which will soon die. Such a cell may well afford to get out of "genic balance." The point I would like to make is that this may be an exceptional situation in many ways, so that it would not be surprising if an empirical rule like DNA constancy does not apply.

Dr. Brachet: I do not feel that the results obtained by Pavan could be entirely explained on the basis of polytenization. There is a differential activity among the bands and obviously the ones which become very active are those which behave somewhat like a nucleolar organizer.

Dr. Mirsky: I quite agree. Even so, it is likely that continuing polytenization is a factor in these cells.

CHROMOSOMAL DIFFERENTIATION *

JOSEPH G. GALL

Department of Zoology, University of Minnesota

INTRODUCTION

The rediscovery of Mendel's laws and the proof of the chromosome theory of inheritance in the early decades of this century brought a resurgence of interest in the fine structure of chromosomes. As early as 1905, C. E. McClung (42) expressed the hope "that it will be possible to establish the relations that exist between body characters and individual chromosomes." He was thinking not only of what we call today genetic mapping, but also of a more direct relation whereby morphological features of particular chromosomes might be related to the expression of certain genes. The remarkable studies of this period quickly laid the foundation for modern views of chromosome structure. Still, however, doubt grew that the ultimate gene differences would ever be directly visualized. The outlook vastly improved when attention shifted from typical mitotic chromosomes to the giant structures found in the larval tissues of certain Diptera, particularly to the salivary gland chromosomes of *Drosophila.* Rapid progress resulted in the localization of known genes within very short segments of the chromosomes and in the demonstration of various structural changes which occur naturally or result from radiation. The culmination of the cytogenetic studies on *Drosophila* came with the detailed studies of the late 1930's which correlated the well-known genetic maps of *Drosophila* with the newly prepared cytological maps.

Throughout this period, however, emphasis remained on the genetic aspects of chromosomes, and practically no attention was given to alterations of genetically identical chromosomes which might accompany diverse functional states. Perhaps it was felt that any functioning of the genes would be expressed only as the release of invisible molecules. But in retrospect we can also see a more subtle restraint which limited the

* Some of the studies reported here were supported by funds from the National Science Foundation, the National Institutes of Health of the U.S.P.H.S., and the Graduate School of the University of Minnesota.

chances of discovering physiological activity in chromosomes. This restraint was simply the types of material studied. For obvious practical reasons chromosomes were observed in their most "condensed" state, usually during the meiotic or mitotic divisions. And the giant chromosomes, furnishing a powerful tool for the geneticist, were popularly studied in the salivary glands of mature *Drosophila* larvae. It now seems that chromosomes in division are in a metabolically inert state, that we must seek them in their most "diffuse" states to see them actively functioning. In the case of the giant banded chromosomes of the Diptera, some do, in fact, show remarkable changes when one looks at them in different tissues or in different periods during larval development. A few papers appearing in the 1930's did lay stress on morphological changes in chromosomes associated with their physiology. For instance, Koltzoff (40) in Russia and Duryee (24) here in the United States emphasized the metabolic aspects of the peculiar lampbrush chromosomes of the vertebrate oocyte. And Poulson and Metz (57), studying the "puffs" and "Balbiani rings" in the salivary gland chromosomes of *Sciara* and *Chironomus,* concluded that these structures might reflect the physiological state of the cell.

Recent studies on these two materials, the vertebrate oocyte chromosomes and the giant larval chromosomes of the Diptera, permit us, I believe, to make tentative suggestions about the differences between "active" and "inactive" chromosomes or chromosome regions. Both materials, at first sight so strikingly different, point to rather similar conclusions, and so it may be that these conclusions can be generalized to other cases.

The general argument which I shall present here concerns both structural and functional aspects of these chromosomes, although in a certain sense these two must be considered together. From the structural standpoint I shall give reasons for believing that the chromatid of classical cytology is at most only a few hundred Ångstroms in width, but millimeters or even centimeters in length in some organisms. The chromatid probably contains deoxyribose nucleic acid (DNA) and basic protein throughout its length. It is capable of complex coiling or folding so that in its contracted state it is visible in the light microscope, either as a whole chromosome or as part of a chromosome. The expanded or unwound state is correlated with synthetic activity, both in terms of reduplication and the elaboration of ribonucleoprotein products. These latter products may accumulate to such an extent around the delicate DNA-protein strand that the whole structure is visible in the light microscope. The unraveling process may involve much or all of the chromosome at once, or it may be limited to very specific regions. It is essentially reversible and correlated

with non-genetic changes in the physiological activity of specific chromosome loci. The latter feature permits us to speculate about the role of the chromosomes in embryonic differentiation, and it is at this point that the discussion of chromosomal differentiation ties in most closely with the topic of the present Symposium.

It should be clear that the scheme outlined here contains much that is common knowledge, while other aspects are quite debatable and may prove to be ultimately untenable. I feel, however, that there is a certain advantage in developing a particular point of view rather than in attempting a general summary of chromosome cytology. Since information on the finest differentiations of chromosomes has come largely from studies on dipteran larval tissues and the oocytes of amphibians, I shall confine most of my discussion to these two tissues.

Definitions

Discussions of chromosome structure are frequently confused by the variety of terms used and the different shades of meaning attached to them. In the recent literature we find, in addition to many others, the words chromonema, genonema, microfibril, chromofibril, and chromatid, as well as half-chromatid, quarter-chromatid, etc. At times these words carry some implication about chemical constitution; at others they are simply morphological. Since any definition must, of necessity, change with increasing knowledge, the important point perhaps is to be consistent and to delimit the implications carefully.

Throughout this discussion, I shall use the terms *fiber* or *strand* in a simple descriptive sense to refer to something seen either in the conventional or electron microscope. The statement, "a fiber connects two granules" means only that at the resolution employed one sees a single line between the granules. The term *chromonema* is sometimes used in this noncommittal fashion, but often it carries genetic or chemical overtones.

On the other hand, I shall use the term *chromatid* with distinct theoretical implications. In the definition I shall assume that the theory of DNA "constancy" is essentially correct as applied to individual chromosomes (12, 46, 64); that is, that any particular chromosome contains a certain amount of DNA or some integer multiple of this amount (the multiple usually some power of 2). A *chromatid* will then be a chromosome or longitudinal fraction thereof which contains the same amount of DNA as an entire anaphase chromosome from the second meiotic division. Thus each prophase chromosome in a typical diploid cell will consist of two chromatids, the anaphase chromosome will contain one chromatid, and the

bivalent chromosomes of meiotic prophase will be made up of four chromatids in two sets of two. The rationale of this definition is simply that the anaphase chromosome of the second meiotic division seems to contain the least common multiple of DNA.

In practice the above definition corresponds to generally accepted usage. It does exclude, however, the simple morphological definition of a chromatid as a "half chromosome." Some authors (e.g., 48) have in the past referred to half an anaphase chromosome as a chromatid. We now know, however, that chromosome duplication, or at least DNA doubling, occurs during interphase (55, 64). Since there is thus no likely structural difference between a chromatid of prophase and an anaphase daughter chromosome, it seems advisable to refer to both by the same term. A definition based on DNA content has the further advantage, at least in theory, of providing an objective measure of the number of chromatids present at any time. Finally, of course, the chromatid is the unit of gene segregation and crossing over.

Polytene Chromosomes

The giant chromosomes found in dipteran larval tissues need no introduction here, as they are one of the best-known cytological objects. Their structure has been subject to much debate since their "rediscovery" in 1933 by Heitz and Bauer (35) and by Painter (49). Actually they were quite accurately described as early as 1881 by Balbiani (5); and a series of papers from that time to the 1930's attests to a continued, albeit minor interest in their structure. Several recent reviews (2, 7, 8) make it unnecessary for me to discuss in detail the numerous papers dealing with these chromosomes. Here I shall take up briefly some of the evidence for their multistranded or polytene condition and shall discuss in more detail the recent interesting studies on the "puffs" and "Balbiani rings" which characterize these chromosomes.

Structure

The polytene chromosomes are of course tremendously longer and thicker than the somatic chromosomes of the same organism. In *Drosophila,* for instance, the total length of the chromosome set is about 7.5 μ in the spermatogonial metaphase, but 1180 μ in the salivary gland (15). One of the first suggestions made to account for their great size was that they consist of a bundle of ordinary chromosomes more or less completely stretched out and lined up accurately side by side (6, 39, 50). A modern and well-documented statement of this polytene or multistrand theory is

found in the recent papers of Bauer and Beermann (7, 8). Briefly, the giant chromosome is supposed to consist of a bundle of hundreds or thousands of fine fibrils accurately aligned with one another along the major axis of the chromosome. A polytene chromosome can be pictured as a typical mitotic chromosome which has both uncoiled and undergone repeated duplication. The bands which cut transversely across the whole chromosome result from the lateral apposition of bead-like enlargements (chromomeres) on the constituent fibrils. Evidence favoring the polytene theory comes from a number of sources, only a few of which will be considered here. In many instances direct visual observation of fixed and stained chromosomes shows evidence of longitudinal fibrillation; fig. 17 in the paper of Beermann (8) shows this to particular advantage. Long ago, however, it was pointed out, particularly by Metz (45), that such fibrils visible in the conventional microscope are too large to correspond to single stretched-out chromatids of a normal chromosome. Fortunately, however, we do not need to rely on this kind of evidence alone, which is at best open to several interpretations. In his careful study of *Chironomus,* Beermann (8) has shown that certain restricted regions of a polytene chromosome may break up into smaller and smaller bundles of fibers, thus affording the most direct possible evidence of their multistranded condition (Figs. 1-3). More indirect evidence comes from a consideration of the nuclear volume and DNA changes which accompany the development of the polytene condition. Hertwig (36) pointed out that the various-sized nuclei in the larval organs of *Drosophila* fall into a rough geometrical series, the largest nuclei having about 512 times the volume of the smallest. More recently, Swift and Rasch (67) found an even more precise geometrical series by estimating the DNA content spectrophotometrically from the intensity of the Feulgen reaction (Fig. 4). These data can be interpreted as reflecting a series of nine to ten "rounds" of chromosome duplication and suggest that the largest salivary gland chromosomes of *Drosophila* contain between 512 and 1024 chromatids. Finally, an examination of many sorts of insect tissues suggests that polyteny may be simply a special case of a more general phenomenon of chromosome duplication without accompanying mitosis (endopolyploidy). Many insect nuclei show very high amounts of DNA (64) and in some cases it is possible to count an exceedingly large number of individual chromosomes, as shown by Geitler (33) in his study of endopolyploidy. In other instances, the reduplicated chromosomes may remain together in loose bundles (51). In view of the wide occurrence of such phenomena in insects generally, it seems likely that a polytene chromosome is an extreme situation where the strands

BR1
BR2
A B C A B C A
1 2
2 3
3 4

A B C
1 2
B C A B C A B C
4 5
5 6

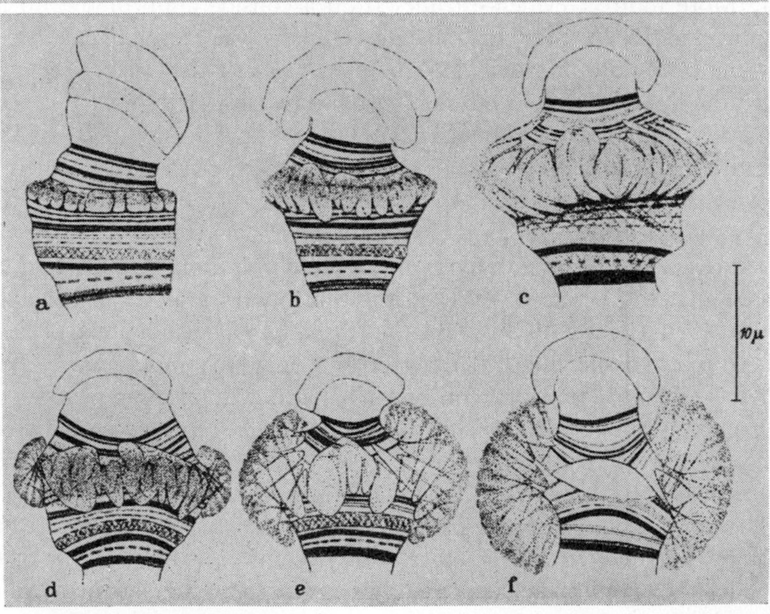
a
b
c
10μ
d
e
f

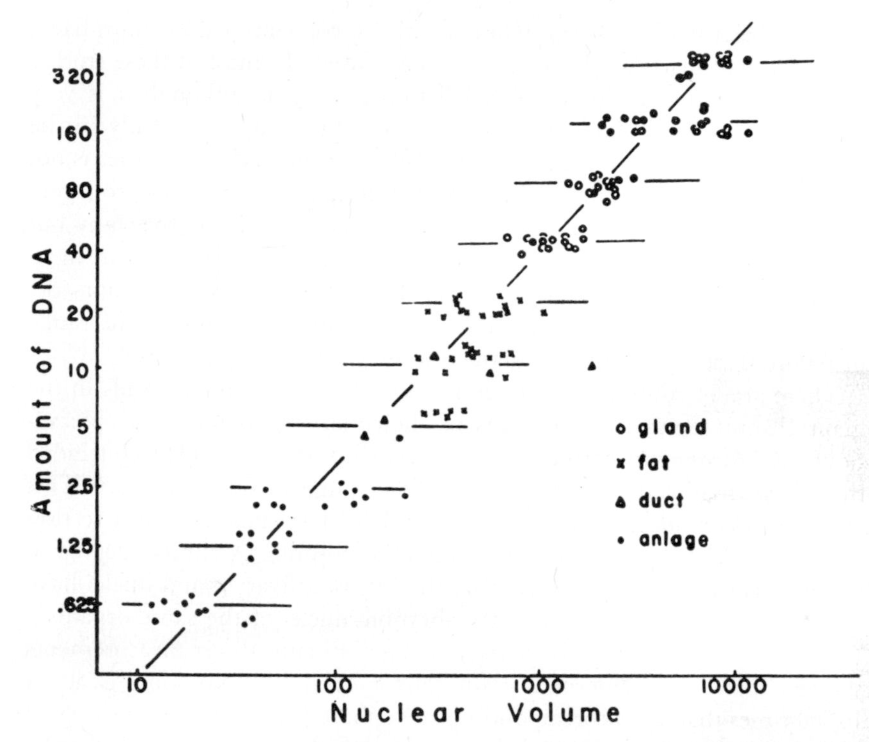

Fig. 4. DNA content as a function of nuclear volume in cells of larval *Drosophila melanogaster*. Estimated spectrophotometrically from the intensity of the Feulgen reaction. The values fall into a regular geometric series, with the largest gland nuclei containing 512 times as much DNA as the smallest anlage nuclei. Data from Swift and Rasch (67).

formed by repeated chromosome duplication remain intimately associated. White (71) has even described a case where a polyploid number of polytene chromosomes are found in a nucleus. Presumably the strands from earlier duplications separated, but those formed later remained together in bundles. These examples by no means exhaust the evidence for polyteny, but indicate some of the strongest arguments in its favor.

Several recent studies of the polytene chromosomes have used the increased resolution of the electron microscope. In some cases surface repli-

---

Fig. 1. Chromosome 4 from the salivary gland of *Chironomus tentans*.

Fig. 2. The same chromosome showing two typical Balbiani rings and a prominent puff. Note particularly that the banding pattern can be followed into the smaller subdivisions of the chromosome; the origin of the rings and puff can be traced to single bands in the unexpanded chromosome (*BR1* and *BR2* in Fig. 1).

Fig. 3. Different degrees of expansion of the same chromosome locus, varying from a small puff in *a* to a fully formed Balbiani ring in *f*. Note the constancy of the banding pattern in the subdivisions of the chromosome. Figs. 1, 2, 3 from W. Beermann (8).

cas have been made (73, 53), while in others, conventional osmium-fixed, thin-sectioned material (11, 32, 37) has been used. In most of these studies some indication of longitudinal fibrillation is evident, although it is very difficult to follow individual fibers for any great length, especially in the sectioned material. The organization of fibers in these chromosomes is not nearly so striking or regular as in such fibrous materials as muscle, collagen, and sperm tails. Indeed, the continuity of individual fibers over any but the shortest lengths (fractions of a micron) is largely a supposition in so far as the electron microscope pictures are concerned. Most authors describe the finest fibers as a few hundred Ångstroms in diameter, the range of reported values being from about 100 Å to 500 Å.

There are, of course, a very large number of such minute strands in the giant chromosomes. On the basis of their electron microscopic observations on *Chironomus* chromosomes, Beermann and Bahr (11) concluded that they "may contain more than 10,000 longitudinal elements." This estimate was made by counting the number of strands in a thin section and extrapolating to include the whole chromosome. A similar degree of polyteny is suggested by the fact that the largest salivary gland nuclei have about 16,000 times the volume of embryonic nuclei of the same organism (diameters in the ratio of about 100 μ to 4 μ). Finally, direct measurements showed that the volume of a giant salivary gland chromosome is about 16,000 times that of its corresponding metaphase pairs (8).

Gay (32) has also estimated the number of constituent strands in polytene chromosomes, in this case from *Drosophila melanogaster*. Taking 500 Å as the diameter of the unit strand, she calculates that the salivary gland chromosome may contain between 1000 and 2000 strands. Her estimate compares nicely with the volume and DNA measurements of Swift and Rasch (Fig. 4) on nuclei of the same fly. As already mentioned, these workers found that the largest gland nuclei contain 512 times the amount of DNA in the smallest anlage nuclei (presumably 1024 times the haploid amount).

One point should be stressed about polyteny as related to the general question of multistrandedness of chromosomes. Both Beermann and Gay find that the total number of strands seen in the electron microscope approximates closely the number of times the volume and/or DNA content of the diploid nucleus has increased. If this numerical relationship were strictly true, then of course we could say that each smallest fibril corresponds to an extended chromatid of a mitotic chromosome. I do not wish to "force" these data, since the estimates of strand number could easily be in error by a factor of two or more in either direction. Nevertheless, taken

at face value, the evidence does not necessarily point to a high degree of multiplicity in the chromatid itself. I shall return to this problem when discussing the lampbrush chromosomes.

Functional Aspects

The polytene chromosomes of many species show local variations in the clarity of the banding, some bands being discrete and sharply bounded, others appearing as diffuse puffs. These modifications have recently been the object of a thorough investigation by Bauer, Beermann, and Mechelke (7-11, 44) and have also been studied independently by Breuer and Pavan (14, 54). Much evidence points to the conclusion that specific modification of the bands occurs in different tissues of an organism and at different times in the life history, and that furthermore these modifications are reversible and are probably related to the functional activity of the cell.

Beermann was the first to show that puffing is not an invariant characteristic of particular bands, but rather that many bands may be either sharp or puffed depending upon the tissue examined. As an example, we may cite a case from *Chironomus tentans* (Fig. 5), where a short segment of chromosome 3 was studied in detail in four different tissues. In these tissues—salivary gland, Malphighian tubules, rectum, and midgut—attention was paid to six specific bands. In each tissue, there was a characteristic pattern of puffing such that any particular locus might be puffed in one,

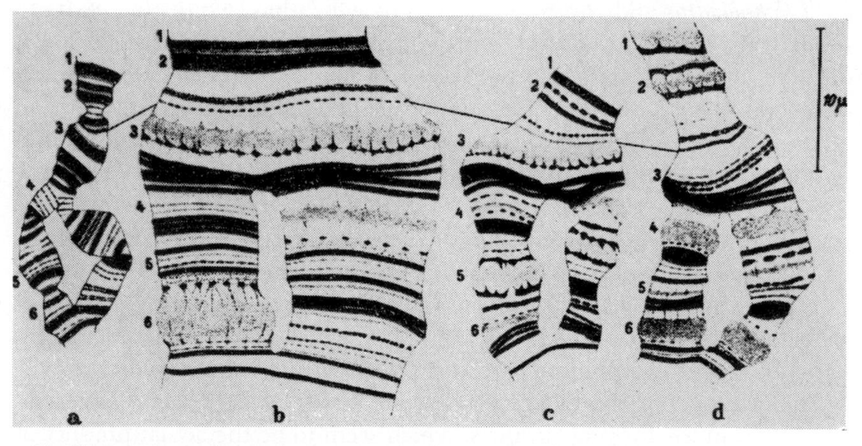

Fig. 5. Drawings of a short region of chromosome 3 in four different tissues of the same individual (*Chironomus tentans*): a. midgut, b. salivary gland, c. Malpighian tubule, d. rectum. Note the bands numbered 1-6, which are distinct in some of the tissues, puffed in others. From W. Beermann (8).

two, or three of the four tissues (puffing at these loci did not occur in the midgut). Beermann's conclusions are as follows: "Diffuse swelling, or 'puffing' of the chromosome is a phenomenon arising from single bands or interband spaces. This, along with the finding that adjacent loci may puff independently, constitutes the first direct morphological demonstration of the fact that giant chromosomes consist of linearly arranged, independently reactive genetic units of the order of magnitude of the bands, in other words, that bands or less probably interbands are gene loci."

Puffs on a vastly more spectacular scale, but still possessing certain basic similarities to those just described, have been known for many years as "Balbiani rings," in reference to the fact that they were seen and described by the first investigator of polytene chromosomes. The typical Balbiani ring appears at first glance to be an annular mass of material surrounding an otherwise normal chromosome. Closer analysis shows, however, that in the region of the Balbiani ring the chromosome actually breaks up into a large number of fine strands which extend out laterally into a more diffuse area (see Figs. 1, 2, 3). Certain features suggest that these rings may differ in their functional significance from the more typical puffs. So far, they have been found only in the salivary gland cells, where there may be from one to three per chromosome set. Beermann has assumed that they are related to the very high synthetic activity of the larval salivary gland, perhaps supplying some sort of precursor needed in the production of the salivary secretion. This view is very much strengthened by observations on *Trichocladius* and *Acricotopus,* each of which has two distinct parts to the salivary gland. In *Acricotopus,* which was studied by Mechelke (44), one lobe of the salivary gland produces a brown secretion at the beginning of metamorphosis, while the remainder of the gland, which differs also in other respects, does not contain the secretion. In the brown lobe are found two typical Balbiani rings and a very large puff; in the other cells, only two Balbiani rings. Most significantly, however, the loci showing these structural modifications are quite different in the two cell types. The situation in *Trichocladius* (9) is quite comparable, the salivary gland in this case possessing six very large specialized cells with their own pattern of Balbiani ring formation. Thus, in both forms specific and prominent chromosomal differentiations are correlated with cellular modifications.

The periphery of the Balbiani ring contains Feulgen-negative materials, sometimes in the form of droplets, which seem to be the actual product or products of this locus. Beermann (8) showed that a short exposure of *Chironomus* larvae to a temperature of 5°C, followed by a return to room temperature, caused a marked accumulation of droplets around these regions of the chromosome. He interpreted this to mean that cold affects

the rate of dispersal of the product more than its rate of formation. In any event, the situation shows clearly that something is produced by the locus at a fairly high rate. In their study of *Rhynchosciara,* Breuer and Pavan (14) noted that the region of large puffs is surrounded by material which stains with the pyronin component of Unna's pyronin methyl green mixture. That much of this material contains ribose nucleic acid (RNA) can be shown quite simply by enzymatic digestion used in conjunction with basic-dye staining (65). Figs. 6 and 7 show the Balbiani ring on the small nucleolar chromosome of *Chironomus* sp. In Fig. 7 we see the distribution of basic dye, azure B used at *p*H 4 (27), after treatment of the sections with RNAase. The staining is limited to parts containing DNA. In Fig. 6, the same section observed with the phase contrast microscope, we see the unstained nucleolus (large mass) and the Balbiani ring. Both these latter structures are intensely basophilic in control sections which were not treated with the enzyme.

Using the electron microscope Beermann and Bahr (11) have demonstrated the presence of numerous fine granules, about 300 Å diameter, in a Balbiani ring region of *Chironomus.* Similar granules, although usually somewhat smaller, are, of course, well known as a component of the microsome fraction of homogenized cells (52) and are presumably identical with the small granules associated with the lamellae of the ergastoplasm or endoplasmic reticulum. Because of their RNA content, these granules are responsible for much of the usual cytoplasmic basophilia. Similar granules are a frequent component of nucleoli, which likewise are known to contain RNA. It now seems possible that the RNA of the chromosomes, like that of the nucleoli and the cytoplasm, is organized into small granules.

That chromosomes contain RNA has been known for some time on the basis of staining characteristics and chemical analysis of isolated material (38, 47). More recently, several studies have shown that salivary gland chromosomes incorporate adenine-C-14 and P-32 into their RNA. Pelc and Howard (56) showed differential uptake of adenine-C-14 by certain bands in the salivary gland chromosomes of *Drosophila.* Control slides involving enzymatic digestion with RNAase prior to making the autoradiographs proved that the incorporation was acutally into RNA and was not simply a reflection of DNA synthesis associated with an increasing degree of polyteny. These same chromosomes showed differential uptake of methionine-S-35 into certain bands, although no attempt was made to see if the same bands simultaneously incorporated both adenine and methionine.

Taylor et al. (68, 69), using autoradiographic techniques, have carried out an extensive and careful set of studies on the RNA metabolism of

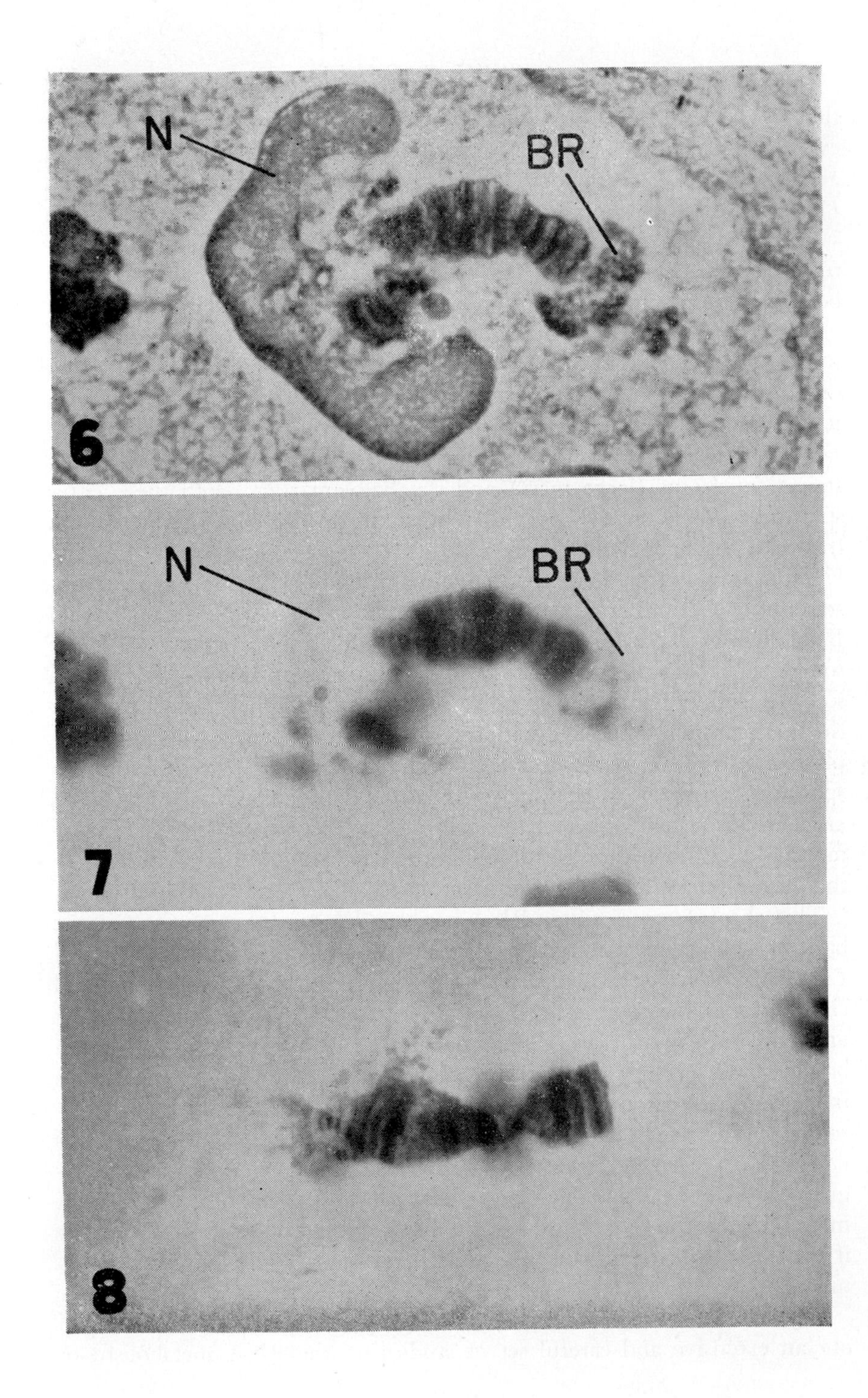
N
BR
6
N
BR
7
8

Drosophila salivary gland cells. By counting silver grains in the exposed emulsion these authors have been able to get quantitative information of the rates of incorporation of P-32 into several RNA fractions. In general, they find that the nucleolus initially incorporates P-32 at a higher rate than any other part of the cell. If larvae which have fed for a short time on P-32 are transferred to non-radioactive food, their nuclei gradually lose radioactivity, while at the same time P-32 appears in the cytoplasmic RNA. The rates of incorporation are consistent with the idea that nucleolar RNA is a precursor of cytoplasmic RNA, although these two fractions could have a common precursor.

The most recent study of McMaster-Kaye and Taylor (43) gives further quantitative data on rates of P-32 incorporation into chromosomes, nucleoli, and cytoplasm and suggests that each of these fractions has its own pattern of incorporation.

Taken together, the evidence indicates that the chromosomes contain RNA in various bands and particularly in the Balbiani ring regions. At least some of this RNA is metabolically active, and it seems safe to assume that it is being synthesized in situ. It may well be that the individual gene products are ribonucleoprotein in nature, although we are a long way from demonstrating locus specificity of these products. It hardly seems necessary to point out here the many lines of evidence which implicate ribonucleoproteins as intermediates between the DNA of the genes and the active sites of protein synthesis in the cytoplasm (13, 21).

Lampbrush or Lateral Loop Chromosomes

The giant meiotic bivalents found in the oocytes of many animals have been named "lampbrush" or "lateral loop" chromosomes in reference to the peculiar looped projections which extend laterally from their main axis. Their great size poses certain problems of observation, as recognized long ago by Rückert (63), who studied them in whole isolated nuclei. Duryee (24, 25, 26) was the first to urge observation of the unfixed chromosomes, and he showed the ease with which these giant structures may be isolated manually from the oocyte nucleus. Under phase contrast the

Fig. 6. Salivary gland chromosome of *Chironomus,* phase contrast photograph of sectioned material to show the nucleolus (N) and a prominent Balbiani ring (BR). 1500 ×.

Fig. 7. The same preparation by conventional illumination. Stained with azure B at *p*H 4 after treatment with RNAase. Only the DNA of the bands stains. In control slides not treated with the enzyme the nucleolus and Balbiani ring are strongly basophilic due to their RNA content. 1500 ×.

Fig. 8. Aceto-orcein squash of the same chromosome from another individual. Note how the chromosome breaks up into smaller fibers in the Balbiani ring and nucleolus regions. Cf. Figs. 1, 2, 3. 950 ×.

freshly isolated chromosomes are a beautiful sight indeed, and clearly show points of fine structure that can hardly be guessed from fixed or sectioned material. As an aid to observation, an inverted optical system is almost a necessity, since with this one may observe the chromosomes as they rest freely on the surface of a coverslip (17, 29, 72).

The main structural features, as observed in the light microscope, are now quite clear and may be summarized briefly (16-20, 23-26, 28-31, 34, 72; cf. Figs. 9 and 10). These chromosomes are the longest known, ranging

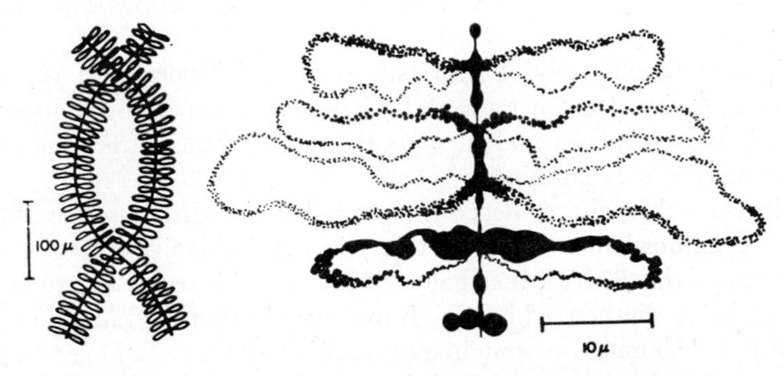

Fig. 9. *Left,* a very diagrammatic representation of a lampbrush chromosome showing the homologues held together at two chiasmata. Hundreds of loop pairs extend laterally from the axis of each homologue. *Right,* a somewhat schematic view of a lampbrush chromosome to show the central axis of chromomeres connected together by a very delicate strand (usually invisible in the light microscope). Loop pairs of differing morphology project laterally from the axis. The loops are more closely spaced on the actual chromosome.

in some species up to a millimeter or more in length. They are actually found in a variety of oocytes, including both vertebrates and invertebrates (18), although they reach their most spectacular dimensions in the salamander. The lampbrush condition is found during the meiotic prophase, so we are in fact discussing meiotic bivalents. When I speak of "chromosome" I shall usually be referring to one homologue of the pair only. The central axis of each homologue consists of a single row of granules (chromomeres in the descriptive sense) connected together by a strand of such fine dimensions that it is generally invisible in the light microscope. The chromomeres themselves are a few micra in length, but generally only 0.5 to 2.0 μ in diameter. Attached laterally to the chromomeres are *pairs* of loops (34) which display an amazing variety of form from locus to locus. The most common loop is an indistinctly fuzzy or granular strand, some 10 to 50 or more micra in total length, frequently showing a thicker and a thinner end at the points of attachment to the chromomere. Some-

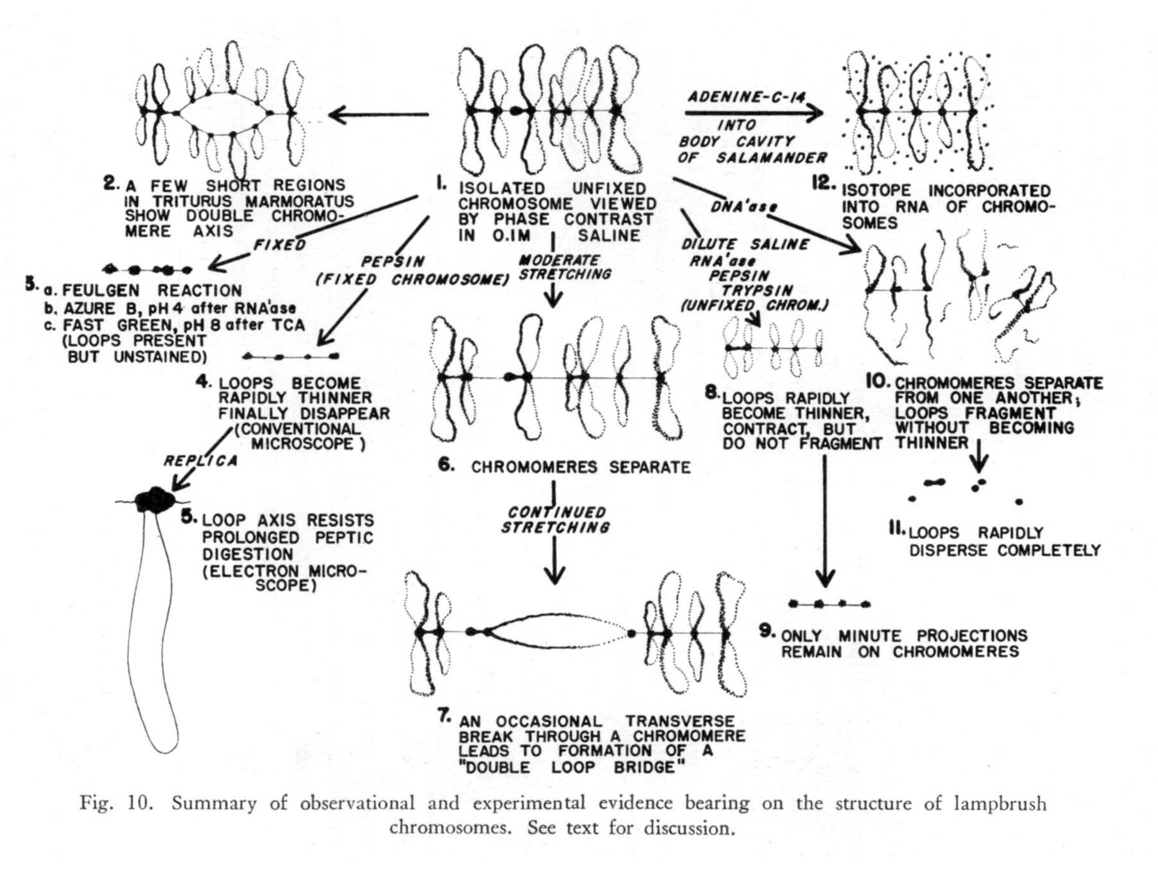

Fig. 10. Summary of observational and experimental evidence bearing on the structure of lampbrush chromosomes. See text for discussion.

times a single pair of loops arises from one chromomere, although particularly in the later stages of oocyte development, when the chromomeres are fewer in number and larger, more than one pair may arise from the same chromomere. The chromomeres were long claimed to be "optical illusions," but they actually differ from the loops in a number of important respects. Thus, the chromomeres are Feulgen-positive, stain by the fast green technique of Alfert and Geschwind (3), and are more or less resistant in the unfixed state to dilute saline, pepsin, trypsin, and RNAase; whereas the loops are negative to the Feulgen reaction and the fast green stain, contain demonstrable amounts of RNA, and are readily dissolved or digested by dilute saline and the enzymes listed.

Of the greatest importance in understanding the structure of the lampbrush chromosomes is the very delicate strand which connects successive chromomeres. I should like to distinguish clearly the evidence that such a strand must exist and must have dimensions generally speaking below the resolving limit of the conventional microscope, and the evidence concerning its actual dimensions, multiplicity, etc., as viewed in the electron microscope. These are of course intimately related questions, but lack of agreement about the fine structure should not obscure the fact that all recent workers, with the exception of Lafontaine and Ris (41), concur that the connections between successive chromomeres are essentially submicroscopic.

When one observes freshly isolated lampbrush chromosomes in a saline solution, the numerous loops tend to obscure the details of the axial structure. However, under three conditions the chromomeres and the regions between them are particularly clear: in stretched regions of the chromosomes, in chromosomes from older oocytes where the loops are much reduced, and in chromosomes isolated in very dilute saline where the loops dissolve. Under these conditions one has no trouble noting that successive chromomeres are separated by a gap which is not transversed by any visible structure (Fig. 11). Such chromosomes are free in the isolating medium

---

Fig. 11. A short segment of a slightly stretched lampbrush chromosome. Note the spaces between chromomeres where the continuity of the axis seems interrupted. Phase contrast view of material fixed in formaldehyde vapor. 1900 ×.

Fig. 12. Low power electron micrograph to show the fine fiber which connects successive chromomeres. The bulk of the loop material has been digested with pepsin to reveal the chromomere axis to advantage. Chromium-shadowed. 5000 ×.

Fig. 13. Higher power view of the interchromomeric fiber from a pepsin-treated chromosome. The fiber diameter is not uniform but ranges from 200-400 Å, with an occasional region of somewhat larger dimensions. Chromium-shadowed. 33,000 ×.

Fig. 14. Similar to Fig. 13, but material dried according to Anderson's (4) critical point method. The fiber diameter here seems more uniform and ranges from 300-400 Å. Chromium-shadowed. 35,000 ×.

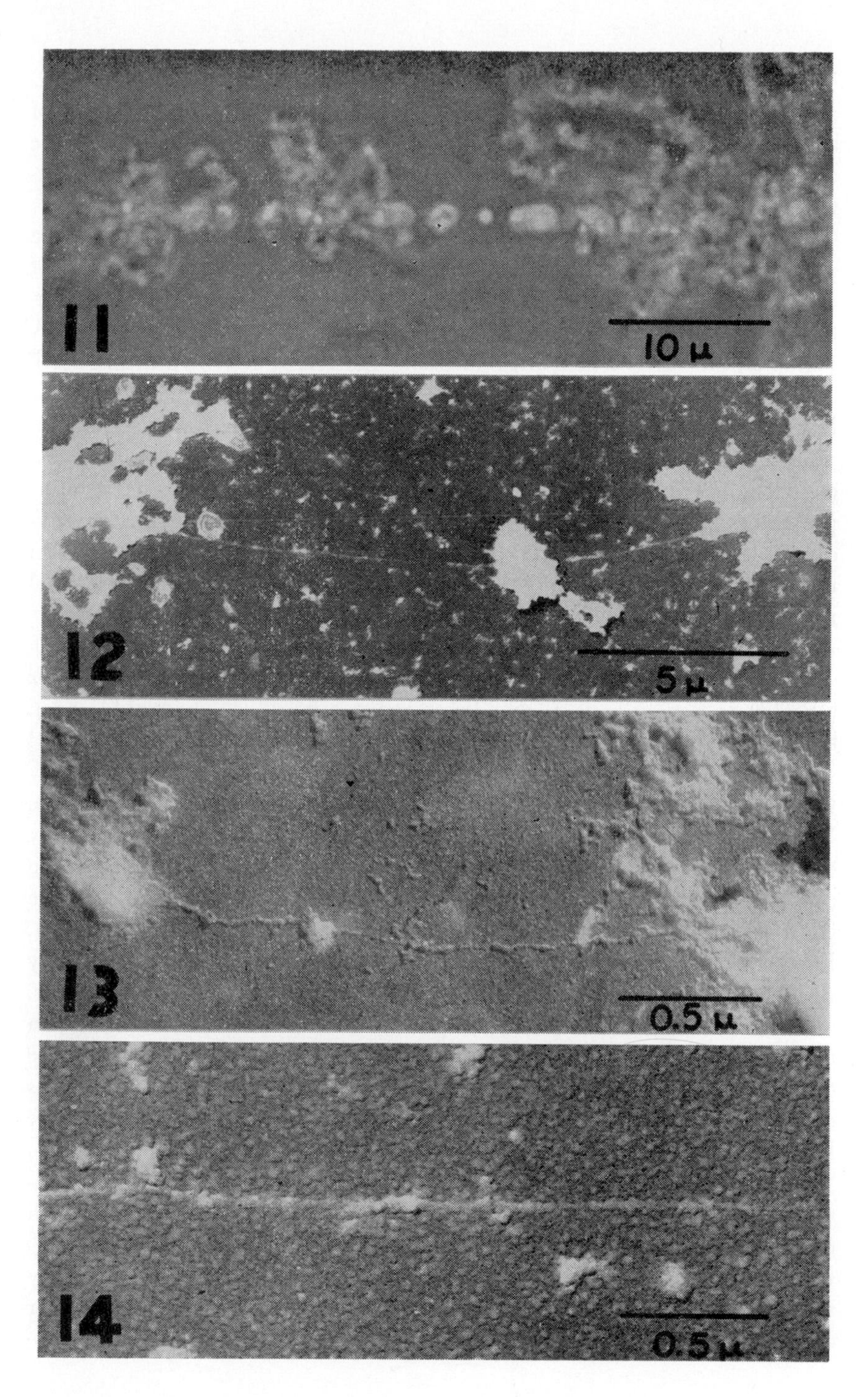
11
10 μ
12
5 μ
13
0.5 μ
14
0.5 μ

and of course would come apart immediately were there not some sort of submicroscopic strand connecting successive chromomeres. It should be added that neither pepsin, trypsin, nor RNAase destroys this fine connection, although as we shall see, it is rapidly attacked by DNAase.

The strand has been photographed in the electron microscope in three different laboratories. Tomlin and Callan (70) found a single strand of about 200 Å diameter in what are probably somewhat stretched preparations. Guyénot and Danon (34) report two connections each 100-150 Å diameter, but often coated with accessory materials. My own original observations (28) indicated a strand of "less than 1000 Å diameter," but later pictures of material dehydrated according to Anderson's (4) critical point method, suggest that 200-400 Å is more nearly correct for the finest connections (Figs. 12-14). However, it is equally clear in all photographs presented to date that the strand is somewhat variable in diameter. My own guess is that the strand (or strands) tend to contract and thicken rather easily and are perhaps seen at true diameter only in slightly stretched regions.

Under certain exceptional conditions the axial continuity of the chromosome is maintained not by such a fine strand as described above, but rather by what is obviously a stretched out pair of loops. Such "double loop bridges" were first described by Callan (17), and they have furnished strong support for a theory of lampbrush structure recently proposed by Callan (17) and by myself (31). Double loop bridges arise as follows. When a lampbrush chromosome is stretched, as may occur accidentally during isolation of the chromosomes from the nucleus, or which can be carefully controlled with microneedles, the chromomeres at first separate from one another and the interchromomeric gaps become evident (17, 26). Further stretching generally causes breaks in the axis. But amazingly enough, these breaks do not involve the interchromomeric connections, but rather occur transversely through the middle of a chromomere. In this fashion a pair of loops is stretched out in the axis of the chromosome to form a "double loop bridge" (see Fig. 10). In these cases the two ends of a loop are separated by a very long gap in the chromosome axis, the length of the gap being simply the total length of the involved loops.

These various observations have led to the theory of lampbrush chromosome structure illustrated in Fig. 15. According to this theory a lampbrush chromosome consists basically of two chromatids of a few hundred Ångstroms diameter. In the region of the loops these chromatids are completely separated from each other and are individually visible only because of their coating of ribonucleoprotein. In the region of the chromomeres the chro-

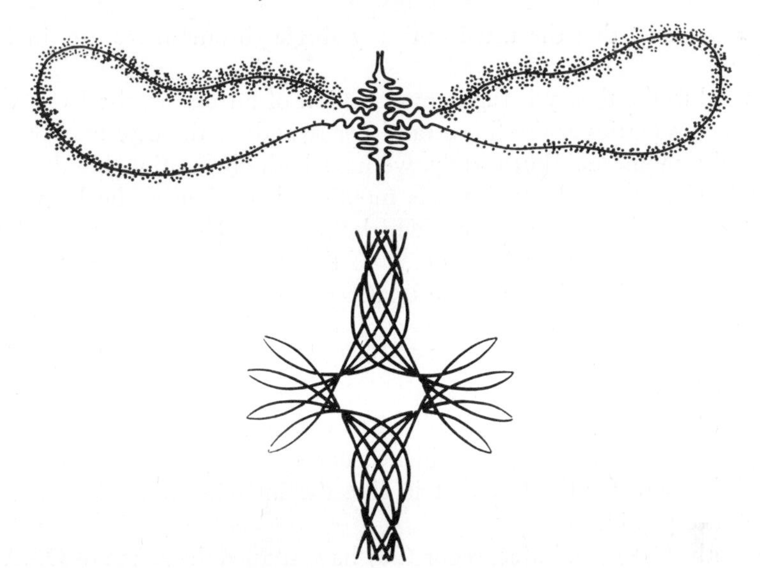

Fig. 15. Diagram of the postulated structure of a lampbrush chromosome.
Fig. 16. Beermann's (8) interpretation of the course of the chromosomal fibers in the region of the Balbiani rings. Compare the lateral looping of the fibers in this case with the loop axes of a lampbrush chromosome.

matids are complexly coiled or folded, but for short distances between chromomeres run more or less straight.

That the loops form part of very long and continuous chromosome strands is an hypothesis first put forward by Rückert (63) in his classic account of lampbrush chromosomes. More recently Ris (58-61) has been the main proponent of this view. The studies of Duryee (26) and my original observations (28, 29) led me at first to reject Ris' formulation, but the stretching experiments of Callan (17) and electron microscopical observations to be discussed shortly have convinced me that the essence of the hypothesis must be retained.

The presence of two chromatids in regions other than the loops is a postulate only and does not rest on experimental evidence. However, we know that in general DNA duplication is completed before prophase of meiosis (55, 64), and so we may suppose that two chromatids are present throughout the length of the lampbrush chromosomes. Furthermore, in *Triturus marmoratus* (17) a few short regions of the lampbrush chromosomes show complete lateral separation not only of the two loops of a pair, but also of the chromomere axes (Fig. 10). For simplicity therefore,

I have assumed that the usual optically single chromomeres are, in fact, double.

Crucial to the theory is the demonstration of an axis in the loops with the same properties as the fine strand (or strands as the case may be) between chromomeres. Fortunately, we have both observational and experimental evidence on this point. As mentioned previously, the loops may be "removed" by several agents which leave the chromomeres and the interchromomeric connections intact. If the theory presented here is correct, then the loop axis should be unaffected by these agents. In point of fact, peptic digestion, which removes all traces of the loops as seen in the light microscope, leaves a very delicate loop axis which has been photographed in the electron microscope (31). The diameter of this axis is somewhat variable in the available pictures but is generally less than 500 Å. We therefore have direct evidence not only for the existence of this strand, but also for the fact that it, like the interchromomeric strand, is resistant to pepsin.

Recently, Callan and Macgregor (20) have studied the action of DNAase on unfixed lampbrush chromosomes, with results which bear on the existence of the loop axis and its chemical composition. DNAase causes a unique and dramatic disintegration of the chromosome structure (Fig. 10). A few minutes after application of the enzyme, the chromosome falls apart into large segments due to breakage of many interchromomeric strands. The process continues until one has only freely scattered chromomeres or short lengths consisting of a few chromomeres each. At the same time the loops fragment into shorter and shorter pieces with no immediate decrease in diameter. Eventually all trace of the loops is lost. It should be emphasized that pepsin, trypsin, and RNAase do not cause breakage of the interchromomeric strands, nor do the loops ever fragment into large pieces in these enzymes. Rather, the loops become thinner and thinner, simultaneously contracting until they are represented by very small projections on the chromomeres (Fig. 10). These observations mean that the continuity not only of the interchromomeric strands but also of the loops is dependent upon the integrity of their contained DNA.

On the basis of the electron microscope evidence and the DNAase experiment, we may conclude that the strands which make up the interchromomeric connections and the axes of the loops are essentially similar in dimensions as well as in composition. The chromomeres themselves resemble the interchromomeric strands and the loop axis in the following features: they are resistant to the same reagents which leave these strands unaffected (dilute saline, RNAase, pepsin, trypsin), and, of course, they

contain DNA as shown by a positive Feulgen reaction. That they consist of a more tightly wound portion of the same strands is an inference based largely on the developmental history of the loops. As this developmental history is also the basis of speculation about the functional role of the loops, I shall discuss them both together in a later paragraph.

The picture of lampbrush chromosome structure which I have outlined here differs somewhat from that presented recently by Ris (59-61) and by Lafontaine and Ris (41). Ris' views on lampbrush chromosome structure have been guided by two general postulates about chromosomes. The first of these is that the chromatid is essentially multiple-stranded (the degree of multiplicity being a species characteristic), and the second that the strands making up a chromosome are uniform throughout their length. In a very general sense, these postulates could be applied to Fig. 15, although a high degree of multiplicity seems unlikely because of the fine dimensions of the chromatid. But as a matter of fact, Ris has used the postulates in quite a different fashion.

Originally (58, 62) he held that the lampbrush chromosome contains a bundle of uniform, independent strands (8 or more) each of which could form separate loops and whose central overlap produced the chromomeres as optical illusions. The demonstration of the paired nature of the loops, implying that a loop corresponds to a chromatid and not some smaller unit, and the numerous lines of evidence proving the existence of the chromomeres, has brought revision of these views. Ris still feels that the chromatid is multiple-stranded and that the strands are structurally uniform. Now, however, the multiple strands are found as very much finer (500 Å) threads making up the entire substance of the loops and presumably continuous with similar, tightly coiled threads in the chromomere. Ris supposes that the 500 Å threads contain RNA in the loop regions but DNA in the chromomeres, and that the loops are formed by intercalary growth within certain regions of the fibers. The evidence for these fibers consists of electron micrographs of whole isolated chromosomes and sections of chromosomes.

The possible existence of fibrous material in the loops will not be denied, although I personally feel that many of the pictures presented could as well be interpreted in terms of granular material. But the question of structural continuity of such fibers throughout the length of the chromosome seems to me clearly refuted by evidence at hand. In particular, the results of digestion experiments, already described, suggest that the structural integrity of the loops is dependent upon DNA. The RNA material may be removed either with dilute saline, proteolytic enzymes, or RNAase with-

out causing fragmentation of the loops or disruption of the interchromomeric strands. The material which holds the chromosome together is clearly quite different from that making up the bulk of the loops.

The dimensions of the interchromomeric strand provide an almost insuperable difficulty to Ris' view: if the loops are made up of 8 or more fibers each 500 Å in diameter, then, of course, these fibers cannot be continuous through a portion of the chromosome itself less than 500 Å in diameter. It is not surprising that Lafontaine and Ris (41) discount the evidence for the existence of such a strand. Rather, they claim that successive chromomeres are connected either by two short strands having dimensions similar to the loop bases (i.e., readily visible in the light microscope), or by successive loops. In the latter case, ends of a loop are supposed to be inserted in two successive chromomeres separated by a gap of a few micra (their Fig. 1). In citing the double loop bridges described by Callan as evidence for their view, these authors confuse the issue, since successive chromomeres in an unstretched chromosome or for that matter in most stretched chromosomes are *not* connected by loops. The gaps which they describe are nothing more than the usual interchromomeric gaps, and careful observation of unfixed material would show that they are not traversed by loops. The same fact can be demonstrated with fixed material (Fig. 11), although here the loops are generally much more tangled and difficult to interpret.

Functional Aspects of the Lampbrush Chromosomes

Evidence has already been presented to show that the loop consists of a very delicate axis about which ribonucleoprotein material is accumulated. It seems very likely that this loop axis is a permanent structural part of the chromosome, unwound during periods of synthesis, folded back into the chromosome axis when inactive. The various loops may correspond rather directly to gene loci. The evidence for these statements will be considered under three headings: structure, synthesis, and genetics.

Structure. The origin and disappearance of the loops should provide us with some evidence bearing on the problem of chromosome activity. The early stages in loop formation are difficult to study because of the small size of the nuclei, but loop regression is easily followed in the later stages of oogenesis. The chromosomes at the first metaphase are essentially typical meiotic chromosomes; that is, they are more or less homogeneous, Feulgen-positive rods with few signs of internal differentiation. They are derived from the lampbrush condition by a gradual reduction in the length of the chromosome accompanied by a decrease in the number and size of

the loops, and a concomitant decrease in the total number of chromomeres. Most significant for the present interpretation is the fact that the loops never detach as such from the chromosome. Rather, it seems that loop regression is accomplished by a discharge of the ribonucleoprotein from the loop and a gradual folding of the loop axis into the chromomere. Essentially the same process occurs during the dissolution of loops in saline of low concentration or in dilute solutions of pepsin or RNAase. Parenthetically it should be remarked that the electron microscopical demonstration of the loop axis was possible only by first fixing the chromosomes in such a way that the loops adhered firmly to a glass slide. In this way many of the loops can be digested by pepsin without the concomitant contraction; they simply become thinner and thinner. The axis alone remains after prolonged digestion and may be visualized in the electron microscope by replica techniques.

Circumstantial evidence for the idea of raveling and unraveling of the loop axis comes from a comparison of chromosomes from young oocytes with those from later stages. The young oocytes contain chromosomes with very large loops but generally small chromomeres. The opposite situation holds later: the chromomeres are large, but the loops are reduced. Such a reciprocal size relationship suggests that the chromomere may form at the expense of the loop axis and vice versa.

One final theoretical argument should be mentioned. It now seems clear that DNA is present in the loops, probably in the loop axis. If the concept of DNA constancy is in fact correct, then it follows that the DNA of the loops must somehow get back into the main body of the chromosome before metaphase. The coiling up of the loop axis into the chromomere would provide such a mechanism.

Synthesis. In all amphibian oocyte nuclei during the later stages of oogenesis the nuclear sap contains an abundance of small granules of various sizes which correspond to quite similar granules found on various lampbrush loops (17, 26, 29). Like the RNA-protein material of the loops, these granules contain cytochemically demonstrable RNA. In some species of salamanders, notably in *T. cristatus carnifex* studied by Callan (17), the loops show an amazing heterogeneity of structure from one locus to the next. Callan has shown that all of the larger granules of characteristic morphology found free in the nuclear sap correspond closely to similar material present on one or more pairs of loops on the chromosomes. The conclusion is almost forced upon us that these free materials are ultimately derived from the loops by some sort of budding process. In *Amblystoma tigrinum,* the nucleolus offers a particularly striking case of the

production of RNA-protein materials from a specific chromosome locus, although here the relationship to a loop is not so clear-cut. The oocyte nucleus of *A. tigrinum,* like the nucleus of all salamanders, contains many hundreds of free nucleoli located some distance from the chromosomes. There has always been considerable question as to whether these nucleoli are really homologous to the usual somatic nucleoli, which are of course attached to a chromosome at a specific locus. In *A. tigrinum* the locus of the somatic nucleoli is known from a careful study made some years ago by Dearing (22). When one looks at this same locus in the lampbrush chromosome, a nucleolus or group of nucleoli, identical to the free extra-chromosomal nucleoli, is found attached laterally to the chromosome axis. The exact mode of attachment is not clear because the highly refractile nature of the nucleolar material obscures the fine detail. But it is quite certain that this locus, responsible for the production of the somatic nucleolus, also produces bodies identical to the free oocyte nucleoli. What we see here is probably an extreme example of RNA-protein production by a particular chromosome region. In point of fact, many of the loops are composed of very large lumps or granules of materials, so that from a morphological point of view, there seems to be a gradation from the typical nucleoli through various sorts of heavily granular materials, to the very faintly granular and "amorphous" loops (cf. 17, 29, 30 for details). Whether one wishes to call all of the larger granules attached to the chromosomes and free in the nuclear sap "nucleoli," as has been customary in the past, seems to be a relatively unimportant question of terminology. They all represent materials derived from the chromosome.

More direct evidence for synthetic activity in the loops is indicated by studies using adenine-C-14 as a precursor for RNA (Gall, unpub.). A few hours after injection of the labeled compound into the body cavity of a female salamander, the RNA of the oocyte nuclei shows strong radioactivity (Fig. 17). Although the concentration of RNA in the cytoplasm is much greater than in the nucleus, as indicated by the intensity of azure B staining, the nucleus is the most radioactive part of the cell. The specific

Fig. 17. Autoradiograph of a section of an immature oocyte of the newt, *Triturus,* eight hours after injection of adenine-C-14 into the coelom. The activity in the oocyte proper is due to incorporation into RNA, as shown by control sections pretreated with RNAase. RNA stained by azure B at *p*H 4, photographed in blue light to reduce the extreme contrast in staining between cytoplasm and nucleus. Note the intense nuclear incorporation despite the relatively low RNA concentration. 400 ×.

Fig. 18. Isolated lampbrush chromosome from same animal used in Fig. 17. Conventional illumination to show grains in the autoradiographic film. Extraction experiments show that the incorporation is into RNA. 550 ×.

Fig. 19. Same as Fig. 18, phase contrast showing the outline of the chromosomes. 550 ×.

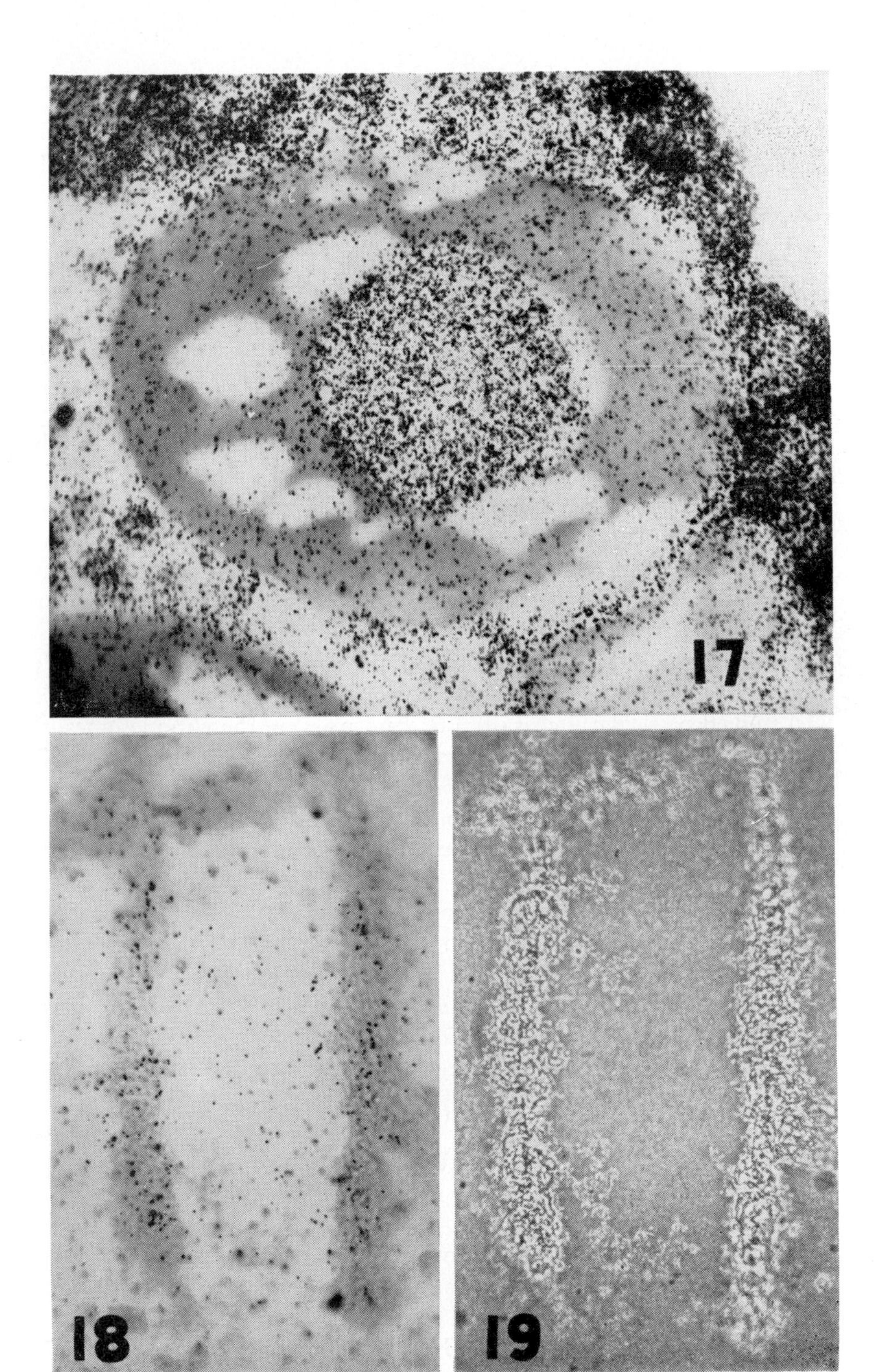

17
18
19

activity of the nuclear RNA is therefore very much higher than that of the cytoplasm. Chromosomes and nucleoli have also been isolated from such radioactive nuclei and fixed onto glass slides before being covered with stripping film. It is clear from the autoradiographs that activity is present not only in the nucleoli, but also in the loops of the chromosomes (Figs. 18, 19). We may reasonably infer, therefore, that synthesis of RNA is taking place directly in the loops.

Genetic. Most of the loops on a typical lampbrush chromosome are rather similar in general morphology. As already indicated, however, characteristic loops differing in total length, and especially in granularity of the ribonucleoprotein materials, occur at specific loci along the length of the chromosome. These loops furnish landmarks by which one may recognize particular chromosomes of the set, and indeed the whole chromosome can be mapped at least partially in terms of loop morphology. These variations suggest that perhaps each loop, or loop pair, represents a different genetic locus responsible for the production of some particular material.

A rather more direct demonstration of the genetic nature of differences in loop morphology has recently been made by Callan and Lloyd (19), who studied particularly characteristic loop pairs on the chromosomes of *T. cristatus carnifex.* Three different conditions have been found with respect to certain loci: loops may be present on both homologues, present on only one, or missing entirely. Significantly, all the oocytes of any one female salamander show the same condition for any one locus. Furthermore, the proportions of individuals with the indicated conditions (homozygous present, homozygous absent, heterozygous) follow expectation on the basis of random distribution of a gene in the population. Thus, we have very strong circumstantial evidence that the directly visualized chromosomal states express gene differences. These same workers have now made crosses between individuals of known constitution to see if the presence or absence of loops segregates in the appropriate Mendelian fashion.

Discussion

Nature of the Chromatid

The evidence from electron microscopy indicates that the interchromomeric fiber of the lampbrush chromosome is only a few hundred Ångstroms in diameter; furthermore, it constitutes the *entire* chromosome in those short regions where it occurs. Now by commonly accepted definition

each homologue of a meiotic bivalent consists of two chromatids. Assuming that the interchromomeric strand is double, as indeed some of the pictures of Guyénot and Danon (34) suggest, we are forced to conclude that the chromatid in these regions is no more than a few hundred Ångstroms in diameter. Callan and Tomlin's data suggest 100 Å, Guyénot and Danon 100-150 Å, and my own pictures, 150-200 Å. It may well be that smaller units exist in these chromatids; the fact that the interchromomeric fiber usually appears single but should correspond to two chromatids is evidence in itself that fibers may be too closely joined for resolution even in the electron microscope. But the strands we are discussing are themselves already near molecular dimensions and it seems most unlikely that any high degree of multiplicity will be demonstrated.

In the case of the salivary gland chromosomes, multiple-strandedness seems well established on a number of grounds. However, the only multiplicity which is certain is that of chromatids, i.e., the DNA content is higher than the diploid amount by some power of 2. We find that the number of strands estimated by Beermann and Gay corresponds closely to the degree of polyteny suggested by volume and DNA measurements. Hence, the component fibril seen in the electron microscope may be a chromatid and not a smaller unit. The evidence, of course, is not so clear in this case as for the lampbrush chromosome. It should be stressed, however, that the presence of multiple strands in the salivary gland chromosomes cannot be used as a general argument for multiple-strandedness of the *chromatid,* unless it is clearly shown that the number of strands exceeds the degree of polyteny. Alfert (2) has stressed essentially this same point.

Fine fibers having a diameter of a few hundred Ångstroms more or less have been described from ordinary mitotic chromosomes and from sperm heads. Figs. 20-21 show such fibers in the spermatid of the grasshopper *Melanoplus,* where they appear on closer inspection to be fine tubules. The mere presence of a number of transversely cut fibers seen in a single electron microscope section, however, tells us nothing about the number of strands in a chromatid. If the chromatids are as long and thin as the evidence just cited would lead us to think, then they must be very complexly woven back and forth in both mitotic chromosomes and sperm heads. We must know the exact geometry of the fiber arrangement before interpreting such pictures in terms of the number of strands. Kaufmann and McDonald (37) claim that mitotic chromosomes consist of a hierarchy of pairs of strands, starting with pairs of the finest (125 Å) threads and proceeding up to quarter chromatids, half chromatids, and finally to the whole chromosome, which presumably contains 32 or more strands.

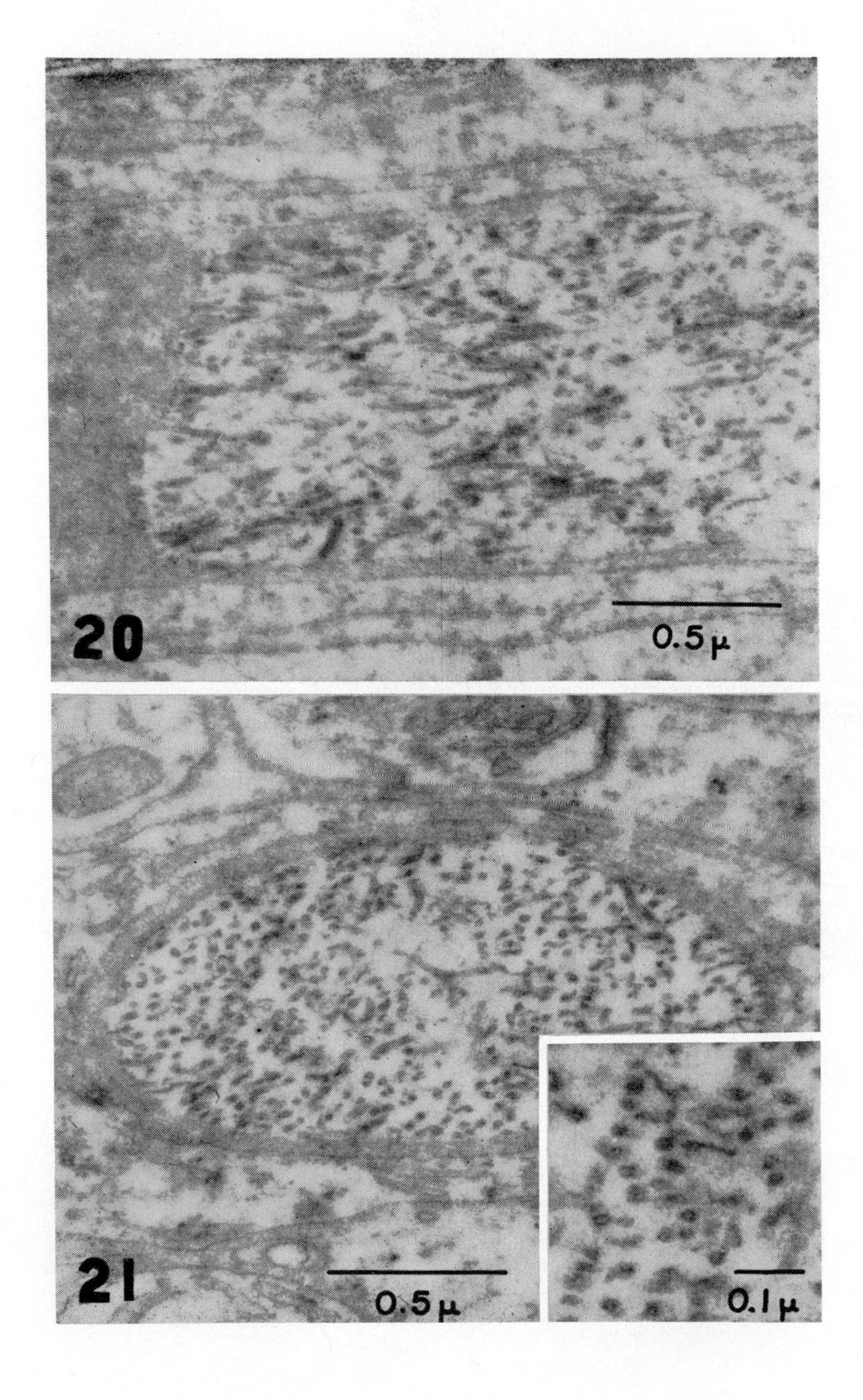
20
0.5 μ
21
0.5 μ
0.1 μ

I agree with these authors that their sections of chromosomes show minute fibrils, but I cannot agree so readily that the geometry of their arrangement is at all evident from the published pictures.

Not only are chromatids of extremely minute diameter, but they are also enormously long. Calculations based on the number of lampbrush loops per chromosome and their average length lead us to believe that the total length of a salamander (*Triturus*) chromosome is of the order of 5 centimeters (31). This calculation completely ignores any length of the chromatid which is wound up in the chromomeres and so is presented as a minimal estimate of length. Beermann and Bahr (11) have estimated that the total length of the strands spun out in a Balbiani ring is of the order of 4 micra, and Beermann (8) has also presented the evidence that this material forms at the expense of a single cross-band. If we count the total number of bands on a salivary gland chromosome, say 1000, and assume that any locus is potentially able to unravel strands several micra in length, we arrive at a figure of several millimeters for the total length of the chromosome. In the salivary gland chromosome we must assume this potentiality for more than a few loci; in the lampbrush chromosomes we can see the expanded regions directly.

Nature of the Functional Unit

The recent elegant studies on polytene chromosomes provide strong reason for believing that the functional unit of the chromosomes is of the general order of magnitude of the bands seen in the light microscope. In the lampbrush chromosome, the functional unit is probably the loop. The similarity between loops and Balbiani rings or puffs is quite striking and has been pointed out already on several occasions (2, 17, 31).

In both, a Feulgen-positive region spins out fibers several micra in length, an estimated four micra for the salivary gland chromosome, up to 200 micra for the longest loops. Ribonucleoprotein accumulates around these fibers but later is lost when the expanded locus regresses to its normal dimensions. Since the fibers which are spun out either demonstrably con-

---

Fig. 20. Longitudinal section of a spermatid from the grasshopper *Melanoplus*. The centriole is the diffusely granular structure to the left; fibers oriented parallel to the axis of the sperm head extend from the centriole anteriorly for a short distance. However, most of the nucleus at this stage is filled with lamellae (not shown in this picture) which are apparently formed by the lateral association of these fibers. 44,000 ×.

Fig. 21. Transverse section of a comparable nucleus showing dotlike cross sections of the fibers. 46,000 ×. Inset: higher magnification of a small region from the transverse section. Here one sees that the fibers are in fact fine tubules whose dimensions are approximately 170 Å total diameter and 70 Å core diameter. 90,000 ×.

tain DNA (lampbrush) or develop at the "expense" of a DNA-containing region (salivary), the process is very likely a change in the degree of folding of the basic chromosome strands and does not involve intercalary growth.

The differences between the Balbiani rings and the lampbrush loops are perhaps related to the type of chromosome in which the changes occur and to the general significance of the cells in which those chromosomes are found. Salivary gland chromosomes contain some thousand or more chromatids; the lampbrush chromosomes, only two. Therefore, when the salivary gland locus unravels, a large number of component loops spread out laterally; when the same state is assumed by the lampbrush locus, only two loops are formed (cf. Figs. 15 and 16).

Beermann argues that the Balbiani rings and puffs are closely related to the activity of the cells in which they occur. He imagines that the pattern of puffing reflects in some fashion the pattern of physiological functions exhibited by each cell type. Many cell types would have certain functions in common and would therefore show greater or lesser activity in some of the same chromosomal loci. Other functions peculiar to individual cell types would be represented by specific chromosomal modifications. The Balbiani rings, for instance, have so far been seen only in salivary gland cells and might be related to the specific and severe demands on these glands involved in the production of the salivary secretion. Somewhat analogous arguments can be brought forward for the egg cell and the lampbrush chromosome. Here, however, we must suppose that a very large number of loci, certainly hundreds, are functional at once. This extreme activity of the chromosomes may well be related to the establishment of many synthetic functions which will be required of the growing and differentiating egg.

Chromosomal Differentiation and Cellular Differentiation

In the preceding discussion I have tried to demonstrate that the lampbrush chromosomes and the polytene chromosomes of the Diptera, at first sight so strikingly different, do in fact exhibit both structural and functional similarities. Both the loops and the puffs provide us with simple observational evidence that chromosomes may undergo differentiation not only as a whole but at rather specific loci. The same question can be asked about the differentiation of these chromosomes that one asks in general about the differentiation of whole cells. Are the changes essentially reversible and therefore in a broad sense of primarily physiological significance, or are they permanent genetic changes?

The polytene chromosomes cannot answer this question directly for the same reason that somatic cells cannot generally answer the question: they are not suitable for breeding experiments. Beermann has ably defended the thesis, however, that the changes in the polytene chromosomes are reversible and are to be interpreted in terms of differential gene activity. His argument rests essentially on those cases in which striking Balbiani rings or puffs may appear at one time in the larval life history and subsequently regress so that the normal banding pattern of the chromosome is restored.

On the other hand, the lampbrush chromosomes offer direct evidence on the question of genetic versus physiological change. Here we see the regression of many hundreds of loop pairs during the latter part of oogenesis, culminating in the appearance of typical meiotic chromosomes at the first metaphase. But most significant is the simple fact that these chromosomes, after the meiotic divisions, furnish half of the genetic material of the next generation. No one would argue that chromosomes undergo permanent genetic changes during the course of meiosis; and so we may conclude that the formation of the loops and their subsequent regression are simply reversible physiological changes.

The two cases thus complement one another. The polytene chromosomes show obvious differentiations related to the cell type in which they are found, as well as to the functional state of that cell. The lampbrush chromosomes, so far studied in only one cell type, show that these changes are reversible and non-genetic.

If we picture the formation of puffs and loops as visible expressions of gene function, then we should expect to find variations in this expression in different strains. Heterozygosity for puffs and for particular loops has been demonstrated by Beermann (8) and by Callan and Lloyd (19). These findings do not contradict the idea that puffing or loop formation *per se* are reversible physiological changes; but rather they add weight to the belief that the functional units seen in the chromosome are indeed also genetic units. We should not expect, of course, all heterozygosity to express itself visibly, since many changes in the genes might affect only the rate of their action or produce some chemical alteration, with no morphological concomitants. The "phenotype" of the chromosome, like the phenotype of individual cells or the organism as a whole, is only a rough guide to its genotype.

Long ago the notion of gene segregation was advanced by Weismann to explain embryonic differentiation. The rise of modern genetics, and especially the evidence from experimental embryology, failed to support his concept. In its place came the idea that all cells of a differentiated or-

ganism contain the same complement of genes, with such obvious exceptions as chromosome elimination. But the latter view left at least two broad possibilities. All the genes might act concurrently in all cells but against different cytoplasmic backgrounds. On this view, cellular differentiation would be largely the result of prior cytoplasmic changes. On the other hand, genes might act at different times or to varying degrees in different types of tissues. The behavior of genes might itself be dependent in part upon cytoplasmic conditions, but in any event the genes would have a more "active" role in the final production of cytoplasmic differentiation. The evidence from the cytology of giant chromosomes seems generally to favor this latter view.

REFERENCES

1. Alfert, M., *J. Cellular Comp. Physiol.*, **36**, 381 (1950).
2. ———, *Intern. Rev. Cytol.* **3**, 131 (1954).
3. ———, and Geschwind, I. I., *Proc. Natl. Acad. Sci. U. S.*, **39**, 991 (1953).
4. Anderson, T. F., *Trans. N. Y. Acad. Sci.*, **13**, 130 (1951).
5. Balbiani, E. G., *Zool. Anz.*, **4**, 637 (1881).
6. Bauer, H., *Zool. Jahrb.*, **56**, 239 (1936).
7. ———, and Beermann, W., *Chromosoma*, **4**, 630 (1952).
8. Beermann, W., *Chromosoma*, **5**, 139 (1952).
9. ———, *Z. Naturforsch.*, **7b**, 237 (1952).
10. ———, *Cold Spring Harbor Symposia Quant. Biol.*, **21**, 217 (1956).
11. ———, and Bahr, G. F., *Exptl. Cell Research*, **6**, 195 (1954).
12. Boivin, A., Vendrely, C., and Vendrely, R., *Compt. rend acad. sci., Paris*, **226**, 1061 (1948).
13. Brachet, J., *Biochemical Cytology*, Academic Press, New York (1957).
14. Breuer, M. E., and Pavan, C., *Chromosoma*, **7**, 371 (1955).
15. Bridges, C. B., *J. Hered.*, **26**, 60 (1935).
16. Callan, H. G., *Symposia Soc. Exptl. Biol.*, **6**, 243 (1952).
17. ———, *Symposium on the Fine Structure of Cells* (Leiden), Intern. Union Biol. Sci. Publ., **B 21**, 89 (1956).
18. ———, *Pubbl. staz. zool. Napoli*, **29**, 329 (1957).
19. ———, and Lloyd, L., *Nature*, **178**, 355 (1957).
20. ———, and Macgregor, H. C., *Nature* **181**, 1479 (1958).
21. Caspersson, T., *Cell Growth and Cell Function*, W. W. Norton, New York (1950).
22. Dearing, W. H., *J. Morphol.*, **56**, 157 (1934).
23. Dodson, E. O. *Univ. Calif. Publ. Zool.*, **53**, 281 (1948).
24. Duryee, W. R., *Arch. exptl. Zellforsch.*, **19**, 171 (1937).
25. ———, in *Cytology, Genetics, and Evolution:* Univ. Penn. Bicentennial Conference, p. 129, Univ. Pennsylvania Press, Philadelphia (1941).
26. ———, *Ann. N. Y. Acad. Sci.*, **50**, 920 (1950).
27. Flax, M. H., and Himes, M. H., *Physiol. Zool.*, **25**, 297 (1952).
28. Gall, J. G., *Exptl. Cell Research*, **Suppl. 2**, 95 (1952).
29. ———, *J. Morphol.*, **94**, 283 (1954).
30. ———, *Symposia Soc. Exptl. Biol.*, **9**, 358 (1955).
31. ———, *Brookhaven Symposia Biol.*, **8**, 17 (1956).

32. Gay, H., *J. Biophys. Biochem. Cytol.,* **2** (Suppl.), 407 (1956).
33. Geitler, L. Endomitose und endomitotische Polyploidisierung. *Protoplasmatologia,* 6 (1953).
34. Guyénot, E., and Danon, M., *Rev. suisse zool.,* **60,** 1 (1953).
35. Heitz, E., and Bauer, H., *Z. Zellforsch. u. mikroskop. Anat.,* **17,** 67 (1933).
36. Hertwig, G., *Z. indukt. Abstamm.-u. Vererblehre,* **70,** 496 (1935).
37. Kaufmann, B. P., and McDonald, M. R., *Cold Spring Harbor Symposia Quant. Biol.,* **21,** 233 (1956).
38. Kaufmann, B. P., McDonald, M., and Gay, H., *J. Cellular Comp. Physiol.,* **38** (Suppl. 1), 71 (1951).
39. Koltzoff, N. K., *Science,* **80,** 312 (1934).
40. ———, *Biol. Zhur.* **7,** 3 (1938).
41. Lafontaine, J. G., and Ris, H., *J. Biophys. Biochem. Cytol.,* **4,** 99 (1958).
42. McClung, C. E., *Biol. Bull.,* **9,** 304 (1905).
43. McMaster-Kaye, R., and Taylor, J. H., *J. Biophys. Biochem. Cytol.,* **4,** 5 (1958).
44. Mechelke, F., *Chromosoma,* **5,** 511 (1953).
45. Metz, C. W., *Cold Spring Harbor Symposia Quant. Biol.,* **9,** 23 (1941).
46. Mirsky, A., and Ris, H., *Nature,* **163,** 666 (1949).
47. ———, and ———, *J. Gen. Physiol.,* **34,** 475 (1951).
48. Nebel, B. R., *Botan. Revs.,* **5,** 563 (1939).
49. Painter, T. S., *Science,* **78,** 585 (1933).
50. ———, *Am. Naturalist,* **73,** 315 (1939).
51. Painter, T. S., and Reindorp, E., *Proc. Natl. Acad. Sci. U. S.,* **26,** 95 (1940).
52. Palade, G., and Siekevitz, P., *J. Biophys. Biochem. Cytol.,* **2,** 671 (1956).
53. Palay, S. L., and Claude, A., *J. Exptl. Med.,* **89,** 431 (1949).
54. Pavan, C., and Breuer, M. E., *J. Hered.,* **43,** 150 (1952).
55. Pelc, S. R., and Howard, A., *Exptl. Cell Research,* **Suppl. 2,** 269 (1952).
56. ———, and ———, *Exptl. Cell. Research,* **10,** 549 (1956).
57. Poulson, D. F., and Metz, C. W., *J. Morphol.,* **63,** 363 (1938).
58. Ris, H., *Biol. Bull.,* **89,** 242 (1945).
59. ———, *Genetics,* **37,** 619 (1952).
60. ———, in *Symposium on the Fine Structure of Cells* (Leiden), Intern. Union Biol. Sci. Publ., **B 21,** 121 (1956).
61. ———, in *The Chemical Basis of Heredity* (W. D. McElroy and B. Glass, eds.), p. 23, Johns Hopkins Press, Baltimore (1957).
62. ———, and Crouse, H., *Proc. Natl. Acad. Sci. U. S.,* **31,** 321 (1945).
63. Rückert, J., *Anat. Anz.,* **7,** 107 (1892).
64. Swift, H., *Intern. Rev. Cytol.,* **2,** 1 (1953).
65. ———, in *Current Trends in Molecular Biology* (R. Zirkle, ed.), Univ. Chicago Press, Chicago (1958).
66. ———, and Kleinfeld, R., *Physiol. Zool.,* **26,** 301 (1953).
67. ———, and Rasch, E., data presented in Alfert (2).
68. Taylor, J. H., *Science,* **118,** 555 (1953).
69. ———, McMaster, R. H., and Caluya, M. F., *Exptl. Cell Research,* **9,** 460 (1955).
70. Tomlin, S. G., and Callan, H. G., *Quart. J. microscop. Sci.,* **92,** 221 (**1951**).
71. White, M. J. D., *J. Morphol.,* **78,** 201 (1946).
72. Wischnitzer, S., *Am. J. Anat.,* **101,** 135 (1957).
73. Yasuzumi, G., Odate, Z., and Ota, Y., *Cytologia,* **16,** 233 (1951).

CHROMOSOMAL REPLICATION AND THE DYNAMICS OF CELLULAR PROLIFERATION—SOME AUTORADIOGRAPHIC OBSERVATIONS WITH TRITIATED THYMIDINE*

W. L. Hughes

Medical Department, Brookhaven National Laboratory, Upton, L. I., N. Y.

Introduction

In autoradiography, a photographic emulsion is placed in contact with a specimen containing radioactivity and is stored in the dark. The radiation, passing through the emulsion, sensitizes silver bromide granules so that they can be reduced to metallic silver by a photographic developer. One then sees a pattern of silver grains lying above the specimen. (The technique (1) employed in the present studies made use of stripping film which was floated over a histological preparation. In some cases Feulgen staining was performed before autoradiography; in other cases the specimen was stained through the emulsion after photographic development.)

Tritium, H^3, with a half-life of 12.3 years, decays to He^3. The β particle produced in this process is one of the least energetic known, having an average energy of only 5,700 electron volts (Fig. 1). The resulting short range of tritium's β particle, while presenting difficulties in many methods for its detection, is of decided advantage in autoradiography because of the high resolution which it permits (2, 3). Even the most energetic β particle from tritium can penetrate only 6 microns in water (or tissue) and only 2 microns in photographic emulsion. However, autoradiographic resolution is even better than this range might indicate because most of the β rays from tritium have much less energy (Fig. 1), and because, in addition, only the two-dimensional projection of their range is seen. Therefore, essentially all of the silver grains activated by tritium lie clustered within a micron of the labeled locus. This is illustrated in Fig. 2a—an autoradiogram of plant chromosomes labeled with tritium (5).

For comparison, Fig. 2 (right) shows an autoradiogram (6) of similar chromosomes labeled as in Fig. 2 (left) except for the substitution of C^{14} for H^3. Note how diffuse the pattern of silver grains has become. The β radiation of C^{14}, while usually considered weak, has an average energy

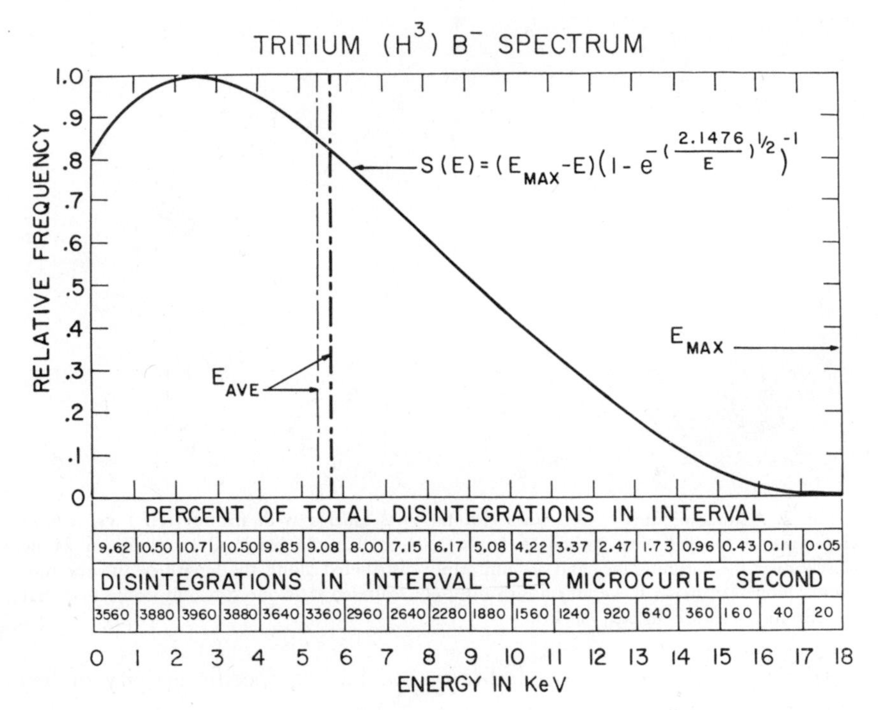

Energy interval (KeV)	0–1	1–2	2–3	3–4	4–5	5–6	6–7	7–8	8–9	9–10	10–11	11–12	12–13	13–14	14–15	15–16	16–17	17–18
PERCENT OF TOTAL DISINTEGRATIONS IN INTERVAL	9.62	10.50	10.71	10.50	9.85	9.08	8.00	7.15	6.17	5.08	4.22	3.37	2.47	1.73	0.96	0.43	0.11	0.05
DISINTEGRATIONS IN INTERVAL PER MICROCURIE SECOND	3560	3880	3960	3880	3640	3360	2960	2640	2280	1880	1560	1240	920	640	360	160	40	20

Fig. 1. Tritium (H^3) β^- spectrum.

of 50,000 electron volts, so that a broad pattern of activated silver grains results.

Hydrogen occurs in almost all metabolites, and methods for its replacement by tritium can usually be devised from published techniques for deuterium exchange (4). When preparing labeled compounds for autoradiography, it is well first to ascertain that specific activities great enough for the problem at hand can be obtained. If one assumes that 20 disintegrations are required on the average to activate one silver grain above a labeled locus, and if the presence of 5 grains is considered sufficient to identify this locus, then the autoradiogram must be exposed long enough for 100 disintegrations to occur in each locus. Since tritium decays at the rate of 0.5 per cent per month, 20,000 tritium atoms must be present in each locus to provide a satisfactory autoradiogram after one month of exposure. If one can label the metabolite which concentrates at the locus intensely enough so that one molecule in fifty is labeled, then 10^6 molecules of metabolite are sufficient to identify the locus. It is perhaps worth

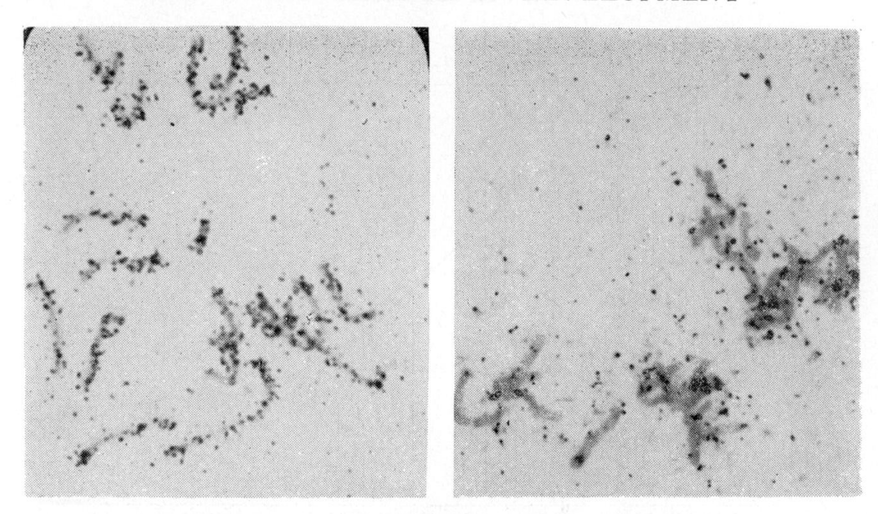

Fig. 2. Autoradiograms of *Bellevalia* chromosomes labeled with tritium (left) vs. *Allium* chromosomes labeled with carbon-14 (right). Note that the black silver grains in 2a lie closely over the chromosomes and are uniformly distributed along the length of the chromosome. However, in 2b the grains are so diffusely scattered that one can only conjecture that the chromosomes are, in fact, labeled.

noting that this labeled metabolite would have a specific activity of 560 curies per mole!

Labeled thymidine with a specific activity in this range has been used in the experiments to be described. The average mammalian nucleus contains 6×10^{-12} g. of deoxyribonucleic acid (7), or there are 3×10^{9} thymine units per nucleus. Therefore, mammalian nuclei can be labeled with tritiated thymidine without affecting the size of the precursor pools (8). However, in the studies with *Escherichia coli* (9), which contain only about 10^{7} thymine units per cell, satisfactory labeling has only been obtained with a thymine-requiring mutant which incorporates the labeled thymidine undiluted.

In attempting to label at high specific activities, radiation damage during the labeling process may present real difficulties. Radiation-induced exchange, as developed by Wilzbach, can produce specific activities from 10 to 100 curies per mole (10). However, the coincident radiation damage precludes higher specific activities by this method, and one must turn to the procedures of organic chemistry. Many substances have been labeled by catalyzed exchange with a labeled solvent. However, 10 curies of pure tritium oxide occupy a volume of only 0.003 cm^3 and this substance irradi-

ates itself at the rate of 10^9 rad/day. Therefore, in using tritium oxide as a source of exchangeable tritium, some inert solvent is necessary. An ideal solvent should lack exchangeable hydrogen. However, solvents in this category, such as dioxane or dimethylformamide, proved ineffective in labeling thymidine, and acetic acid was used instead.

Thymidine was labeled (in the position indicated in Fig. 3) by catalytic

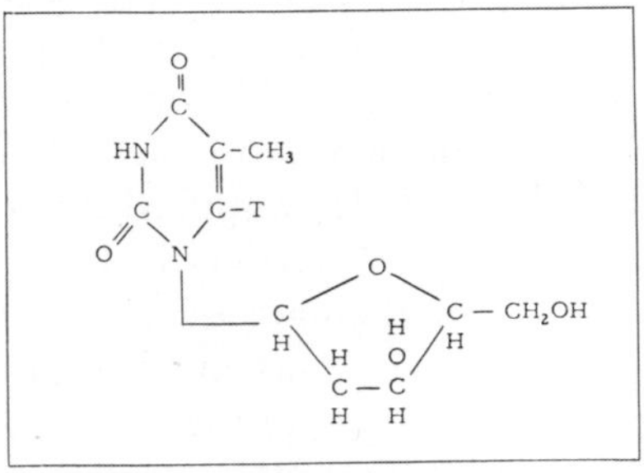

Fig. 3. Tritiated Thymidine.

exchange on reduced palladium black in acetic acid solution containing up to 100 curies of tritium oxide per cm^3. This procedure (11), which is analogous to a published method of labeling purines (12), exchanges tritium for the hydrogen bound to carbon in the pyrimidine ring. Tritium was then removed from the labile positions on oxygen or nitrogen, which were simultaneously labeled, by repeated equilibration with water. The product usually contained large amounts of tritiated impurities which were not readily recognized by paper chromatography. These could be detected by crystallization with carrier thymidine. By careful chromatography on anion exchange resins, a fraction was obtained in which all the activity co-crystallized with added thymidine. Cytidine and deoxycytidine have been labeled in a similar manner.

Tritiated thymidine thus prepared does not exchange its radioactivity even in the presence of acid or alkali. Degradation to thymine retains the label in the thymine fraction. However, the assignment of its position to the ring rather than the methyl group is based on the chemical analogy that cytidine, which contains no methyl group, can be similarly labeled.

The remainder of this paper will describe some applications of tritiated thymidine, to indicate the wide range of physiological processes which it has already illuminated.

Mechanism of Duplication of Deoxyribonucleic Acid

Thymidine is efficiently utilized in the formation of the genetic material, deoxyribonucleic acid (DNA). Current evidence emphasizes the stability of DNA, so that it now stands as a landmark in the shifting currents of physiological processes. While the immutability of the gene has long been recognized, its explanation in terms of a corresponding chemical stability of the genetic material has only recently been forthcoming. Thus radioactive phosphorus has been found preferentially incorporated into the DNA of rapidly dividing tissues (13). However, studies with phosphorus are complicated by its incorporation into many substances besides DNA. Reichard (14) and Friedkin (15) have studied the metabolism of thymidine, whose base, thymine, occurs uniquely in DNA. They have shown that labeled thymidine is utilized almost exclusively for the formation of DNA and that DNA formation occurs in tissues rich in dividing cells. Perhaps the most satisfying evidence for the immutability of DNA comes from studies (5, 9) of the mechanism of chromosomal duplication employing tritium-labeled thymidine. These will now be described in some detail:

Duplication in Plant Cells (5)

Seedlings of *Vicia faba* (English broad bean) were grown in a mineral nutrient solution containing 2-3 μg/ml of the radioactive thymidine. This plant was selected because it has 12 large chromosomes, one pair of which is morphologically distinct, and because the length of the division cycle and the time of DNA synthesis in the cycle are known (16). After growth of the seedlings in the isotope solution for the appropriate time, the roots were thoroughly washed with water and the seedlings were transferred to a nonradioactive mineral solution containing colchicine (500 μg/ml) for further growth. At appropriate intervals roots were fixed in ethanol-acetic acid (3:1), hydrolysed 5 minutes in 1 *N* HCl, stained by the Feulgen reaction, and squashed on microscope slides. Stripping film was applied and exposed one month for autoradiography.

Roots remained in the isotope solution for 8 hours, which is approximately one-third of the division cycle (16). Since about 8 hours intervene between DNA synthesis in interphase and the next anaphase, few, if any, nuclei which had incorporated the labeled thymidine should have passed through a division before the roots were transferred to the colchicine solution. In the presence of colchicine chromosomes contract to the metaphase condition, and the sister chromatids (daughter chromosomes), which ordi-

narily lie parallel to each other, spread apart. The sister chromatids remain attached at the centromere region for a period of time, but they finally separate completely before transforming into an interphase nucleus. Because colchicine prevents anaphase movement and the formation of daughter cells, but does not prevent chromosomes from duplicating, the number of duplications following exposure to the isotope can be determined for any individual cell by observing the number of chromosomes. Cells without a duplication after transfer to colchicine will have the usual 12 chromosomes at metaphase (c-metaphase), each with the two halves (sister chromatids) spread apart but attached at the centromere. Cells with one intervening duplication will contain 24 chromosomes, and those with two duplications will contain 48 chromosomes.

Two groups of roots were fixed. The first group remained in the colchicine solution 10 hours. The second group remained in the colchicine for 34 hours. In the first group, cells at metaphase had only 12 chromosomes, which indicated that none of these had duplicated more than once during the experiment. The chromosomes in these cells were all labeled, and furthermore, the two sister chromatids of each chromosome were equally and uniformly labeled (Fig. 4, left). The amount of radioactivity in the

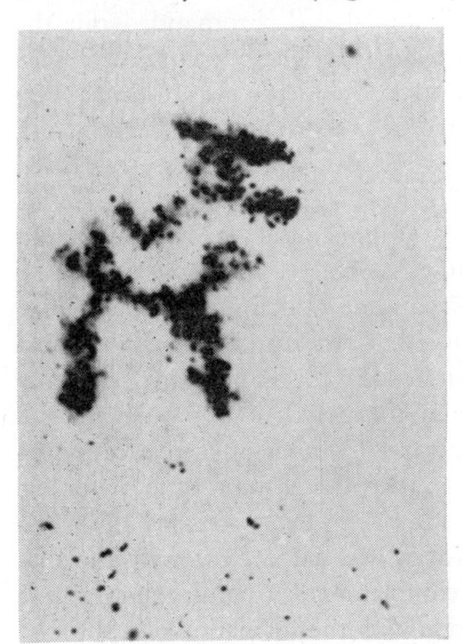

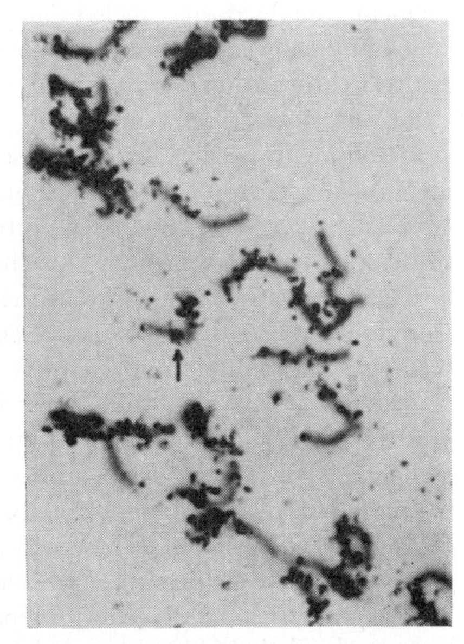

Fig. 4. Autoradiograms of first and second generations of plant chromosomes labeled with tritiated thymidine. *Left,* Duplication with labeled thymidine, showing uniform distribution of label. *Right,* Second duplication of labeled chromosomes in the absence of labeled thymidine, showing labeled and unlabeled chromatids.

chromosomes varied from cell to cell, as would be expected in a non-synchronized population of cells, but within a given cell the label in different chromosomes was remarkably uniform. This is perhaps more clearly demonstrated in Fig. 2 (left), an autoradiogram of similarly labeled chromosomes in *Bellevalia*. (The nucleus shown was slightly further advanced in mitosis so that most of the daughter chromosomes have separated.)

In the second group, cells contained either 12, 24, or 48 chromosomes. Those with 12 chromosomes usually were not labeled, but when labeling occurred, sister chromatids were uniformly labeled as in the first group. In cells with 24 chromosomes, all chromosomes were labeled; however, only one of the two sister chromatids of each was radioactive (Fig. 4, right). Evidently the pool of labeled precursor in the plant had been quickly depleted after the plant was removed from the isotope solution, and these cells with 24 chromosomes had gone through a second duplication in the absence of labeled thymidine.

In the few cells with 48 chromosomes, analysis of all 48 was not possible. However, in several cases where most of the chromosomes were well separated and flattened, approximately one-half of the chromosomes of a complement contained one labeled and one non-labeled chromatid, while the remainder showed no label in either chromatid. The appearance of cells with 48 chromosomes in a 34-hour period in colchicine also indicates that there was some variation in the predicted 24-hour division cycle.

In cells with 24 and 48 chromosomes a few chromatids were labeled along only a part of their length, but in these cases the sister chromatids were labeled in complementary portions (Fig. 4, right, arrow). This can be described as sister chromatid exchange.

These results indicate (1) that the thymidine built into the DNA of a chromosome is part of a physical entity that remains intact during succeeding replications and nuclear divisions, except for an occasional chromatid exchange; (2) that a chromosome is composed of two such entities probably complementary to each other; and (3) that after replication of each to form a chromosome with four entities, the chromosome divides so that each chromatid (daughter chromosome) regularly receives an "original" and a "new" unit. These conclusions are made clearer by the diagrams in Fig. 5. Beginning with two complementary non-labeled strands in a chromosome, the two strands separate with the formation of a complementary labeled strand along each original strand. At metaphase, when the two pairs of strands separate, each chromatid will appear labeled, although it contains both a labeled and a non-labeled strand. After the next

replication, in the absence of labeled thymidine, separation of the two pairs at metaphase will reveal a labeled and an unlabeled chromatid. Following another replication only one-half of the chromosomes will contain a labeled chromatid, as demonstrated in those cells with 48 chromosomes.

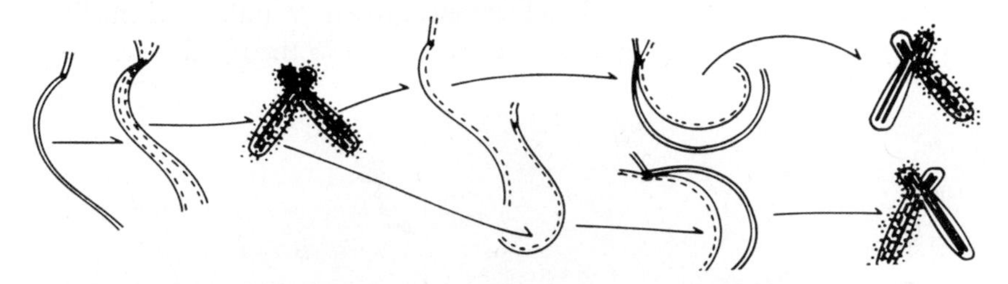

Fig. 5. Diagrammatic representation of mechanism of duplication.

It is immediately apparent that this pattern of replication is analogous to the replicating scheme proposed for DNA by Watson and Crick (17). We cannot be sure, of course, that separation of the two polynucleotide chains in the double helix is involved, for the chromosome is several orders of magnitude larger than the proposed double helix of DNA. However, at least in the case of bacterial DNA, labeled with N^{15}, separation of the individual chains does seem to occur (18).

Duplication in Bacteria

Our own studies with *E. coli* 15 T– labeled with tritiated thymidine (9) seem to indicate a similar mechanism for the duplication of DNA in bacteria.

A log phase culture of *E. coli* 15 T– was added to a glucose-mineral medium containing 2-4 micrograms of tritiated thymidine per milliliter. Following at least 100-fold growth at 37°C in the labeled medium, two types of experiments were performed. In the first, the cells were washed in saline and grown in medium containing excess unlabeled thymidine. Direct cell counts from aliquots were taken at the time of inoculation and every thirty minutes thereafter. Each time a doubling of the population of the culture occurred, as determined by the direct cell count, smears were made. These were fixed by heating and washed with water; autoradiograms were made by the stripping film technique. After various exposure times, varying from 5 to 40 days, the slides were developed and stained with 0.04% crystal violet. In the second type of experiment, labeled cells were isolated micromanipulatively on nutrient agar medium which contained excess unlabeled precursor. Progeny lines were obtained from these

isolated cells. Growth was stopped by drying the agar medium, and stripping film autoradiograms were made after fixing in 3:1 ethyl alcohol—glacial acetic acid and a series of alcohol-water solutions.

Both experiments revealed very clearly that the distribution of the incorporated tritium among the daughter cells grown on unlabeled medium was very heterogeneous (Fig. 6). At least as soon as the third generation,

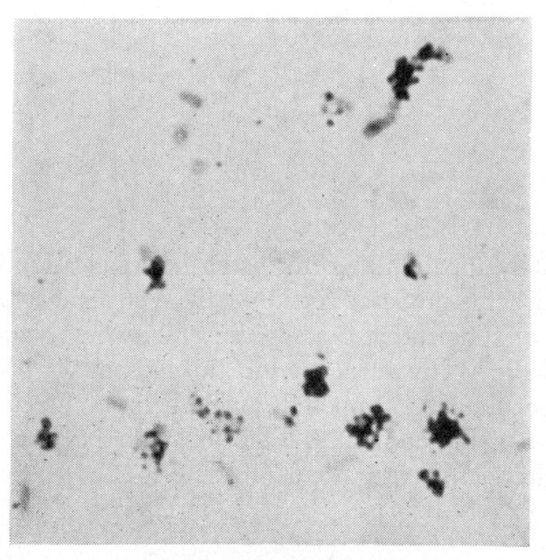

Fig. 6. Autoradiogram of *Escherichia coli* 15 T– labeled by several generations of growth in tritiated thymidine and then grown for about 3 generations in non-radioactive medium. Note that some cells are unlabeled, while in other cases the silver grains are so numerous as to obscure the bacterial cell.

and possibly sooner, one found cells with no label in the presence of those containing considerable label. In the liquid culture experiment, all-or-none splits, where one of an unseparated pair of cells exhibited heavy label (6-14 grains) while the other had no grains above it, were observed occasionally. Such all-or-none splits were also seen in the micromanipulation experiments where the sibling relations in the progeny line were known. These micromanipulation experiments indicate that the heterogeneity observed in bulk culture experiments is not primarily a result of cell death (from radiation or any other cause) or of differences in growth rates for individual bacteria. It should also be noted that at the first division on non-radioactive medium, no case of all-or-nothing distribution has yet been seen, even though attempts were made to select the smallest possible labeled cells as the sources of a progeny line.

The observation that uniform dilution of tritiated thymidine during bacterial growth does not occur would seem to indicate that relatively large amounts of parental DNA can remain functionally associated in transmissions to daughter cells. While the data do not clearly establish a functional two-strandedness for bacterial DNA like that found for the plant chromosomes, the lack of all-or-nothing splits at the first generation and their appearance in later generations are in harmony with this possibility.

Sequences of Events in Cell Proliferation

In addition to providing information on the mechanism of DNA synthesis, tritiated thymidine is also proving useful in relating the chronology of other events within the cell to DNA synthesis. Thus, if labeled thymidine is available to cells for only a very short interval, the subsequent appearance of labeled nuclei in cells of any recognizable morphological type indicates that those cells were making DNA when the label was available. Hence this interval of the cell's life cycle is measured. Since cells once labeled are presumably labeled forever, subject only to dilution of the label at each cell division, labeled cells may also be followed chronologically through diverse morphological forms. Their migration from their zone of origin to that of function and final death may also be elucidated. Studies along these lines are being performed on mammalian cells in tissue culture and also on intact mammals.

Tissue Cultures of Mammalian Cells

In tissue culture the labeling period may be reduced to a few minutes by transferring the cells to an unlabeled medium. Thirty per cent of the cells of a culture of HeLa cells were labeled following a few minutes' exposure (19). Since the cells in such a culture are completely asynchronous, DNA synthesis must require the same fraction (30%) of the generation time. After further incubation in cold medium, labeled mitoses (Fig. 7) began to appear at 3 hours, but did not reach a maximum until after 6 hours. These intervals then measure the minimum and maximum time between the completion of DNA synthesis and the appearance of a mitotic figure (19, 20). The variation in this time must reflect a similar variation among individual cells in the length of this metabolic phase. Extension of these studies to longer times appears to reveal variation in other phases of the generation cycle.

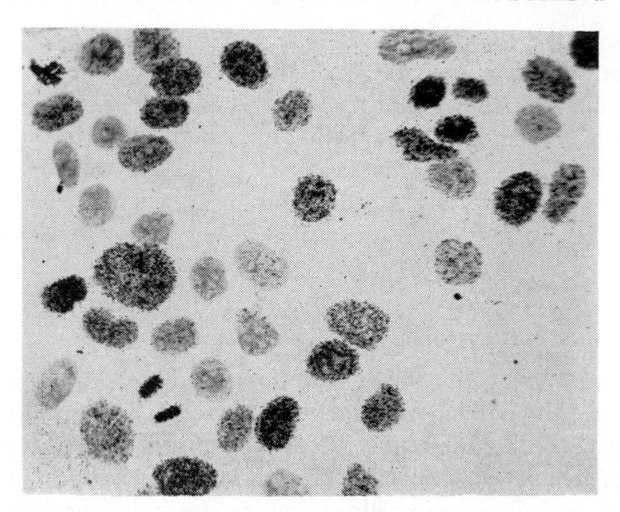

Fig. 7. Autoradiogram of a culture of HeLa cells grown in tritiated thymidine, showing labeled and unlabeled nuclei.

Intact Mammals

In mammals (mouse and human) the tritium of labeled thymidine appears to be built into DNA or converted to water during the first hour following injection. Therefore, any cells subsequently found labeled must have been making DNA preparatory to cell division immediately following injection. Autoradiograms of histological sections made a few hours after injection showed a wide variation in the number of labeled cells and thereby permitted the ready identification of the zones where cells are generated (8). The number of labeled cells in young adult mice exceeded that which might have been predicted from previous data on mitotic indices (21). The following section describes some of the findings (8) when young adult male mice were injected intraperitoneally with 0.7 μc of tritiated thymidine per gram mouse and sacrificed at intervals of from 7 to 48 hours after injection.

Seven hours after injection of the thymidine solution, labeled cells were found in the generative zones of the gut: the basal layer of the forestomach (which is lined with stratified epithelium) (Fig. 8a), the gland necks of the fundus, the crypts of the pyloric region (particularly the lower third, except for the cells at the very bottom of the crypts), the crypts of the small bowel (including the region occupied by the Paneth cells—however, no label was seen in cells containing granules) (Fig. 8b), and the crypts of the colon. The fraction of labeled cells ranged from about one-fifth, in

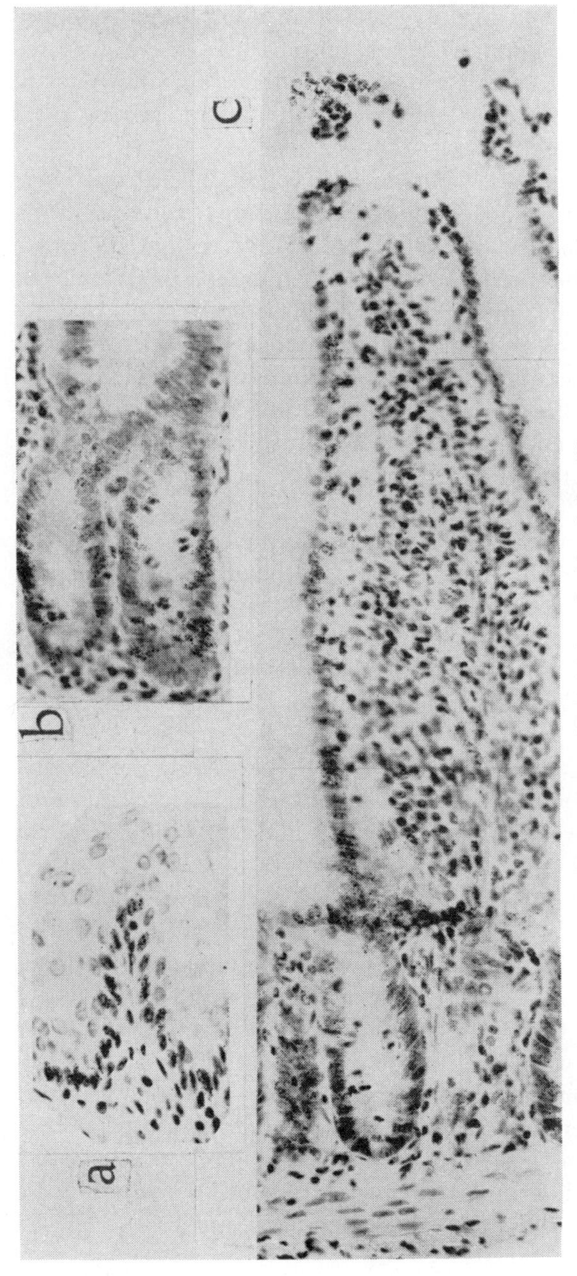

Fig. 8. Autoradiograms of mouse gut after injection of tritiated thymidine.
a. Forestomach 7 hours after injection. Label in basal cell layer.
b. Jejunum 7 hours after injection. Label in crypts only.
c. Jejunum 48 hours after injection. Label diluted in crypts and distributed along entire villus.

the forestomach, through one-third to one-half, in stomach and colon, to about two-thirds, in the jejunum. The amount of label per cell appeared to be fairly uniform. Most mitoses seen at this time were strongly labeled (in a subsequent series, labeled telophases were found as early as 2 1/2 hours after injection).

In preparations taken 14 to 48 hours after injection, labeled cells were seen to have moved from the generative to the functional zones; concomitantly, the number of labeled cells in the generative regions decreased, as did the amount of label per cell (Fig. 8c). An exception seems to be the colon, where a moderate number of heavily labeled cells remained after 48 hours near the bottom of the crypts. The movement of labeled cells was not very regular. This was best seen in the jejunum, with its large percentage of labeled cells: the zone behind the leading edge was characterized by patchy labeling, and the distance to which the label progressed varied considerably among villi and even on the two sides of a single villus.

In fundus, pylorus, jejunum, and colon, the distance from generative zone to surface was covered in less than 2 days, as shown by the appearance in the lumen of desquamated labeled cells 48 hours after injection. In the same 48 hours, in the forestomach, the label moved into the prickle cell layer but did not reach the surface. In the depth of the fundus glands, a few labeled cells were found at this time, but no fully differentiated chief and parietal cells.

The percentage of labeled mitoses was nearly 100 per cent in the preparation taken 7 hours after injection; it was very low 14 hours after injection, and showed irregular variations (between 20% and 60%) in subsequent samples.

In the spleen the most heavily and frequently labeled cell was the normoblast; the label seemed to stay constant for some time, but appeared reduced at 48 hours. Labeled megakaryocytes were found in all preparations, the percentage labeled possibly increasing with time up to about 60 per cent. In the malpighian follicles, a few reticulum cells and about 10 per cent of the lymphocytes were labeled; there were some groups of labeled cells in the germinal centers. The amount of label in lymphocytes was smaller than in the generative cells of the gastro-intestinal tract. During the first day after injection, the percentage of labeled lymphocytes increased and had decreased at 48 hours. A few doughnut-shaped myelocytes were labeled in all specimens; at 48 hours, there were large numbers of labeled mature granulocytes.

In the first series of animals, the pancreas contained label only in some

duct cells; in a later series (not fasted) several well-labeled cells and mitoses were found. Occasionally fibroblasts and rarely smooth muscle cells were labeled in all preparations. A labeled liver cell was infrequently found. An occasional labeled cell was found in Brunner's glands. Even neurons, usually considered incapable of division, were occasionally labeled (22, 23).

If a cell population is homogeneous and completely asynchronous, then the percentage of labeled cells present after a brief labeling period measures the percentage of the total generation time during which cells can take up thymidine and use it for DNA synthesis. If the generating zones of the gut are thus considered as homogeneous populations of cells, it follows from our results that the synthetic time must vary from 20 per cent to 70 per cent of the generation time in different regions. If the durations of the periods of synthesis in these different regions are similar, then the rate of cell renewal must vary directly with the fraction of labeled cells. In agreement with this, labeled cells moved more rapidly out of the heavily labeled crypts of the jejunum than out of the more sparsely labeled basal epithelium of the forestomach.

With regard to intensity of labeling, throughout the gastro-intestinal tract, those cells that were labeled at all appeared to be labeled with equal intensity, also suggesting similar synthetic rates. By way of contrast, lymphocytes were weakly labeled. This may possibly be interpreted as indicating a slower synthetic rate for the lymphocyte. However, in addition to the inaccuracies resulting from variation in autoradiographic efficiency, variation in cellular uptake of the isotope or in size of the precursor pool might explain this difference.

The time required for the appearance of labeled mitotic figures following injection measures the interval between completion of DNA synthesis and the beginning of mitosis. Since some mitoses were labeled 2 1/2 hours after injection and all were labeled 7 hours after injection, all cells must proceed into mitosis within 7 hours following the completion of DNA synthesis. In the subsequent intervals studied, the percentage of labeled mitoses decreased to a low value at 14 hours and then varied between 20 per cent and 60 per cent. It is possible that further studies over more frequent time intervals may show a rhythmic variation in labeling which should correspond to the generation time.

Before concluding this discussion it may be well to point to possible complications produced by radiation from the incorporated tritium. In tissue culture, inhibition of cell division has been observed following the uptake of tritiated thymidine (24), but only when the incorporation exceeded many hundredfold that required for autoradiography. More than

10^7 tritium atoms per cell are required to inhibit growth, whereas 10^5 or less will provide satisfactory autoradiograms. However, some effects of radiation, such as chromosome breaks, occur at much lower levels of radiation. These have been observed with C^{14}-labeled thymidine (6). Perhaps sister chromatid exchanges observed in the tritium-labeled plant chromosome (5) and the fractional transfer of the tritiated DNA of *E. coli* (9) are also subtle evidence of radiation injury. Further studies are necessary to clarify this situation.

Conclusions

While the studies reported have been performed on "adult" tissues, their implications in embryology are obvious, and it is hoped that others will find this report useful not only for its contents but also in suggesting new tools for embryology. Thus autoradiography shortly after the injection of tritiated thymidine would permit a quantitative appraisal of rates of cellular proliferation in various parts of the embryo, and subsequent sampling of labeled embryos should help elucidate problems of cell migration and tissue differentiation. The transplantation of labeled cells could provide proof of the viability of transplants and also could permit one to follow the migration of donor cells and thus to determine the origin (donor vs. host) of each cell in the accepted graft.

Finally, it should be noted that other tritiated metabolites should elucidate other biochemical processes at the cellular level, although the situation may be complicated by intracellular turnover, which is lacking in DNA. We are beginning such studies with similarly labeled cytidine as a precursor of RNA and with tritiated arginine as a precursor of protein. Relative to Gall's paper, perhaps most interesting has been the finding that, in *Vicia* roots, cytidine was initially incorporated only in nucleoli (Fig. 9) (25). However, after a few hours the label left the nucleolus and was distributed throughout the cytoplasm, suggesting that RNA may be synthesized in the nucleolus and then transported to functional sites in the cytoplasm.

Acknowledgments

This paper is a synthesis of reports from several biological and medical research programs utilizing tritium for autoradiography. The author has had the privilege of acting as "liaison" between these groups, which seemed too diverse for a joint paper, and so the author has assumed sole responsibility for this report; but it should be reiterated that credit both for the results and for the concepts expressed belongs equally to his collaborators. Particular appreciation is due Drs. R. B. Painter, J. H. Taylor, and P. S. Woods for their courtesy in making recent, still unpublished, results available.

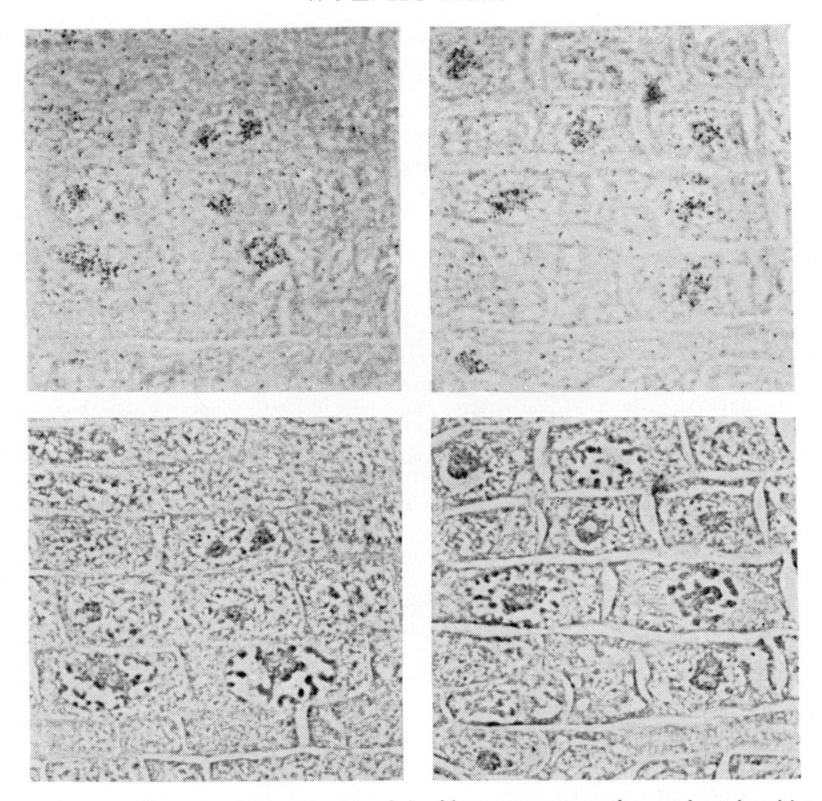

Fig. 9. Autoradiograms (upper photographs) of bean roots grown for one hour in tritiated cytidine. Label is confined almost exclusively to the nucleolus, as can be verified by the lower photographs, focused on the tissue below the autoradiogram.

REFERENCES

1. Doniach, I. and Pelc, S. R., Autoradiograph Technique, *Brit. J. Radiol.,* 23: 184-192 (1950).
2. Robertson, J. S., and Hughes, W. L., Intranuclear Irradiation with Tritium-Labeled Thymidine, *Proc. Biophysical Society's First Meeting* (in press).
3. Fitzgerald, P. J., Eidinoff, M. L., Knoll, J. E., and Simmel, E. B., Tritium in Radio-autography, *Science,* 14: 494 (1951).
4. Kamen, M., *Isotopic Tracers in Biology,* Academic Press, New York, (1957).
5. Taylor, J. H., Woods, P. S., and Hughes, W. L., The Organization and Duplication of Chromosomes as Revealed by Autoradiographic Studies Using Tritium-Labeled Thymidine, *Proc. Natl. Acad. Sci. U. S.,* 43: 122-128 (1957).
6. McQuade, H. A., Friedkin, M., and Atchison, A., Radiation Effects of Thymidine 2-C^{14}, *Exptl. Cell Research,* 11: 249-264 (1956).
7. Vendrely, R., in *The Nucleic Acids,* (Chargaff, E., and Davidson, J. N., eds.) Vol. II, p. 155, Academic Press, New York (1955).

8. Hughes, W. L., Bond, V. P., Brecher, G., Cronkite, E. P., Painter, R. B., Quastler, H., and Sherman, F. G., Cellular Proliferation in the Mouse as Revealed by Autoradiography with Tritiated Thymidine, *Proc. Natl. Acad. Sci. U. S.,* 44:476 (1958).
9. Painter, R. B., Forro, F., and Hughes, W. L., Distribution of Tritium-Labeled Thymidine in *Escherichia coli* During Cell Multiplication, *Nature,* 181: 328-329 (1958).
10. Wilzbach, K. E., Tritium Labeling by Exposure of Organic Compounds to Tritium Gas, *J. Am. Chem. Soc.,* 79: 1013 (1957).
11. Verly, W. G., and Hunebelle, G. have described a similar procedure, *Bull. soc. chim. Belges,* 66: 640 (1957).
12. Eidinoff, M. L. and Knoll, J. E., The Introduction of Isotopic Hydrogen Into Purine Ring Systems by Catalytic Exchange, *J. Am. Chem. Soc.,* 75: 1992 (1953).
13. Hevesy, G. and Ottesen, J., Rate of Formation of Nucleic Acid in the Organs of the Rat, *Acta Physiol. Scand.,* 5: 237-247 (1943).
14. Reichard, P. and Estborn, B., Utilization of Deoxyribosides in the Synthesis of Polynucleotides, *J. Biol. Chem.,* 188: 839-846 (1951).
15. Friedkin, M., Tilson, D., and Roberts, D., Studies of Deoxyribonucleic Acid Biosynthesis in Embryonic Tissues with Thymidine C^{14}, *J. Biol. Chem.,* 220: 627 (1956).
16. Howard, A. and Pelc, S. R., Nuclear Incorporation of P^{32} as Demonstrated by Autoradiographs, *Exptl. Cell Research,* 2: 178-187 (1951).
17. Watson, J. D. and Crick, F. H. C., Genetical Implications of the Structure of Deoxyribonucleic Acid, *Nature,* 171: 964 (1953).
18. Meselson, M. and Stahl, F. W., Replication of DNA in *Escherichia coli, Proc. Natl. Acad. Sc. U. S.,* 44:671 (1958).
19. Painter, R. B., Drew, R. M., and Hughes, W. L., unpub.
20. Firket, H. and Verly, W. G., Autoradiographic Visualization of Synthesis of DNA in Tissue Culture with Tritium-Labeled Thymidine, *Nature,* 181: 274-275 (1958).
21. LeBlond, C. P. and Walker, B. E., Renewal of Cell Populations, *Physiol. Revs.,* 36: 255-276 (1956).
22. Kahle, W. has observed labeled nuclei in the neurons of the hippocampus (mouse), pers. commun.
23. Messier, B., LeBlond, C. P., and Smart, I., Presence of DNA Synthesis and Mitosis in the Brain of Young Adult Mice, *Exptl. Cell Research,* 14: 224 (1958).
24. Painter, R. B., Drew, R. M., Hughes, W. L., Inhibition of HeLa Growth by Intranuclear Tritium, *Science,* **127**:1244 (1958).
25. Woods, P. S. and Taylor, J. H., pers. commun.

DISCUSSION

Dr. Cowden: I would like to ask a two-part question of Dr. Gall. The first part of the question concerns the incorporation of labelled adenine. In its incorporation into the cells, does it go into the chromosomes, or into the nucleolus first?

Dr. Gall: These studies have just been done, actually, and I can't tell you the time sequence of the incorporation. There was incorporation into the nucleoli after 8 hours and there was also incorporation into the chromosomes.

Dr. Cowden: The second part is: I think that both Dr. Swift and Dr. Brachet as well as myself have noted that in the metaphase chromosomes basophilia after DNAse treatment seems to reach a peak. How do you reconcile this with your situation where you have more RNA observable in the uncoiled, interphase

condition than in the metaphase meiotic chromosomes of other materials in which RNA is found maximally in metaphase.

Dr. Gall: You do find RNA in metaphase chromosomes but I don't think that proves there are not larger quantities in some interphase chromosomes. I think that the normal interphase cell shows you plenty of RNA and it may in fact be minimal at metaphase. I don't know if there are any quantitative data on that.

Dr. Cowden: I think that Dr. Swift has some in the 14th Growth Symposium.

Dr. Gall: Is RNA maximal at metaphase?

Dr. Swift: Well, we reported it so in our graph, but you will notice that there was a statement below in the paper saying it was impossible to eliminate spindle substance from our measurements, and that metaphase values were thus too high. What I really feel is that RNA is probably maximal at diplotene, and stays high until anaphase when it drops off.

Dr. Gall: Well, the lampbrush chromosomes are prophase chromosomes, they are in the diplotene stage, so these are not interphase chromosomes in the strict sense of the word.

Dr. Spiegelman: I made a mental calculation and perhaps you have done the same with more care; namely, how long would a DNA Watson-Crick model be? Would these lampbrush chromosomes be of approximately the same order of magnitude?

Dr. Gall: Yes, they would be about the same order of magnitude.

Dr. Spiegelman: Perhaps, we can carry this comparison on to compare the DNA content for chromosomes of different sizes.

Dr. Gall: No, I haven't done that, but what I have done is to make the actual estimation for the salamander I have worked on. The DNA length is about 90 centimeters per chromosome. Comparing this with the 5 centimeter length of the chromosome, you must remember that the latter is gotten by measuring only the loops and if there is any amount of strand wound up in the granules, which I think there must be, they may well be of the same order of magnitude. In fact, I don't see any reason for not postulating that the thing is one or two strands, but I know that is a very heretical view.

Dr. Spiegelman: I wonder whether you could then give supporting evidence for this, using the sort of tricks that are used in microbial systems of labeling with very hot P^{32}. The suggestion is that you do have a backbone of the same nature as in the Watson-Crick model, and therefore you should see breaks. If you can label with very hot P^{32} and then freeze your material for awhile to allow decay to occur, you should then see the breaks in your preparations.

Dr. Gall: I haven't given any thought to such experiments, but I think that something of the sort should be done now that we know there is DNA throughout the whole chromosome.

Dr. Vincent: Could I make some comments about nucleoli that might be pertinent if it won't take too long? I have a little evidence here on biochemical

analyses of starfish nucleoli which might be pertinent, I think, within the framework of this conference. First of all, take this as the nucleolus: (See Figure 1). It has essentially three compartments that I can find: one is a single

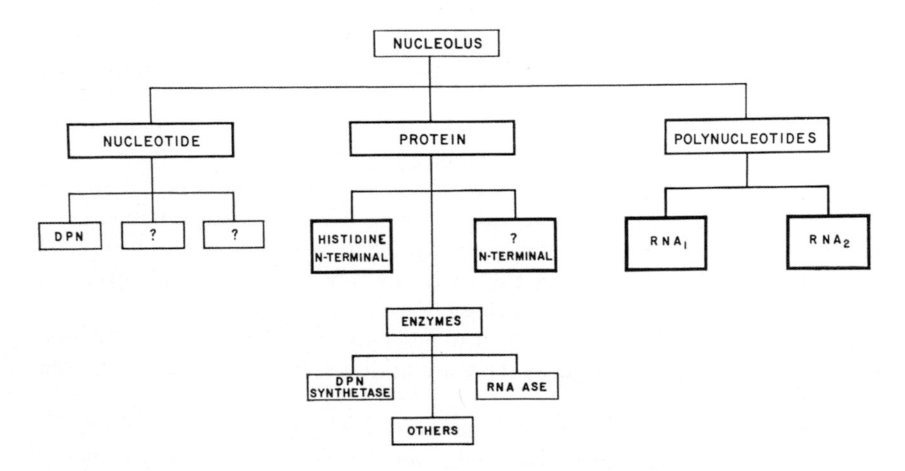

nucleotide and, as indicated earlier, in Dr. Brachet's laboratory, it allows these starfish nucleoli to synthesize DPN. The second compartment is polynucleotide and this is what is called RNA, and I shall call it RNA; and the third one is a protein compartment.

Now we can subdivide two of these compartments at least, and certainly the nucleotide compartment can be subdivided even more to not only DPN but also all of the other mononucleotides which may be significant in the formation of high-energy bonds.

The polynucleotide fraction has been separated by myself in these nucleoli into what I designated RNA_1 and RNA_2 in which the RNA_1 fraction is a fraction which picks up radiophosphate, at least, from an incubation medium very rapidly (this is in the intact egg) and reaches equilibration in a very short time. RNA_2 picks up radiophosphate and incorporates it more slowly and it carries on incorporation over a long period of time and so one can plot the specific activities of RNA_1 and RNA_2 as shown in Figure 2. From curves such as this I think we can conclude that RNA_1 did not contribute to RNA_2, otherwise the specific activity would never reach this particular level of 2.

Now the protein fraction also has at least two major components. I have just been working on N-terminal end-group analyses of the proteins of starfish nucleoli. One finds two end-groups in starfish nucleoli. I take this to mean that we have just two major species of protein present. One of these proteins is a protein which comes out with RNA_1 and it has as its N-terminal end-group histidine. This protein accounts for about 5% to 10% of the total nitrogen of the nucleolus. Thus, the other protein is a very large component of the nu-

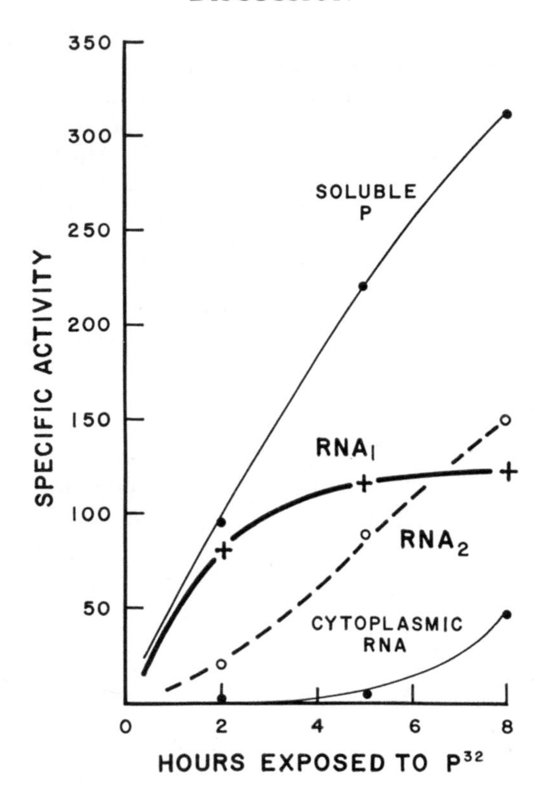

cleolus, in fact some 90% of the nucleolus, and it contains an N-terminal amino acid which I have not yet been able to identify. I might mention in this case it is interesting that it differs from the major cytoplasmic protein of these eggs, the yolk, for the yolk protein has glycine as its N-terminal amino acid. Outside of that, these two proteins appear to resemble each other very much. So, we have then a rather interesting situation in the starfish nucleolus where, if it performs a large number of functions, it must do this with a small number of proteins.

A comment that I would like to make as pertinent to Dr. Mirsky's earlier comment is that we have here a small quantity of protein which is not fractionated any further yet, other than to say it is related to the RNA_1 fraction. The RNA_2 component—that is this one which is very slow in its incorporation of radiophosphate into RNA—appears to be associated mostly with this protein with the unknown end-group which constitutes 90% of the nucleolar protein. This particular protein is an acid protein, rich in glutamic acid, resembling casein very much in its over-all components.

One might make one comment then in respect to Dr. Allfrey's and Dr. Mirsky's experiments. The combination of these two curves, that is, the curves

of incorporation of RNA_1 and RNA_2 as graphed on the blackboard, gives almost the identical curve that Dr. Allfrey and Dr. Mirsky gave for their "nucleolar RNA." On this basis, then, I would suggest that if the nucleolus that exists in other cells than starfish eggs is similar to the one that I am dealing with here, we might have the nucleolar protein Dr. Mirsky is dealing with possibly containing an extra RNA component similar to this RNA_1.

If one takes this RNA component here (RNA_1) and analyses it even further one finds, at least the data I have seem best to be interpreted in this manner: that phosphate entering this nucleus, or this nucleolus, is tied up in this RNA_1 fraction and later reappears in the acid-soluble nucleotide fraction. This leads me to make the suggestion that only this particular fraction of RNA here (RNA_1) acts as a phosphate acceptor for this nucleolus, or for the nucleus, which later then redistributes the phosphate into smaller nucleotide fractions.

DR. MARKERT: What is the appearance of these chromosome loops under the electron microscope after RNAse treatment? Are histones present?

DR. GALL: I haven't looked at those under the electron microscope yet. The ones I showed you were pepsin-treated.

ORIGIN AND STRUCTURE OF INTERCELLULAR MATRIX[1]

Mac V. Edds, Jr.
Biology Department, Brown University,
Providence, Rhode Island

There are at least two reasons why it is appropriate to consider intercellular matrices in this symposium. First, there are few other materials to which so many significant embryological roles have been assigned. Secondly, numerous recent investigations of these matrices, pursued from the most diverse points of view, have provided new and exciting information which deserves careful evaluation by embryologists.

It is a striking fact that although the importance of the ground substance in embryonic differentiation was pointed out over forty years ago (2), and although embryologists have widely accepted the concepts of Weiss (e.g., 45-47) concerning its role in morphogenesis, we still know almost nothing of how this role is exercised. Grobstein (14) has outlined a provocative hypothesis of the interaction of intercellular matrices during embryonic induction. And Weiss (46), Holtfreter (22), and Moscona (29) have all discussed the possible significance of this material in the affinities and disaffinities of embryonic cells. These various proposals present a compelling challenge. What do we now know about intercellular matrices which could explain their roles in development—and what do we still need to learn?

In trying to answer these questions, it will not be possible even to mention all of the relevant investigations. The intention rather is to gather together a few selected examples which seem to be particularly instructive. As the discussion progresses, it will become apparent that in the present state of our knowledge we are long on speculation and short on explanation. There appear to be opening up, however, fields of research which may in time yield information of crucial significance for our understanding of morphogenesis.

First, a word about definitions. The terms intercellular matrix and ground substance have been used interchangeably with a lack of precision

[1] Unpublished research mentioned in this paper was supported by a research grant (A-1755) from the National Institute of Arthritis and Metabolic Diseases, Public Health Service.

not unfamiliar to biologists. In this discussion, "ground substance" designates the optically homogeneous, viscous material which permeates the spaces between the various cells of an organism. "Intercellular matrix" will include the ground substance plus the various fibrous and mineral components which are embedded in it (cf., 9). Obviously, we deal with a motley collection of substances which will have to be carefully dissected in each particular case.

Ground Substance

The ground substance is a complex mixture composed of water and salts, substances in transit between cells and the vascular system, and such diagnostic compounds as acid mucopolysaccharides, soluble precursors of collagen and elastin, and other proteins. The amount of ground substance varies greatly in different regions and at different ages; it is generally more conspicuous in young tissues and is gradually replaced by fibrous components in later life.

Origin and Fine Structure

The structural homogeneity which characterizes the ground substance in ordinary histological preparations is borne out by electron microscopic study. Granular or fibrous structures may be visualized after special treatments (1) or in dried films of extracted materials (8, 43), but the available evidence is against any visibly structured elements in the natural state (e.g., 15, 35, 36).

It has been widely accepted that the ground substance originates as a secretion of mesenchyme cells and some of their derivatives, especially fibroblasts and mast cells. In early stages of development, however, a transparent cell-free jelly occurs between ectoderm and entoderm (3), and the elaboration of ground substance should not be conceived as the exclusive property of cells of mesodermal origin. Moreover, evidence from electron microscopy confirms the earlier views of histologists that small amounts of a homogeneous "cementing" material is laid down between many different kinds of cells. Even in the adult connective tissues, where accumulations of ground substance are particularly conspicuous, specific contributions by other cell types cannot be ruled out. In fact, it would be rather surprising if the special character of the parenchymal cells of various organs was not in this fashion impressed upon the connective tissues with which they are associated.

The most often studied chemical components of the ground substance, the mucopolysaccharides, do, however, appear to arise particularly from

fibroblasts and possibly mast cells (26). This view is supported, for example, by the recent studies of Grossfeld et al. (19) on mass cultures of fibroblasts from human embryonic skin and bone. These investigators found that large amounts of mucopolysaccharide, including both chondroitin sulfate and hyaluronic acid, accumulated in the medium. Tissue culture offers a potentially valuable but so far little exploited technique for studying the biosynthesis of polysaccharides (18).

Mucopolysaccharides in Ground Substance

Knowledge of the composition of the ground substance is based both on chemical isolations and on histochemical procedures (for reviews, see 9, 21, 28). The histochemical methods, though providing some important information about the localization of certain chemical groups, are generally conceded to lack specificity, even in conjunction with enzymatic digestion. There is, however, little doubt about the presence in ground substance of the acid mucopolysaccharides and carbohydrate-protein complexes described by histochemists.

Chemical analyses have stressed the mucopolysaccharides. Although these compounds are clearly of major importance in the functioning of ground substance, they actually represent only a small fraction of the dry weight of connective tissue (some 0.5 to 5%; 28). The exact amount of mucopolysaccharide in ground substance is unknown; no one has succeeded in isolating ground substance in sufficiently pure form for this type of analysis.

Types of Mucopolysaccharides

The number of distinct mucopolysaccharides in connective tissue is also unknown. Due to the pioneering work of Meyer (28) and his associates, it is clear that these substances constitute a family, and the number already isolated is imposing. Hyaluronic acid and its isomer chondroitin represent a class of non-sulfated acid mucopolysaccharides. The sulfated compounds include at least three chondroitin sulfates (A, B, C), in addition to heparin and keratosulfate. All these compounds are high molecular weight polymers; upon hydrolysis they yield hexosamines, and uronic, acetic, and sulfuric acids. In some cases, the chemical description of the monomer units is nearly complete. Hyaluronic acid, for example, is a polymer of hyalobiuronic acid, a disaccharide containing glucosamine and glucuronic acid; its structure has been established by Weissmann (28). The repeating units of other mucopolysaccharides contain such uronic acids as galacturonic, mannuronic, or iduronic acid and such alternate hexosamines as galactosamine.

The occurrence of iduronic acid in chondroitin sulfate B is noteworthy because of the close similarity of this acid to ascorbic acid. Chondroitin sulfate B is one of the most typical components of connective tissue, while ascorbic acid, as is well known, has been implicated in connective tissue maintenance and collagen synthesis (e.g., 13). If ascorbic acid is a precursor of iduronic acid, it would serve not as a vitamin but as an essential nutrient (28).

The various connective tissues contain diverse amounts and proportions of the mucopolysaccharides referred to above. In each case analyzed by Meyer, typically different proportions of hyaluronic acid and one or more of the chondroitin sulfates were encountered. The point is well exemplified by a recent comparative study of the bovine cornea and sclera (32). In the cornea, keratosulfate (lacking a uronic acid) is the major component; chondroitin sulfate A and chondroitin are present in lesser amounts. The sclera contains no keratosulfate but is rich in chondroitin sulfate B and yields lesser amounts of chondroitin sulfates A and C.

Mucopolysaccharide Molecules

As macromolecules, the mucopolysaccharides are elongate, flexible particles. They have a high negative charge, and hence a strong affinity for cations and water. Depending on local physical and chemical changes they readily undergo depolymerization and repolymerization, or form reversible linkages with other compounds. Their role in the regulation of water and inorganic ion metabolism has often been acknowledged. Dorfman, for example, has pointed out that "a change in concentration or molecular size of such a substance is obviously of great importance in modifying the capacity of connective tissue to bind water and salts" (9, p. 82). Polatnick, LaTessa, and Katzin suggest that the differences between corneal and scleral mucopolysaccharides are related to the "more closely controlled state of hydration of the cornea" (32, p. 364). This may also be the significance of the varying mucopolysaccharide compositions of other connective tissues. But the possibility is open that constant ratios exist between particular mucopolysaccharides and the protein moieties of some mucoprotein complexes, and that these variations therefore have an altogether different significance. In so far as this matter has been studied, the existence of such a ratio between collagen and mucopolysaccharides is uncertain (cf. 28, 42). But at least in the case of the corneal and scleral analyses considered above, a rather constant ratio between non-collagenous protein and mucopolysaccharides is indicated; the cornea contains about 2.5 times as much mucopolysaccharide as the sclera and also has a pro-

portionately larger amount of non-collagenous soluble protein; the collagen fractions in the two tissues, however, show only minor differences (33).

Mucopolysaccharide-Protein Complexes

Although our knowledge of the chemistry of mucopolysaccharides is far from complete, enough information is at hand to suggest that these compounds create more problems for embryologists than they solve. There are, for example, no clear hints that the properties of these substances bear directly on such matters as the specificity of cellular interactions, embryonic induction, or guidance during cell migrations. However, the ground substance is not just a collection of free mucopolysaccharides. On the contrary, it is becoming increasingly apparent that most mucopolysaccharides are complexed with proteins (e.g., 27). This obviously opens possibilities for speculations about specificity, but unfortunately, little of an exact nature is yet known.

Recent analyses of cartilage provide examples of the current status of information about mucoprotein complexes in the ground substance. Bernardi (7) has concluded that about one-third of the chondroitin sulfate (mainly A) of cartilage is linked to a non-collagenous protein, the rest apparently being associated largely with collagen. From analyses of viscosity, sedimentation, and light scattering, Bernardi infers that chondroitin sulfate and polypeptides are joined end-to-end in linear chains.

Partridge and Davis (31) have also shown that at least part of the chondroitin sulfate of cartilage is in firm chemical combination with a non-collagenous protein. This protein has been isolated and its amino acid composition determined. It is altogether different from collagen, being rich in tyrosine and low in both glycine and proline. The protein moiety is apparently influential in forming molecular aggregates, since solutions of the complex rapidly become less viscous upon treatment with proteolytic enzymes. Previous studies (30, 41) had indicated that the ability of these chondroitin-sulfate–protein preparations to combine reversibly with collagen is destroyed by heating or dilute alkali. It therefore seems likely that these linkages with collagen depend not on free chondroitin sulfate but on the mucoprotein complex.

However praiseworthy the analytical work on which these statements are based, it is at once evident that there is no obvious and immediate relation between the known properties of the macromolecules occurring in the ground substance and the developmental events we are seeking to explain. The elongate shape and flexibility of these molecules, their ion-binding characteristics, the ease with which their carbohydrate and protein

moieties may associate or dissociate under varying conditions of *p*H or ionic strength, the dynamic equilibria of synthesis and degradation which we may visualize during growth and differentiation—all tell us that we are dealing with a responsive and critical population of substances. But beyond this, the path is dark and sign-posts are lacking.

Fibrous Components

Collagen is the most abundant and most studied fibrous component of the intercellular matrices. Due to the interest shown in this substance during the past fifteen years by biologists, biochemists, and biophysicists, we now have a remarkably full catalogue of information about it (for reviews, see 4, 5, 20, 34, 40).

For the purposes of this discussion, three important points must be made. First, as Schmitt (37, 38), Gross (16), and others have pointed out, collagen has become a prototype among fibrous proteins—not only because of the intensity with which it has been studied but also because of its significance as a model for studies of morphogenesis at the macromolecular level. Next, collagen participates in the formation of a variety of fibrous fabrics, some with an astonishing complexity of fine structure which also pose intriguing morphogenetic problems. Finally, the often suggested but rarely analyzed relation between collagen and the mineralization of an intercellular matrix is turning out to be even more intimate than previously suspected. Each of these points deserves brief comment.

Collagen Fibrogenesis

A collagen fibril is an array of adlineated collagen molecules, the tropocollagen particles of Schmitt, Gross, and Highberger (39). The individual molecules are composed of three helically coiled polypeptides strongly linked by hydrogen bonds; they are some 3000 Å long and 14 Å wide. Glycine, proline, and hydroxyproline are conspicuous among the amino acid residues of collagen, the last-named acid being regarded as virtually diagnostic.

The native fibril of adult vertebrate collagen has a cross-banded pattern with an average axial period of about 640 Å. The bands have been attributed to zones of relative molecular disorder resulting from the interactions of long side-chains which repeat regularly along the laterally associated tropocollagen particles (4, 40). In a series of exciting experiments growing out of observations first made by Nageotte, Schmitt and coworkers (40) have demonstrated that collagen which has been dissolved

in appropriate solutions can be caused by a number of treatments to reconstitute into fibrils of precisely ordered structure. The treatments include alterations in *p*H or ionic strength, as well as the addition of one of several organic compounds (e.g., chondroitin sulfate, ATP, glycoprotein, or heparin). Depending on the exact conditions employed, the fibrils reconstitute as one of several naturally occurring types with 640 Å, 220 Å, or no axial periods; or as one of at least two unnatural types with periods of 2600 to 3000 Å, that is, approximately the length of the individual tropocollagen particles.

These diverse patterns are interpreted as resulting from the aggregation of elongate molecules which, being polarized, become arranged either in parallel or antiparallel arrays. The molecules are assumed to lie either with their ends in register or staggered by some specific fraction of their length. The important conclusion was reached that the type of fibrillar structure formed depends critically on two factors: one, the built-in properties of the individual collagen macromolecules; and two, the chemical environment which determines the degree of ionization, the interactiveness of specific side chains, and the like. Although it has been claimed that mucopolysaccharides are involved in the biogenesis of collagen fibrils or in stabilizing the linkages between adjacent collagen molecules (e.g., 23), there is no really cogent supporting evidence. Schmitt, Gross, and Highberger have emphasized particularly that "the precipitation of collagen fibrils by various substances is no proof that these substances form an essential part of the structure of native collagen or are involved in its biogenesis" (40, p. 150).

In the intact organism, fibrogenesis presumably involves comparable events. That is, collagen macromolecules which have been synthesized in fibroblasts are deposited in the immediately adjacent ground substance, where they then aggregate into fibrils. Whether any fibril formation occurs intracellularly is still undecided despite several electron microscopic investigations (for literature, see 24). No matter where collagen fibrils first emerge as electron optically visible elements, the main point of the in-vitro work just discussed is that once definitive collagen macromolecules are available, no specific external factors are required to fabricate them into fibrils. The structural order of the fibril will emerge spontaneously. The physical and chemical environment in which the molecules interact imposes limits on the type of fibril which will form. But the detailed specificity of the interaction, and hence the configuration of the final product, depends on the collagen particles themselves.

Ordered Fibrillar Aggregates

The appearance during development of oriented fibrillar aggregates depends in part on prevailing patterns of tension (e.g., 47), and in part on interactions between individual fibrils and the ground substance in which they are embedded. A developing tendon is a case in point. As Jackson (24) has shown, collagen fibrils each about 80 Å in diameter appear in parallel bundles in the metatarsal tendons of the 8-day chick embryo. The diameter of the fibrils increases progressively with age, an especially rapid increase occurring between the 12th and 18th days. Diameters of some 400 Å are encountered by hatching, 750 Å in the adult bird.

The individual fibrils are embedded in a structurally homogeneous ground substance; they lie in the characteristic hexagonal pattern assumed by closely packed, equidistant cylindrical rods. At any given stage, all fibrils have essentially the same diameter; that is, they are growing laterally at equal rates. As development proceeds, the relative amount of interfibrillar material diminishes; the fibrils thus become ever more closely packed, until in the adult they are separated by distances only a fraction of their diameters.

The growth of the fibrils must therefore be presumed to involve the following types of events. Tropocollagen particles, synthesized in neighboring fibroblasts, continuously permeate the ground substance and become equally distributed around the growing fibrils. Some of these particles adhere to the fibrillar surfaces, aggregate end-to-end and side-to-side with others of their kind, and thus add in an orderly manner to the bulk of the fibrils.

However, some fibrils lie within a few Ångström units of a fibroblast; others near the center of a bundle lie several hundred Ångström units from the nearest source of collagen molecules. Conditions in the interfibrillar region immediately adjacent to the fibrils clearly favor the aggregation of the collagen molecules and their accretion on the fibrils. It is therefore not easy to understand how equal rates of growth are maintained by all fibrils of a given region (35). If the diffusion of collagen molecules were a limiting factor in the growth of the fibrils, then a gradient of diameters—decreasing toward the center of each bundle—would be expected. Since there is no such size gradient, growth control must involve some other mechanism. The simplest hypothesis to account for the facts would assume that collagen molecules en route from the source of supply are in some respect incomplete and hence unable to aggregate on fibrils until "activated." The details of activation are irrelevant; they could include some

nucleation involves a specific stereochemical configuration resulting from a particular state of aggregation of collagen macromolecules" (12, p. 861). By combining metastable solutions containing calcium and phosphate ions with tropocollagen in solution, or with one of the various types of reconstituted collagen fibrils described above, it was demonstrated that crystallization of hydroxyapatite occurred only on fibrils with the native 640 Å axial period. Neither the individual macromolecules nor fibrillar aggregates of any other type served as nucleation centers. The identity of the inorganic crystals was established by x-ray and electron diffraction and by chemical analysis. It must be assumed, therefore, that when collagen molecules have become so aligned as to form fibrils of the native type, they then present surface groups or sites whose configurations are sterically adapted to the crystal lattice of hydroxyapatite.

The reconstituted fibrils used in this study were prepared with collagen from a number of sources which do not normally become calcified. Thus, whatever the barrier to mineralization of such tissues, it cannot be attributed to the collagen molecules themselves, since despite their origin, they induce the formation of hydroxyapatite if properly aggregated. However, collagen fibrils which are directly isolated from tendon (i.e., *not* reconstituted), do not calcify when exposed to solutions of calcium and phosphate ions even at concentrations where spontaneous precipitation occurs. It is tempting to attribute this difference in the behavior of reconstituted and original fibrils to mucopolysaccharides associated with the latter. Considerable interest will therefore attach to future efforts to dissect this hypothetical inhibitory action of mucopolysaccharides by treatments which remove or modify them.

We thus return to our starting point—the ground substance and the presumably critical but poorly known properties of the mucopolysaccharides and mucoprotein complexes which it contains. In each of the examples which we have considered, these substances apparently play a crucial but tantalizingly obscure role. By turning from the function of the ground substance in events which have often received the attention of embryologists to events in the domain of ultrastructure and macromolecules, we have uncovered a number of fascinating new puzzles, perhaps without greatly clarifying the older problems. But the success already achieved by dealing with morphogenetic events at the new level fosters the hope that some of the less precisely characterizable problems with which embryology has been concerned will ultimately find solutions which can be expressed in at least equally satisfying terms.

REFERENCES

1. Asadi, A. M., Dougherty, T. F., and Cochran, G. W., *Nature,* **178**, 1061-1062 (1956).
2. Baitsell, G. A., *J. Exptl. Med.*, **21,** 455-479 (1915).
3. ———, *Quart. J. Microscop. Sci.,* **69,** 571-589 (1925).
4. Bear, R. S., *Advances in Protein Chem.,* **7,** 69-160 (1952).
5. ———, *Symposia Soc. Exptl. Biol.,* **9,** 97-114 (1955).
6. Bell, E., *Proc. Biophys. Soc.,* in press (1958).
7. Bernardi, G., *Biochem. Biophys. Acta,* **26,** 47-52 (1957).
8. ———, Cessi, C., and Gotte, L., *Experientia,* **13,** 465-466 (1958).
9. Dorfman, A., in *Connective Tissue in Health and Disease* (G. Asboe-Hansen, ed.), p. 81-96, E. Munksgaard, Copenhagen (1954).
10. Edds, M. V., Jr., *Proc. Natl. Acad. Sci. U. S.,* **44,** 296-305 (1958).
11. Ferry, J. D., Katz, S., and Tinoco, J., *J. Polymer Sci.,* **12,** 500-510 (1954).
12. Glimcher, M. J., Hodge, A. J., and Schmitt, F. O., *Proc. Natl. Acad. Sci. U. S.,* **43,** 860-867 (1957).
13. Gould, B. S., and Woessner, J. F., *J. Biol. Chem.,* **226,** 289-300 (1957).
14. Grobstein, C., in *Aspects of Synthesis and Order in Growth* (D. Rudnick, ed.), p. 233-256, Princeton University Press, Princeton (1955).
15. Gross, J., *Ann. N. Y. Acad. Sci.,* **52,** 964-970 (1950).
16. ———, *J. Biophys. Biochem. Cytol.,* **2** Suppl., 261-274 (1956).
17. ———, *J. Exptl. Med.,* **107,** 265-277 (1958).
18. Grossfeld, H., *Exptl. Cell Research,* **14,** 213-216 (1958).
19. ———, Meyer, K., Godman, G., and Linker, A., *J. Biophys. Biochem. Cytol.,* **3,** 391-396 (1957).
20. Gustavson, K. H., *The Chemistry and Reactivity of Collagen,* Academic Press, New York (1956).
21. Hale, A. J., *Intern. Rev. Cytol.,* **6,** 193-263 (1957).
22. Holtfreter, J., *Ann. N. Y. Acad. Sci.,* **49,** 709-760 (1948).
23. Jackson, D. S. *Biochem. J.,* **56,** 699-703 (1954).
24. Jackson, S. Fitton, *Proc. Roy. Soc. (London),* **B, 144,** 556-572 (1956).
25. McLean, F. C., *Science,* **127,** 451-456 (1958).
26. McManus, J. F. A., in *Connective Tissue in Health and Disease* (G. Asboe-Hansen, ed.), p. 31-53, E. Munksgaard, Copenhagen (1954).
27. Meyer, K., *Discussions Faraday Soc.,* **13,** 271-275 (1953).
28. ———, *Harvey Lectures,* **51,** 88-112 (1957).
29. Moscona, A., remarks at Harvard Cancer Conference (1957).
30. Muir, H., *Biochem. J.,* **62,** 26P (1956).
31. Partridge, S. M., and Davis, H. F., *Biochem. J.,* **68,** 298-305 (1958).
32. Polatnick, J., La Tessa, A. J., and Katzin, H. M., *Biochim. Biophys. Acta,* **26,** 361-364 (1957).
33. ———, ———, and ———, *Biochim. Biophys. Acta,* **26,** 365-369 (1957).
34. Randall, J. T., *Nature and Structure of Collagen,* Academic Press, New York (1953).
35. ———, *J. Cell. Comp. Physiol.,* **49** Suppl., 113-127 (1957).
36. Rothman, S., *Physiology and Biochemistry of the Skin,* University of Chicago Press, Chicago (1954).
37. Schmitt, F. O., *Proc. Natl. Acad. Sci. U. S.,* **42,** 806-810 (1956).
38. ———, *J. Cell. Comp. Physiol.,* **49** Suppl., 85-104 (1957).
39. ———, Gross, J., and Highberger, J. H., *Proc. Natl. Acad. Sci. U. S.,* **39,** 459-470 (1953).
40. ———,———, and ———, *Symposia Soc. Exptl. Biol.,* **9,** 148-162 (1955).

41. Shatton, J., and Schubert, M., *J. Biol. Chem.*, **211**, 565-573 (1954).
42. Slack, H. G. B., *Biochem. J.*, **65**, 459-464 (1957).
43. Sylvén, B., and Ambrose, E. J., *Biochim. Biophys. Acta,* **18,** 587 (1955).
44. Waugh, D. F., *J. Cell. Comp. Physiol.*, **49** Suppl., 145-164 (1957).
45. Weiss, P., *Amer. Naturalist,* **67,** 322-340 (1933).
46. ———, *J. Exptl. Zool.*, **100**, 353-386 (1945).
47. ———, in *Chemistry and Physiology of Growth* (A. K. Parpart, ed.), p. 135-186, Princeton University Press, Princeton (1949).
48. ———, *Proc. Natl. Acad. Sci., U. S.*, **42,** 819-830 (1956).
49. ———, *J. Cell. Comp. Physiol.*, **49** Suppl., 105-112 (1957).
50. ———, and Ferris, W., *Proc. Natl. Acad. Sci. U. S.*, **40,** 528-540 (1954).
51. ———, and ———, *J. Biophys. Biochem. Cytol.*, **2,** Suppl., 275-282 (1956).

DISCUSSION

DR. STEINBERG: Dr. Edds, in the earlier part of your discussion you suggested that possibly all cells are capable of producing ground substance. You mentioned in particular the work of Drs. Weiss, Grobstein, and Holtfreter on the role of the so-called ground substance in contact guidance and in induction and possibly in tissue affinities. Do you mean to imply that the intercellular matrix which is studied in connective tissues is present not only in connective tissue spaces, but also between, let us say, epithelial cells of the organism? In other words, do you mean to say that all of the cells in a particular tissue are surrounded by something which we might loosely term intercellular cement?

DR. EDDS: Yes, embryonic cells are imbedded in this ground substance; this is commonly accepted. I was trying to suggest that information from studies of adult connective tissues may provide hints which will help us to understand its role in the embryo.

DR. STEINBERG: I have recently been through some of the literature on the so-called intercellular cement which has been presumed by many to glue the cells of the organism together. It seems to me that the idea of such a ubiquitous cement is a conceptual extension of observations actually made in connective tissue. The presence of such cement between other kinds of cells in different tissues has not really been substantiated. In particular, if one examines electron micrographs of cells in various tissues, one finds that these cells are in very close approximation to one another. The distance in general between the osmiophilic layers of adjacent cell membranes is roughly 200 Ångstroms. This is about the same distance that we find between the two membranes of the nucleus, between the layers of closely packed endoplasmic reticulum, between the membrane pairs constituting the cristae or the outer walls of mitochondria, or between the closely packed layers of myelin, which as we know are Schwann cell membranes. And, of course, this 200 Ångstrom distance between cells is only the maximum possible distance between them, for there may be nonstaining layers between the paired osmiophilic ones. Tissue cells seem, there-

fore, to be as closely approximated as the structure of lipoprotein membranes will permit. Consequently it seems unreasonable to me to assume that there is a proteinaceous, matrix-like cement, distinct from the cell surfaces, between them. Would you care to comment on this?

Dr. Edds: As far as the 200 Ångstroms space is concerned, this is still pretty big when we consider molecular dimensions, even of the macromolecules we are discussing.

Dr. Steinberg: Of course this is only the maximum possible intercellular distance. The presence of a non-osmiophilic component external to the osmiophilic one would reduce or extinguish the apparent "space."

Dr. Edds: Yes, of course. One still does not know what lies within it, however. There is one matter I would like to comment on which I was not able to include in my talk; that is, the situation in the basement membrane of the epidermis of the frog embryo. I cannot see this membrane under the highest resolution of the light microscope until about Shumway stage 19, no matter how I stain it. However, I can find it earlier just by going to the embryo and stripping off the epidermis with ultrasound. I didn't think there was any membrane and it was surprising to find it before it was optically detectable in sections. In fact, this "invisible" basement membrane is thick enough to dissect from the embryo. But it is dissolved by the technique which I was using to study it microscopically. So, I think one has to be very cautious about conclusions concerning the physical existence of these substances until one has explored several different ways of revealing their presence or their absence.

Dr. Afzelius: As an electron microscopist I would like to comment on this 200 Ångstrom distance between cells. This distance might be what actually exists between living cells and then again it might be many, many other things. The possibilities of artifacts are, of course, manifest when one uses the conventional techniques of the day in electron microscopy.

I would now like to comment on the question asked after Dr. Allen's fine paper. Someone asked what happened to those cortical granules of the sea urchin egg that were not extruded during fertilization. I am convinced that the cortical granules which are acid mucopolysaccharides according to the histochemist do not all contribute to the fertilization membrane. Over half of them form the so-called hyaline layer. This layer is homogeneous or slightly fibrous in the electron micrographs. It has been known since 1900 that this layer can be dissolved away, after which the blastomeres will fall apart. If one examines the two-cell stage of the sea urchin egg, the cells seem to be stuck together by a cell cement of acid mucopolysaccharide from the hyaline layer and in the closest places they are only 250 Ångstroms apart. This observation might have some bearing on the problem which has been raised. If one washes away this substance, then the blastomeres fall apart. If they are left alone, however, the blastomeres remain together by this intercellular cement. Therefore, in the case of the cortical granules, you might have a nice oppor-

tunity to study materials which may be possible precursors of the ground substance which has been discussed here.

DR. EDDS: That may well be possible. However, I have a feeling that this system may be too minute for such studies. Possibly in vitro culture systems will be useful for studies of biosynthesis. I am afraid that the embryologist has little chance to make a contribution to this field by using cortical granules because the amounts of materials are so very small.

DR. WEISS: I would like to comment briefly on this question raised about intercellular cement. In tissue culture we find that epithelial cells of the same kind form an island which may contain only 4 or 5 cells. We can see that these cells will mill around, will shift their positions relative to one another, and yet the island will remain compact and retain its identity. It seems pretty difficult to explain this in any terms other than assuming that there is an envelope of some kind which surrounds the island. The mode of recognition which keeps cells together cannot be a cement because they are not cemented. They shift constantly relative to one another and yet they retain a common geometrically simple contour. This implies that there must be a ground mat which holds them together. Now Dr. Moscona in our laboratory before he left studied this and in the cases where he could find this envelope under the microscope it stained with periodic acid Schiff. The point I want to make is that the idea of cell glue or cell cement is largely an artifact.

DR. MARKERT: Do you have any evidence concerning the metabolic stability of the intercellular matrix?

DR. EDDS: I am relatively unfamiliar with this aspect of the ground substance but it has been studied extensively, for example by Dorfman. His investigations show that mucopolysaccharides are relatively labile constituents.

DR. ALLEN: I would like to suggest a system for the possible study of the biosynthesis of acid mucopolysaccharides. The sea urchin cortical granules are probably too small, as you suggested, but the fish cortical alveoli, which supposedly contain the same kinds of substances, are extruded from the egg and form the colloid of the perivitelline space. These egg alveoli are large enough and probably concentrated enough to work with. They range from 4 or 5 microns up to 25 or 30 microns in size and show a very intense PAS reaction. They are formed at a very early stage of oogenesis and Dr. Norman Kemp has shown that they come from the primary yolk vesicles.

I would also like to ask a question concerning the remark made about possible false-positive reactions with the PAS stain, and metachromasia. I was wondering if you have any information on what kinds of substances give false-positive reactions.

DR. EDDS: As I understand it, the important step in the PAS reaction is the cleavage of a carbon-carbon bond having adjacent OH or OH and NH_2 groups. Since there are a large number of compounds which can be oxidized at such a site, there is always difficulty in interpreting the results of the technic.

Dr. Lenhoff: I think that it should be mentioned that embryological studies involving collagens may offer advantages. Since the amino acid hydroxyproline is found almost uniquely and in high concentrations in proteins belonging to the collagen family, it is possible to follow changes in the collagen content of cells and tissues by carrying out the relatively simple and specific chemical assay for hydroxyproline. Thus, cytological changes may be concomitantly followed by the more quantitative chemical assay.

In our own laboratory, Mr. Edward Kline and I have begun to pursue a related problem while studying the differentiation of the nematocysts of *Hydra littoralis*. This problem arose from our observation of radioautographs of C^{14}-labeled hydra which demonstrated that specific labeled "loci" in the body tube migrated and concentrated in the batteries of the tentacles. In an attempt to identify the labeled material as the nematocysts, a method was developed for the isolation of these stinging organoids. An analysis of the purified capsules of the previously described "chitinous" nematocysts demonstrated the presence of over 20% hydroxyproline and of a similar amount of proline; these results suggested that the capsule of the nematocyst is an unusual member of the collagen family. Since other studies indicate that hydroxyproline is not present in significant quantities in other hydra proteins, it appears feasible to investigate problems such as nematocyst differentiation and migration, tentacle regeneration, and reconstitution by quantitatively following hydroxyproline.

Dr. Edds: I am glad you gave me an opportunity to comment on hydroxyproline because I have become interested in just this feature of the collagen molecule. Collagen is the only animal protein which we know of that is characterized by a particular amino acid. For this reason, it lends itself to chemical analyses by people who may not be adept at the more complex procedures of protein chemistry. Even if one is not an expert protein chemist it is therefore possible to develop considerable precision in tracing the development of collagen merely by following the one amino acid, hydroxyproline.

Dr. Scheiderman: I should like to remark, Dr. Edds, that F. C. Steward and his colleagues have found that in rapidly growing tissue of many plants, and I believe carrot is one of them, hydroxyproline is found in large quantity in certain proteins. The situation with respect to hydroxyproline here is quite different from that in collagen, but in any case, hydroxyproline is really not unique to collagen.

Dr. Edds: Thank you. Of course, I should have qualified my reply by saying that hydroxyproline is found in a few other restricted places. If anyone can tell the collagen chemists what hydroxyproline is doing in these plant tissues I am sure it would make them very happy.

Dr. Hadorn: Has anybody examined the ground substance in the jelly fish? That would seem to be a very desirable object to study in this respect.

Dr. Edds: I do not know of any such studies.

DR. BRACHET: I believe that Dr. Bouillon, in Brussels has looked at the jelly fish under the electron microscope. His conclusion was that the mesoglea fibres are not made out of collagen, but that they rather resemble the elastic tissue of the vertebrates.

CYTOPLASMIC PARTICULATES AND BASOPHILIA[1]

HEWSON SWIFT
Whitman Laboratory, Department of Zoology
University of Chicago

INTRODUCTION

Certain particulate components of the cytoplasm (mitochondria, basophilic inclusions, Golgi material) are, with few exceptions, of universal occurrence in all cells. They frequently possess shapes or distributions characteristic of different tissue types, and in many cases change in specific fashion with differentiation and the physiological conditions of the cell. In spite of their wide occurrence, our knowledge of the form and function of cell particulates is still fragmentary, although it has been immeasurably increased in recent years by studies with the electron microscope and from biochemical investigations on isolated cell fractions.

1. Mitochondria

Almost 50 years ago Warburg found that certain metabolic enzymes were inextricably bound to cell particulates. In the intervening years of work on isolated mitochondria, begun by Bensley and Hoerr (6) and continued by Claude (17) and his co-workers, the importance of mitochondria as enzyme carriers has been thoroughly established. The enzymes of mitochondria are diverse, functioning in synthesis and hydrolysis, as well as in oxidative metabolism (71). The morphology of mitochondria has also been thoroughly studied with the electron microscope, chiefly after osmium fixation. In the great majority of cells they appear to be limited by a "double membrane" of two dense layers enclosing a less dense space. They contain a number of inner lamellate structures (cristae), or filaments, that have been considered either to be extensions of the inner

[1] The author is greatly indebted to Dr. Ellen Rasch for invaluable collaboration in every phase of the work described here. Figs. 2, 5, 11, and 20 were photographed by Dr. Rasch; Fig. 24 was taken by Dr. L. E. Roth; Fig. 29 by Mr. W. Ferris; Fig. 35 by Dr. L. Herman; and Figs. 36 and 37 by Dr. A. Ruthmann. The writer expresses his appreciation to these associates for their kind permission to publish this material. Aided by Grants C-1612 and C-3544 of the U. S. Public Health Service, and the Abbott Memorial Fund.

limiting membrane (48), or as separate structures in contact with it (74). In spite of the wide morphological variation encountered among different tissues, these characters define a surprisingly consistent class of particulates, present in all cells except for those in certain terminal states, such as mature erythrocytes or the cells of outer squamous epidermis.

In most tissues there are also particulates that bear a doubtful relation to typical mitochondria, such as the "microbodies" (68) and "dense bodies" (45) of rat liver, "components I and II" of mouse small intestine epithelium (92), and the "globoid bodies" of HeLa cells (35). Further characterization of such components, and of their enzyme composition if any, must await more subtle isolation procedures, and the further development of enzyme localization techniques for the electron microscope.

Many basic questions concerning mitochondria still remain unanswered. For example, we know next to nothing about mitochondrial origin, although evidence has been presented of their formation from preexisting mitochondria (85, 31), from the cell membrane (31), or from microbodies (68), to name a few current concepts. Is the mitochondrion itself the site of enzyme synthesis, or merely of its aggregation? In this connection the cinematographic observations of Frédéric and Chèvremont (25) on temporary connections between mitochondria and the nuclear membrane are of interest. Mitochondria show morphologies specific for their tissue type. It would be interesting to know how such differences occur in differentiation, whether new types of mitochondria arise, or preexisting embryonic types are modified. These and many other problems await further study.

2. *Golgi Apparatus*

Fine-structure studies have also penetrated somewhat the classical cloud of confusion surrounding the Golgi apparatus far enough to provide a consistent morphological picture. From studies with the light microscope, often employing unpredictable cytological methods, Golgi substance has variously been considered to be fibrous, vacuolar, lamellar, or canalicular, as lipid droplets (3), or as myelin figures produced during fixation (51). In light of this disorder, the constant pattern of Golgi fine structure is most welcome. In the electron microscope after osmium fixation Golgi bodies appear as a series of densely packed parallel double membranes, often slightly expanded at their ends, surrounded by numerous small "vacuoles" or "granules" roughly 50 mμ in diameter. Since these small vacuoles have limiting membranes similar to the lamellae, it is possible that the two types of structure represent different phases of the same material. In some cases the lamellae may be expanded by large vacuoles of

low density, and the whole complex may be surrounded by a dense area of cytoplasmic ground substance (78).

In some tissues, such as mouse epididymis (20), Golgi components are aggregated into characteristic bodies U-shaped in section, and located near the distal nuclear margin. In the small intestine mucosa they exist as several unconnected plate-like structures lying parallel to the cell axis (92), and in rat hepatic cells as somewhat less organized complexes lining the bile canaliculi (23). Similar structures also occur in plant cells, for example, the "dictyosomes" shown by Porter (60). In spite of different arrangements within the cell, the characteristic Golgi morphology is usually readily recognized. An old dispute concerning the Golgi nature of the dictyosomes of certain spermatocytes has thus been adequately resolved, and the acroblast formed from the aggregation of dictyosomes is clearly Golgi-like in structure (12). There are, however, certain membrane complexes showing morphological differences from the usual Golgi pattern, such as the stacked, short lamellar aggregates of flagellates (70), or the smooth-contoured whorls in rat motor neurons (54), whose Golgi nature seems unclear.

A number of cytochemical studies have confirmed the high phospholipid content of Golgi material. Evidence for two different lipid fractions has been presented, one soluble and the other insoluble in 70 per cent alcohol (20). The presence of polysaccharides has been suggested on the basis of the periodic acid-Schiff reaction (30), but lipids have also been considered responsible for this finding (72). The presence of alkaline phosphatase in the Golgi zone of certain epithelial cells has been described on the basis of histochemical tests (22, 46), and also from the isolated Golgi fraction (72). None of these findings are very helpful in elucidating Golgi function. The obvious change in Golgi material with secretion has frequently been demonstrated, for example, by Moore, Price, and Gallagher (44) in rat prostate. Golgi involvement in acrosome synthesis, at least in some spermatids, also seems indicated. However, pilocarpine injection produced no obvious changes in the Golgi apparatus in pancreas, although in acinar cells a series in size and density could be arranged from small Golgi vacuoles to fully formed zymogen granules (78). Except for a poorly defined role in secretion, possibly in condensing or partitioning products synthesized elsewhere, we are almost completely ignorant of Golgi function.

3. Cell Membranes

It is evident from a number of electron microscope studies that cell membranes are not merely passive boundaries. They are strikingly convoluted

in many tissues (55, 65), and may extend into "microvilli" at free cell surfaces (90, 92), affording good morphological support to physiological concepts of active transport and absorption. Such findings suggest that cell membranes frequently invaginate to form cytoplasmic channels and intracellular vesicles, taking fluids or large particulate materials across cell membranes by pinocytosis, phagocytosis, or extrusion. Certain cell inclusions thus may continually arise from internal blebbing of cell membranes (31, 50, 90). Where such processes occur between cells it seems possible that large chunks of cytoplasm may freely be exchanged. The importance of such processes in cell interaction, for example in embryonic induction, is as yet completely unexplored.

4. Basophilic Components

Our knowledge of the RNA-containing structures of the cytoplasm has emerged spasmodically over a long period. A number of early studies indicated that basophilic cell components (i.e., those stainable with basic dyes) must somehow be associated with synthetic processes. For example, in his studies on gland cells Garnier (28) considered that the filamentous, lamellate, or whorled structures comprising the "ergastoplasm" were important in the process of secretion. In subsequent studies the term ergastoplasm was also applied to filamentous or flocculent inclusions found in a variety of other animal and plant cells, including starfish oocytes and embryo sacs of lily (63), where the "ergastoplasm" was thought to be engaged in the elaboration and transformation of various cell substances. In his studies on annelid oocytes, Lillie (40) suggested that the highly basophilic particles, which he called "microsomes" after Hanstein (34), were in some way associated with yolk synthesis. Similar conclusions were reached for other cell types by numerous investigators, although in many cases the "microsomes" were inadequately differentiated from mitochondria and other cytoplasmic materials. Finely granular or filamentous components of the cytoplasm have also been called "chromidia" (36), because their staining properties were similar to certain components of the nucleus. Goldschmidt (32), among others, considered that the "chromidial apparatus" was formed from basophilic components extruded from the nucleus, and that it possessed a synthetic or trophic function. Several later workers refuted this theory, chiefly on the grounds that chromidia were probably mitochondria.

It has been known for many years (43) that the basophilia of certain cell structures was due to their nucleic acid content. In addition, van Herwerden (87) showed that cytoplasmic basophilia could be depressed if tissues

were first treated with ribonuclease. Our more recent interest in the function of RNA, however, dates from the findings of Caspersson and Schultz (14) from ultraviolet absorption studies, and from the studies of Brachet (10) with basic dyes and ribonuclease. These authors have repeatedly stressed the presence of high concentrations of RNA in cells engaged in active secretion or growth. Further evidence for the involvement of RNA in protein synthesis has come largely from the studies on isolated RNA-containing components, begun by Claude (17). These studies have now expanded into a highly important analytic approach to biochemical mechanisms of protein synthesis.

The RNA-containing components of the cytoplasm occur in a variety of forms. They have been isolated from cell homogenates by a number of different methods that affect in various ways their composition and structure. The "small granule" fraction isolated from rat liver by Claude (18), was considered to contain particles more or less homogeneous in size, averaging about 200 mμ in diameter, and containing a high concentration of lipoproteins and RNA. To these particles Claude applied the name "microsomes," using a term frequent in the older cytological literature, but for structures he felt were below the level of light microscope visibility. Later more extensive fractionation studies demonstrated that the microsomal fraction was far from homogeneous in composition, but could be divided into subfractions of varying RNA and lipoprotein content (15, 47). Ribonucleoproteins were also isolated as very much smaller particles, 5 to 24 mμ in diameter, of high density, essentially free of lipids. These fine particles were called "ultramicrosomes" by Barnum and Huseby (4), and "macromolecules" by Petermann and Hamilton (56), who distinguished different classes of particles on the basis of density and charge. With desoxycholate the fine particles were readily recovered from the microsomal fraction, leaving behind a membranous complex of lipoproteins (91). It is of interest to note, however, that considerable RNA may remain within the membranous component, after the fine particles have been removed (16).

That labeled amino acids were most rapidly incorporated into the proteins of the "microsomal" fraction was shown by Borsook (9) and later by many others, as a clear indication of the importance of these particulates as sites of protein synthesis. Ability to incorporate amino acids was later found to reside mainly in the fine particle fraction, and only slightly in the lipoprotein membranes (41). This incorporation was demonstrable in vitro, where it was rapidly depressed by ribonuclease, and was thus dependent on the integrity of RNA (41, 91). It is also interesting to note

that cholesterol synthesis in the lipoprotein membranes, as determined by labeled acetate incorporation, was independent of the presence of the fine particle components, and unaffected by ribonuclease (11). Thus although nucleoprotein particles and lipoprotein membranes are in intimate association in the microsomal fraction, protein synthesis in the particles and cholesterol synthesis in the membranes seem largely independent.

Basophilic components of the cytoplasm, as seen in the electron microscope, possess a varied and complex morphology. Disagreement in the current literature concerning matters of their classification and interpretation attest to our present state of ignorance. In studies on whole cells, grown in tissue culture, Porter, Claude, and Fullam (61) described strings of small vesicles and tubules that were disposed as a network throughout the cytoplasm, but were absent from the outermost extensions of the cell. This vesicular system was later called the "endoplasmic reticulum" (62), a descriptive term obviously quite appropriate to this component as found in cultured cells. The development of adequate sectioning techniques precipitated a flood of observations on tissue sections. In many tissues investigators described vesicles, tubules, lamellae, and membranes arranged in a variety of ways (21, 8, 75). In a study comparing sections with whole cultured cells, Palade and Porter (52) identified a series of membrane-lined vesicles with the endoplasmic reticulum. Although in sections the vesicles usually appeared as isolated entities, analysis of serial sections showed that, at least in some cases, vesicles were interconnected and the "reticular" nature of the system was still evident. Tissue sections also demonstrated that vesicles frequently occurred in the form of large flattened sacs or "cisternae," and that in some cells, for example, in acinar cells of pancreas or in the parotid gland (58, 89), the cisternae were stacked to form complex arrays of parallel lamellae. In describing these structures, Porter (60) and Palade (50) have emphasized the occasional interconnections visible between parallel cisternae. They thus felt that "the main feature of the system" is that it forms a reticulum permeating the entire cytoplasm. In addition, these authors (50) continue to use the name "endoplasmic reticulum" because they have not been able to find a better term, although admittedly the concept of an endoplasm is inappropriate to most tissue sections.

The concept of the endoplasmic reticulum has been gradually expanded in the light of additional findings. The correspondence between the distribution of cell basophilia and the lamellar or vesicular systems was recognized, and the endoplasmic reticulum was thus considered as a component responsible for cytoplasmic basophilia (19, 58, 89). In many cases, the

membranes of the endoplasmic reticulum were further seen to be associated with fine particles 10 to 15 mμ in diameter, with a distribution characteristic of the tissue, and lining the outer surface of the cisternae or vesicles (49, 77). In addition, particularly in embryonic and tumor cells, these particles occurred freely distributed in the cytoplasm, and not associated with the membranes. It was suggested that the RNA responsible for cell basophilia occurred in this particulate component rather than in the membranes (49), and that the particles were probably homologous with the "ultramicrosomes" of Barnum and Huseby (4).

In other investigations it was evident that cytoplasmic vesicles also existed to which no granules were attached. Their lining membranes were thus smooth contoured, as seen in sections, as opposed to the particle-lined "rough" membranes. In most cases these smooth structures were clearly distinguishable as elements of the Golgi material (20), but in some cases single cisternae, for example in rat liver (50) or rat motor neurons (54), appeared to be particle-lined in some places and smooth in others. In addition, membrane complexes of the endoplasmic reticulum have been described as being in continuity with infoldings of the cell membrane at the periphery (50) and also with the nuclear membrane (88). The endoplasmic reticulum has thus been considered as "a continuous net-work of membrane-bound cavities permeating the entire cytoplasm from the cell membrane to the nucleus" (50). As such, the system includes both basophilic "rough" membranes, and "smooth" elements of the Golgi apparatus, the nuclear membrane, and infoldings of the cell membrane. All are considered to be interconnecting or "reticular," but differentiated into recognizably different components in specific areas of the cell.

This is a sweeping concept, postulating that all the membrane systems of the cell are combined into one integrated system. If the conclusion is sound that all of these membranous components are essentially interconnecting, then it is certainly of value to stress this aspect with a single generic term. The concept of the endoplasmic reticulum has been criticized, however, on several grounds. First, the name has been considered unsuitable, since the structures included are "not reticular, and there is little reason to talk about endoplasm in tissue cells" (76). Second, there have been objections to the use of a generic name for several different cell components that in the great majority of cases can be clearly distinguished by their fine structure. Third, several investigators have failed to find the reported interconnections between the membrane systems of different types (76, 77, 92). Partly because of these criticisms, other investigators have used different terms in describing these components. The name

"ergastoplasm" has been used for the stacks of lamellae characteristic of acinar pancreas, salivary gland, and hepatic parenchymal cells, since these structures are obviously comparable with the basophilic bodies originally studied by Garnier (8, 89). However, use of the term "ergastoplasm" was criticized by Sjöstrand and Hanzon (77), since it implies a function as yet unverified. Sjöstrand (76) and Zetterqvist (92) have preferred to use the completely neutral name *α-cytomembranes* for the particle-lined components, *β-cytomembranes* for membranes connected with or derived from the cell membrane, and *γ-cytomembranes* for the lamellar or vesicular membranes of the Golgi complex. These membrane components were considered to be readily distinguishable by their morphology and characteristic disposition in the cell; no connections between them were reported.

The electron microscope has helped to characterize the "microsomes" of Claude (18). As isolated from rat liver homogenates, the microsomal fraction appeared to contain a collection of particle-lined vesicles, occurring singly or in strings (79). It thus seemed likely that microsomes were largely the fragmented portions of the particle-lined membrane system, although considerable contamination from fragments of mitochondria and Golgi vesicles was also found (7). Similar conclusions have been reached by other investigators (53). The word "microsome," as now pre-empted by biochemists, is an entity created in the centrifuge and defined by its chemistry. In this sense it should obviously not be employed for structures in intact cells (7).

In spite of the complex morphology it has demonstrated, the electron microscope has so far added little to our concepts of the function of basophilic components. Postulated functions for the endoplasmic reticulum include: (1) providing a membrane surface for enzyme distribution; (2) providing compartments in the cytoplasm for segregation of certain metabolites; and (3) acting as an interconnected system for rapid diffusion (60). It has also been assigned a function in conduction of the excitatory impulse in muscle (59). Other suggestions have been somewhat more in line with the cytochemical evidence relating microsomes with protein synthesis. Sjöstrand and Hanzon (77) have assumed that the membranes and particles of the exocrine pancreas cells are important in enzyme synthesis, and that the Golgi apparatus, mitochondria, zymogen granules, and the cell membrane are primarily involved in the secretion process. In general, the vagueness of all such theories serves to emphasize the wide gap that still exists between our concepts of function at the biochemical level and our knowledge of cell morphology.

Results

Although the problem is discussed with growing frequency, we still are largely ignorant concerning the role played by the nucleus in the origin of cytoplasmic RNA. Some observations are reported here on two aspects of the problem: cytochemical studies have been made on the RNA of amphibian liver with microphotometry and radioautography; and the morphology of basophilic components of amphibian liver and pancreas cells has been investigated with the electron microscope.

1. Cytochemical Observations

RNA occurs inside the nucleus as a component of the nucleolus, but also in association with the chromosomal material. As mentioned by Dr. Gall, in the polytene chromosomes of *Drosophila* and *Chironomus* it forms in the expanded puffs (73, 82), and it occurs in the lateral loops of the lampbrush chromosomes of amphibian oocytes (76). In some cells RNA also occurs in the nuclear sap. The chromosomes in amphibian oocyte nuclei may be centrifuged to one side of the nucleus, so as to leave a diffuse material that stains faintly for RNA in the non-chromosomal portion. Many workers have suggested that RNA is first formed at these nuclear sites, and later extruded into the cytoplasm (33, 37, 42).

As shown by several investigators (39), when rats are starved or fed low protein diets, the RNA of the cytoplasm is depleted, and upon refeeding normal levels are restored. In an attempt to analyze the role of the nucleus in this restoration process, we have measured by microphotometry the amount of RNA in nuclear and cytoplasmic fractions of single liver cells. *Ambystoma tigrinum* larvae, which were used for these studies, were reared under constant conditions from a single batch of eggs. They were starved for 3 weeks prior to refeeding. RNA was estimated on tissue sections by azure B binding after the removal of DNA by deoxyribonuclease (Worthington, 0.02% in 0.003 *M* magnesium sulfate, *p*H 6.5, at 25°C for 1 hour). The cytoplasmic RNA was measured by the two-wavelength method to avoid error due to non-random dye distribution. Details of the methods and calculations used have been presented elsewhere (83, 84). A total of 6 larvae were studied.

After refeeding, the cells increased in size and total protein content, and the amounts of stainable RNA in nucleus and cytoplasm showed marked changes. Microphotometric determinations on three different liver cell components—nucleoli, nuclei (excluding nucleoli), and cytoplasm—are

graphed in Fig. 1. At maximum stimulation (36 hours) the relative amounts in nucleolus, nucleus, and cytoplasm were 1, 4.7, and 82 respectively. Thus both of the nuclear RNA fractions we have measured showed roughly parallel changes during the recovery process. We can also say that the nucleolus contributed only about one-fifth of the total stainable RNA of these nuclei.

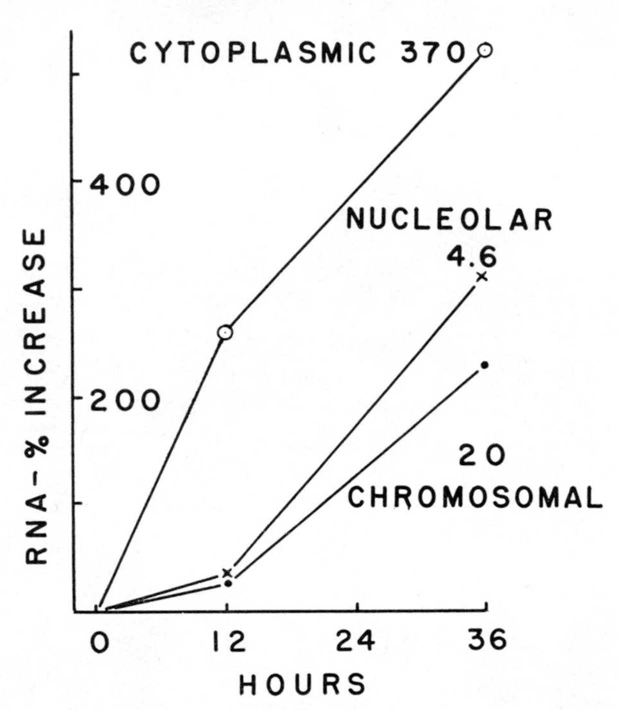

Fig. 1. RNA levels, plotted as percent increase over control values, of refed *Ambystoma tigrinum* larvae after starvation for 3 weeks. Larvae were all about 3 cm. in length. Each point represents the mean of from 10 to 20 measurements. RNA was determined by microphotometry of tissue sections stained with azure B (84). The total RNA, in relative photometric units, is also indicated for the 36-hour determinations.

To characterize the nuclear RNA fractions further, incorporation of adenine-C^{14} into the RNA of salamander tissues was studied by radioautography (Fig. 2). Two adult *Triturus viridescens dorsalis* were injected with 2.5 μc of adenine-8-C^{14} (1 mc/mM) in Holtfreter's solution, and were sacrificed 5 hours later. Tissues were fixed in acetic alcohol (1:3), and paraffin sections were cut at 4μ. Deparaffinized tissues were treated with 5% trichloroacetic acid at 3°C for 5 minutes, thoroughly washed and

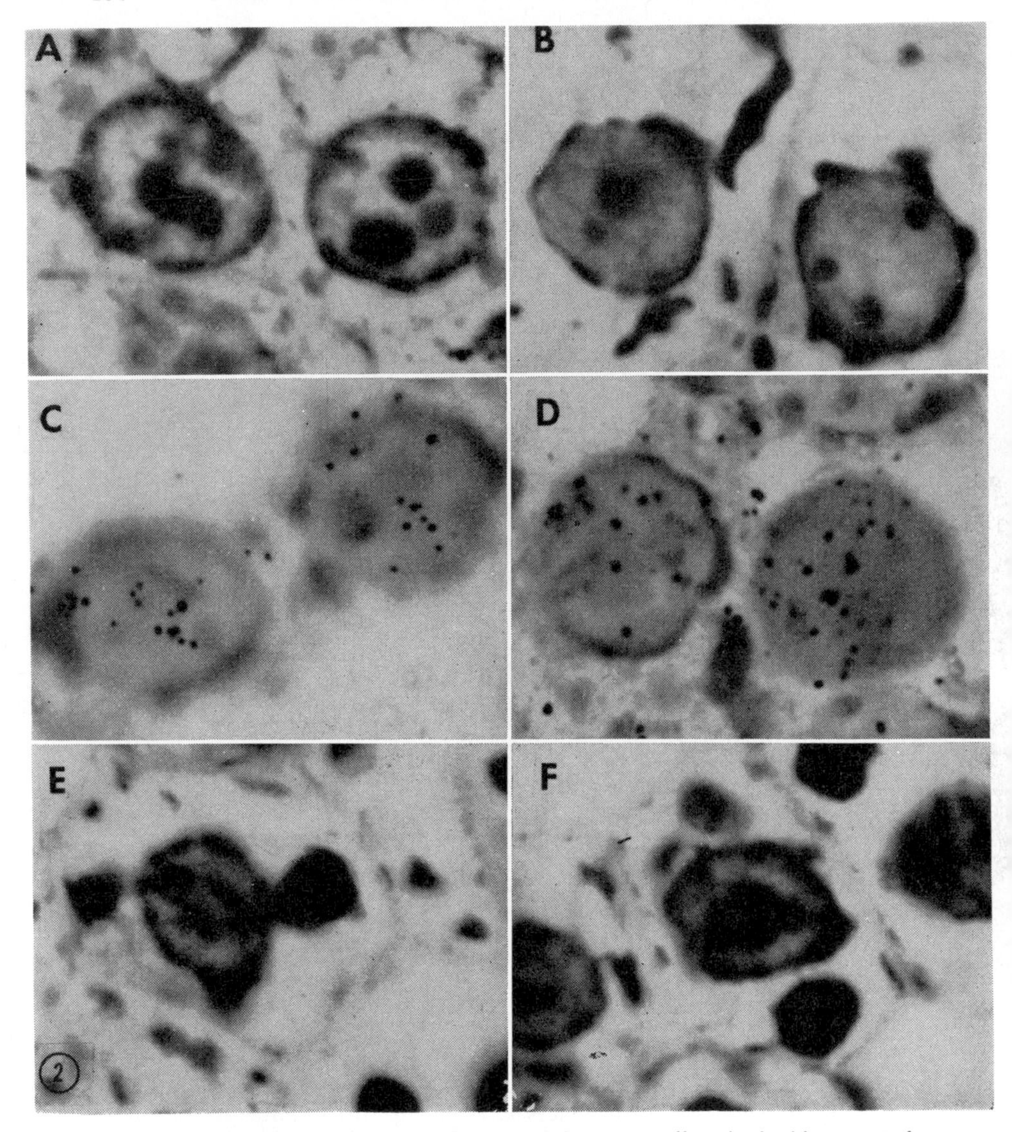

Fig. 2. Adult *Triturus* liver. Magnification 1,800 ×. A. Cells stained with azure B for RNA and DNA. B. Same, except the DNA has been removed with deoxyribonuclease before staining. Note diffuse RNA staining of nuclei. Central clumps of chromatin are practically unstained, but are faintly outlined by the RNA. C and D. Radioautographs showing incorporation of adenine-C^{14} into nuclear RNA. E and F. Sections of the same tissue shown in A, but after treatment with Holtfreter's solution for 3 hours. Nuclei are shrunken, and basophilic inclusions in the cytoplasm are enlarged.

air-dried before covering with Kodak, Ltd. stripping film. Control sections were also treated with ribonuclease (Armour, 0.1% at *p*H 6.5 for 1 hour at 25°C) before covering. Slides were stored for 6 weeks before development. RNA was estimated on adjacent sections by azure B binding as before; DNA was removed with deoxyribonuclease (Worthington, 0.02% at *p*H 6.5 for 90 minutes at 25°C) before staining. Results of these determinations are summarized in Table 1. Photographs of the stained cells are shown in Fig. 2.

TABLE 1

RNA Amounts and Relative Specific Activity in *Triturus* Liver and Pancreas Cells[1]

Tissue	RNA-azure B (photometric units)	Relative specific activity
Liver (animal #1)		
Nucleolus	2.0	0.81
Nucleus	10.0	4.0
Cytoplasm	124	0.21
Liver (animal #2)		
Nucleolus	1.8	1.1
Nucleus	13.5	2.7
Cytoplasm	90	<0.2
Pancreas (animal #2)		
Nucleolus	3.9	0.73
Nucleus	15.0	5.0
Cytoplasm	221	0.37

[1] Slides were measured at a wavelength of 550 mμ for nuclei and nucleoli; cytoplasm was measured with the two-wavelength method at 510 and 550 mμ. Photometric units equal extinction per micron section thickness multiplied by the volume in cubic microns (83). RNA values represent means of 15 measurements. Relative specific activities are given as grains per μ^2 per unit of RNA-azure B concentration, computed as extinction per micron section thickness, as determined on adjacent sections. Each value represents the mean of 30 to 40 counts on single nucleoli, nuclei, or on random areas 6.6 μ in diameter taken in the cytoplasm. These values assume stoichiometry of the RNA-dye complex.

In adult *Triturus* liver and pancreas, as in *Ambystoma* larval liver, nuclear RNA occurred outside of the nucleolus, associated with the chromosomes. The relative specific activity of this fraction, determined by relating absorption measurements on dye concentration to the number of autograph grains per μ^2, was also considerably higher than nucleolar RNA. These studies indicate that the fraction we have called "chromosomal RNA" comprises a large part of the RNA of the nucleus and shows a relatively high rate of incorporation. It should be emphasized, however, that the computations of relative specific activity assume stoichiometry of

dye-RNA binding. We feel that this is justified, since absorption curve analysis has shown Beer's law to hold for this method (24, 80).

Estimates of RNA and DNA per nucleus were also made using ultraviolet light at 260 mμ (Figure 3). Measurements were performed on untreated and deoxyribonuclease-treated slides to obtain DNA absorption by difference. Slides were further treated with 5% trichloroacetic acid at 90°C for 15 minutes to remove RNA, and the RNA was also computed by difference. These determinations indicated a DNA/RNA ratio of 1.5 for nuclei (excluding nucleoli). Comparative DNA-Feulgen measurements on diploid rat liver and *Triturus* liver nuclei showed that the *Triturus*

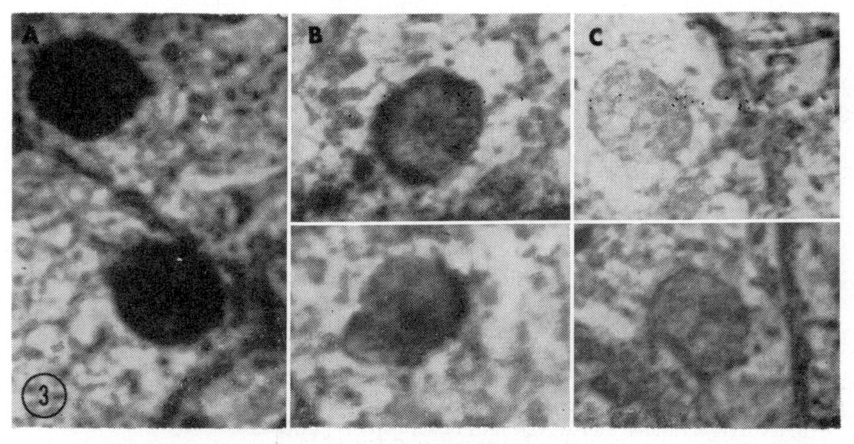

Fig. 3. Ultraviolet photographs of adult *Triturus* liver, taken at 260 mμ. A. Untreated tissues. B. An adjacent section after treatment with deoxyribonuclease. C. An adjacent section after treatment with trichloroacetic acid (5% at 90°C for 15 minutes) to remove both nucleic acids. The decrease in density between B and C represents absorption due to RNA.

diploid value was 16.4 times that of the rat. Assuming the rat contains 6×10^{-9} mg. DNA per diploid nucleus (86), then *Triturus* contains 9.8×10^{-8} mg. DNA per nucleus, and the RNA per nucleus of this animal (excluding the nucleolus) was 6.8×10^{-8} mg. Our DNA figure is slightly higher than that given by Gall (26), the difference being largely attributable to the different reference value used. Our values are also for a different subspecies of *Triturus viridescens.*

From visual observations on slides stained for either DNA or RNA, it was obvious that distributions were different within the nucleus. DNA was aggregated into several very dense clumps in the nucleus center, but also occurred diffusely around these clumps, and showed smaller concen-

trations near the nuclear membrane. RNA, in addition to the 1 to 4 nucleoli, was largely absent from the dense clumps, and was most evident in areas where the DNA concentration was low (Fig. 2, B). RNA occurred in the cytoplasm in a few dense lamellar or more rarely spherical bodies. These frequently occurred against the nuclear membrane and scattered through the cytoplasm, or less often along the cell membrane (Fig. 2,B).

In the process of studying incorporation into liver explants, it was apparent that in Holtfreter's solution these basophilic inclusions of the cytoplasm often increased in size (Fig. 2, D, E). This process was considered to be a condensation from the faint diffuse basophilia of the background cytoplasm, and apparently did not involve an increase in the total RNA of the cell. In hypotonic medium (0.3% Holtfreter's solution) the cells increased in volume with imbibition of water, and the inclusions became vacuolate and disperse, although the cell did not return completely to its original appearance. Somewhat similar aggregates have been described as forming around the nucleus of sea urchin eggs in hypertonic media (68a), and in guinea pig spermatocyte cytoplasm in Tyrode solution (36a).

2. Electron Microscopy

So far, the electron microscope has added little to our understanding of the mechanisms of nuclear control of cell processes. The detail presented in the nuclear membrane region is largely too complex and too poorly understood for functional interpretation. A few specific observations, however, have been considered of possible importance in nuclear-cytoplasmic interaction. Fine particles have been reported in the nucleolus (58), nuclear sap (27), and along the inner edge of the nuclear membrane (88), and bear at least a superficial resemblance to particles in the cytoplasm. The nuclear membrane, in a wide variety of tissues, has been shown to contain discontinuities, which some have interpreted as "pores" (88), although others have felt that the presence of actual holes in the nuclear membrane has not been convincingly demonstrated (76). Projections from the nuclear membrane have also been mentioned as possibly a sign of nuclear-cytoplasmic exchange (57). A morphological similarity between the nuclear membrane and the cisternae of the cytoplasm has been demonstrated. This has been interpreted as indicating either that the nuclear membrane is essentially cytoplasmic in origin, being merely another modification of the endoplasmic reticulum (50, 88), or that cisternae and cytoplasmic vesicles may originate from the nuclear membrane by a process of blebbing or delamination (5, 29).

Many of the observations reported here have been made on amphibian liver or acinar cells of the pancreas, although other material has been added for comparative purposes. In these cell types the nuclei were variable in appearance, probably influenced by the physiological state of the cell, but also by its fixation in osmic acid and other aspects of preparation. Nucleoli were usually the most dense intranuclear structures. In both tissues the nucleoli frequently contained peripheral areas having in the electron microscope a coarse thread-like appearance surrounding a more dense and roughly circular center. Adjacent sections stained for nucleic acids (Figs. 4-6) indicated that RNA occurred in both regions but was more concentrated in the thread-like areas. Vesicular regions of lower electron density occasionally occurred adjacent to the nucleoli. These contained only protein and no measurable nucleic acid. There was no evidence for nucleolus-associated chromatin, such as is present in many mammalian cells.

In many cells the nucleus contained chromatin areas, usually of uniform density, surrounded by less dense and less regular interchromatin regions. In addition, some nuclei showed very dense "heterochromatic" clumps around the nuclear membrane. These clumps closely resembled the thread-like nucleolar substance in fine structure, but when studied on adjacent stained sections showed the presence of DNA and no RNA. Nuclear sap areas contained thread-like extensions from the chromatin, and also irregular clusters of particles varying in diameter up to about 50 mμ (Figs. 6, 7, 14, 15). These particles were frequently distributed around clumps of chromatin, so as to resemble the distribution of "chromosomal RNA" stained for the light microscope. For this reason we have suggested that they might be the site of this RNA fraction (84). Further studies have shown that the largest of these particles are no longer apparent when thin sections are treated for 3 hours with 3% hydrogen peroxide, a treatment that removes certain lipid inclusions from osmium-fixed tissue, but little or no RNA. It thus seems likely that some of these particles contain an osmophilic component that is possibly lipid in nature (Figs. 10, 18).

The nuclear membrane appeared somewhat variable from cell to cell. In many cases it was clearly double with the inner and outer components separated by an area of low density. The inner membrane often appeared denser, probably because of chromatin fibrils that were packed against it. In some cells this gave a double appearance to the inner membrane (Fig. 8). In sections of sufficient thinness the nuclear membrane was visibly interrupted at certain places, where inner and outer membranes were joined (Figs. 7-9, 21, 22, 29).

In oblique cuts through the nuclear membrane the discontinuities were

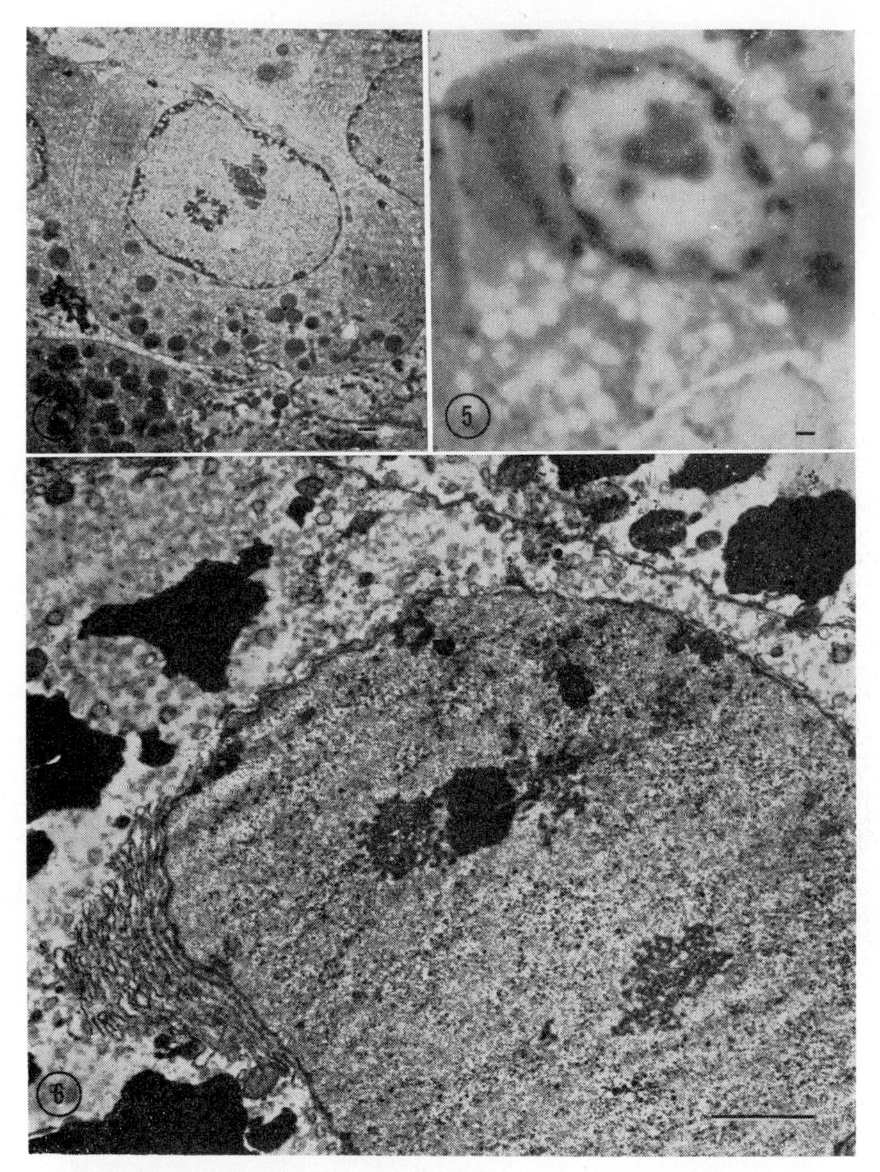

Figs. 4, 5. Larval *Ambystoma tigrinum* pancreas, showing the same cell in adjacent sections as seen with the electron microscope, and with the nucelic acids stained for the light microscope with azure B. Note that whorled structures at either end of the nucleus are basophilic, while the secretory granules do not stain. Fig. 6. Larval *Ambystoma* liver cell. Note the heterogeneous nucleolus, the interchromatin areas of the nucleus containing dense particles, and the lamellar basophilic body against the nuclear membrane. The irregular black areas in the cytoplasm are probably lipid inclusions.

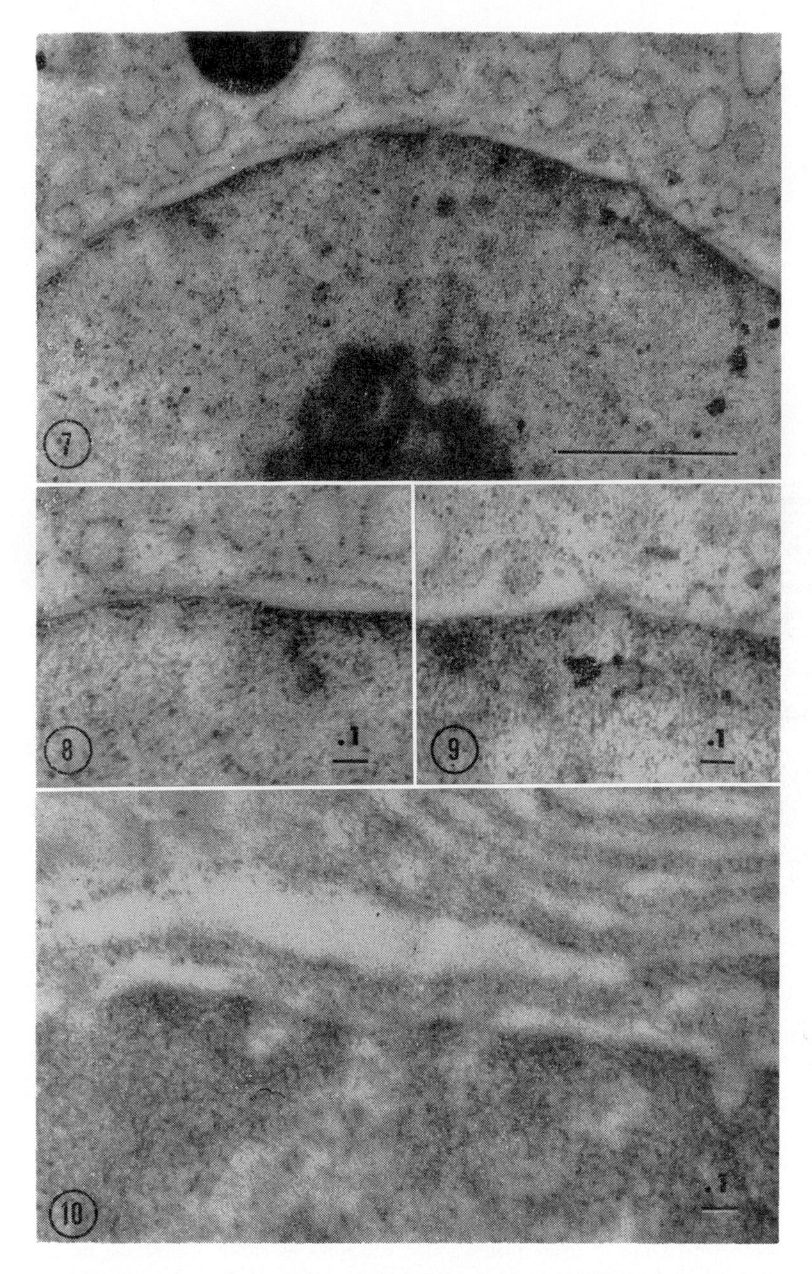

Figs. 7-9. Larval *Ambystoma* pancreas. The nuclear membrane contains a darkly outlined inner component, which appears double in Fig. 8, probably because of filamentous material lying in contact with it. Fig. 9 shows a section through an annulus. The inner and outer nuclear membranes appear to join, and there is a characteristic region of reduced density in the nucleus adjacent to the annulus. Fig. 10. The same tissue as in Figs. 7-9, except that the section has been treated for 3 hours with 3% hydrogen peroxide. Obvious particles in the interchromatin areas are absent. The section shows portions of five annuli. Note their association with less dense areas of the nucleus and their contact with cytoplasmic cisternae.

seen to be surrounded by dense rings of material, or "annuli," as reported by many authors for a wide variety of tissues (1, 13, 38). The structure of annuli in the nuclear membrane of several tissue types is shown in Figs. 22 to 33, A. Several points are of interest. Annuli were usually present where interchromatin areas were against the nuclear membrane, and much less often when the membrane was in contact with clumps of chromatin, a relation also pointed out by Porter (60). When annuli occurred amid chromatin material, small areas of lower density were almost always present in the adjacent chromatin (Figs. 9, 10). The annulus center frequently contained a small dense central body, as described by Afzelius (1) (Fig. 33). The annulus wall in oblique section presented a variable morphology. In some cases it apparently contained small rings or "subannuli" about 20 mμ across. These might be interpreted as cross sections through small filaments possessing relatively electron-light centers (Figs. 23; 33,A).

From comparisons with other cell types, additional characteristics of annuli were evident. The annulus in some tissues extended as a tube or rod a considerable way down inside the nucleus, and out into the cytoplasm (1, 81). In some cases, as in the snail and spider oocytes shown in Figs. 22, 23, 25-28, the "annular tubule" apparently widened out in the cytoplasm. When the nuclear membrane was cut obliquely, annular tubules were transected at different levels, and thus their organization above and below the nuclear membrane was evident. Annuli thus cut at different levels possessed different morphologies. This was particularly evident in the onion telophase nucleus section shown in Fig. 30. Here the annuli were most evident at the level of the nuclear membrane, as opaque circular structures, usually with a dense center. The annular tubule apparently extended down into the nucleus, between chromatin areas where it usually became smaller in cross-section and less distinct in organization. In the cytoplasm it became paler and more expanded, and again less distinct. In the spider oocyte the extensions sometimes appeared as an amorphous cloud of material, as described by André and Rouiller (2).

In some tissues, namely, the *Triturus* pancreas and spider oocyte, the annular tubule had a wall that closely resembled in structure certain small vesicles or tubules occurring in the cytoplasm (Figs. 11, 25, 26).

Annuli in some cases were associated with fine particles (27, 88), although the relation between such particles and the annular tubule was often difficult to interpret. In the pancreas section shown in Fig. 11, the projections, that were probably annular tubules, clearly contained particles on the outer surface. In some cases there was a suggestion of a spiral row of particles around the projection. In rat liver and onion root oblique cuts

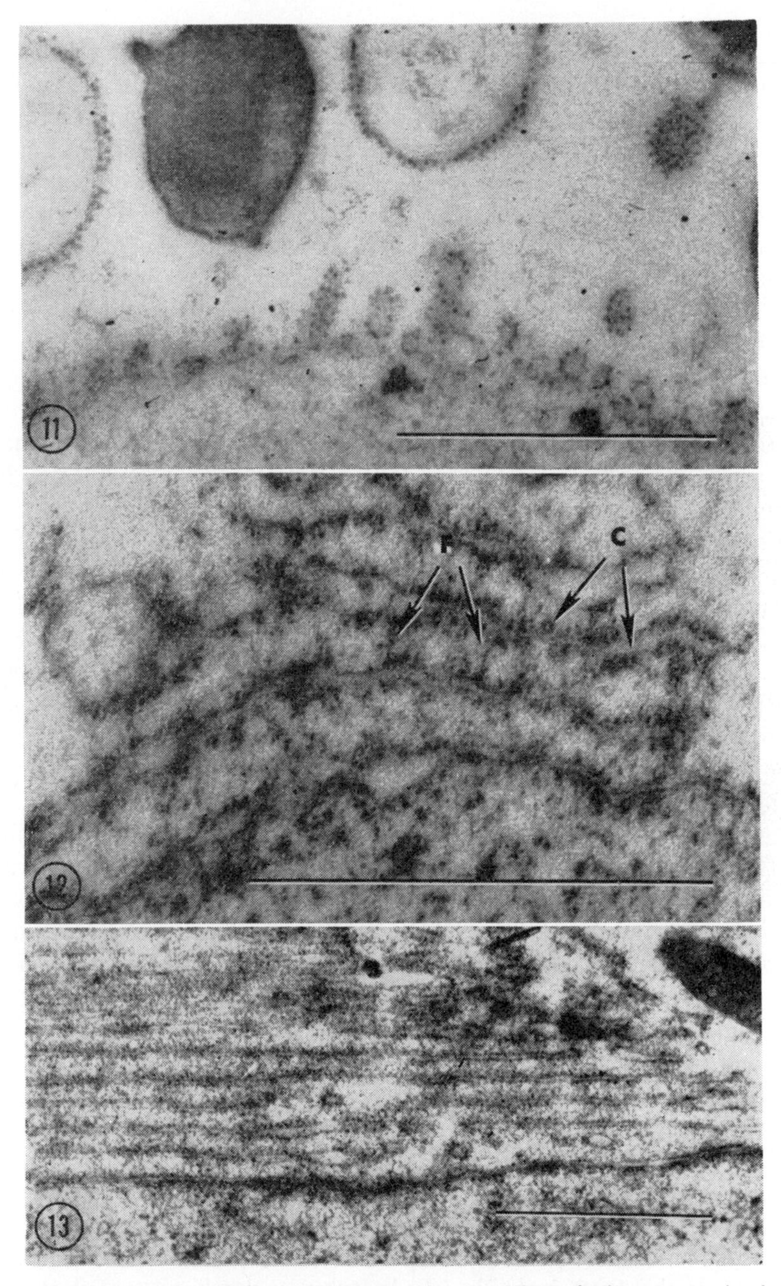

Fig. 11. Nuclear margin of larval *Ambystoma* pancreas. The projections are associated with small particles. Note the cytoplasmic vesicles also with particle-lined membranes. The dark body is a secretory granule with a characteristic smooth limiting membrane. Fig. 12. A small lamellar aggregate on the margin of a larval *Ambystoma* liver nucleus. Note the rather poorly defined filamentous component F, connecting the membranes perpendicular to them. Arrows at C indicate small circles, possibly filaments in cross section. Fig. 13. A similar lamellar body from the pancreas of the same animal, seen at lower magnification.

through nuclei frequently demonstrated rings of particles of a similar diameter to the annulus, as pointed out by Watson (88) (Figs. 30, 33). Particles were also arranged in semicircles or spirals. These arrangements, in both rat liver and onion root, appeared more commonly near the nucleus, and rarely further out in the cytoplasm, where particles usually showed less regular groupings. Although in some cases these rings, semicircles, or spirals were in contact with cisternal membranes, in other cases no such attachment was apparent, and they rather appeared to lie detached in the cytoplasm, possibly surrounding projecting annular tubules.

Annuli apparently form in telophase, as the nuclear membrane forms, as shown in both onion root and embryo chick somites (Figs. 29, 30). Short annular tubules are evident in the chick annuli shown in Fig. 29. The chick nuclear membrane arises apparently by the coalescence of a series of cytoplasmic vesicles. Telophase nuclei were, as might be expected, more compact than interphase nuclei, and the interchromosomal areas were practically absent. Where annuli occurred, however, interchromosomal areas were often evident.

The relation between the nuclear membrane region and adjoining areas of cytoplasmic basophilia was complex, variable, and difficult to analyze. In amphibian liver most nuclei contained orderly nuclear membranes, but in a number of cells this region was irregular and the nuclear membrane was interrupted for wide areas, particularly in relation to the interchromatin regions (Fig. 14). The cytoplasm surrounding the nuclei contained numerous small vesicles, in some cases grouped into somewhat irregular lamellar aggregates. Although the actual point of the nuclear margin was difficult to recognize, some vesicles apparently occurred inside the nucleus (Fig. 15). Since nuclei of this type were interspersed with cells where nuclear membranes were intact, it seems unlikely that disruption of the membrane can be attributable to poor fixation or other artifacts.

In other cells, stacks of cisternae frequently occurred against the nucleus. These regions were intensely basophilic when studied on adjacent sections, stained for the light microscope, and are homologous to the dense perinuclear bodies shown in Fig. 2. Similar aggregates also occurred against the cell membrane, but these were usually smaller and less frequent. In most instances the membranes were not obviously particle-lined, although at high magnification they may appear finely granular (Fig. 17). In many cases they occurred in relation with a more or less amorphous electron-dense material that occurred in the spaces between cisternae (Fig. 16). In other cases there was a suggestion that filaments, approximately 150 mμ in diameter, ran through the cisternal membranes at right angles to them

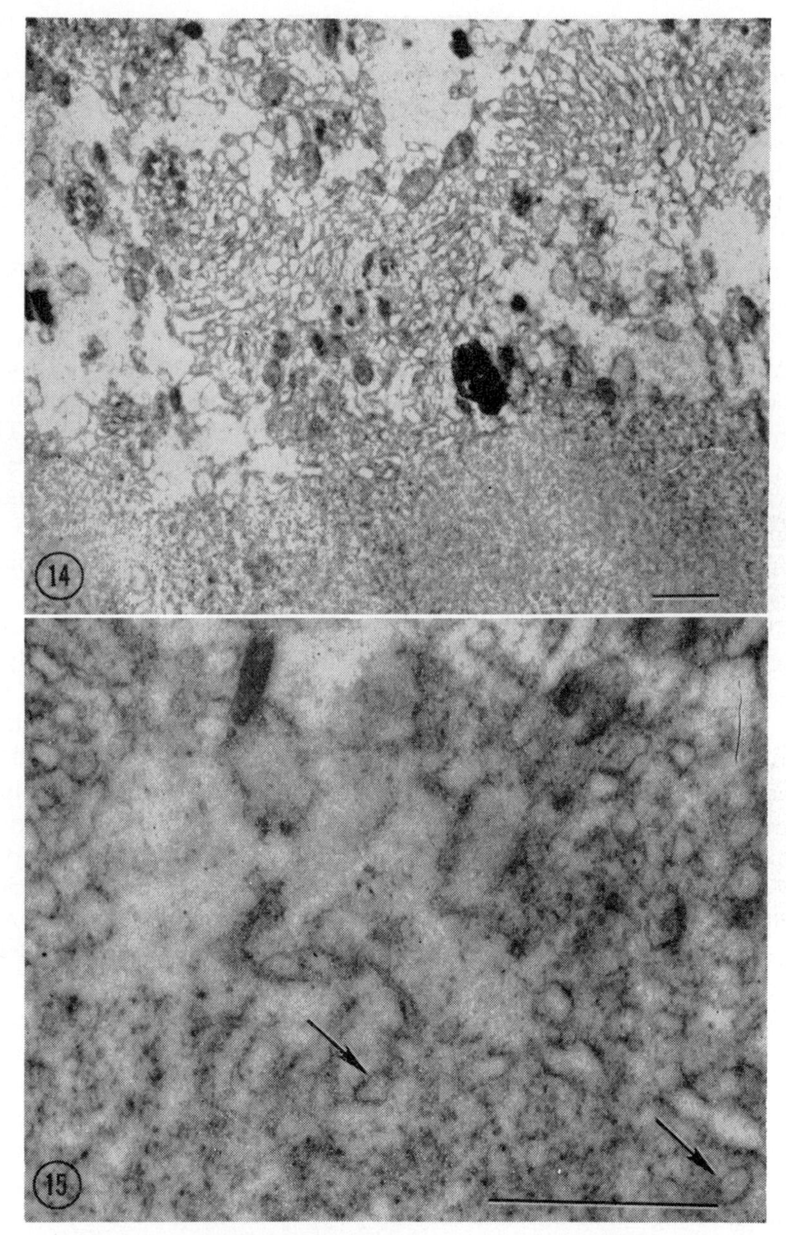

Figs. 14, 15. Nuclear margin from the liver of a starved *Ambystoma* larva 24 hours after refeeding. The nuclear membrane area is poorly defined. Small vesicles (Fig. 15, arrows) occur in association with the interchromatin areas, apparently lying slightly inside the nucleus.

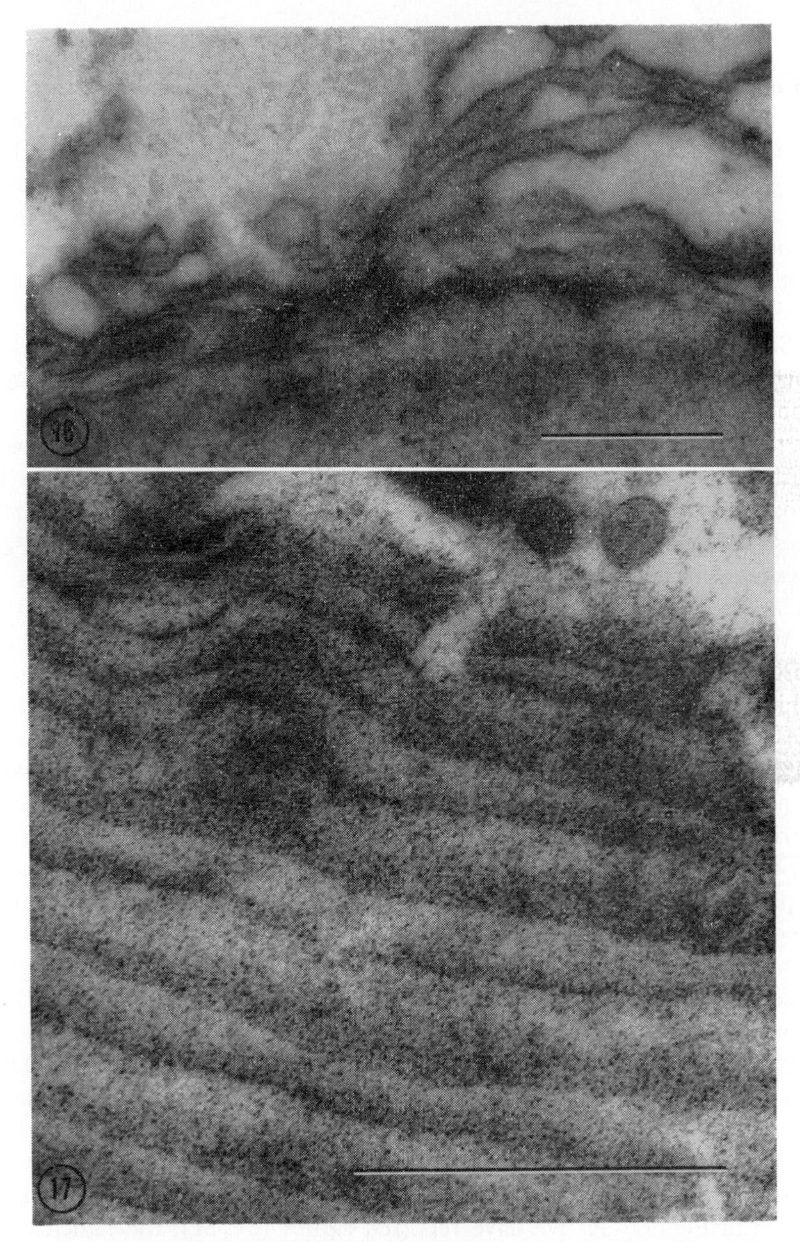

Figs. 16, 17. Lamellar aggregates from the liver of a starved *Ambystoma* larva, 24 hours after refeeding. Membranes are cut transversely in Fig. 16, and obliquely in Fig. 17. Lamellae are associated with a dense, faintly granular material, but contain no definite particles. These lamellae appear basophilic, as seen in adjacent sections.

(Figs. 12, 13). In a few favorable cases such fine filaments also appeared to penetrate the nuclear membrane and similar structures were also visible inside the nucleus. Where filaments were in contact with membranes, areas of greater electron density usually surrounded the filament. Where such an area was cut obliquely a ring or oval of dense material was evident in contact with the membrane. These could easily be interpreted as particles, but at least in some cases may be the filamentous component cut transversely (Fig. 12).

Somewhat similar stacks of cisternae were also seen against the nuclear membrane in *Triturus* pancreas (Fig. 18). Such lamellar arrays usually appeared to contain particles between adjacent cisternae. In the cytoplasm of the same cells whorls of membranes also occurred, lined with typical particles, about 15 mμ in diameter, as found in guinea pig pancreas by Sjöstrand and Hanzon (77) and many others. In a few regions, however, these "particles" also appeared to stretch in a linear fashion between adjacent membranes, so as to suggest the presence of short filaments rather than a regular series of particles (Fig. 20).

We were anxious to see the distribution of RNA in relation to these particles, and consequently a number of thin sections were prepared from which the osmium was removed by treatment with 3% hydrogen peroxide for 3 to 12 hours (Fig. 10), followed by "staining" for RNA with 10% ferric chloride in 0.1 *N* HCl. After treatment from 1 to 3 hours, sections were differentiated for 3 to 10 minutes in 0.1 *N* HCl to remove excess ferric chloride (83a). Results of this treatment are shown in Figs. 18, 19, 21, and 31. These micrographs must be interpreted with caution, since it is possible that the position of RNA may be altered during the staining process. In general, the stainable material was distributed as the particulate component, but appeared more finely dispersed in fine dots and lines between the cisternae. This work is still preliminary.

In other tissues, as in amphibian liver and pancreas, filamentous components were also observed in association with basophilic inclusions. This was particularly evident in lamellar bodies found in snail oocytes, where poorly defined filaments, about 15 mμ in diameter, were seen oriented at right angles to lamellae (Fig. 24). These filamentous components showed some resemblances to the projecting walls of the annuli of the same cell, as shown in Fig. 22. As we have reported earlier (64, 81), the lamellae in these cells also contain annuli. A quite different arrangement of filamentous material was seen in the lamellae of amphibian (*Ambystoma*) thyroid, where filaments about 20 mμ in diameter appeared in intimate association with basophilic lamellar structures, running along the membranes

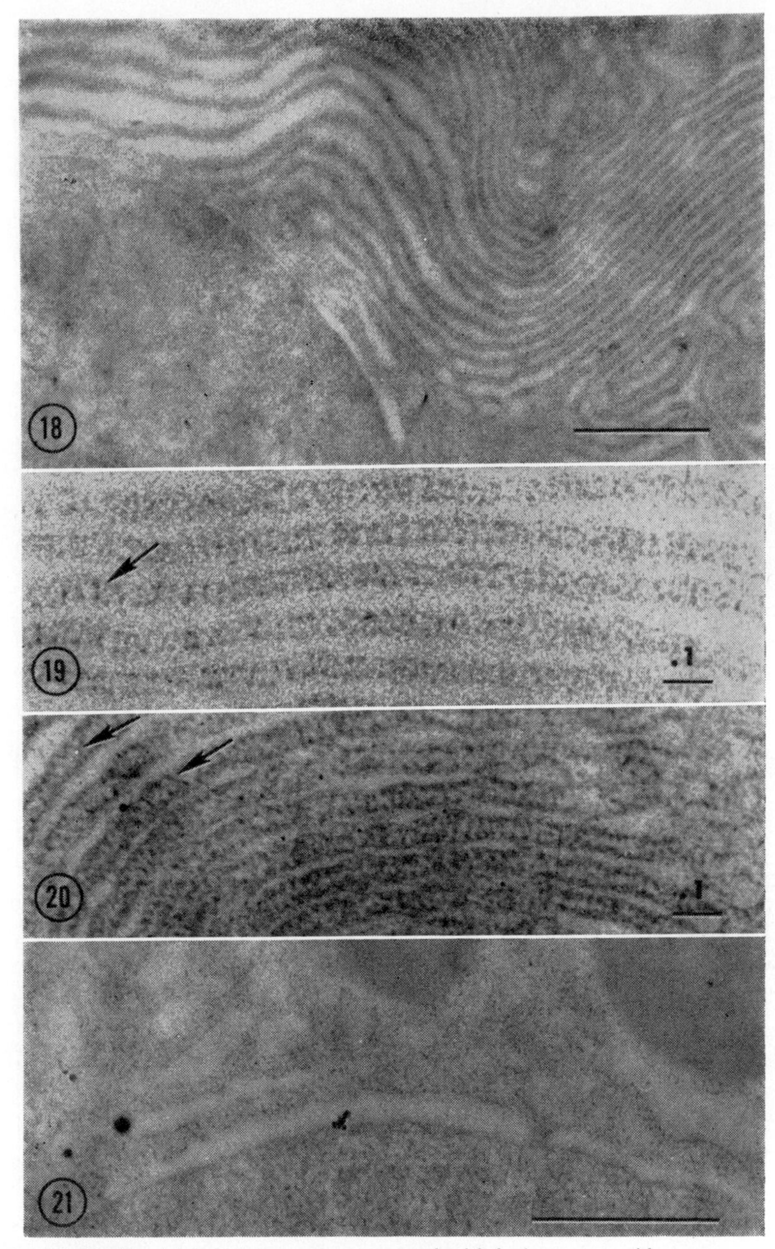

Figs. 18, 19, 21. Adult *Triturus* pancreas, treated with hydrogen peroxide to remove osmic acid, and then stained with 10% ferric chloride to visualize nucleic acids. Fig. 20. An untreated control section. As visible in Figs. 19 and 21, densities after staining are finely distributed as irregular lines and dots, following the distribution of the cisternae. In some places dense material appears as short filaments between cisternal membranes (arrows).

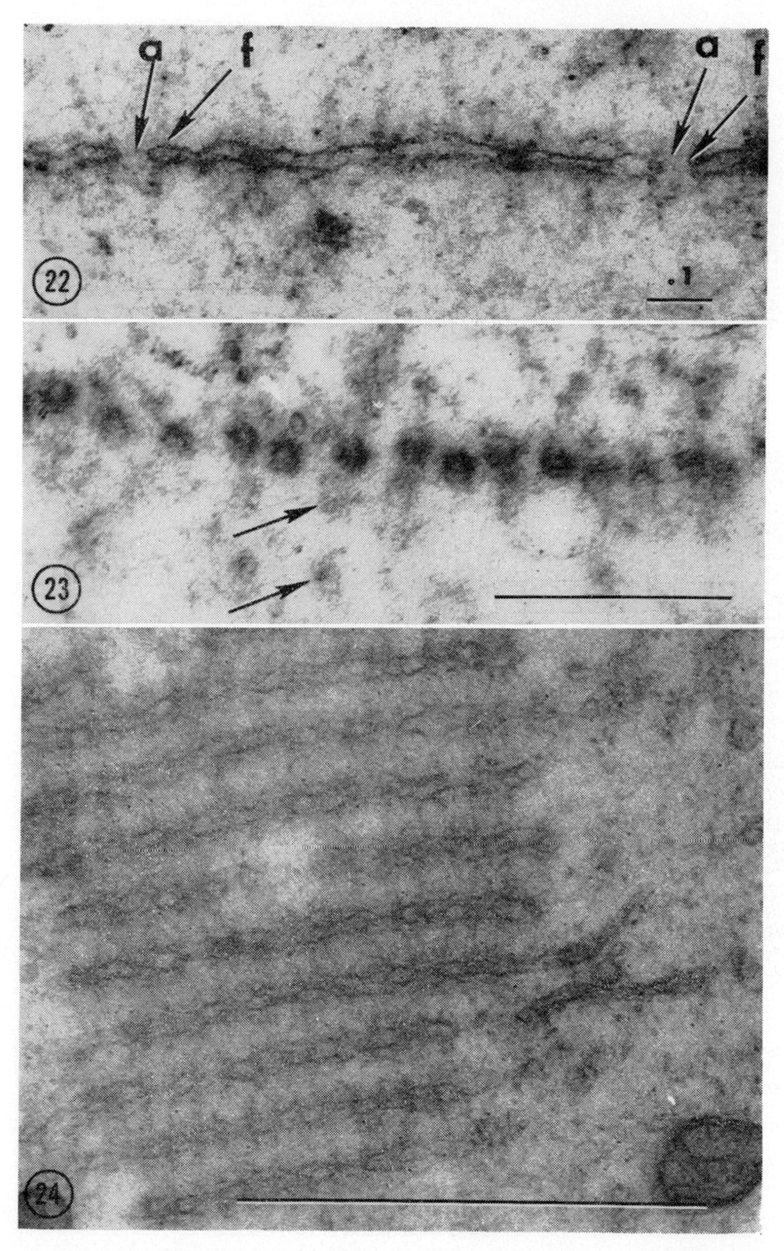

Figs. 22-24. Oocytes of the helicid snail *Otala lactea.*

Fig. 22. Cross section of the nuclear membrane showing a section through two annuli (a). Note the faint filamentous material (f) at either side of the annulus, and also at other places along the membrane. Cytoplasm above. Fig. 23. An oblique cut through the nuclear membrane, showing annuli. Annular tubules have been cut across as they project into the nucleus (arrows). Fig. 24. Lamellar inclusion in oocyte cytoplasm, showing interconnecting filamentous structures. (Micrograph by L. E. Roth).

and apparently forming a part of them (Fig. 35). These filaments appeared to be outlined by very fine dense particles arranged along the membrane, with a diameter that was variable from cell to cell, in Fig. 35 averaging roughly 5 mμ. Another interesting filament membrane relationship, also highly basophilic, has been found in crayfish (*Cambarus*) spermatocytes (69). Here the filaments occurred in a lattice-like array, traversed by lamellae at right angles to them. In some cases the lamellar and filamentous structures merged into one another, suggesting that they may be two different types of aggregation of the same components, or at least have certain constituents in common. The lamellar component was further associated with cytoplasmic vesicles of two types, either single-walled or doubled-walled. In double-walled vesicles the two membranes were separated by the width of one filament, and in fact when such membranes were cut across, rings and ovals of dense material in the membranes suggest that filament integrity is still maintained inside the membrane (Figs. 36, 37). No particulate component was evident in these inclusions.

In tissues where fine particles are present they may occur both in association with membranes and away from them. In the case of regenerating muscle cisternae (Fig. 34), the particles were arranged along poorly defined filaments that project at right angles to the membrane. The arrangement of particles in linear clusters, also suggestive of some filamentous orientation, occurred in a wide variety of tissues, such as onion root cells, although in this tissue membranous components were not apparent in the cytoplasm (Fig. 30). In rat liver, when cisternal membranes were cut in tangential section, rows of fine particles were often evident (Fig. 32), somewhat similar to those seen in the amphibian thyroid. This orientation suggests that the particles may be outlining a convoluted filamentous component lying in the membrane. In addition, small rings of particles were frequent between and on the lamellae, as a characteristic of this tissue. It is at present extremely difficult to reconstruct a three-dimensional conception of particle arrangements from thin sections through this complex structure. It seems possible, however, that these small rings of particles could represent sections through convoluted filaments lying between cisternal membranes (Fig. 32). In sections stained for RNA with ferric chloride the distribution of stain was similar to the distribution of fine particles, except that convoluted lines of dense material were present instead of rows of particles, and the cisternal membranes themselves seemed to bind the ferric ions. Mitochondria were completely unstained (Fig. 31). This distribution may be caused in part by changes in RNA distribution during staining. It suggests, however, that RNA may occur in areas where obvi-

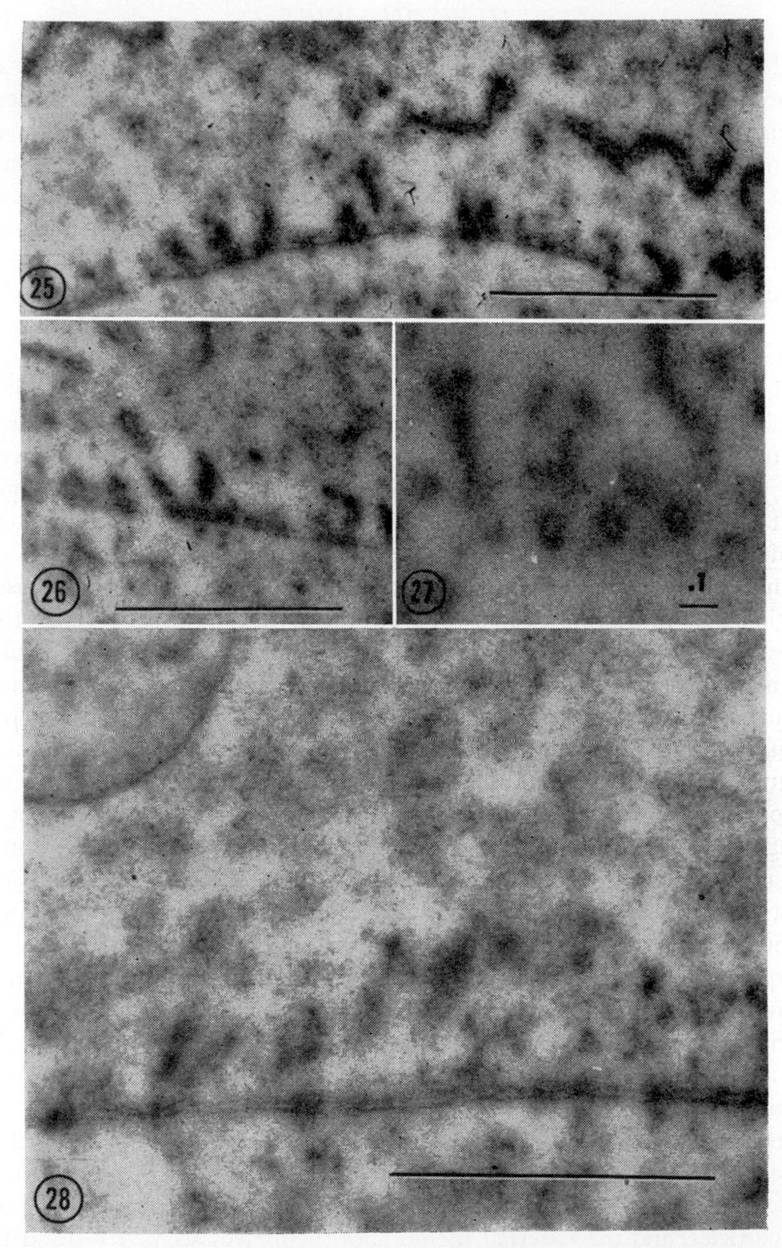

Figs. 25-28. Oocytes from the spider *Theridion tepidariorum*, showing projecting annular tubules. The nucleus is below and the cytoplasm above. In Figs. 25 and 26 note the similarity between some of the projections and vesicles in the cytoplasm.

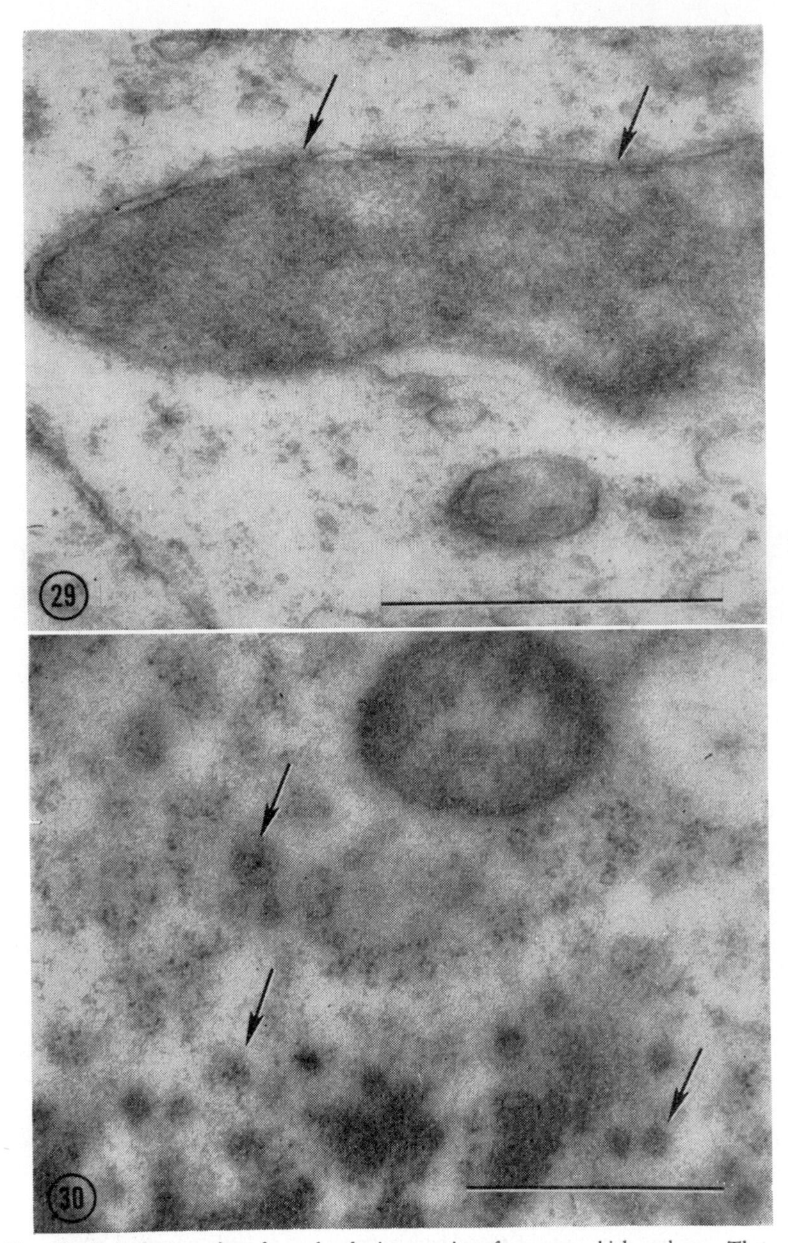

Fig. 29. Telophase nucleus from developing somite of a young chick embryo. The membrane has not completely formed below but annuli are apparent at upper surface (arrows). Notice the less dense nuclear areas in association with the annuli. (Micrograph by W. Ferris).

Fig. 30. Oblique section through a late telophase nucleus of an onion root. Annuli are most evident at the level of the nuclear membrane, but annulus-like structures occur in the nucleus (below) and in the cytoplasm a considerable distance from the nuclear margin (arrows).

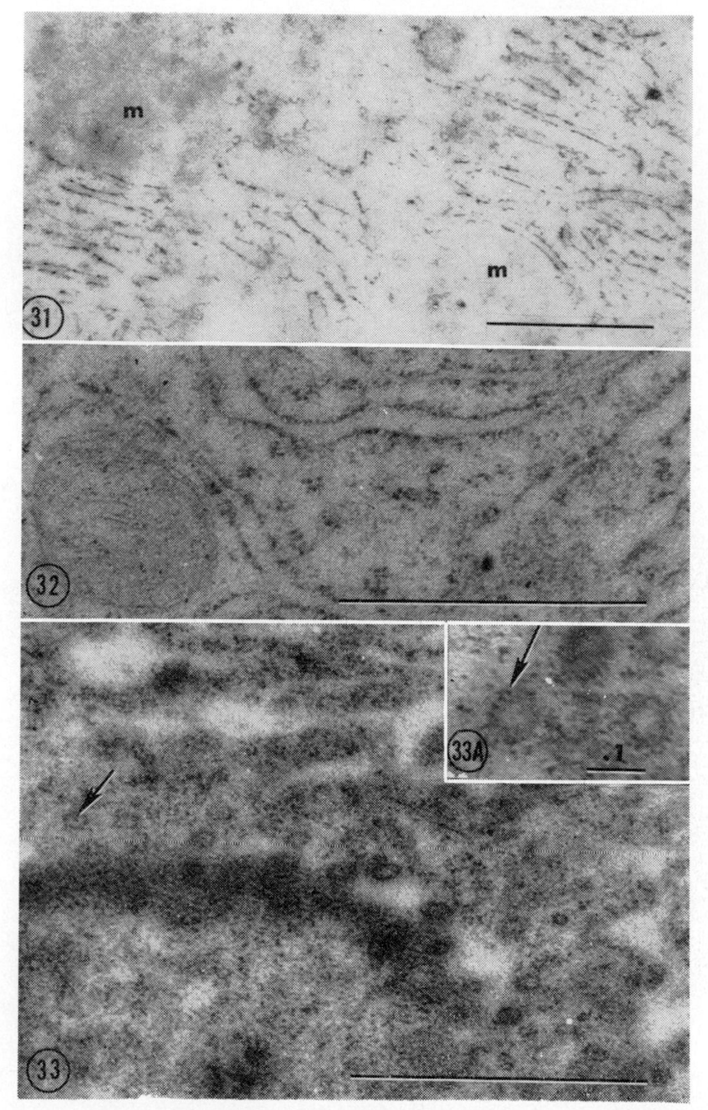

Figs. 31 to 33. Rat hepatic cells. Fig. 31. Section treated with hydrogen peroxide to remove osmic acid and then stained with ferric chloride to visualize nucleic acids. The distribution of stain is similar to the distribution of fine particles, except that convoluted lines of dense material are present instead of rows of particles, and cisternal membranes themselves seem to bind the ferric ion. Note that the mitochondria (m) are completely unstained.

Fig. 32. Note the small rings of particles which could represent sections through convoluted filaments lying between cisternal membranes, and rows of particles at lower right.

Fig. 33. Oblique section through nuclear membrane, showing rings of particles of similar diameter to annuli. Note that the annular center contains a small dark central body (arrow).

Fig. 33A. Annuli in cross section showing subannuli (arrow).

ous particles are lacking. It is interesting to note that Chaveau, Moulé, and Rouiller described RNA as being present in the membranous component of rat liver homogenates (16).

Discussion

From the observations presented, several conclusions can be drawn. In *Triturus* liver and pancreas there is a large RNA fraction associated with the chromosomes. This component surrounds the clumped chromatin and fills the interchromatin regions. It also actively incorporates adenine-C^{14}. Where interchromatin regions lie in contact with the nuclear membrane, small dense rings or annuli are most evident.

Annuli, at least in some tissues, arise in telophase as the nuclear membrane forms, and persist as a characteristic component of the nuclear membrane throughout interphase. They are complex structures, frequently with visible extensions (annular tubules) projecting into the nucleus and out into the cytoplasm. Telophase nuclei may appear compact, with the interchromatin areas absent. As the nucleus grows in volume the interchromatin areas become apparent. This suggests that annuli, at least during the telophase through early interphase period, may be sites for the entrance of materials from the cytoplasm. In spite of this, annuli are not simple pores in the nuclear membrane. They often contain a small "central granule" visible in cross sections of the annular tubule, and in some tissues, such as onion root, have dense centers.

In some tissues (salamander pancreas, spider oocytes) there is a resemblance between the fine structure of vesicles or tubules in the cytoplasm and the projecting annular tubules of the nuclear membrane. It thus seems possible that some cytoplasmic components may originate from annular tubule material by a process of extension of these structures. Strings of cytoplasmic vesicles, as in the "endoplasmic reticulum" of whole cultured cells, could arise in this way. We have reported earlier (81) that annulate lamellae, in which structures resembling annular tubules are incorporated, apparently break down into cytoplasmic vesicles formed in part by the tubule wall.

The annular tubule occasionally appears made up of a circle of filaments, appearing in cross section as small rings (subannuli). Above and below the annulus these filaments become vague in outline and irregularly arranged. Filamentous structures also form a part of several types of cytoplasmic basophilic inclusions. In snail oocytes, and in lamellae lying against the nuclear membrane in salamander liver and pancreas, filaments

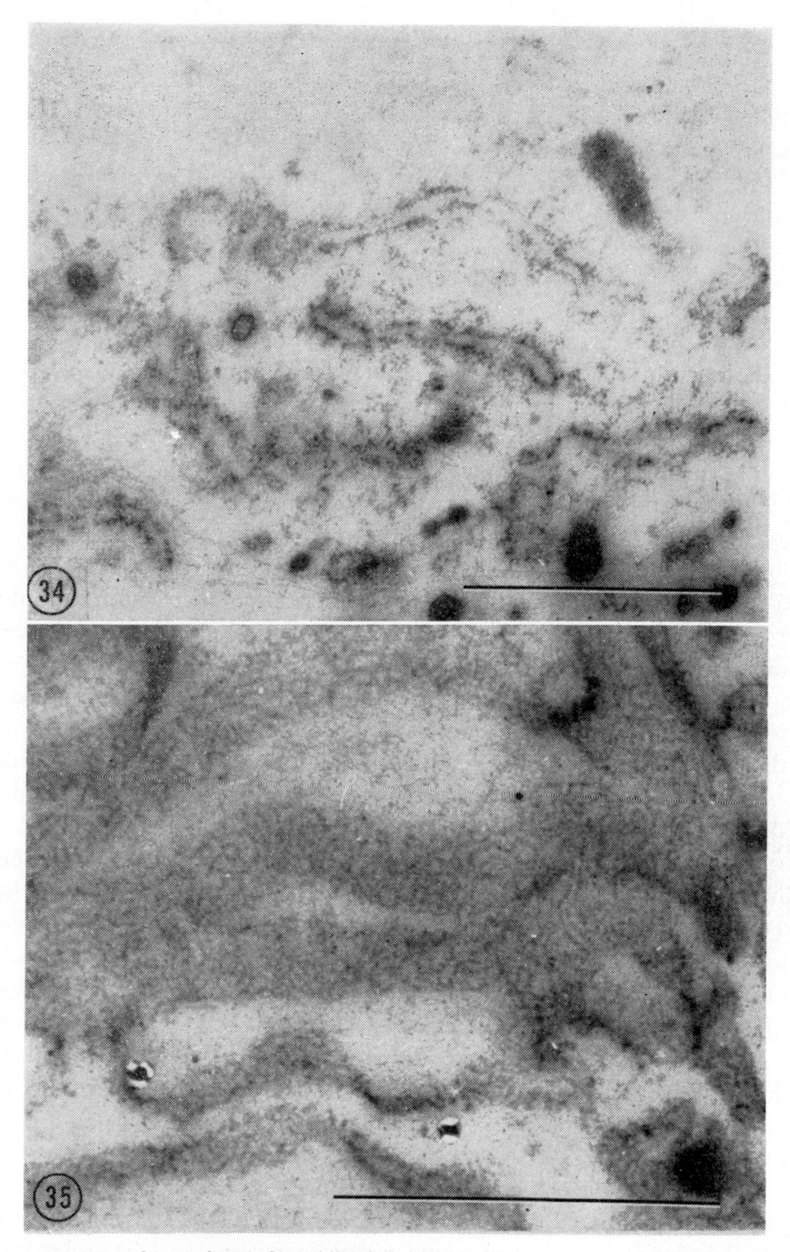

Fig. 34. Area of sarcoplasmic basophilia from regenerating mouse muscle. Cisternae show particles arranged along poorly defined filaments that project at right angles to the membranes.

Fig. 35. Filaments in association with basophilic lamellar structures of the cytoplasm in adult *Ambystoma tigrinum* thyroid treated with 0.1 mg. of thyroid-stimulating hormone for 10 days. Here the filaments appear outlined by fine dense particles arranged along the membranes. (Micrograph by L. Herman).

run perpendicular to the plane of the lamellae. They occasionally appear to penetrate lamellae, and to traverse the nuclear membrane. A similar basophilic structure occurs in crayfish spermatocytes, except that the filaments are regularly packed in a lattice-like arrangement, traversed by evenly spaced double membranes (69). In amphibian thyroid lamellae the filamentous structures, instead of running perpendicular to the lamellae, appear to lie within the lamellar membrane in a convoluted pattern. In some respects these lamellar membranes thus appear to be composed of fused filamentous components. In crayfish spermatocytes the continuity between filaments and lamellae lends support to this interpretation.

The relation between these filamentous structures and the fine particles often considered responsible for cell basophilia is not clear. In many cases the membranes of cytoplasmic vesicles are clearly particle-lined (as in Fig. 11). Where cisternae are closely opposed, however, and the membranes properly oriented with the section plane, the "particles" lining adjacent cisternae may appear to merge into short filaments. This linear orientation of short filaments perpendicular to the lamellae may merely be a secondary ordering, influenced by association with the membranes. On the other hand, since filaments are occasionally demonstrable in the perinuclear lamellae of the same tissue, it may indicate that the "particulate" material in the closely packed cisternal aggregates is also predominantly filamentous in nature. Sjöstrand and Hanzon (77), in a schematic diagram of the α-membranes, have shown the particles with an elongate shape. We feel that this configuration is equally well interpreted as an oblique section through a filament, oriented perpendicular to the membrane. Although a great deal more work is needed before the fine structure of these components, and their manner of change, becomes clear, we may conclude that in certain tissue types the "rough profiles" of "particle-lined" membranes are possibly equally well considered to be membrane-filament complexes.

In many basophilic cell types, areas of diffuse basophilia appear to be associated with more or less disordered areas of dense material. These show a variety of forms, from the largely amorphous clouds seen in spider oocytes, to the particles in onion root. This dense material in the cytoplasm never appears completely random in distribution. Particles are frequently aggregated into small strings or clusters. In a few cases, e.g. in liver (Fig. 32) or muscle (Fig. 34), particles appear in rings or short rows, as if outlining a filamentous component of lower electron density.

It is easy to conclude from these few examples that the concept that cytoplasmic RNA occurs only as regular particles is inadequate. In the

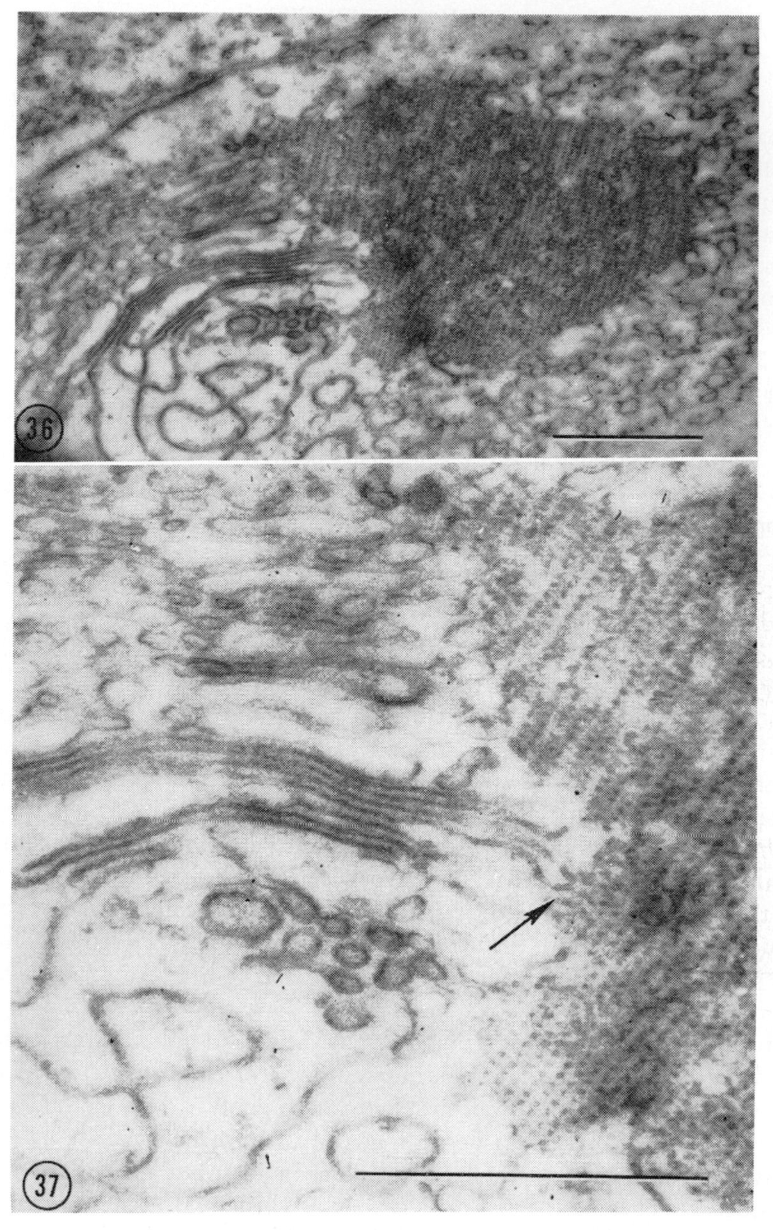

Fig. 36. Basophilic body in cytoplasm of crayfish (*Cambarus virilis*) spermatocyte. Note the lattice-like arrangement of filamentous units in cross section.

Fig. 37. Same, but at higher magnification. Note also the transition of lamellae and filamentous components (arrow). (Micrographs by A. Ruthmann).

various basophilic components described briefly above, some contain no resolvable particles at all, and in others the particles are extremely small, or absent from some basophilic regions of one cell and present in others. Particle size may be in part a matter of fixation, but this possibility can probably be ruled out when variations occur consistently within single cells. One probably should further differentiate between large particles (14 to 20 mμ in diameter), which we have suggested may represent filaments in section, and smaller particles (usually below 10 mμ in diameter), which apparently lie along the filaments, as for example in amphibian thyroid.

In studies of rat liver during refeeding after starvation, Fawcett (23) described the formation of membranous components that at first lacked the associated fine particles. For this reason he has suggested that the "membranous framework" of the basophilic inclusion may arise before they acquire RNA. Somewhat similar observations have been made by Rouiller and Bernhard (68). In the light of our findings that the lamellae of amphibian liver are in some cases smooth-contoured but nevertheless basophilic, it seems possible that rather than a change from nonbasophilic to basophilic with accumulation of particles, the change may somehow be associated with the function of these components in protein synthesis. In the whorled structures found in neurone cytoplasm by Palay and Palade (54), particles were present in some areas and absent in others. This is possibly another instance of the change from nonparticulate to particulate membranes. Such structures could be the basis for considering the "rough profiles" and Golgi membranes to be part of one interconnecting system, the endoplasmic reticulum (50). In our material the Golgi membranes were almost invariably distinguishable from the membranes associated with basophilic inclusions, whether or not they contain obvious particles.

We had hoped that the RNA staining for electron microscopy might indicate that filamentous RNA material might be associated with filament centers, as suggested for chromosomal structures by Ris (66). The stained sections are difficult to interpret, but in rat liver and amphibian pancreas no evidence was found for this hypothesis.

Whether or not the RNA-filament association emphasized here is important in nuclear-cytoplasmic exchange is unclear. Certain processes of the cell involve the active extension of filamentous structures, for example, the formation of chromosomal fibers between centrosome and centromere, or the fibrillar systems of ciliate protozoa (67). It is possible that similar extensions of filaments from nucleus to cytoplasm could act in the transfer

of information. In this connection the filamentous material apparently radiating from nucleoli may be of interest (82).

Summary

Studies on RNA of amphibian liver and pancreas, with microphotometry and radioautography, have indicated a significant and active nuclear RNA fraction outside of the nucleoli, in association with the chromosomes. Electron microscope studies on these and other tissues have indicated that RNA occurs in association with filamentous and lamellar structures which may or may not contain fine particles. It is suggested that extensions from the nuclear membrane (annular tubules), and filamentous structures, may function in nuclear-cytoplasmic exchange.

REFERENCES

1. Afzelius, B. A., *Exptl. Cell Research,* **8,** 147 (1955).
2. André, J., and Rouiller, C., in *Electron Microscopy, Proceedings of the Stockholm Conference, September 1956* (Sjöstrand, F. S. and J. Rhodin, eds.), p. 162, Academic Press, New York (1957).
3. Baker, J. R., *Quart. J. Micros. Sci.,* **90,** 293 (1949).
4. Barnum, C. P., and Huseby, R. A., *Arch. Biochem. and Biophys.,* **19,** 17 (1948).
5. Bennett, H. S., *J. Biophys. Biochem. Cytol.,* **2** (Suppl.), 99 (1956).
6. Bensley, R. R., and Hoerr, N. L., *Anat. Rec.,* **60,** 449 (1934).
7. Bernhard, W., Gautier, A., and Rouiller, C., *Arch. anat. microscop. morphol. exptl.,* **43,** 236 (1954).
8. ———, Haguenau, F., Gautier, A., and Oberling, C., *Z. Zellforsch. u. mikroskop. Anat.,* **37,** 281 (1952).
9. Borsook, H., Deasy, C. L., Haagen-Smit, A. J., Keighley, G., and Long, P. H., *J. Biol. Chem.,* **184,** 529 (1950).
10. Brachet, J., *Compt. rend. soc. biol.,* **133,** 88 (1940).
11. Bucher, N. L. R., and McGarrahan, K., *J. Biol. Chem.,* **222,** 1 (1956).
12. Burgos, M. H., and Fawcett, D. W., *J. Biophys. Biochem. Cytol.,* **1,** 287 (1955).
13. Callan, H. G., and Tomlin, S. G., *Proc. Roy. Soc.* (*London*), **B, 137,** 367 (1950).
14. Caspersson, T., and Schultz, J., *Proc. Natl. Acad. Sci. U. S.,* **26,** 507 (1940).
15. Chantrenne, H., *Biochim. et Biophys. Acta,* **1,** 437 (1947).
16. Chaveau, J., Moulé, Y., and Rouiller, C., *Exptl. Cell Research,* **13,** 398 (1957).
17. Claude, A., *Cold Spring Harbor Symposia Quant. Biol.,* **9,** 263 (1941).
18. ———, *Biol. Symposia,* **10,** 3 (1943).
19. Dalton, A. J., *Am. J. Anat.,* **89,** 109 (1951).
20. ———, and Felix, M., *Amer. J. Anat.,* **92,** 277 (1953).
21. ———, Kahler, H., Striebich, M. J., and Lloyd, B., *J. Natl. Cancer Inst.,* **11,** 439 (1950).
22. Deane, H. W., and Demsey, E. W., *Anat. Rec.,* **93,** 401 (1945).
23. Fawcett, D. W., *J. Natl. Cancer Inst.,* **15** (Suppl.), 1475 (1955).
24. Flax, M., and Himes, M., *Physiol. Zool.,* **25,** 297 (1952).
25. Frédéric, J., and Chèvremont, M., *Arch. Biol.* (*Liége*), **63,** 109 (1953).
26. Gall, J., *Brookhaven Symposia,* **8,** 17 (1955).
27. ———, *J. Biophys. Biochem. Cytol.,* **2,** (Suppl.), 393 (1956).

28. Garnier, C., Medical Thesis, Nancy (1899).
29. Gay, H., *Proc. Natl. Acad. Sci. U. S.,* **41,** 370 (1955).
30. Gersh, I., *Arch. Pathol.,* **47,** 99 (1949).
31. Gey, G., *Harvey Lectures,* **50,** 154 (1956).
32. Goldschmidt, R., *Zool. Jahrb.,* **21,** 49 (1904).
33. Goldstein, L., and Plaut, W., *Proc. Natl. Acad. Sci. U. S.,* **41,** 874 (1955).
34. Hanstein, J., *Das Protoplasma,* Heidelberg (1880).
35. Harford, C. G., Hamlin, A., Parker, E., and van Ravenswaay, T., *J. Biophys. Biochem. Cytol.,* **2** (Suppl.), 347 (1956).
36. Hertwig, R., *Arch. Protistenk.,* **1,** 1 (1902).
36a. Ito, S., and Revel, J. P., *Anat. Rec.,* **130,** 319 (1958) (Abstr.).
37. Jeener, R., and Szafarz, D., *Arch. Biochem.,* **26,** 54 (1950).
38. Kautz, J., and deMarsh, Q. B., *Exptl. Cell Research,* **8,** 394 (1955).
39. Lagerstedt, S., *Acta Anat., Suppl.,* **9,** 1 (1949).
40. Lillie, R. R., *Wilhelm Roux' Arch. Entwicklungsmech. Organ.,* **14,** 477 (1906).
41. Littlefield, W., Keller, E. B., Gross, J., and Zamecnik, P. C., *J. Biol. Chem.,* **217,** 111 (1955).
42. Marshak, A., and Calvet, F., *J. Cell. Comp. Physiol.,* **34,** 451 (1949).
43. Matthews, A., *Amer. J. Physiol.,* **1,** 445 (1898).
44. Moore, C. L., Price, D., and Gallagher, T. F., *Amer. J. Anat.,* **45,** 71 (1930).
45. Novikoff, A. B., Beaufay, H., and deDuve, C., *J. Biophys. Biochem. Cytol.,* **2** (Suppl.), 179 (1956).
46. ———, Korson, L., and Spater, H. W., *Exptl. Cell Research,* **3,** 617 (1952).
47. ———, Podber, E., Ryan, J., and Noe, E., *J. Histochem. and Cytochem.,* **1,** 27 (1953).
48. Palade, G. E., *J. Histochem. and Cytochem.,* **1,** 188 (1953).
49. ———, *J. Biophys. Biochem. Cytol.,* **1,** 59 (1955).
50. ———, *J. Biophys. Biochem. Cytol.,* **2** (Suppl.), 85 (1956).
51. ———, and Claude, A., *J. Morphol.,* **85,** 35 (1949).
52. ———, and Porter, K. R., *J. Exptl. Med.,* **100,** 641 (1954).
53. ———, and Siekevitz, P., *J. Biophys. Biochem. Cytol.,* **2,** 171 (1956).
54. Palay, S., and Palade, G. E., *J. Biophys. Biochem. Cytol.,* **1,** 69 (1955).
55. Pease, D. C., *J. Biophys. Biochem. Cytol.,* **2** (Suppl.), 203 (1956).
56. Petermann, M. L., and Hamilton, M. G., *Cancer Research,* **12,** 373 (1952).
57. Pollister, A. W., Gettner, M., and Ward, R., *Science,* **120,** 789 (1954). (Abstr.).
58. Porter, K. R., *J. Histochem. and Cytochem.,* **2,** 346 (1954).
59. ———, *J. Biophys. Biochem. Cytol.,* **2** (Suppl.), 163 (1956).
60. ———, *Harvey Lectures,* **51,** 175 (1957).
61. ———, Claude, A., and Fullam, E. F., *J. Exptl. Med.,* **81,** 233 (1945).
62. ———, and Kallman, F. L., *Ann. N. Y. Acad. Sci.,* **54,** 882 (1952).
63. Prenant, A., Bouin, P., and Maillard, L., *Traité d'histologie,* vol. **5,** Masson & Co., Paris (1905).
64. Rebhun, L., *J. Biophys. Biochem. Cytol.,* **2,** 93 (1956).
65. Rhodin, J., Correlation of ultrastructural organization and function in normal and experimentally changed proximal convoluted tubule cells of the mouse kidney, Thesis, Karolinska Institutet, Stockholm (1954).
66. Ris, H., in *The Chemical Basis of Heredity* (McElroy, W. D. and B. Glass, eds.), p. 23, Johns Hopkins Press, Baltimore (1957).
67. Roth, L. E., Ph. D. Thesis, Univ. of Chicago (1957).
68. Rouiller, C., and Bernhard, W., *J. Biophys. Biochem. Cytol.,* **2** (Suppl.), 355 (1956).
68a. Runnström, J., *Exptl. Cell Research,* **8,** 49 (1955).
69. Ruthmann, A., *J. Biophys. Biochem. Cytol.,* **4,** 267 (1958).
70. Sager, R., and Palade, G. E., *J. Biophys. Biochem. Cytol.,* **3,** 463 (1957).
71. Schneider, W. C., *J. Histochem. and Cytochem.,* **1,** 212 (1953).

72. ———, and Kuff, E. L., *Anat. Rec.*, **92**, 209 (1954).
73. Schurin, M., Ph. D. Thesis, Univ. of Chicago (1957).
74. Sjöstrand, F. S., *Nature*, **171**, 30 (1953).
75. ———, *Nature*, **171**, 31 (1953).
76. ———, *Intern. Rev. Cytol.*, **5**, 455 (1956).
77. ———, and Hanzon, V., *Exptl. Cell Research*, **7**, 393 (1954).
78. ———, and Hanzon, V., *Exptl. Cell Research*, **7**, 415 (1954).
79. Slautterback, D. B., *Exptl. Cell Research*, **5**, 173 (1955).
80. Swift, H., in *The Nucleic Acids* (E. Chargaff and J. N. Davidson, eds.), Vol. 2, p. 51, Academic Press, New York (1955).
81. ———, *J. Biophys. Biochem. Cytol.*, **2** (Suppl.), 415 (1956).
82. ———, in *Current Activities in Molecular Biology* (R. E. Zirkle, ed.), Univ. Chicago Press, Chicago (in press).
83. ———, and Rasch, E., in *Physical Techniques in Biological Research* (Oster, G. and A. W. Pollister, eds.), **3**, 353, Academic Press, New York (1956).
83a. ———, and ———, *RCA Scient. Instr. News*, **3**, 1 (1958).
84. ———, Rebhun, L., Rasch, E., and Woodard, J., in *Cellular Mechanisms in Differentiation and Growth* (D. Rudnick, ed.), Princeton Univ. Press, Princeton (1956).
85. Tahmisian, T. N., Powers, E. L., and Devine, R. L., *J. Biophys. Biochem. Cytol.*, **2** (Suppl.), 325 (1956).
86. Thomson, R. Y., Heagy, F. C., Hutchinson, W. C., and Davidson, J. N., *Biochem. J. (London)*, **53**, 460 (1953).
87. Van Herwerden, M. A., *Arch. Zellforsch.*, **10**, 431 (1913).
88. Watson, M. L., *J. Biophys. Biochem. Cytol.*, **1**, 257 (1955).
89. Weiss, J. M., *J. Exptl. Med.*, **98**, 607 (1953).
90. Yamada, E., *J. Biophys. Biochem. Cytol.*, **1**, 445 (1955).
91. Zamecnik, P. C., and Keller, E. B., *J. Biol. Chem.*, **209**, 337 (1954).
92. Zetterqvist, H., *Ultrastructural Organization of the Columnar Absorbing Cells of the Mouse Jejunum*, Thesis, Karolinska Institutet, Stockholm (1956).

DISCUSSION

Dr. Brachet: I should like to thank Dr. Swift for his excellent presentation of such a stimulating paper, and for showing us these most excellent electron photomicrographs.

Dr. Lehmann: Bairati and I have shown for instance that in amoeba the fine structure of fibrillar and chromidia-like formations are very poorly preserved by buffered osmium tetroxide (Bairati and Lehmann, *Protoplasma, 45,* 525, 1956). The same is true for the plasmalemma. In *Tubifex* astral and spindle structures disappear practically after osmium fixation. On the contrary the lipid-containing mitochondria or the nuclear membrane in amoeba is very well preserved by buffered osmium tetroxide. Here again the problem of the association of unsaturated lipids with certain cell structures emerges. This leads to the question whether osmium tetroxide is only a good histochemical reagent to unsaturated lipids and whether other cell structures like spindles and asters require better adapted fixatives. Dr. Swift, are you aware of this problem?

Dr. Swift: I would like to talk with you about some of these things later. There are a couple of things, though, I might say now. Osmium, as you know,

in addition to lipid binding, is also bound by proteins. In fact, you can greatly enhance the electron density of proteins in sections by floating them on an osmic acid solution. Therefore I think we are showing more with osmic acid fixation than just the lipid, though unsaturated lipid inclusions stain very darkly of course. Concerning the electron density of basophilic components, the fine particles appear dark even after acetic-alcohol fixation, so some of this electron density is due to the components of the particle itself. The rest may well be due to osmic acid binding by protein. It is my opinion, and I am no authority on this, that once you isolate the fine particulate component from liver or pancreas microsomes, as Zamecnik and associates have done, that these contain relatively little lipid. Is that not right, Dr. Mirsky? I think several workers have found nearly equal amounts of RNA and protein and virtually no lipid in the fine particle component. Most people, I think, would tend to believe that the lipids were in the membranes with which the fine particles are often associated, and not in the particles themselves. We have no indication that these particles, or other components poor in lipids, are not adequately fixed by osmic acid.

Dr. Novikoff: It is unfortunate that time limitation kept you from discussing a topic of great interest to embryologists: the origin of mitochondria.

I would like to ask two specific questions: (1) Did the "microbodies" show areas of high electron density in sections not treated with ferric chloride? and, (2) did you mean to imply that mitochondria possess no RNA?

Dr. Swift: In the first place one has to interpret our nucleic acid staining for the electron microscope carefully. It is messy at this particular level, since the osmic acid fixative penetrates tissue blocks very poorly and very slowly, and you have a fixation gradient. This means that different regions of the same block stain differently. We take a normally fixed tissue block and section it for the electron microscope. These serial sections are then treated in various ways. A control section is untreated, another is floated on 3% hydrogen peroxide for 3 to 12 hours, which removes most or all of the osmic acid. After this treatment the density of rat liver microbodies is greatly reduced, but is increased again if sections are stained with ferric chloride. On the other hand, if sections are treated with perchloric acid before staining, to remove RNA, the microbodies don't stain. On the basis of this purely operational definition we tentatively suggest that microbodies contain RNA.

Dr. Novikoff: No, quite the contrary. We have put ourselves out on a thin limb, by suggesting that mitochondria of rat liver have little or no RNA. This was based on parallel decreases in RNA and esterase activity (used as a microsomal marker) when the isolated mitochondrial fraction was repeatedly washed. However, similarly indirect evidence has led investigators in at least three other laboratories to conclude that the low level of RNA in washed fractions was not due to microsomal contamination but was intrinsic to mitochondria.

Dr. Swift: Oh yes, I see what you mean. We have seen in our liver sections the very dark particulates you and deDuve have called dense bodies. In our

material these seem to be different from the microbodies, if one uses the term as applied by Rouiller and Bernhard. Microbodies usually do not contain the fine dense particles you have suggested might be ferritin.

On the other hand, typical liver mitochondria, in our sections, contain no stainable components in them at all, and this seems to indicate they have no RNA. But they are very intimately associated with RNA on the membranes which are often wrapped around them. Do you disagree with this?

DR. NOVIKOFF: Oh, I am very happy with this. We had been way out on a limb. As we purified our mitochondrial preparations the RNA content got to the point where I considered it to be insignificant. However, data from other laboratories indicated that this isn't so, so I am very pleased to hear your data.

DR. SWIFT: If you consider a microbody to be an incipient mitochondrion, then RNA may be associated with mitochondrial formation.

DR. MIRSKY: I want to say one thing about the nucleolus. In particular I would like to speak about the nucleolar organizer. You remember the beautiful work of Barbara McClintock showed that the material for the nucleolus probably came from all over the chromosomes to the nucleolus organizer site where it formed the definitive nucleolus.

DR. SWIFT: The matrix theory as presented by McClintock has been refuted rather adequately by several recent studies.

DR. MIRSKY: I have read the papers by the South American workers criticizing McClintock, but her figures show that nucleolar material probably comes from the chromosomes. When the nucleolar organizer is damaged, one can see material accumulated on the chromosomes.

DR. SWIFT: Dr. McClintock's is a very beautiful and important paper, but I would like to point out that there is now considerable evidence against her suggestion that the nucleolar locus "organizes" chromosomal matrix material to form the nucleolus. For example, lagging chromosomes in the monosomic wheat strains studied by Dr. Crosby-Longwell (*Amer. J. Bot.* 44:813, 1957) often produce small separate nuclei. In some cases such small nuclei form nucleoli of their own, but with nuclei formed from some chromosomes no nucleoli at all are formed. It thus seems likely that the matrix is not involved in nucleolus formation, but rather that nucleoli are the synthetic products of particular chromosome loci. The fact that multiple nucleoli arise in cells containing a damaged "organizer" locus, seems better interpreted as the result of competition between potential nucleolus-forming sites. The fact that potential loci compete in nucleolus formation has been shown by McClintock and several others. That is, the same chromosome may normally form a large nucleolus, but when it is combined with chromosomes containing a "stronger" locus, for example through hybridization, it may form only a small nucleolus or none at all.

DR. ALLEN: I have one very short comment on the lamellar bodies that you showed in oocytes. The egg of *Spisula* has a very high viscosity as measured by

the centrifuge method. If you centrifuge one of these eggs at about 200,000 times g for 5 minutes, with some difficulty you can stratify the cytoplasmic components. If you now look at one of these oocytes with the polarizing microscope, you see that there is a very intensely birefringent ring around the nucleus. When I saw this some years ago, I attributed it to strain birefringence on the advice of Dr. Inoue. From some recent electron micrographs by one of your former students, Dr. L. Rebhun, it has become apparent that these are the lamellar bodies that have been aligned due to centrifugal force, probably due to collisions with various cytoplasmic components among which these structures are lying. It struck me that this might be an interesting way to test for the presence of these lamellar bodies in living cells without having to go to the bother of electron microscopy.

Dr. Swift: Yes, that is a very nice idea.

Dr. Brachet: Well, I think that this session has been a very successful one and that certainly developmental cytology has been making a lot of progress and is going to make much more. And we all have been working very well and very hard, especially the speakers, and I wish to thank them and all those who took part in the discussion.

Part II

CELLULAR AND TISSUE INTERACTIONS IN DEVELOPMENT

EMBRYONIC INDUCTION [1]

TUNEO YAMADA
Biological Institute, Faculty of Science
Nagoya University,
Nagoya, Japan

INTRODUCTION

At the present time a vivid revival of interest in the mechanism of embryonic induction may be witnessed. New approaches are being made from different angles. According to the method adopted, the following groups of investigations may be distinguished in this field: (a) study of exchange of substances between the inducing and reacting systems by isotope technique; (b) elucidation of the physical nature of the agent mediating induction by the use of a filter with known porosity; (c) demonstration of the diffusible agent of the organizer by culture in vitro of the embryonic cells; (d) morphological study of the cells in inductive interaction by electron microscopy; and (e) isolation and characterization of the substances responsible for regional induction by adult tissues. In the present paper some of the recent progress made in the last-mentioned group of experiments will be reviewed and discussed together with some of the data obtained in other groups of experiments.

Holtfreter (13) was first to show that some differentiated tissues of various animals give strong inductive effects which are either neural or mesodermal, when implanted in the *Triturus* gastrula. Experiments subsequently performed along this line by Chuang, Toivonen, and their followers have revealed that the inductive effects of many of these tissues are regionally specific. However, no general relationship was found to exist between the regional effect of an organ and its embryological derivation. The first attempt at chemical characterization of the factor responsible for regional effects was made by Toivonen, who chose the liver and kidney tissue of the guinea pig as source materials. It had been shown by

[1] The research reported in this paper was supported by a science research fund of the Education Ministry and by a grant from the Rockefeller Foundation.

The writer wishes to express his thanks to Dr. E. Babbott for her kind help in preparing the manuscript.

TABLE 1

REGIONAL INDUCTIVE EFFECTS

	Regionality (Lehmann)	Regionality (Dalcq)	Structures
A	Archencephalic	Acrogenetic	Forebrain, eye, nose
D	Deuterencephalic	Deutogenetic	Midbrain, hindbrain, ear vesicle
SC	Spino-Caudal	Tritogenetic	Spinal cord, tail-notochord, tail-somites
TM	Trunk-Mesodermal[1]	———	Trunk-notochord, trunk-somites, pronephros, blood islands

[1] According to Yamada (40).

Toivonen (28) himself that the former tissue induces forebrain, eye, nose, and lens (archencephalic (19) or acrogenetic (4) structures), while the latter tissue induces spinal cord, tail-notochord, and tail-somites (spino-caudal (19) or tritogenetic (4) structures), or midbrain, hindbrain, and ear vesicle (deuterencephalic (19) or deutogenetic (4) structures). According to Toivonen's earlier papers (29), the factor responsible for archencephalic induction is relatively thermostable, soluble in petroleum ether, accompanies the nucleoproteins in fractionation, endures protracted ethanol treatment and is readily dialysable, while the factor responsible for spino-caudal induction is thermolabile, not extractable with petroleum ether, non-dialysable, and is inactivated by formalin and proteolytic enzymes. The work was continued by Kuusi (16, 17, cf. 1) in a series of extensive experiments. She tested inductive effects of cell components separated by differential centrifugation, nucleohistone samples, saline extracts, tissues treated with formalin, and homogenates treated with ribonuclease by implanting the samples into the blastocoel of the early amphibian gastrula. After formalin treatment both tissues lost their spino-caudal and deuterencephalic effects and showed a low frequency of archencephalic effects. On the other hand, ribonuclease failed to produce clear suppression of any type of induction. Kuusi observed a large difference between the effects of the kidney tissues and those of the various fractions extracted from the latter. The tissue or the residue of centrifugation was very often characterized by the spino-caudal and deuterencephalic effects, while the fractions separated from the kidney tissue indicated mostly archencephalic and deuterencephalic tendencies. This led her to conclude that centrifugal separation of the spino-caudal factor from the tissue is more difficult than that of the archencephalic factor. Yet she succeeded in obtaining from the supernatant fraction of the kidney spino-caudal effects as well as archencephalic and deuterencephalic ones. Considering various data, she maintained that archencephalic and spino-caudal factors are chemically distinct, and that

the former is represented by granules containing pentose nucleic acid (PNA) and the latter by a protein. In a later paper she tested the inductive effects of the homogenates of the kidney, which were tested with some reagents for suppressing certain active groups of protein contained therein (17). In recent papers Kuusi (18) has reported her efforts toward getting into solution the factors responsible for the mesoderm-inducing effects of guinea pig bone marrow. We shall discuss these results later.

Using the extract of the chick embryo as source material, Tiedemann and Tiedemann (26) succeeded in isolating various protein fractions with either archencephalic or spino-caudal and deuterencephalic effects. Extraction with phenol, pyridine, and ethanol, precipitation with trichloroacetic acid and ammonium sulfate and high speed centrifugation were the chief techniques adopted by these German workers for isolation of the fractions.

In our own laboratory, research is being carried out to separate and characterize the factors responsible for regional induction by liver, kidney, and bone marrow of the guinea pig. The results to be presented here in some detail have been obtained with the collaboration of Dr. Y. Hayashi, Mr. K. Takata and Miss C. Takata.

The Testing of Inductive Effects

In contrast to the experiments mentioned above, in which the sample was introduced into the blastocoel of a whole gastrula, in the present study the sample was tested on the isolated ectoderm of the early gastrula cultured in vitro. This procedure excluded possible interference with the regional effect by the host, which has been demonstrated to occur upon implantation of an inducer in the whole embryo by Chuang (2, 3) and Vahs (34). Other complications which might be caused by the presence of endoderm, mesoderm, and blastocoel fluid in the direct vicinity of the sample, and the difficulty of controlling the direct contact of the ectoderm with the sample were also avoided in our experiments. The samples were always tested in solid form. The solutions were precipitated with ethanol and the precipitate was collected, washed in Holtfreter's solution, and tested. A piece of the sample measuring about 0.4 mm. in diameter was enclosed between two pieces of the isolated ectoderm each measuring about 1 mm. in diameter. The ectoderm pieces fused to give rise to a vesicle. The explants were cultured in Holtfreter's solution adjusted to *p*H 7.3 for 10 to 14 days at 15°C. All explants were fixed and studied in sections. The technique allows a reliable morphological evaluation of the inductive effects. Its drawback consists in the quantitative assay, although the total frequency

of induction gives in most cases a measure for the inductive ability of the sample. A technique for quantitative assay is now being worked out. As the donor of the ectoderm, early gastrulae of *Triturus pyrrhogaster* were used exclusively. In Holtfreter's solution the ectoderm of the species differentiated only epidermal cells clustered irregularly (38, 10).

Morphogenetic Effects of Kidney Pentose Nucleoprotein

Preliminary experiments (41) indicated that a piece of ethanol-treated guinea pig kidney evoked spino-caudal and deuterencephalic structures in the isolated ectoderm, as it had in the insertion experiments of Toivonen (28). The same regional effects were obtained by an ethanol precipitate of the 0.14 *M* NaCl extract. Moreover, an acid-precipitable fraction of the extract containing the bulk of the pentose nucleic acid (PNA) present in the extract revealed the same effect. Comparing the inducing ability of the cytoplasmic fractions of the tissue prepared by differential centrifugation, the "small microsome" fraction containing the highest amount of PNA was found most effective in inducing spino-caudal structures (39). These results were taken to suggest that the pentose nucleoprotein (PNP) of the original extract might be responsible for the induction. This led us to prepare from the saline extract a sample of PNP by precipitating with streptomycin sulfate and subsequent washing and dialysis. The ethanol precipitate of this sample induced spino-caudal and deuterencephalic structures in the isolated ectoderm at a high frequency (43). The sample, which indicated a typical nucleoprotein absorption curve, was found to contain a considerable amount of PNA (245 PNA-P μg. per mg. protein-N) and to be free of DNA (cf. also 25). In electrophoresis, the sample indicated a single boundary whose mobilities were calculated by K. Takata to be $-6.1 \sim -6.3$ for the ascending limb and $-5.3 \sim -5.4$ for the descending limb (in cm^2/sec./volt $\times 10^{-5}$, *p*H 7.5, borate or phosphate buffer, $\mu = 0.2$, 4°C).

The sample was further purified by centrifuging at 100,000 g for 1 hr., and the supernatant containing a higher amount of PNA was precipitated with ethanol and tested (Table 2). An intensive inducing effect was registered, in which the deuterencephalic tendency was dominating. A moderate tendency of the spino-caudal type and a weak tendency of the archencephalic type were also noted (see p. 232).

In an earlier paper, Hayashi reported that a ribonuclease treatment of a phosphate extract of the kidney removed a large part of the PNA present in the extract, but did not appreciably reduce the spino-caudal and deuterencephalic effects of the extract (10). This was in accordance with the

TABLE 2

MORPHOGENETIC EFFECTS OF SUBFRACTIONS OF PENTOSE NUCLEOPROTEIN PREPARED BY ULTRACENTRIFUGATION FROM THE KIDNEY
(Yamada, Hayashi, and Takata)
100,000 × g, 1 hr.

	Supernatant	Sediment
PNA content (PNA-P μg./mg. protein-N)	358.7	124.6
No. of available explants	85	87
Total induction	84 (99%)	86 (99%)
Spino-caudal induction	25 (29%)	16 (18%)
Deuterencephalic induction	56 (66%)	72 (83%)
Archencephalic induction	9 (11%)	24 (28%)
Non-regional induction	6 (7%)	1 (1%)

results that Kuusi (16) obtained after a ribonuclease treatment of the homogenate of the tissue. On the other hand, trypsin and chymotrypsin suppressed the inducing ability of the kidney tissue and its extracts (42). These experiments harmonize with each other in suggesting that the spino-caudal and deuterencephalic effects of the kidney extract are due not to its PNA but to its protein component. This conclusion was further supported by the experiments in which PNA isolated from the kidney of the guinea pig was found to possess only weak morphogenetic effects on the isolated ectoderm (44). In no case was a spino-caudal or deuterencephalic effect observed (cf. also 27).

MORPHOGENETIC EFFECTS OF LIVER PENTOSE NUCLEOPROTEIN

Hayashi (11) fractionated the 0.14 *M* NaCl extract of guinea pig liver, which showed considerable inductive effect of the archencephalic type alone, into two fractions by adding streptomycin sulfate. The pentose nucleoprotein fraction precipitable with streptomycin sulfate caused archencephalic structures at a higher frequency than the original extract, while the non-precipitable fraction induced these structures at a lower frequency. In a later series of experiments a liver PNP sample induced not only archencephalic but also deuterencephalic structures (cf. 30). In any case, we have here an interesting situation, that from the liver and kidney of the guinea pig with an identical technique PNP samples were isolated, which have distinctly different morphogenetic effects corresponding to the effects of the source materials. Also in the case of liver PNP, the electrophoretic pattern indicated a single boundary. The mobilities of the sample[2] as calculated by K. Takata did not significantly differ from the above reported

[2] —6.0 ~ —6.1 for the ascending limb, and —5.1 ~ —5.3 for the descending limb. For further data see p. 220.

values for kidney PNP. However, as in the sedimentation diagram some heterogeneity was observed, the sample was separated into the supernatant and sediment by ultracentrifugation. The supernatant, containing a large amount of PNA, showed deuterencephalic and archencephalic effects in a very high percentage of cases, while the sediment, containing a smaller amount of PNA, gave archencephalic and non-regional neural effects in a lower percentage of cases (Table 3). Probably the supernatant represents the bulk of PNP, and the sediment contains some protein contaminating the original sample of PNP.

TABLE 3

THE INDUCTIVE EFFECT OF SUBFRACTIONS OF A SAMPLE OF LIVER PENTOSE NUCLEOPROTEIN SEPARATED BY MEANS OF ULTRACENTRIFUGATION (HAYASHI AND TAKATA)

	100,000 × g precipitate	100,000 × g supernatant	173,490 × g precipitate	173,490 × g supernatant
PNA-P μg./mg. N	10.2	92.7	21	197.5
No. of available explants	53	59	31	37
Neural induction	38 (72%)	59 (100%)	21 (68%)	36 (96%)
Non-neural induction	12 (23%)	0	5 (16%)	1
Archencephalic	29 (55%)	20 (34%)	17 (55%)	9 (24%)
Deuterencephalic	5 (9%)	42 (71%)	9 (29%)	27 (73%)
Induction without regional character	20 (38%)	5 (8%)	5 (16%)	5 (14%)

The obvious question to be asked was whether the induction by the nucleoprotein sample is due to its nucleic acid or its protein component. In order to answer the question, effects of proteolytic enzymes and ribonuclease on the inductive ability of the sample were studied by Hayashi. He succeeded in removing the bulk of PNA present in the PNP sample with ribonuclease in the following two series of experiments. In the first series an ethanol-precipitated sample of liver PNP was used as the substrate (series A). As shown in Table 4, no significant difference was observed

TABLE 4

EFFECT OF RIBONUCLEASE ON THE INDUCTIVE ABILITY OF PENTOSE NUCLEOPROTEIN FROM THE LIVER (HAYASHI)

	Series A		Series B	
	Control	Treated	Control	Treated
PNA content (PNA-P μg./mg. protein N)	86.6	3.5	148.6	0.84
No. of available explants	25	33	49	52
Neural induction	25 (100%)	33 (100%)	49 (100%)	52 (100%)
Archencephalic induction	24 (96%)	27 (82%)	7 (14%)	8 (15%)
Deuterencephalic induction	1 (4%)	3 (9%)	40 (82%)	40 (77%)
Non-regional induction	1 (4%)	4 (12%)	8 (18%)	9 (17%)

in the inducing ability of the sample. A better removal of PNA was attained by treating a liver PNP sample purified by ultracentrifugation with ribonuclease without previous ethanol-precipitation (series B). Even in this sample practically free of PNA, no reduction of inducing ability was detected as compared with the control sample.

The results were in accord with Hayashi's earlier work, in which an extract of guinea pig liver showed, after incubation with ribonuclease and deoxyribonuclease, an inducing frequency comparable to that of the untreated sample (10). That the treatment with ribonuclease does not affect the inductive power of tissues and their homogenates has been repeatedly observed in experiments with whole embryos (16, 5, 35).

Thus no indication was obtained for an active participation of PNA in the induction by the liver. On the other hand, the importance of protein in induction was clearly evidenced in the experiments with pepsin and trypsin (12). Hayashi incubated a liver PNP sample with 0.1% pepsin at *p*H 4.0 and 28°C for 30, 60, and 120 minutes. After incubation, the *p*H was adjusted to 7.5 and ethanol was added to the mixture (Table 5). The

TABLE 5

EFFECTS OF PEPSIN ON THE INDUCTIVE ABILITY OF LIVER PENTOSE NUCLEOPROTEIN (HAYASHI)
Enzyme 0.1%, *p*H 4.0, 28°C.

	Control	Pepsin 30 min.	Pepsin 60 min.	Pepsin 120 min.
No. of available explants	70	51	31	47
Neural induction	66 (94%)	45 (88%)	17 (55%)	20 (43%)
Archencephalic induction	53 (76%)	25 (49%)	9 (29%)	6 (13%)
Deuterencephalic induction	9 (13%)	2 (4%)	0	0
Non-regional induction	13 (19%)	21 (41%)	19 (61%)	34 (72%)

precipitate was tested on the isolated ectoderm and the effects were compared with those of the control sample, to which enzyme in inactive condition was added after a sham incubation. The result indicated a progressive suppression of the regional inductive ability of the sample, although even after 120 minutes no complete suppression was achieved.

In the case of the trypsin series, incubation was done at *p*H 7.6 and 28°C for 30, 60, and 120 min. with 0.01% enzyme. After each incubation period, ethanol was added and the precipitate thus obtained was heated in 95% ethanol for 5 min. at 85°C, in order to effect inactivation of the enzyme. In the control series after incubation without the enzyme, trypsin was added and immediately followed by ethanol. The precipitate thus obtained was heated in ethanol as in the experimental series. As shown in

TABLE 6

Effects of Trypsin on the Inductive Ability of Pentose Nucleoprotein from the Liver (Hayashi)
Enzyme 0.01%, *p*H 7.6, 28°C.

	30 min.		60 min.		120 min.
	Control	Exper.	Control	Exper.	Exper.
No. of available explants	45	35	50	45	53
Neural induction	45 (100%)	16 (46%)	46 (92%)	5 (11%)	3 (6%)
Archencephalic induction	43 (96%)	12 (34%)	42 (84%)	3 (7%)	0
Deuterencephalic induction	2 (4%)	0	0	0	0
Non-regional induction	0	10 (29%)	8 (16%)	12 (27%)	11 (21%)

the table, a progressive inactivation of the inducing ability was clearly demonstrated. In this series, after 120 minutes of incubation, the regional effects of the sample had completely vanished.

The Substance Responsible for the Mesoderm-Induction by the Bone Marrow

As stated above, Toivonen (31) demonstrated that guinea pig bone marrow induces almost exclusively mesodermal structures from the presumptive ectoderm. Recently Kuusi (18) has published papers concerning the chemical nature of the bone marrow factor. In her attempt to get the factor in the extract, Kuusi obtained induction of mesodermal structures by a phosphate extract of the tissue. However, a saline extract of the tissue proved to be very weak in morphogenetic effects. Without knowing the work of Kuusi, we started in 1956 a series of experiments aiming at the isolation and characterization of the bone marrow factor. Before going further it may be convenient to point out that most of the mesodermal structures evoked by a freshly prepared sample of guinea pig bone marrow are those characteristic for the trunk-region, and are easily distinguished from the mesodermal structures induced, for instance, by guinea pig kidney, which are caudal in nature. Hence the present writer (40) proposed that the typical structures induced by the bone marrow be called the "trunk-mesodermal structures" and be distinguished from the caudal mesodermal structures which are included in the spino-caudal type (Table 1). Probably the trunk-mesodermal effects are further given by the bone marrow of the rat (24) and mouse (14, 15), and also by the skin of the adult frog (7, 8, 21).

Contrary to Kuusi's results (18), the 0.14 *M* NaCl extract of the bone marrow of the guinea pig gave in our case a high percentage of trunk-mesodermal induction in the isolated ectoderm after ethanol-precipitation (see Fig. 5). Two series of fractionations were done with the saline extract

as the starting sample. In the first series, streptomycin sulfate was added to the extract in order to precipitate PNP. After washing, dialysis, and ethanol-precipitation the PNP sample, containing a large quantity of PNA (399 μg. PNA-P/mg. protein-N), was tested on the isolated ectoderm. Contrary to our expectations, the sample proved to be a very weak inducer, giving rise only infrequently to small neural or mesodermal structures (Fig. 1). On the other hand, the fraction not precipitable with streptomy-

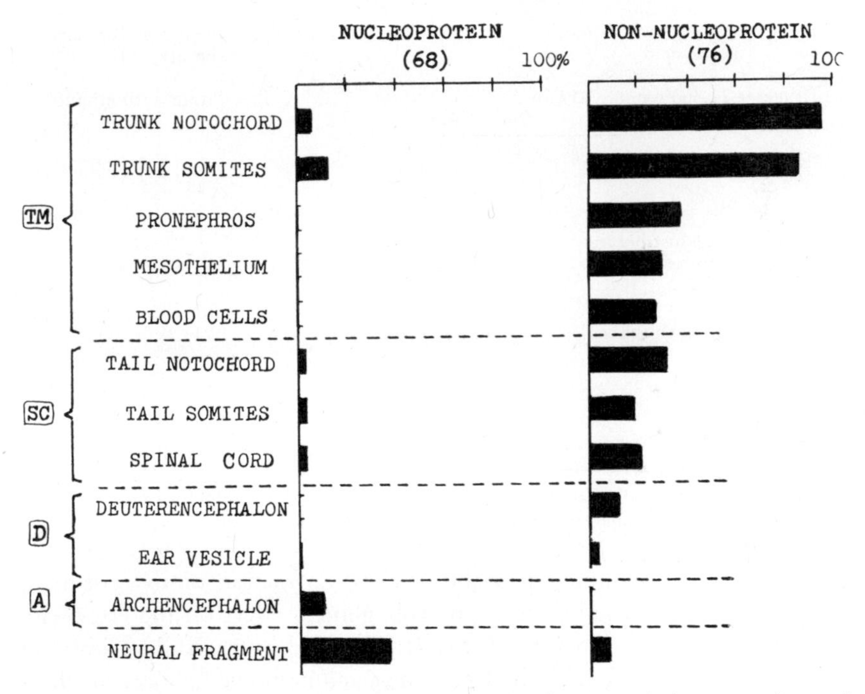

Fig. 1. Inductive effects of the pentose nucleoprotein fraction and the non-nucleoprotein fraction of the bone marrow extract. The frequency is expressed as the percentage of explants carrying a particular structure among the total number of explants of the respective series (in parentheses). This explanation applies also to Figs. 3, 5, and 7.

cin sulfate and possessing only a small quantity of PNA (12 μg. PNA-P/mg. protein-N) revealed an intensive activity of mesodermization on the isolated ectoderm. The results, repeatedly confirmed, imply that the bone marrow factor is not represented by the streptomycin-precipitable PNP fraction.

In the second series of fractionations, the sediment and supernatant were prepared from the saline extract according to the scheme of Fig. 2. The

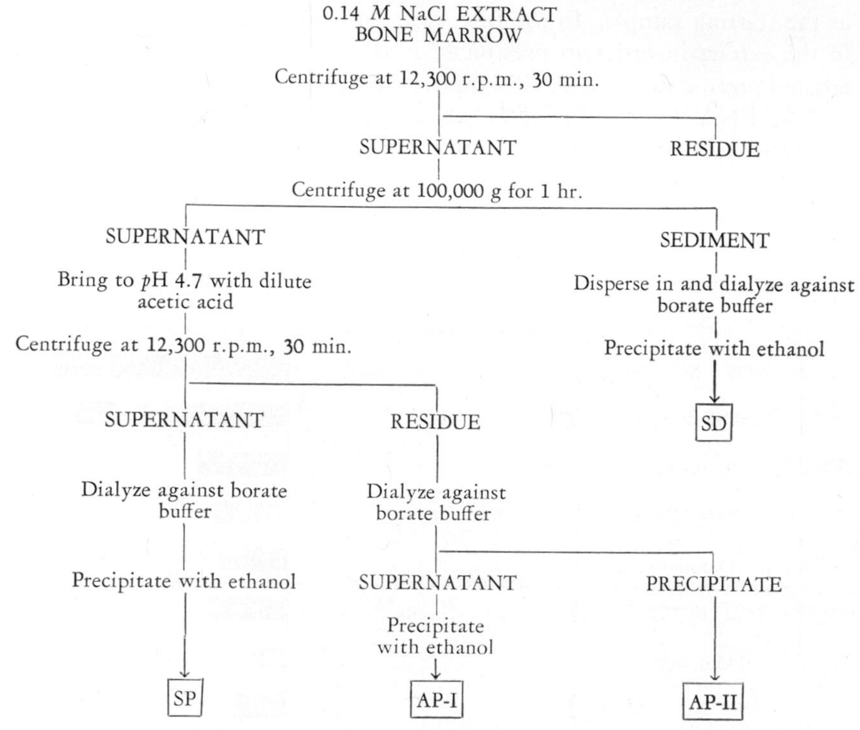

Fig. 2. The scheme of fractionation of the bone marrow extract. SD, final sediment; SP, final supernatant; AP, acid-precipitable fraction.

former fraction, containing probably the PNP fraction of the last-mentioned series, exerted only a weak morphogenetic effect on the ectoderm. The supernatant fraction was further fractionated by carefully acidifying with acetic acid to *p*H 4.7. The final supernatant showed almost no morphogenetic effects on the ectoderm. The fraction precipitated at *p*H 4.7 was suspended in a borate buffer and dialyzed. After the dialysis the part of the sample which was in solution was separated from the sediment found in the dialysis bag. The former was called acid-precipitable 1 (AP-I) and the latter acid-precipitable 2 (AP-II). Both samples caused very intensive induction of the trunk-mesodermal type when tested after ethanol-treatment (Fig. 3). Thus the active substance present in the original saline extract was recovered in the acid-precipitable and non-dialyzable fraction of the supernatant obtained by centrifuging at $100,000 \times g$ for 1 hour. The data of chemical analysis (Table 7) imply that only about one-eighteenth

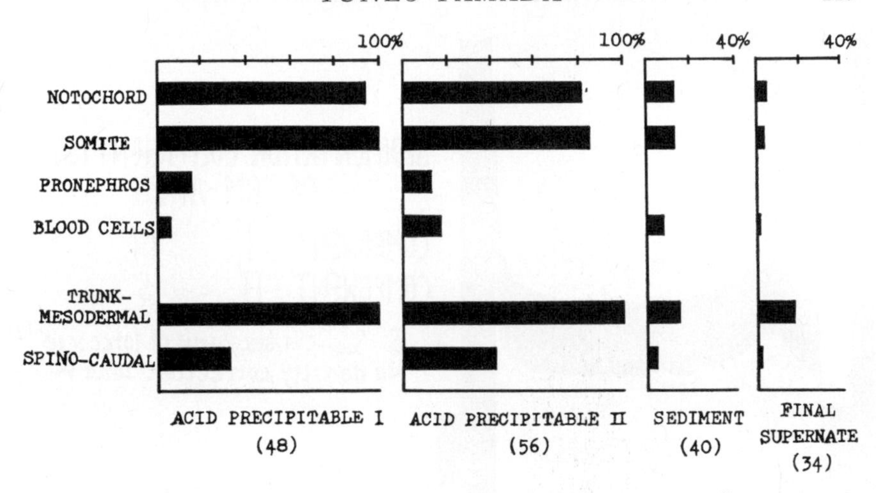

Fig. 3. Inductive effects of the bone marrow fraction, separated according to the scheme of Fig. 2.

of the protein-N present in the original saline extract is accounted for by the acid-precipitable fraction.

In the sedimentation diagram of sample AP-1, a major component with $S_{20} = 5$ was found accompanied by a minor component with $S_{20} = 11$ (Fig. 4). A sample of AP-1 was fractionated into the supernatant SII and sediment SI by centrifuging at $220{,}000 \times g$ for 1 hour, and both subfractions were tested for morphogenetic effects on the isolated ectoderm. The data shown in Fig. 5 indicate strong trunk-mesodermal effects by both subfractions.

A sample of AP-I was studied in a Tiselius apparatus (Fig. 6). Five components were recognized whose mobilities are given in Fig. 6. The slower-moving components (D and E) were separated as one fraction

TABLE 7

Analytical Data on the Fractions of the Bone Marrow Extract

Samples	PNA-P μg. per mg. protein-N	Total protein N (mg.)	Total PNA-P (μg.)
0.14 *M* NaCl extract	19.1	88	1680
Supernatant fraction	9.7	—	—
Acid non-precipitable of supernatant (BM-SP)	6.0	—	—
Acid precipitable of supernatant (BM-API)	12.4	5	62

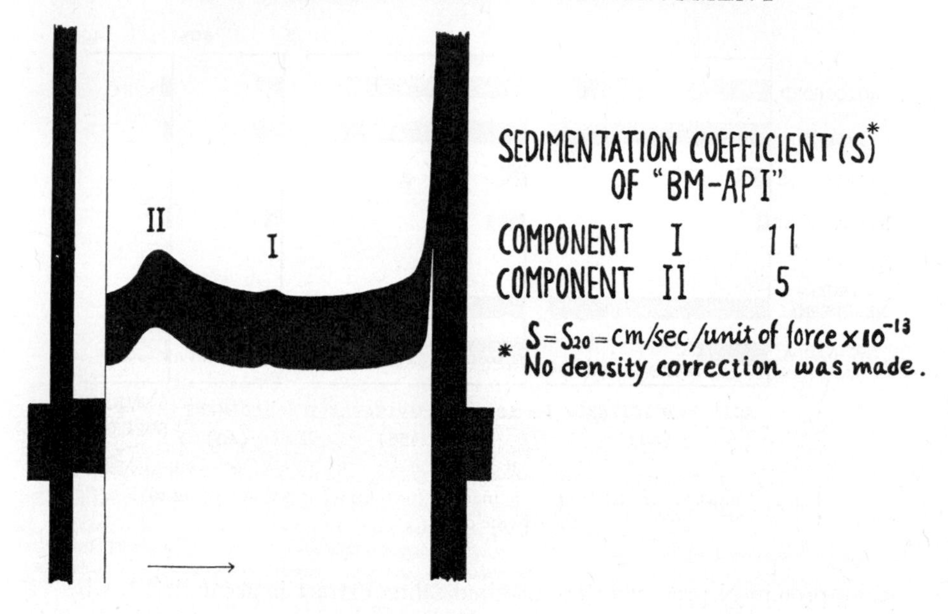

Fig. 4. Sedimentation pattern of bone marrow AP-I.

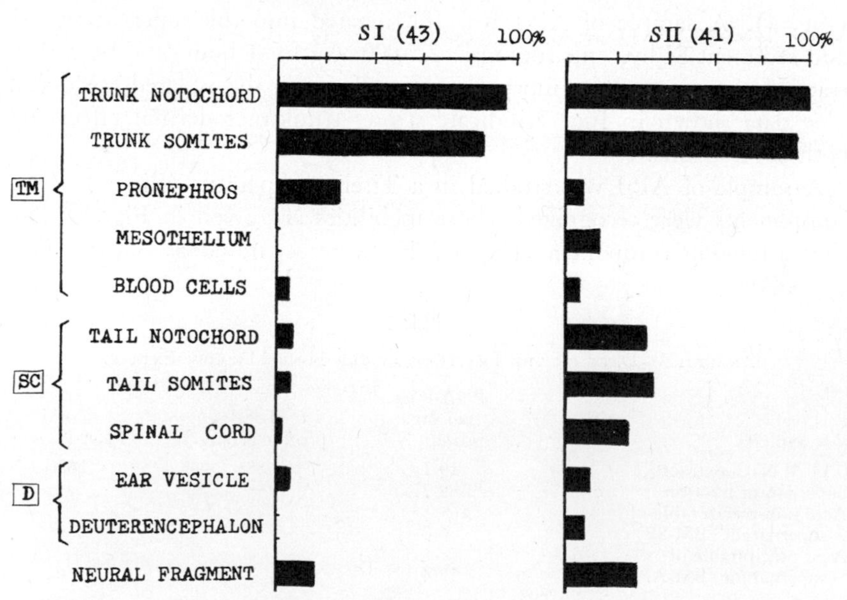

Fig. 5. Inductive effects of the subfractions of AP-I separated by ultracentrifugation.

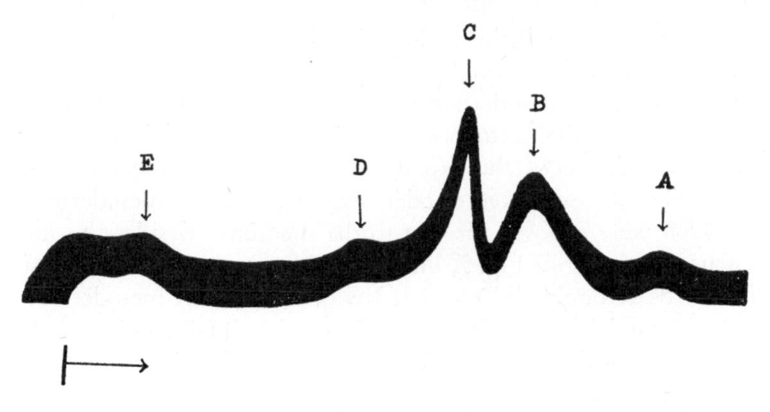

Fig. 6. Electrophoretic pattern (ascending) of BM–AP-I. 0.14 μ borate buffer at pH 7.5 after 70 min. in a field of 9.5 volts per cm. Ascending Mobilities of the Components of "BM–AP-I," in cm./sec./volt $\times 10^{-5}$.

A	B	C	D	E
−9.2	−7.4	−6.1	−4.4	−1.9

(D and E bracketed: S-E)

from the descending limb after ethanol-precipitation. This sample (S-E) caused intensive mesodermization of the isolated ectoderm (Fig. 7). We have not been successful so far in testing the morphogenetic effects of the fast-moving components.

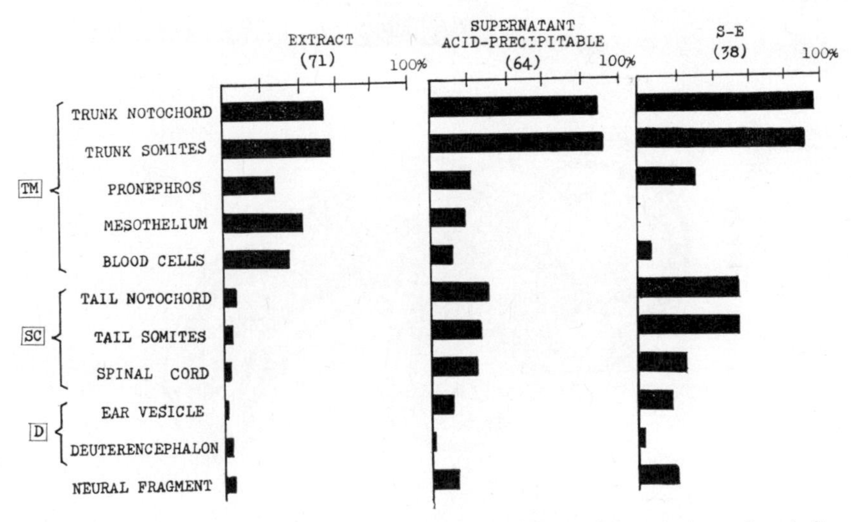

Fig. 7. Inductive effects of the original extract, fraction AP-I and S-E, an electrophoretically separated subfraction of the latter.

Under the influence of the acid-precipitable fraction not only were practically all the explants induced, but the main part of the isolated ectoderm was converted into mesodermal structures. In most of the explants the only cells retaining their ectodermal nature were those of the thin epidermis covering the surface of the explant. In a smaller number of cases the whole mass of the explanted ectoderm was turned into mesodermal structures which were exposed directly to the medium. Besides the mesodermal structures listed in Fig. 7, limb buds, blood vessels, and mesenchyme could also be recognized. Associated with these trunk-mesodermal structures, spino-caudal ones such as the tail notochord, tail somites, and spinal cord appeared in the series of the bone marrow fractions. In most cases both types of structures were continuous, giving rise to a more or less organized axis with cephalocaudal polarity (Fig. 8, B).

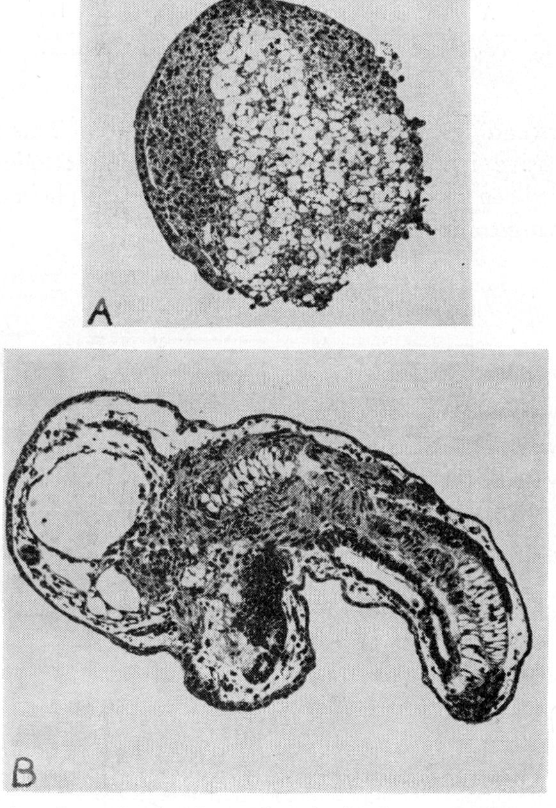

Fig. 8. A. Induction of notochord and mesoderm by fraction S_1. B. Induction of notochord, myotome, and spinal cord by fraction S-E.

From the beginning of our work on bone marrow induction, I had been attracted by occurrence of a group of yolk-rich cells within the induced mesodermal tissue. The problem is now under investigation with the collaboration of Miss C. Takata. Recently we have obtained convincing

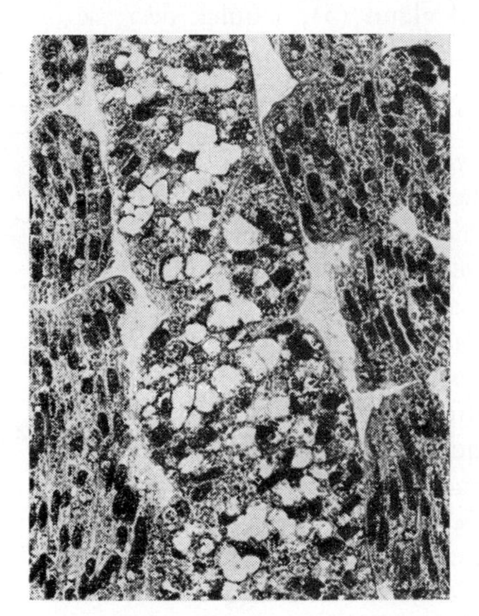

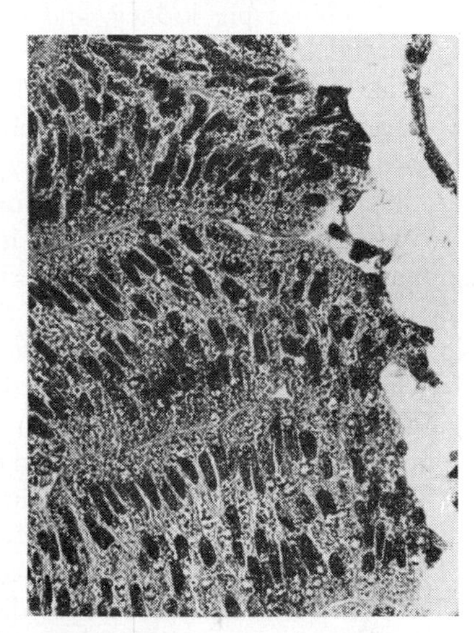

Fig. 9. Induced myotomes *left* and notochord with somites *right* in the explants of series S-E.

data showing induction of endodermal tissues from the ectoderm by the bone marrow fractions. In favorable cases differentiation of the pharynx and stomach was indicated in the explant containing a piece of acid-precipitable fraction. Those endodermal structures appear always closely associated with the trunk-mesodermal tissues but not with other types of induced structures. In her recent paper Kuusi (18) pointed out that the bone marrow extract enhanced differentiation of the host endoderm at the site of implantation. It remains to be decided whether this acceleration has something to do with the induction of endodermal tissues observed in our experiments.

Progressive Change in Regional Effects

Chuang (2, 3) was first to show a progressive change in the regional effects of the adult tissue caused by heat treatment. According to him the mesodermal induction was the first to vanish, while the induction of brain, nose, and eye not only withstood heating but showed an increase in frequency. Recently Vahs (33) has studied the effects of heating on induction

by the mouse kidney. Classifying the effects in terms of regionality, he reached the conclusion that heat suppresses the deuterencephalic effects but increases the archencephalic effects under his experimental conditions. It was shown further that during a long ethanol-treatment of mouse kidney (35, 6), guinea pig kidney, and parotid gland (5), a quick decrease of spino-caudal effects and a later decrease of deuterencephalic effects were evident. A gradual increase in archencephalic effects kept the total induction frequency at the original level.

A comparable shift of regionality by various treatments occurs not only on the level of the tissue but also on the level of the extract (41) or of a fairly homogeneous sample. For instance, in the case of our sample of kidney PNP, the spino-caudal effects were easily suppressed and the deuterencephalic effects enhanced, if the sample was left in solution for a longer time or kept more than several days in ethanol before testing. This fact helps to explain why the fractions separated from the kidney of the guinea pig after a longer procedure often showed a lower frequency of spino-caudal effects and a larger frequency of deuterencephalic effects (cf. Table 2 and p. 220). Even archencephalic effects could appear. A complete suppression of spino-caudal effects and a concomitant appearance of archencephalic effects were noted upon treating the sample of kidney PNP with acetic anhydride, according to the method suggested by Hugh for acetylating protein.[3] Hayashi found that a similar change in regional effect can be evoked in the same sample by treating it with pepsin. Upon addition of the enzyme to a neutral solution of kidney PNP, suppression of the spino-caudal tendency, increase of the deuterencephalic tendency, and appearance of the archencephalic tendency were demonstrated. When the sample was incubated with pepsin at *p*H 4.0, a quick disappearance of the spino-caudal and slower disappearance of the deuterencephalic tendency were noted. In the course of incubation the archencephalic effects also diminished. The results suggest that the presence of pepsin under sub-optimum conditions causes a change in the protein part of PNP, which is reflected in the change of its regional effects. The enzymatic activity of pepsin seems to suppress all types of regional induction, by acting strongly on the spino-caudal one and weakly on the archencephalic one. Using a sample of liver PNP with deuterencephalic effects, Hayashi (12) observed the disappearance of deuterencephalic effects after a short heat treatment. A similar effect of pepsin has been reported by Tiedemann and Tiedemann

[3] However, Kuusi (17) observed no clear shift of regionality when she treated the kidney homogenate in the same way.

(26) for protein fractions of chick embryos, which induce primarily spino-caudal structures.

According to Toivonen (32) and Kuusi (18), the bone marrow of the guinea pig is different from the above-mentioned tissues and their fractions in that it loses its inductive effects altogether when heated, without converting its inductive quality. This claim is based on the experiments of Toivonen (32) that ethanol-treated bone marrow tissue lost all its mesodermal effects and induced only insignificant epidermal structures after immersion in 80°-90°C water for 10 minutes. However, by steaming a thin layer of bone marrow tissue, the present writer (40) could confirm that during the first 150 seconds of treatment the tissue quickly changes its regional effects, and induces trunk-mesodermal, spino-caudal, deuterencephalic, and archencephalic structures in sequence (Fig. 10), before the

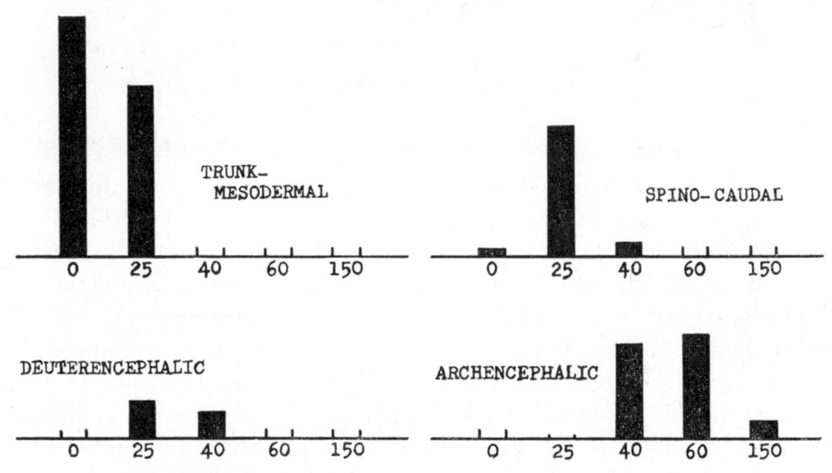

Fig. 10. Regional effects of bone marrow tissue steamed for 0, 25, 40, 60, and 150 seconds respectively (Yamada).

total induction frequency drops to a very low level. Probably Toivonen observed in his last-mentioned experiment only the very end of this sequence of events. Nonetheless we have to admit that the bone marrow factor is more heat-sensitive than the factors of other tissues studied so far. A similar conversion of the regional effect of an inducer of the trunk-mesodermal type was demonstrated earlier by Okada (21), when he observed the induction of various neural structures by the heat-treated frog skin.

When the acid-precipitable fraction of the supernatant which carries the inducing activity of the bone marrow (p. 226) was steamed for 40 seconds and the inductive effects were compared with those of the untreated sample, the spino-caudal effects and deuterencephalic effects were found to be increased at the expense of the trunk-mesodermal effects. Thus also in the case of the bone marrow it is likely that the progressive change in regional effects observed in the tissue is based on the comparable change in its active component. An extensive study on this point is being planned.

Summarizing the results reviewed above, various treatments convert the regional effects according to the sequence of regional types represented in Fig. 11. In many cases the progressive change in regional effects proceeds without any change in the total induction frequency. In the case of steaming the bone marrow or of pepsin-treatment of kidney PNP, a progressive decrease in the total induction frequency accompanied the progressive regional change. Many results presented above speak for the possibility suggested by us earlier (41, 42) that these progressive changes in regional effects are due to comparable changes of the active component of the tissue, which is probably a protein. It is tempting to assume that the protein molecule responsible for induction goes through a series of changes in configuration or in any other physical property, which are reflected in the regional effects.

TRUNK-MESODERMAL
↓
SPINO-CAUDAL
↓
DEUTERENCEPHALIC
↓
ARCHENCEPHALIC

Fig. 11. The sequence of regional types of induction.

It may be pointed out that on the surface of an early gastrula of the urodele, the area having the prospective significance of archencephalic structures is located near the animal pole, followed by the prospective areas of the deuterencephalic, spino-caudal, and mesodermal structures in sequence toward the vegetal pole. That the sequence of the regional types observed in various inducing samples upon various treatments follows the vegetal-animal sequence of the corresponding areas can hardly be a mere coincidence. It may be added that even the induction of the endodermal structures by the bone marrow factor fits in well with this sequence.

The Specificity of the Inductive Phenomena

As to the specificity of the induction studied in the present paper, the following remarks may be pertinent. First, in all types of inducing sample discussed above, the effect observed is region-specific but not organ-specific or tissue-specific. Also, during the course of step-wise purification of the samples, no indication was obtained to speak for any concomitant segregation of the factor inducing one specific organ. Among the large number of induction experiments with various adult tissues hitherto reported, no reliable case of organ-specific induction has been found. The claim that the thymus of the guinea pig is a specific inducer of the lens (28) could not withstand later critical experiments (23). Also in the extensive experiments of Kuusi (16, 17, 18) and of Tiedemann and Tiedemann (26), in which more or less purified samples with inductive ability have been obtained, the effects which have been reported are region-specific but not organ-specific. Induction of several distinct organs or tissues belonging to one or two regionalities by a fairly homogeneous sample could be interpreted by assuming a secondary induction of some of these structures by one structure which alone is primarily induced by the sample. This interpretation is however at least not always applicable, because in all regional types of heterogeneous induction most of these structures have been induced directly from the inducing sample, independently from other structures. Thus we are forced to admit that the inducing sample initiates in the ectoderm a morphogenetic activity which is characteristic for a particular region, but not for an individual organ or tissue. Thus the segregation of the whole explant induced by a sample into a number of organs and tissues belonging to the same regionality may be most readily understood by assuming a gradient of morphogenetic activity, which is established within the explant according to the topographical relation to the sample, and which brings forth a different morphogenesis on its different levels.

This idea is supported by observations on the relative frequencies of various structures of one regional type in a series of induction experiments with the samples containing various concentrations of the active substance. Observations by Hayashi (11) suggest that samples with a higher concentration of the active substance of the archencephalic type induce the eye and forebrain more readily, whereas samples with a weaker concentration tend to induce the mesenchyme and melanophores more frequently. These observations confirm the earlier results of Yamada (38). A comparable situation is suggested also for the tissue of the trunk-mesodermal type: by a sample of lower concentration of the active substance (for instance,

the extract of Fig. 7) the blood islands and mesothelium are more readily induced than by a sample of higher concentration (for instance, S-E of Fig. 7); while the opposite holds for the notochord and somites. Furthermore, the topographical relationship between various mesodermal rudiments induced within an explant often reminds us of the normal dorsoventral distribution of the rudiments, as Okada (21) pointed out in his experiments with frog skin. The same is true for all other types of regionality (38, 11). These facts accord with the assumption of a gradient of morphogenetic activity.

Secondly, the specificity of induction caused by our sample is limited by the phenomenon which has been called the shift of the regional type. This tends to widen the range of the morphogenetic effects of a particular sample. In the case of the bone marrow factor, in particular, almost all the principal organ rudiments belonging to three germ layers may be induced from the presumptive ectoderm by this factor if it is applied under fresh and modified conditions.

Concluding Remarks

The results reported in this paper concerning the bone marrow factor seem to raise the question whether in the normal organizer cells a similar substance is present at a higher concentration and directs differentiation and mediates induction.[4] The demonstration of Niu (20) that a substance or substances are discharged from the developing organizer cells into the medium and cause the ectoderm cells cultured in the medium to differentiate in a neural, mesectodermal, or mesodermal direction, may be interpreted as suggesting such a possibility. The recent work of Grobstein (9) indicates that the tubule-inducing effects of the spinal cord on the metanephrogenic mesenchyme of the mouse embryo can be transmitted without any cytoplasmic contact between the two tissues, and suggests that some substance responsible for the induction and separable from the cell body is transferred from the acting system into the reacting system. A transfer of protein from the organizer into the ectoderm cells is also made probable by some of the recent isotope experiments (cf. 37). However, facts are known which indicate that the hypothetical factor involved in the normal organizer, or other normal inducers if present, must be chemically different from the bone marrow factor—for the morphogenetic substances found in the adult tissues are stable toward ethanol-treatment, but the amphibian

[4] As the bone marrow factor is known to be active as an antigen (36, and oral communication of Dr. Kawakami), it may be interesting to study the effect of the antiserum against the bone marrow factor on the differentiation of the normal organizer.

organizer loses its characteristic effects when treated with ethanol. It was shown by Okazaki (22) that a piece of the organizer loses its inducing effect when devitalized by a mild method, such as treatment with subzero ethanol or freezing-drying, and that the archencephalic inducing ability can be secondarily evoked in such a piece by a subsequent treatment with 5°C ethanol. Thus the inducing ability exhibited by a "dead organizer" may have nothing to do with the original inducing ability. Further, it must be pointed out that also in the specific induction of the later embryonic period the inducer loses its effect upon devitalization, while the adult tissues are capable of "specific" induction after devitalization. In any case, the question raised above needs more coordinated information from the different fields suggested in the Introduction.

REFERENCES

1. Brachet, J., Kuusi, T., and Gothié, S., *Arch. Biol.*, **63**, 429 (1952).
2. Chuang, H. H., *Wilhelm Roux' Arch. Entwicklungsmech. Organ.*, **139**, 556 (1939).
3. ———, *Wilhelm Roux' Arch. Entwicklungsmech. Organ.*, **140**, 25 (1940).
4. Dalcq, A. M., *Acta Anat.*, **30**, 242 (1957).
5. Engländer, H., and Johnen, A. G., *J. Embryol. Exptl. Morphol.*, **5**, 1 (1957).
6. ———, ———, and Vahs, W., *Experientia*, **9**, 100 (1953).
7. Fujii, T., *J. Facul. Sci. Imp. Univ. Tokyo*, Sec. IV, **5**, 425 (1941).
8. ———, *J. Facul. Sci. Imp. Univ. Tokyo*, Sec. IV, **6**, 451 (1944).
9. Grobstein, C., *Exptl. Cell Research*, **13**, 575 (1957).
10. Hayashi, Y., *Embryologia*, **2**, 145 (1955).
11. ———, *Embryologia*, **3**, 57 (1956).
12. ———, *Embryologia*, **4**, 33 (1958).
13. Holtfreter, J., *Wilhelm Roux' Arch. Entwicklungsmech. Organ.*, **132**, 307 (1934).
14. Kawakami, I., and Mifune, S., *Mem. Fac. Sci. Kyushu Univ., Ser. E*, **2**, 21 (1955).
15. ———, and ———, *Mem. Fac. Sci. Kyushu Univ., Ser. E*, **2**, 141 (1957).
16. Kuusi, T., *Ann. Zool. Soc. Zool. Botan. Fennicae Vanamo*, **14**, 1 (1951).
17. ———, *Arch. Biol.*, **64**, 189 (1953).
18. ———, *Arch. Soc. Zool. Botan. Fennicae Vanamo*, **11** (2), 136 (1957); **12** (1), 73 (1957).
19. Lehmann, F. E., *Einführung in die physiologische Embryologie*, Verlag Birkhäuser, Basel (1945).
20. Niu, M. C., in *Cellular Metabolism in Differentiation and Growth* (D. Rudnick, ed.), p. 155 (1956).
21. Okada, Y. K., *Proc. Japan Acad.*, **24**, 22 (1948).
22. Okazaki, R., *Exptl. Cell Research*, **9**, 579 (1955).
23. Rotmann, E., *Naturwiss.*, **30**, 60 (1942).
24. Saxén, L., and Toivonen, S., *Ann. Med. Exptl. et Biol. Fennicae (Helsinki)*, **34**, 235 (1956).
25. Takata, K., and Osawa, S., *Biochem. et Biophys. Acta*, **24**, 207 (1957).
26. Tiedemann, H., and Tiedemann, H., *Hoppe-Seyler's Z. physiol. Chem.*, **306**, 7 (1956).
27. ———, and ———, *Hoppe-Seyler's Z. physiol. Chem.*, **306**, 132 (1957).
28. Toivonen, S., *Ann. Acad. Sci. Fennicae, Ser. A*, **55**, 3 (1940).
29. ———, *Rev. Suisse Zool.*, **57**, Fasc. Suppl. 41 (1950).

30. ———, *Experientia,* **8,** 120 (1952).
31. ———, *J. Embryol. Exptl. Morphol.,* **1,** 97 (1953).
32. ———, *J. Embryol. Exptl. Morphol.,* **2,** 239 (1954).
33. Vahs, W., *Z. Naturforsch.,* **10,** 412 (1955).
34. ———, *Biol. Zentr.,* **75,** 360 (1956).
35. ———, *Wilhelm Roux' Arch. Entwicklungsmech. Organ.,* **149,** 339 (1957).
36. Vainio, T., *Ann. Acad. Sci. Fennicae, Ser. A,* **35,** 7 (1957).
37. Waddington, C. H., and Mulherkar, L., *Proc. Zool. Soc. Bengal,* Mookerjee Memor. vol., 141 (1957).
38. Yamada, T., *Embryologia,* **1,** 1 (1950).
39. ———, *Symposia Soc. Cellular Chem.,* **4,** 1 (Jap.) and 147 (Eng. résumé) (1956).
40. ———, *Experientia,* **14,** 81 (1958).
41. ———, and Takata, K., *J. Exptl. Zool.,* **128,** 291 (1955).
42. ———, and ———, *Exptl. Cell Research,* **3,** (Suppl.), 402 (1955).
43. ———, and ———, *Embryologia,* **3,** 69 (1956).
44. ———, ———, and Osawa, S., *Embryologia,* **2,** 123 (1954).

INDUCTIVE SPECIFICITY IN THE ORIGIN OF INTEGUMENTARY DERIVATIVES IN THE FOWL

JOHN W. SAUNDERS, JR.[1]
Department of Biology, Marquette University, Milwaukee, Wisconsin

INTRODUCTION

The domestic fowl bears a variety of regionally distinctive integumentary derivatives. The body is covered with feathers, the head is adorned with the comb, beak, and wattles, and the feet are armed with scales and claws; a small claw tips Digit II of the wing. These skin derivatives are of dual origin; the comb and wattles comprise thickened and highly vascular modifications of the dermis, with a thin epidermal covering; the feathers, scales, and claws, on the other hand, are chiefly epidermal structures, each associated with a more obscure dermal portion.

The feathers are of particular interest. They are arranged in tracts (pterylae) separated by featherless areas (apterylae). Each tract contains feathers of a distinctive range of structural and physiological characteristics, ordered in parallel rows long both longitudinal and diagonal coordinates (Fig. 1). Within each tract there are graded variations in structure and physiological features (size, degree of asymmetry, hormone thresholds, etc.) from feather to feather along each row. Each feather is thus an unique component of an orderly pattern (1, 3).

The origin of this pattern presents a challenging problem. More than two decades ago, Professor Willier and his colleagues sought to analyze the embryonic origin of spatial distribution and tract-specificity in feathers by grafting skin ectoderm from the head to the wing bud in embryos of genetically different breeds of fowl. The grafts contributed little or no epidermis to the host, however, and hence did not affect the regional characteristics of feather structure at the graft site. On the other hand, they frequently "infected" the host tissues with melanoblasts, prospective pig-

[1] This research has been supported in part by research grants (C1481-C5, C6) from the National Cancer Institute of the National Institutes of Health, by a grant (G2253) from the National Science Foundation, and by grants from the American Cancer Society, Milwaukee Division.

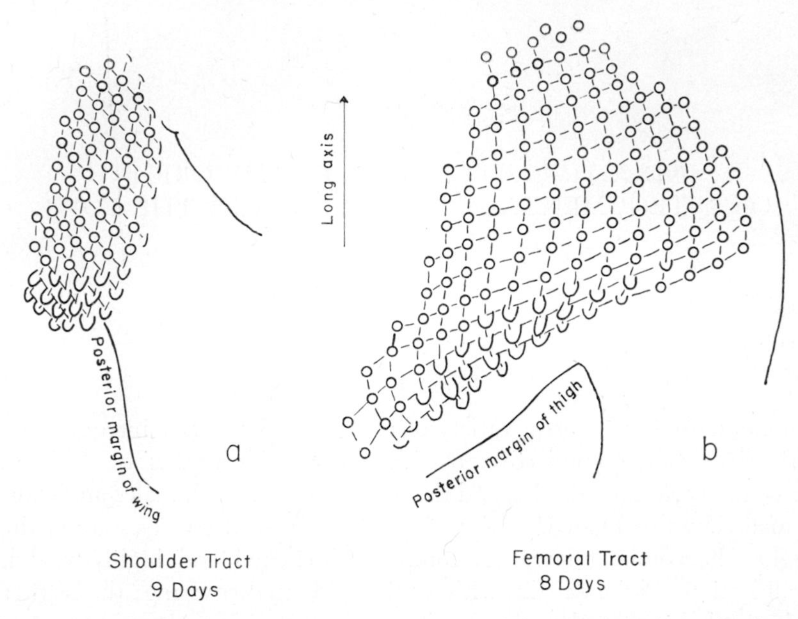

Fig. 1. "Grid" patterns showing the arrangement of feather germs in *a,* the *humeral* and *b,* the *femoral* feather tracts of the chick, traced from camera-lucida drawings. The feather germs form a pattern of intersecting coordinates.

ment cells, of donor origin, and accordingly brought about the formation of donor-colored feathers in the region of the implant. This observation led to a most successful analysis of the role of the migratory pigment cell in the origin of color patterns in the plumage of birds (11-16, 24, 26-30), but further work on the origin of the distribution pattern and tract-specificity of feather germs was deferred.

This being so, it would seem particularly appropriate that, in a Symposium Volume honoring Professor Willier, some attempt should be made to pursue the analysis which he originally projected. This report, based chiefly on work initiated in his laboratory and originally under his direction, takes up this analysis as an aspect of the general problem of the origin of regional specificity in the epidermis and its derivatives. It treats chiefly of (1) ectoderm-mesoderm interactions in the locus of origin of the feather germ; (2) the order in which tract-specific feather characteristics are established; and (3), the regionally specific inductive action of the mesoderm in the origin of distinctive epidermal derivatives, i.e., kinds of feathers, scales, claws.

Induction of Tract-Specific Feather Characteristics

Ectoderm-Mesoderm Relationships in the Mature Feather

The familiar contour feather is a bilaterally organized epidermal structure which develops in intimate association with a vascular mesodermal papilla located at the base of a pit in the skin, the feather *follicle*. When the feather of an adult bird is plucked or moulted, the denuded dermal papilla becomes encircled by a ring of epidermal cells, the *collar*, originating from the adjoining lining of the follicle. From this epidermal collar is regenerated a new feather similar in size, structure, and physiological characteristics to the one that was lost.

The dermal papilla permanently resides at the base of the follicle and is essential to feather formation; a follicle from which it has been removed will not regenerate a feather. Apparently, therefore, the dermal papilla induces feather formation in the epidermis. Furthermore, it determines the bilateral organization of the feather vane, for rotation of the dermal papilla in the base of the follicle brings about a corresponding rotation of the regenerating feather which it induces (10).

On the other hand, when a dermal papilla from a follicle of the distinctive "saddle" feather tract is grafted to a follicle of the "breast" tract from which the papilla was previously removed, a breast feather is formed. Conversely, grafting a dermal papilla from the breast tract to an empty follicle in the saddle tract results in the formation of a saddle feather. Clearly, therefore, the inductive action of the dermal papilla is generalized, or non-specific, and the tract-specific characteristics of the feather are the property of the follicular epidermis (23).

Embryonic Origin of the Feather Germs

The spatial distribution of feather germs, the inductive activities of the dermal papillae, and the definitive response capacities of the follicular ectoderm might reasonably be expected to originate during embryonic development. Accordingly, it is appropriate to describe briefly the embryonic origin of the feathers.

The feather germs first appear in the back skin as early as 6½ days of incubation, and by the tenth or eleventh day the tract patterns of the future plumage are essentially complete. Within each feather tract, the first primordia appear as a row of mesenchymal condensations, usually oriented longitudinally with respect to the embryonic axis. On each side of this

"row of origin" (7) secondary rows of mesodermal condensations appear, each occupying a position corresponding to the space between condensations in the primary row; thus diagonally intersecting coordinates are formed (cf. Fig. 1). Additional rows are added in a similar manner, extending the tract until its pattern is complete.

Meanwhile the ectoderm overlying each dermal condensation becomes thicker. Proliferation of both the ectoderm and the dermal condensation forms the conical feather papilla which projects above the level of the skin, usually sloping somewhat posteriorly in the direction of orientation of the definitive feather. Subsequently, each primordium sinks into the skin so that its insertion is at the base of a pit, the follicle. There the dermal condensation forms the dermal papilla and pulp of the down feather; the proliferating ectoderm of the germ forms the feather vane.

The down feather is superficially a radially symmetrical structure, but the manner of its origin forecasts the future bilateral organization of the juvenile and adult feathers. The first barb-vane ridges arise on the side of the feather papilla which forms the outer obtuse angle of its incidence with the skin (8, 9, 24). This is the *dorsal* side, the site of origin of the rachis of the definitive feather. Further, the melanophores first become aligned in rows along the dorsal side (24) of the germ, and alkaline phosphatase in the feather pulp shows a greater initial activity dorsally (6, 9).

Details of the formation of the down and its replacement by the juvenile and adult plumage are well known (2, 4, 5, 8, 24). They are not particularly pertinent to this report and will not be described.

Factors Determining the Origin of Feather-Germ Loci

The intimate association of epidermal and mesodermal elements in the origin of the feather suggests that mutual interactions between these layers are responsible for determining the feather-germ loci. This has been shown experimentally. Feather formation is not initiated by either ectodermal or mesodermal elements of the embryonic skin cultured alone in vitro on media which will support the differentiation of feather germs in intact skin (22). Also, mesoderm of the dorsal surface of the wing bud in vivo will not organize a typical corium or dermal papillae in the absence of the covering ectoderm (21, 25).

On the other hand, since the first signs of feather-germ formation are seen in the mesoderm, it is reasonable to suggest that mesodermal factors may be responsible initially for determining where feather germs will form. This has also been demonstrated (18). Rectangular blocks of tissue (ectoderm plus subjacent mesoderm) were excised from the dorsal side of the

wing bud in the 3½-day chick and replaced by mesodermal isolates of similar size and shape taken from the prospective thigh region of the leg bud. Ectoderm from the regions of the wing bud adjoining the graft then healed over the implant, and the resulting wings frequently showed feather papillae in the normally apterous region adjacent to the distinctive shoulder tract (Fig. 2). It is clear, therefore, that feather formation is induced

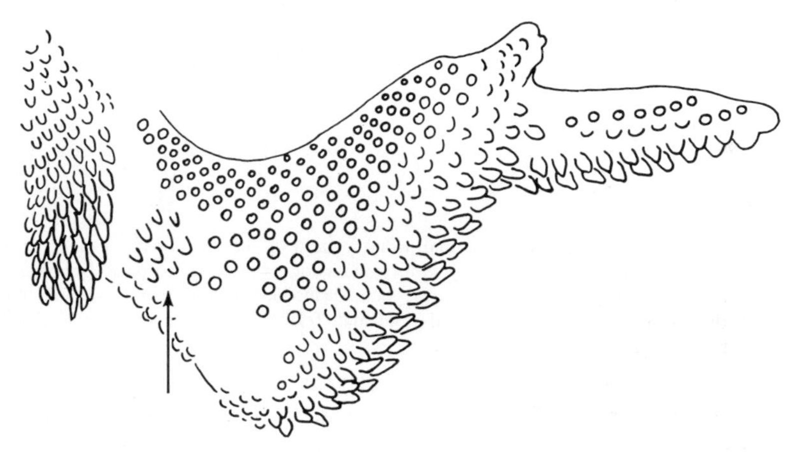

Fig. 2. The induction of supernumerary feather germs (arrow) in epidermis of the normally apterous region of the upper arm by an implant of prospective thigh mesoderm. Camera lucida drawing of the 10-day embryonic wing.

by mesoderm for, in these cases, feather germs developed in ectoderm which normally would not form feathers. Hence, the locus of feather-germ formation is probably controlled initially by mesodermal factors.

Under some conditions, however, the ectoderm may also affect the site of feather-germ formation. When epidermal wounds are made on the dorsal side of the wing bud distal to the shoulder tract, the coordinate pattern of feather germs in the tract is frequently distorted in the direction of the wound (Fig. 3). Presumably this effect results from shifting of the ectodermal layer with respect to the underlying mesoderm of the prospective feather tract during wound-healing movements. The embryonic ectoderm is thus an active partner in feather-germ formation (21).

The Progressive Organization of a Feather Tract

Since mesodermal factors apparently bear the initial responsibility for the origin of feather-germ loci, it follows that the number and spatial distribution of feather germs in the various tracts are under mesodermal con-

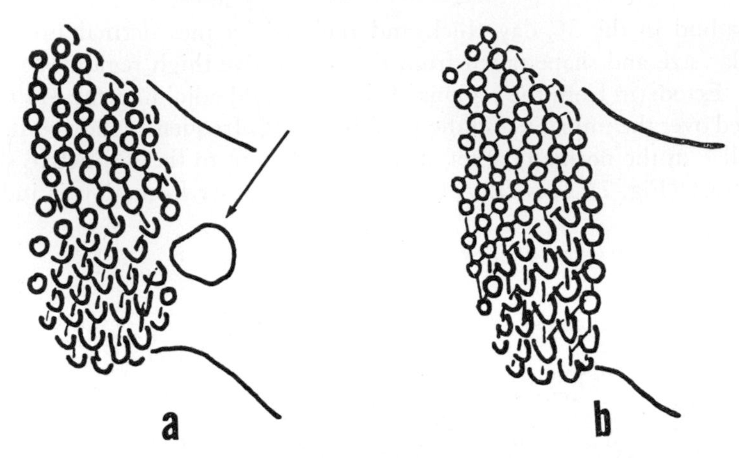

Fig. 3. Effects of a persisting epidermal wound (arrow) on the orderly arrangement of feathers in the humeral tract. *a,* 10-day embryonic wing; epidermis stripped lateral to the shoulder tract at stage 24+ (ca. 4½ days); note distortion of the antero-posterior coordinates of the humeral-tract pattern. *b,* the normal feather arrangement in the shoulder tract. Camera lucida drawings of the specimens.

trol. It is also of interest to learn whether other aspects of feather-tract organization, such as the structure, orientation, size relationships, and physiological characteristics of the feathers are determined by mesodermal factors and, further, to examine the sequence in which characteristics of the feather tracts are fixed.

The humeral (shoulder) feather tract, which originates from materials located proximally on the wing bud, was chosen for this analysis. This is a well-defined tract (cf. Fig. 1) which has been thoroughly studied (1), and its prospective materials are readily accessible to experimental manipulation during the young wing-bud stages. In embryos of stages 17 to 24 (3 to 4½ days of incubation), rectangular blocks of mesoderm (with or without the covering ectoderm), comprising chiefly materials of the postero-lateral quadrant of the shoulder tract and distally adjoining apterium, were excised from the dorsal side of the right wing bud to a depth of approximately 0.1 mm., rotated 180° in the horizontal plane, and replaced in situ. The operation thus displaced materials of the future humeral tract distally and in reversed antero-posterior and medio-lateral orientation (Fig. 4). Simultaneously, it shifted materials of the prospective apterium into the region of the humeral tract.

The results of these experiments were analyzed in a large number of adult and embryonic specimens (20). Many of them showed completely

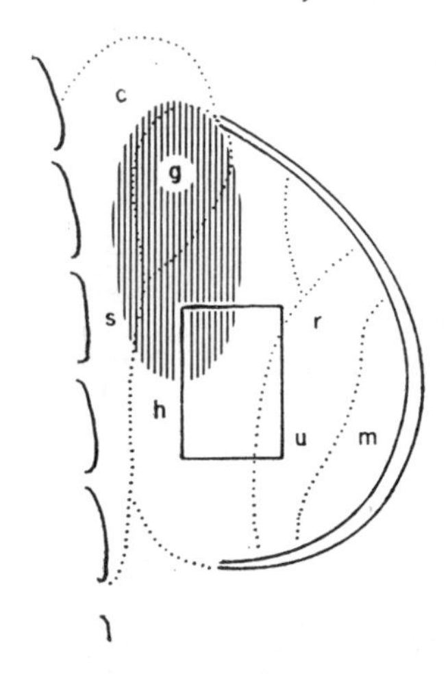

Fig. 4. Fate map for wing bud in stage 21 (adapted from Saunders, 17). The rectangular outline indicates the wing parts affected by the reorientation operation. The approximate location of the materials of the humeral tract is designated by vertical hatching. Mapped skeletal areas are enclosed by dotted lines: *c*, coracoid; *g*, glenoid region; *h*, humerus; *m*, manus; *r*, radius; *s*, scapula; *u*, ulna.

normal patterns of feather distribution. In others (*Type I*), the humeral tract was defective, usually lacking from 2 to 25 feather germs in the postero-lateral quadrant, but the feathers of more distal wing parts were normally arranged. Approximately one-half of the specimens likewise had defective humeral tracts but, in addition, bore distinctive feathers, structurally like those of the humeral tract, in the apterous region distal to it (*Type II*). These feathers, presumably of humeral-tract origin and displaced distally by the operation, emerged simultaneously with feathers of the humeral tract in the juvenile plumage and were directed posteriorly or postero-distally. They showed normal dorso-ventral relationships; i.e., the dorsal aspect of each feather was dorsally oriented. In some favorable cases it could be shown that the normal antero-posterior order of feather sizes in the displaced group of humeral-tract feathers was reversed: larger feathers, normally found at the posterior edge of the tract, were located anteriorly in the displaced group. Finally, a few specimens (*Type III*) showed defective humeral tracts and displaced feathers, as described above, but among the displaced feathers the apices of at least some were directed anteriorly, conforming to the original axial relationships of the reoriented isolate. In the only bird of this kind which hatched and achieved the adult plumage, dorso-ventral axiation of the displaced feathers was appropriate to the feather slope (i.e., dorsal sides dorsally oriented).

The results of one group of experiments, ordered with respect to the developmental stages of the embryos at the time of operation, are summarized in Fig. 5. Analysis of the frequency with which the various feather patterns were found, as a function of the stage of operation, shows: (1) a

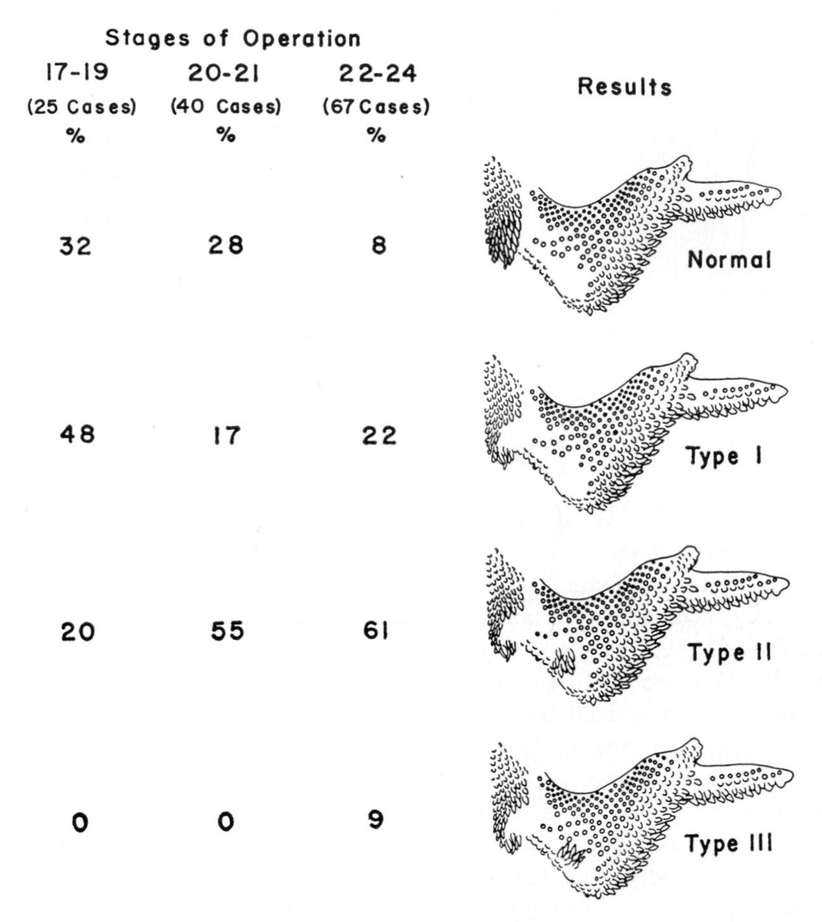

Stages of Operation
17-19
20-21
22-24
(25 Cases)
(40 Cases)
(67 Cases)
%
%
%
Results
32
28
8
Normal
48
17
22
Type I
20
55
61
Type II
0
0
9
Type III

Fig. 5. Effects of the reorientation operation on the distribution and orientation of feather germs in the wing bud. Atypical feather patterns designated as Types I, II, and III, were redrawn, with suitable modifications, from a camera-lucida tracing of the normal pattern.

progressive loss of the ability of the humeral tract to reorganize its typical pattern after the reorientation operation; (2) a progressive increase in the ability of displaced parts of the prospective humeral tract to differentiate the characteristic structure, spatial order, and time of emergence of its feathers in a new location; and (3), in the latest stages treated, a loss of the capacity to regulate the initial direction of feather outgrowth.

It is noteworthy that the dorso-ventral organization of the individual feather-germ does not appear to be correlated necessarily with the slope of the newly-emerged papilla. This is suggested by the fact that in embryonic

specimens which showed some feather papillae of reversed slope after the reorientation operation, there were also feather papillae which were apparently forced into a more normal orientation through mechanical factors of crowding. Also, among cases hitherto unreported, in which blocks of tissue entirely within the humeral tract were reoriented 180°, rosettes of feather papillae, variously oriented, were observed; but, in adult specimens, dorso-ventrality always corresponded to feather slope regardless of direction (i.e., dorsal sides dorsally oriented). It follows, therefore, that any causal connection between feather slope and dorso-ventrality is effective at the time the direction of feather slope is finally fixed, or later, and not during the initial outgrowth of the feather papilla. [This raises the question whether other evidences of dorso-ventrality (e.g., order of origin of barb-vane ridges, or distribution of melanophores) in the newly-formed feather papilla are necessarily related to the future dorso-ventral organization of the feather germ. An answer to this question is now being sought in appropriate experiments.]

These results suggest that the properties of the prospective humeral tract are progressively established in the following sequence: (1) the delimitation of the tract area; (2) the structural properties, space-size distribution, and time of emergence of the prospective feathers; (3) the orientation of their initial outgrowth with respect to the body axis; and (4) the establishment of their dorso-ventral organization. Clearly, the differentiation of these properties occurs first in the embryonic mesoderm, for the effects of the reorientation operation are the same regardless of whether the ectoderm is rotated along with the mesoderm. The mesoderm subsequently induces in the ectoderm the appropriate tract-specific response properties.

Regionally Specific Inductive Action of Feather-Tract Mesoderm

Since, in the adult bird, each feather generation arises from the epidermis of the follicle as a consequence of the non-specific inductive action of the dermal papilla, and since each feather is an unique component of an orderly pattern, it follows that there are differences from follicle to follicle in the response properties of the epidermis. These epidermal response patterns arose, as shown above, through the inductive action of the mesoderm during early developmental stages; therefore, it must further follow that during the origin of the feather tract the mesoderm associated with each prospective feather germ gives different inductive cues to its overlying epidermis. (Presumably these inductive cues also determine the sequence of structural changes which characterize the successive feather generations of the juvenile plumage; that is, the embryonic induction establishes a pat-

tern of changing epidermal responses to non-specific inductive action of the dermal papilla, and the response pattern becomes stabilized only in the adult feather follicle. There is a possibility, however, that specific influences of the dermal papilla in the juvenile bird affect the characteristics of feathers regenerated during juvenile moults. This should be studied.)

This conclusion has been examined further by means of experiments in which a mesodermal isolate excised from the prospective thigh feather tract in the 3- to 4-day chick was grafted to the dorsal surface of the wing bud from which an isolate of similar size and shape was previously removed (1). The thigh mesoderm became covered with wing ectoderm after the operation and induced in it the formation of typical thigh feathers, in some cases clearly replicating the particular gradient pattern of change from feather to feather characteristic of a portion of the normal thigh tract. This result occurred at all levels of the wing from shoulder to wrist. It is apparent, therefore, that mesoderm of the prospective thigh feather tract exercises a regionally specific inductive action on its covering ectoderm. Likewise, there is a graded variation in this inductive specificity from one prospective feather locus to another, such that the epidermal component of each feather follicle in the adult bird forms a distinctive feather vane which is a component of an orderly pattern of structural variation within the feather tract.

The regional response properties of the epidermis are thus entirely dependent on the nature of the mesodermal stimulus. It is important, however, to recognize that these response properties are subject to genetic limitations. For example, when an isolate of mesoderm from a normal White Leghorn embryo is grafted to the wing bud of a host homozygous for silky (a gene affecting feather structure), the wing epidermis responds to the mesodermal induction by forming feathers of the silky type (1).

Time of Inductive Action

Results of the foregoing experiments clearly indicate that the potentiality of mesoderm to give specific inductive cues to the epidermis of the prospective feather tract is differentiated long before there are morphological signs of incipient feather formation. But, they do not provide evidence of the time at which these potentialities are exercised or the manner in which the inductive action is carried out. It seems possible, however, that specification of the future epidermal response may be induced as soon as the dermal condensations are formed and epidermal outgrowth of the feather papilla begins. At this time there occurs a complex interplay of inductive reactions between mesodermal and ectodermal components of

the feather germ, as demonstrated by experiments in vitro. These reactions are of such interest as to merit further discussion.

The mesodermal condensations of the first feather germs of the back skin appear in embryos of stage 30 (6½ days), or slightly before. Small isolates of back skin explanted to tissue culture media at this time form typical feather papillae but differentiate poorly, if at all, when explanted at earlier stages. Furthermore, when ectoderm from undifferentiated skin is explanted in combination with skin-mesoderm in which the dermal condensations have just formed, feather germs develop. It would appear, therefore, that the initial outgrowth of feather germs may be induced by the dermal condensations in vitro (22).

This initial inductive action of the mesodermal condensations on the overlying epidermis is apparently of short duration. When isolates of mesoderm from embryonic skin in which the epidermal response has begun are associated in vitro with epidermis (from a younger donor) which has not been induced, feather germs are not formed. But, epidermis which has initiated feather formation is itself inductive, for when combined with mesoderm which has not yet formed dermal condensations, it induces their origin and typical feather germs arise (22). It is possible, of course, that these relationships do not occur in vivo and that, although the mesodermal component of the feather germ may lose its inductive capacity shortly after it is formed, it subsequently regains it, for, as noted above, the dermal papilla, a derivative of the original mesodermal condensation, induces the formation of successive feather generations in each follicle after hatching.

Specific Induction of Scales and Claws

Whereas the foregoing sections show that regionally specific differences in the character of the plumage in the fowl have their origin in specific inductive actions of the mesoderm, the question now arises whether other integumentary derivatives likewise arise in response to regionally specific mesodermal influences. An answer to this question has been sought in experiments in which mesodermal tissues of the prospective foot, typically associated with the origin of scales and large claws, have been combined with ectoderm of the wing, which does not normally form these structures.

In the 3- to 4-day embryo, mesoderm of the apical region of the leg bud, which forms the foot, was stripped of ectoderm, excised, and grafted to the apex of the wing bud subjacent to the apical ectodermal ridge (1). The graft was thus initially supplied with wing ectoderm of the apical ridge, and subsequently became covered with ectoderm regenerating from the proximal portions of the wing bud. In most of the resulting embryos, the

wings terminated in abnormal toes bearing scales and large claws characteristic of the foot.

In other experiments grafts of apical leg-bud mesoderm from older (ca. 4½ days) donor embryos were implanted in the shoulder region of the wing bud. In these cases, also, wing-bud ectoderm covered the graft, and scales and large claws formed on toe-like structures which developed proximally on the wing. Since epidermis of the wing normally does not form scales and long claws, it is clear that these structures differentiated in response to a specific inductive action of the leg mesoderm.

Origin of Regional Differences in Inductive Specificity

It is now appropriate to give particular attention to the differences observed when mesoderm from different proximo-distal levels of the leg bud is grafted to the wing bud in association with ectoderm of wing-bud origin. As shown in the foregoing sections, mesoderm originating from the proximal portion of the leg bud (prospective thigh) induces typical thigh feathers in the wing ectoderm at all levels of the wing from shoulder to wrist. Mesoderm of the distal portion of the leg bud, however, in suitable grafts to the shoulder or the wing-bud apex, induces scales and claws in the wing ectoderm.

These results emphasize, perhaps more dramatically than others reported here, the striking differences in inductive specificity which are exercised by closely associated regions of the embryonic mesoderm. The origin of these differences is a problem which currently offers a better opportunity for analysis than those more subtle differences which result in the induction of tract-specific and follicle-specific feather characteristics which have been treated in a considerable part of this report.

It should be noted, however, that no great progress has been made as yet in this analysis, and the only evidence contributing appreciably to the problem has been obtained from experiments on the developmental role of the apical ectodermal ridge (17). This structure, which caps the apical zone of the young limb bud, acts as the inductor of limb outgrowth (19, 31-33); it elicits the sequential formation of materials for the prospective limb parts in proximo-distal sequence in the apical mesoblast. During the outgrowth of the limb bud, therefore, the apical zone is a region of intensive morphogenetic activity and might reasonably be expected to modify the inductive specificities of tissues implanted in it.

This has proved to be the case. Grafts of prospective thigh mesoderm, which would normally induce thigh feathers in the covering ectoderm, were implanted at the apex of the wing bud subjacent to the apical ecto-

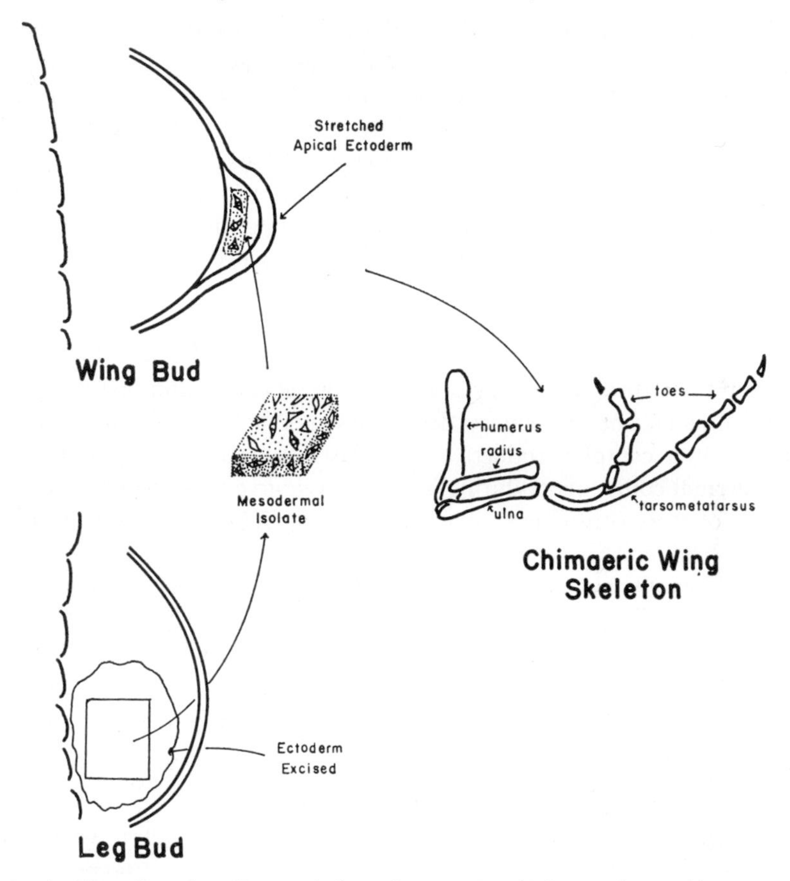

Fig. 6. The effect of grafting an isolate of prospective thigh mesoderm subjacent to the apical ectodermal ridge of the wing bud. The skeleton of the chimaeric appendage was traced from an enlarged x-ray photograph of the disarticulated wing shortly after hatching.

dermal ridge (Fig. 6). In the resulting chimaeric wings the grafts differentiated typical foot parts in the region of the manus and induced the formation of warty and overlapping scales and large claws in the wing ectoderm. This occurred, however, only when the implant developed in intimate association with the apical ectodermal ridge. When a small amount of mesoderm was interposed between the graft and the apical ridge, foot parts were never formed; instead, the implant developed at more proximal wing levels and usually induced the formation of typical thigh feathers in the wing ectoderm. From these results it is apparent that suitable implants of prospective thigh mesoderm may retain their ability to

differentiate leg-specific qualities in the wing environment. In the special circumstance of contact with the apical ridge, however, the thigh-specific regional potentialities of the implant are not realized; instead, the graft differentiates foot parts and the inductive specificities which provide for their appropriate armor of scales and claws. Thus the origin of regional differences in inductive specificity in the integumentary mesoderm is related to the morphological differentiation of its underlying skeletal parts. The latter, however, differentiate under the influence of the apical ectodermal ridge.

Conclusions

From these studies one may draw the general conclusion that the regionally distinctive integumentary derivatives in the fowl arise as the consequence of a complex inductive interplay between their epidermal and mesodermal components during early embryonic development. The cooperation of these components is schematized in Fig. 7. The ectoderm is an

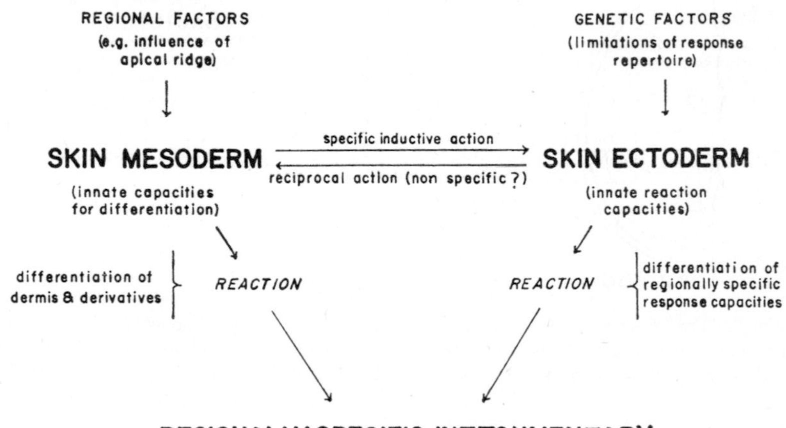

Fig. 7. Scheme of the interaction between embryonic ectoderm and mesoderm in the origin of regionally specific integumentary derivatives in the fowl.

active partner in the process, but the potentialities for qualitative regional differences develop initially in the mesoderm, which then induces a specific epidermal response.

It remains a challenging problem for the future to determine the factors responsible for the origin of inductive specificities in the mesoderm, and

the mechanisms whereby the mutual influences of the epidermal and mesodermal components of the skin are exercised in the differentiation of the complex integumentary system. These problems possibly will be attacked successfully through application of the newer methods of biochemical and biophysical analysis.

REFERENCES

1. Cairns, J. M., and Saunders, J. W., *J. Exptl. Zool.,* **127,** 221-248 (1954).
2. Davies, H. R., *Morphol. Jahrb.,* **15,** 560-645 (1889).
3. Fraps, R. M., and Juhn, M., *Physiol. Zool.,* **9,** 378-406 (1936).
4. Goff, R. A., *J. Morphol.,* **85,** 443-482 (1949).
5. Hamilton, H. L. (ed.), *Lillie's Development of the Chick,* 3rd edition, Henry Holt & Co., New York (1952).
6. ———, and Koning, A. L., *Am. J. Anat.,* **99,** 53-80 (1956).
7. Holmes, A., *Am. J. Anat.,* **56,** 513-535 (1935).
8. Jeffries, J. A., *Proc. Boston Soc. Nat. Hist.,* **22,** 203-241 (1883).
9. Koning, A. L., and Hamilton, H. L., *Am. J. Anat.,* **95,** 75-180 (1954).
10. Lillie, F. R., and Wang, H., *Physiol. Zool.,* **14,** 103-135 (1941).
11. Rawles, M. E., *J. Genet.,* **38,** 517-532 (1939).
12. ———, *Proc. Natl. Acad. Sci. U. S.,* **26,** 86-94 (1940).
13. ———, *Physiol. Zool.,* **17,** 167-183 (1944).
14. ———, *Physiol. Zool.,* **18,** 1-16 (1945).
15. ———, *Physiol. Zool.,* **20,** 248-269 (1947).
16. Ris, H., *Physiol. Zool.,* **14,** 48-66 (1941).
17. Saunders, J. W., *J. Exptl. Zool.,* **108,** 363-404 (1948).
18. ———, *Anat. Rec.,* **111,** 450 (1951).
19. ———, Cairns, J. M., and Gasseling, M. T., *J. Morphol.,* **101,** 57-88 (1957).
20. ———, and Gasseling, M. T., *J. Exptl. Zool.,* **135,** 503-528 (1957).
21. ———, and Weiss, P., *Anat. Rec.,* **108,** 581 (1950).
22. Sengel, P., *Experientia,* **13,** 177-182 (1957).
23. Wang, H., *Physiol. Zool.,* **16,** 325-354 (1943).
24. Watterson, R., *Physiol. Zool.,* **15,** 234-259 (1942).
25. Weiss, P., and Matolsty, A. G., *Nature,* **180,** 854 (1957).
26. Willier, B. H., and Rawles, M. E., *Proc. Natl. Acad. Sci. U. S.,* **24,** 446-452 (1938).
27. ———, and ———, *Physiol. Zool.,* **13,** 177-199 (1940).
28. ———, and ———, *Yale J. Biol. and Med.,* **17,** 321-340 (1944).
29. ———, and ———, *Genetics,* **29,** 309-330 (1944).
30. ———, ———, and Hadorn, E., *Proc. Natl. Acad. Sci. U. S.,* **23,** 542-546 (1937).
31. Zwilling, E., *J. Exptl. Zool.,* **128,** 423-441 (1955).
32. ———, *J. Exptl. Zool.,* **132,** 151-171 (1956).
33. ———, *J. Exptl. Zool.,* **132,** 173-187 (1956).

DISCUSSION

DR. HOLTFRETER: I want to congratulate you, Dr. Yamada, on your beautiful results. They are novel and most revealing. At the same time they are puzzling, leaving many of the old problems still unanswered. As an old-timer in this field I may be permitted to put your findings into a wider context.

As many of you know, the quest for the chemical nature of the inductive

agents operating in *normal* amphibian development (and this, I may insist, is our goal) has been tortuous and disheartening. Some two decades ago this inquiry started out with a dazzling bang. Embryologists at various places discovered almost simultaneously that a frightening diversity of artificial unrelated stimuli can imitate the effects of the living inductive tissues of the embryo. In most instances, however—and this is important for my subsequent remarks—the stimuli, such as tissue extracts or pure chemicals, would produce only the neuralizing, brain-inducing ("archencephalic") effects of the natural inductors.

The story became more involved. Very early two interconnected observations were made. (1) Devitalization of the natural inductors by heating, freezing, or various chemicals did not readily inactivate their neuralizing power but quickly destroyed their notochord—somite-inducing or "mesodermizing" power. (2) A great variety of tissues from all sorts of adult animals, including man and guinea pig, when grafted into an amphibian gastrula, could perfectly replicate the effects of either the archencephalic or the mesodermizing inductors of the embryo. The latter activity vanished in the adult tissues about as quickly by heat treatment as it did in the natural spino-caudal inductor.

From these observations it has been concluded by some authors that the multitude of effective adult tissues contain (for no apparent morphogenetic reason) the same inductive agents as are operating in the embryo. The search for the chemical nature of the agents went off on a new tangent. From now on, except for some abortive attempts at characterizing the inductors of the embryo proper, most researchers took to model experiments. They tested the activity of various extracts or fractions from readily available mammalian tissues, such as liver or kidney of the guinea pig. It was thought implicitly that if these chemically identifiable preparations can act like living inductors they would provide clues to the chemical nature of the latter.

Let us be aware of this sleight-of-hand procedure. From all we know about phenocopies, parthenogenesis, carcinogenesis, and, more fundamentally, about the potential side-tracking of enzymatic reactions, there is no *a priori* reason to assume that the effective agents present in adult tissues are identical with, or even related to those acting in normal induction.

This sceptical attitude became strengthened when it turned out that a great variety of biologically alien, so-called unspecific chemical agents can elicit normal conversion of gastrula ectoderm. Such agents were alkali or acids, versene or distilled water, alcohol, detergents, or what not. Who would dare attempting an identification of any one of these foreign agents with those employed by the embryo? And yet, what is the sense of making experiments if we cannot relate them rationally to the mechanisms of the embryo?

Other methodological difficulties have been pointed out in previous reviews. They offer further serious obstacles in interpreting our experimental results. Due to these difficulties many embryologists have given up in despair. But you, Dr. Yamada, and a few others have courageously followed up this line of ap-

proach, trying to specify the chemical compounds engaged in amphibian induction by resorting to experiments with adult mammalian tissues.

The saving grace of your endeavors lies, I believe, in the fact that your various preparations not only neuralize the ectoderm explants—as many slightly damaging shock treatments would do—but that some of them bring about mesodermal and even entodermal transformations. For one thing, your results support the view that embryonic induction is not simply due to a trigger mechanism, or represents an alternative choice, say between epidermal and neural differentiation. Whatever the chemical nature of your inductive preparations may be, they produce qualitatively different results. One may infer, indeed, that in normal development, too, the different structures are induced by different inductive agents. Comparable to the ubiquitous auxins, the very substances of the embryonic inductors may indeed occur throughout the organic world.

Dr. Cohn: I would like to ask Dr. Yamada what was the precision of the assay used to fractionate the various extracts that he made.

Dr. Yamada: In the case of the acid-precipitable fraction of the bone marrow-supernatant both the light and heavy fractions were found to be active in our test. However, it might be that one is the real inducer and the others are just contaminated by small amounts of the first component. We need a quantitative assay technique for determning this and other similar questions. We are now trying hard to work out such a method. We realize that the test of morphogenetic effects used in the present study is suited for morphological evaluation of the inductive effects, but not for quantitative study.

Dr. Grant: Most of your fractionation began with nucleoprotein, is that right? In other words, you have a salt extract with protein.

Dr. Yamada: Yes. In the case of liver and kidney an electrophoretically homogeneous sample of ribonucleoprotein has the inducing effect.

Dr. Grant: Do you have any indication that protein other than nucleoprotein will serve as inducing agent?

Dr. Yamada: Yes. The ribonucleoprotein fraction has been found to be effective only in the liver and kidney. In the bone marrow the same fraction of nucleoprotein has nothing to do with induction. Even in the case of kidney and liver it might be that there are other fractions which have a similar effect. For instance, we have obtained very clear spino-caudal effects by the kidney nucleus fraction separated by ordinary differential centrifugation. But as the sample was contaminated with whole cells, we don't use this result as a basis of argument.

Dr. Novikoff: I would like to ask how the 0.14 *M* salt extract was prepared. Was it a soluble extract?

Dr. Yamada: This is soluble. We use different methods of preparation but ordinarily we use unbuffered sodium chloride, centrifuging it at about 3,000 g.

DR. NOVIKOFF: The reason I ask is, I think if we start with soluble material, it may be questionable whether we should subsequently use the word "microsomes" for a particulate fraction. I don't wish to argue with this. This is a beautiful piece of work and has nothing to do with what we are calling a particular fraction, but I remember Hewson Swift's use of the word "microsomes" and it is bad enough when we get out of the cells certain materials which are in the cells if we call those microsomes but we confound the problem, I think, if we start with a soluble extract of particulates, presumably of the cell, and we treat them subsequently in the centrifuge and call the resulting pellet "microsomes." Now the word "microsomes," as Swift pointed out, had a past which is both venerable and confusing, and was resurrected by Claude.

DR. YAMADA: What we know is only that it contains a large amount of RNA. What I wanted to indicate with the designation was just to give you an idea of the magnitude of the centrifugal force we use for sedimenting this fraction. I agree with your suggestion.

DR. NOVIKOFF: Would it not be better that a pellet obtained from a salt extract be called "sediment" or "precipitate"? The term "microsome" is confusing enough, even for cell particulates isolated from homogenates.

DR. YAMADA: Yes. Perhaps better to call it a sediment.

DR. NIU: I want to congratulate Dr. Yamada for contributing so much to the problem of embryonic induction. We are also doing some simple experiments on the subject. First of all let me mention our purpose. As an embryologist, I am a little more interested in the physiological functioning of nucleoproteins or nucleic acids. Of course we have been approaching this problem in a different way. Many of you know of the technique we are using. To begin with, we have been interested in "ribonucleoprotein" and so we tried to isolate "ribonucleoprotein" as Dr. Yamada did. I use the term ribonucleoprotein in quotation marks because I don't know how pure it is. But I do know the following properties. It has an ultraviolet absorption spectrum typical of nucleoprotein. Of course, this curve varies somewhat from sample to sample. A second property is its ratio of nitrogen to phosphorus. According to our experiments this ratio varies from 5 up to 50. The content of RNA in these samples is about 5-20 percent. We want to know which part of this preparation is active. To my mind there are three ways to study this. The first method, and one which Dr. Yamada employed, is to use an enzyme, either a proteolytic enzyme or ribonuclease to hydrolyze the substrate. We have followed Dr. Yamada's work closely along these lines and can say that we have confirmed what he has obtained, but with some precautions. For instance, trypsin treatment in our system removes all of the activity. However, this enzyme is still in the system. When we added trypsin inhibitor, the activity returned. Following treatment with ribonuclease we still found activity but that activity was lower than in the control. Therefore it is clear that RNA-ase has some effects on the sample but

this effect is not complete. In other words, after RNA-ase treatment some RNA is still present in the sample. Since RNA-ase is destructive to living cells and lower concentration has no inducing effect, it appears that the loss of activity is due to the loss of RNA by treatment with RNA-ase. As to what is the active factor, you may draw your own conclusion. It immediately occurred to us that we should isolate some RNA by a newer method. It is the Kirby method which is published in the *Biochemical Journal.* With this RNA we had some specific activity but the activity was higher in the preparation of ribonucleoprotein. In the RNP we found 70% of the activity and only 30% residing in the RNA. The effects of these two were qualitatively the same but quantitatively different. If the isolated RNA is combined with a foreign protein, such as serum albumin, or a plant protein, then the activity is increased considerably. I don't know the mechanism involved here, but do think that pinocytosis may have something to do with it. It should be mentioned that if you prepare RNA you have to really be careful that you don't dry it or the activity of the fraction is lost. Finally, the concentration of RNA is extremely important. At the optimal concentration RNA initiates ectodermal differentiation. A factor of 5 or 10 will change the picture completely. Higher concentration tends to produce inhibitory effect. I certainly would appreciate hearing Dr. Yamada's comments on our work.

Dr. Yamada: Do you know about the work by Tiedemann and Tiedemann who tested nucleic acids prepared with phenol and came to the conclusion that they are not responsible for regional induction? Were the techniques the same or were they different?

Dr. Niu: Yes. It is interesting to note that they obtain low activity in their dried RNA. Using phenol, we also extracted protein from 9-day chick embryos. The solubility of this extract is too low to be tested in our assay system.

Dr. Yamada: I think your result is extremely important. Up until now we have tested no nucleic acid which was prepared in your way. What we used was the guanidine-hydrochloride method. This is the only one we have tested carefully enough and so it may be that the difference in preparation might be important in this case. How do you explain your result with the protease series?

Dr. Niu: I think Dr. Hayashi might be better able to answer that question. However, we compared ectodermal explants explanted into medium containing ribonucleoprotein treated with trypsin with explants placed in similar medium to which had also been added soy bean inhibitor. After two days, the explants in medium containing only trypsin became free-swimming vesicles. With inhibitor, however, the explants had attached to the glass and later gave rise to outgrowths which may contain special structure, neural tissue, or both.

Dr. Yamada: I was told by Tiedemann that he tried also soy bean inhibitor in his experiments using trypsin. Trypsin alone suppressed the inducing ability

of his sample. In the presence of soy bean inhibitor this effect of trypsin was inhibited. He concluded that the enzymatic activity of trypsin was responsible for suppressing the inducing ability.

Dr. Niu: That pleases me very much.

Dr. Yamada: Of course, this hasn't been published yet.

Dr. Brachet: I would like to make the point that it is really important to know what trypsin and its inhibitors are really doing. I wonder if Dr. Yamada, or any of the other people here, has considered this question by looking at the liberation of amino acids or nucleotides from the material which was treated with these enzymes. In other words, which materials are being released by the action of these enzymes? I would also like to say that I think it would be valuable to study the combined action of ribonuclease and trypsin on the explants. I think that it is very difficult to remove all of these enzymes from the solid preparations you are using, and it then becomes very important to know what the enzyme itself is doing. Finally, I would like to make briefly a comment on something Dr. Niu mentioned, that is that he gets an increased activity of RNA when he adds a non-specific protein to the preparation. This might be due to pinocytosis induced by the nonspecific protein. In our own experience with the amoebae, we have found that if you add RNA to the medium, say, for instance, labeled RNA, you get very little uptake whatsoever. However, if you add some protein to the RNA in the medium, this increases the pinocytosis of the amoebae and the uptake becomes considerable. So I would just like to offer as a suggestion that the effect of the protein in your system, Dr. Niu, is to increase pinocytosis, which may in turn increase the uptake of RNA by a factor of three or four.

Dr. Yamada: Thank you very much Dr. Brachet for the very important suggestion. I would like to comment on your question about the effect of the enzymes on the cells in the explants. For a control we always used a sample to which the enzyme was added after a sham incubation. The enzyme in these particular cases was always treated with heat. Compared with the sample without added heat-treated enzyme there was no significant difference in the outcome of induction.

Dr. Brachet: However, these enzymes can be heated to a great degree and still retain their activity, say trypsin, for instance. They are both very thermostable enzymes.

Dr. Yamada: We compared the heat-treated and non-heat-treated series of trypsin-incubation of the liver ribonucleoprotein sample for inductive ability. In the not heat-treated sample we get a complete suppression of induction. But if the enzyme is heat-treated after the incubation period, there is still a clear suppression of induction probably due to enzyme action on the sample during incubation. On the other hand, addition of heat-treated enzyme to the reaction mixture after a sham incubation does not cause a clear change in induction,

when compared with the original untreated sample. This suggests a heat inactivation of the enzyme even if it is not complete.

DR. NIU: Dr. Brachet, I am very glad you made the point on the use of non-specific proteins to increase the rate of pinocytosis by cells. We were very fortunate to have Dr. Holtfreter with us for a few days. I was happy to hear of his work on induced pinocytosis in amoeba. It is highly possible that this may well be what is going on.

DR. WEISS: The organism is to us still very much of a black box which responds to an experimental input Y with a signal X without revealing the complete network of connections and the route that has led from Y to X. Most attention in the problem of induction has been given to the identification of various Y's. I would like to get back to the other side of this question. Now we have been concerned mostly with what kind of substance produces a given "X" reaction. We have administered these substances to the black box, ignorant of what goes on inside, and then we observed the end result. With one kind of substance one got one particular type of reaction, with another substance one got another particular type of reaction. I think it is very significant that Dr. Yamada has shown us today the same substance, put through a series of treatments, can produce in this black box any particular reaction, depending upon the previous treatment. This removes the stigma of specificity from the chemical quality of the substance. In addition, if Dr. Niu is right, that the reaction of these materials differs according to the method of preparation, then again this contradicts specificity in the sense of a one-to-one matching reaction between the substance and the reacting system. Now where does this leave us? I would like to ask a question and it is this: what do we know about what happens between the time when we apply the substance and the time when we see the results of its action? Naturally, it will make a considerable difference just how fast the cell picks up this material, and just how fast it gets through the three or four or more reacting steps it may have to go through after it has gotten into the cell. All of these things must be taken into consideration. Now, to what extent can the different results we heard about be explained by differences in the penetration reaction kinetics, and so on, of the agent Y—for instance, extracts from bone marrow or some other source—and by the different stage of development of the reacting system—our black box—at the time when it is actually "hit" by Y, when the crucial event takes place? What do we know about progressive changes in our reacting systems irrespective of what agent we might apply to them? What effect do these materials you have extracted have on ectoderm taken from different stages, say from early and late gastrulae? How does this affect the type of results you get? The reacting system is usually treated as if it were stagnating, as if it were dead in a way. I think Dr. Holtfreter has shown that the ectoderm which is in these explants, although it may not form neural tissue or undergo specific differentiation types,

is changing in competence—meaning constitution—and the reacting system is therefore different when taken from different stages.

Dr. Yamada: We don't have any experiments on this point but I would like to mention the work of Toivonen and his group in this respect. They put bone marrow on their explants of some stage for different lengths of time. They found that the results obtained were qualitatively the same irrespective of the length of time the bone marrow was applied to the explant. They left the bone marrow on from several hours to several days and the effect was always of the trunk-mesodermal type. What did change, however, was the frequency with which the effect was noted; increasing time of application gave a greater frequency of effect.

Dr. Weiss: When you say frequency, do you mean that it was different types or the same type increasing in frequency. It seems to me that I remember that Toivonen showed that there were some admixture of types here.

Dr. Yamada: Yes, but I think that this was insignificant. What was quite apparent to me was that, in general, the time of application did not affect the quality of the induction noted. Another example is that studied by Johnen in Cologne. She studied the effect of kidney on gastrula ectoderm for different durations of time. When there is only a short period of contact with ectoderm she gets archencephalic effects, but if she leaves the sample on for a longer time she gets spino-caudal effects. Thus the effect seems to be qualitatively changing with different lengths of time but she feels that this may only be a quantitative difference and she interprets this along the lines which Nieuwkoop has suggested.

Dr. Holtfreter: I think it would be most desirable if we could reduce some of these troubles to changing properties of the reacting system in time, but I am not sure that this is the complete story.

Dr. Weber: I should like to ask a question concerning heat treatment of the bone marrow extract. I think it would be of interest to find out what happens to the extract after different lengths of heat treatment in biochemical terms. Are there progressive changes in these proteins or peptides, for instance, which could be correlated with the regional inductions obtained? Have you any information about this point?

Dr. Yamada: No, I am afraid that has not been done, but of course it should be. Our approach has been to use different treatments and it was interesting that a number of different treatments such as high salt concentration, longer ethanol-treatment, addition of pepsin at *p*H 7 and so on gave rise to the same kind of effects and we feel that something "spontaneous" is happening to the proteins. Not only tissues or extracts but fairly purified samples show this sequential change in regional effects after various treatments. We are planning to study the change of the sample, which is responsible for the change in regional effects, after we get a reasonably purified sample of the bone marrow factor.

Dr. Hayashi: Going back to the earlier discussion I would like to make a few comments to the questions raised by Dr. Niu. As Dr. Yamada mentioned we always added the same amount of enzyme to the control samples after incubation as that used in the experimental series. Only in the case of experiments with trypsin both the control and experimental samples were heated after incubation (and after the addition of trypsin to the control samples) in order to inactivate the enzyme. In preliminary experiments the control sample, to which trypsin was added and which was used without inactivating treatment, was found to lose its inductive effect almost completely. This might suggest either that trypsin absorbed to the sample acted directly on the reacting ectoderm or that the enzyme digested the implanted sample after implantation. Anyway, the control sample which was treated with heat for 5 minutes in 95% ethanol after the addition of trypsin retained its inductive effect. We also have controls on the effect of simple heat-treatment of the sample without the enzyme. This heat-treatment suppressed the deuterencephalic effect of the sample and shifted the regional inductive effect toward archencephalic. Thus, as far as the heat-treatment was involved we could only test the effect of trypsin on the archencephalic activity of the sample. Unfortunately, we could not use soyabean inhibitor because it is so expensive for us.

In the cases of ribonuclease-treatment and pepsin-treatment, no enzyme-inactivating treatment was used because the control samples of liver ribonucleoprotein, to which the enzymes were added after incubation, retained their inductive activities almost unchanged. However, in the case of kidney ribonucleoprotein we found that the mere addition of pepsin to the sample suppressed to some extent its spino-caudal effect, shifting the regional effect toward deuterencephalic. This suggests a more labile nature of the spino-caudal factor than the archencephalic factor of the kidney nucleoprotein.

As to the question of the effective concentration of RNA, I should like to say that we tested many ribonucleoprotein samples containing varying amounts of RNA and got results indicating that the inductive effect of those samples is largely dependent upon the nature of the protein-component and not upon the presence or amount of RNA in the sample. For example, we got almost the same regional effect at a comparable frequency with protein samples which were extensively reduced in their RNA content by ribonuclease-treatment as with the original ribonucleoprotein samples having high RNA content. Also in the case of pepsin-treatment, experimental samples which contained increased amounts of RNA (relative to the protein-moiety) showed only weak inductive effect. This fact indicates that the proteolytic enzyme did degrade the protein-moiety of the ribonucleoprotein and thus suppressed the inductive effect of the sample. We cannot completely exclude the possibility that RNA had something to do in the process of induction, but even if it participates it seems evident that some integral structure of protein is indispensable for the induction

of regional structures in the ectoderm at least under the experimental conditions we adopted.

I also tested the inductive effect of protein samples, which were derived from the liver ribonucleoprotein after removing RNA by phenol-treatments (Kirby's method and the method of Westphal et al. as described by Tiedemann and Tiedemann). With those protein samples I could not get any induction at all. The loss of inductive effect seems to me to be caused by severe denaturation of the sample and not to be caused by removal of RNA.

DR. NIU: I realize now that our discussion is coming to quantitative aspect of inducers. If so, it would be wise to discuss the problem on a quantitative basis. Unfortunately, time does not permit us to do so.

DR. STREHLER: How did you determine what concentration of protein or other substances to use? Did you use the same amount of protein in each one of these cases or was it the concentration you ended up with in a particular fraction?

DR. YAMADA: This type of experiment must be very curious for biochemists. For testing morphogenetic effects we have to put a solid sample into the ectodermal explant. When a supernatant fraction was to be tested, cold 90% ethanol was added to make 70% and the precipitate developed was gathered by centrifugation and applied (undiluted) to the ectoderm, after careful washing in the culture medium. In all series roughly 0.01 mg. (in dry weight) of such a sample was given to an ectodermal explant of approximately 1 mm. diameter.

DR. HOLTFRETER: Dr. Yamada, I wonder if you get any results using non-precipitated whole fractions?

DR. YAMADA: We have not yet obtained regional induction by putting fluid sample in the culture medium. But there are some experiments of von Woellwarth in Germany and Kawakami in Japan speaking for regional inductive effects of chick embryonal extract added to the culture medium.

DR. COHEN: I am still not clear as to the quantitative methods which you use, Dr. Yamada. Were there increments of solid put on the reacting system and did the differences in quantity reveal any different effects? Just how can you quantitate these effects in your assay system?

DR. YAMADA: Well, we tried to put approximately the same amount of solid material onto the explant. However, a very serious difficulty in even becoming semi-quantitative in this system is the difficulty in obtaining the reacting explants in uniform size. Even though we take them from the same region of the gastrulae it is very difficult to precisely control how much material we have. So we are aware that this test is not quantitative enough, although it allows a reliable identification of the induced structures. We are working out another test technique which gives us quantitative informations.

DR. COHEN: What I am thinking of is the concentration in the medium.

Dr. Yamada: I think I told you that we do not add the material in solution but that we add it as a solid material to the reacting system.

Dr. Cohen: Well, do you quantitate it by taking one, two, or three times a given amount of solution and then adding all the precipitate obtained from those samples?

Dr. Yamada: No, we did not do that, because from earlier experiments we know that that type of test does not work in this method. After the technique of quantitative assay will be worked out, we are planning to do that type of experiment.

Dr. Cohen: I would like to say that however exciting it may seem to be to look for stimulating compounds which produce these effects, it seems to me that the same kind of results could be explained on the basis of specific inhibitors which act upon the right system at the right time. Thus when you add something to a system of this complexity the effect may be due to an inhibitor or a stimulating factor, and both of these possibilities must be taken into account when you interpret your results.

Dr. Racker: I would like to re-emphasize a point brought up by Drs. Cohn, Strehler and Cohen, namely, the quantitative evaluation of inducers. I have recently read some of the literature on the purification of inducers and noted that although serious attempts are being made to grade the effects in a quantitative manner, which is undoubtedly difficult, few attempts are made to express these data in terms of dry weight or any other suitable unit of material. One is reminded of the earlier days in the field of enzymology when emphasis was placed on concentration rather than purification, and the meaning of specific activity was not generally recognized.

Dr. Niu: Well, Dr. Racker, in our work we know precisely the amount of RNA we used, the RNA content of nucleotprotein and particularly the specific structure induced by the freshly isolated substances.

A DEVELOPMENTAL ANALYSIS OF CELLULAR SLIME MOLD AGGREGATION[1]

MAURICE SUSSMAN[2]
Northwestern University,
Evanston, Illinois

INTRODUCTION

Aggregation is a stage in the developmental cycle of the cellular slime molds (Acrasiales). It is a device by which heretofore independent myxamoebae are brought together into a compact mass, a single organized, multicellular entity, whose terminal expression is a fruiting body. The process is illustrated by the time lapse series of photomicrographs shown in Fig. 1. The entire developmental cycle is shown schematically in Fig. 2.

This system is considered by the writer to exemplify cellular differentiation and to possess attributes that permit a rigorous, quantitative analysis thereof. Because the writer comes to the subject of developmental biology by the unorthodox route of microbial genetics, it may be of interest to examine his rationale for these statements.

We start with the observation that morphogenesis in multicellular systems is invariably accompanied by a sequential and progressive emergence of many new cell types. These specialized cells may persist as constituents of the terminal structure or may appear only transiently, play a specific role in the developmental sequence, and then disappear. Any such phenotypic modifications are adjudged to be within the domain of cellular differentiation. Whether the new phenotypes are readily reversible or, on the contrary, are irreversible by any presently known means is not considered to be of significance in defining this domain. Inclusion is based solely upon whether or not the new cell type can be shown to play a causal role in the construction or functioning of the terminal entity.

What kind of information, then, could provide a complete description of

[1] The investigations summarized in this paper were supported by grants from the National Cancer Institute and the Office of Naval Research.

[2] Present address: Department of Biology; Brandeis University, Waltham, Mass.

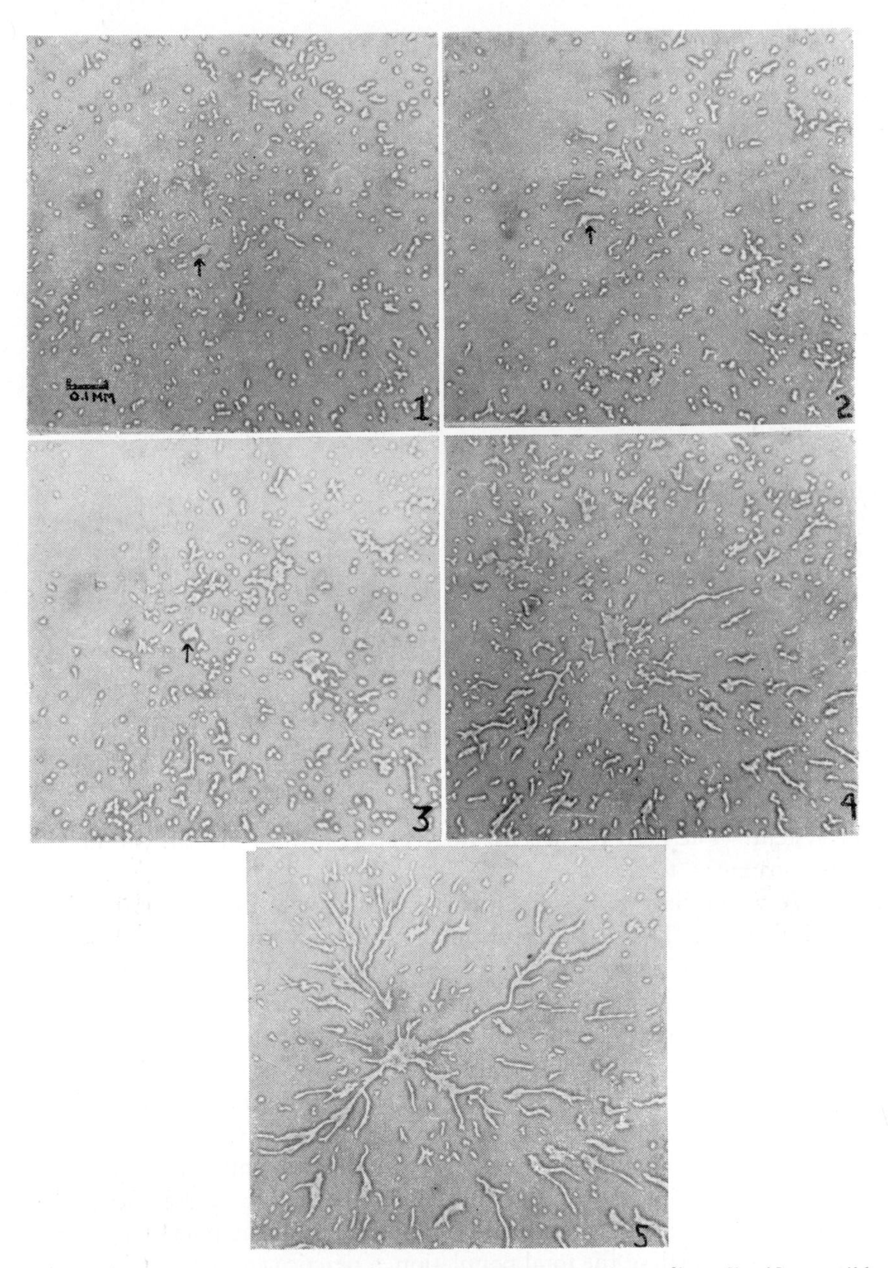

Fig. 1. Time lapse photomicrographs of aggregation by *Dictyostelium discoideum* wild type. The arrows point to the cell at which the aggregative center formed. The myxamoebae had been incubated on washed agar for periods of 9.5, 10.4, 10.75, 11.5, and 12.25 hours, respectively. (Sussman, Ennis, and Sussman, 1958).

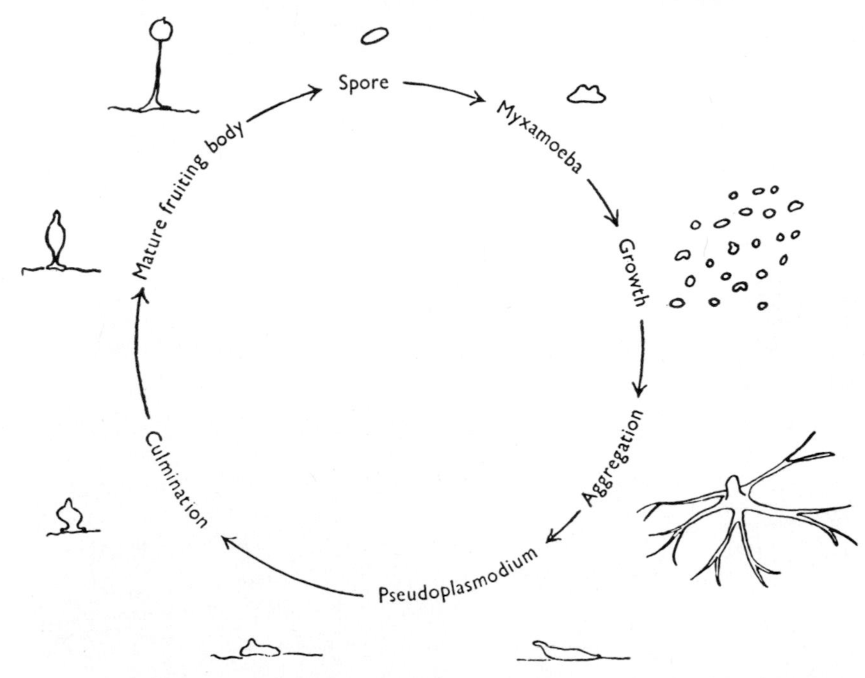

Fig. 2. A schematic diagram of the developmental cycle of *D. discoideum*. (Sussman, 1954).

the system? The need for at least three classes of information is immediately apparent:

1. We would have to describe the new phenotypes in quantitative, biochemical terms. This is necessary since ultimately we must explain the physiological role played by each in the developmental sequence and the manner in which it was derived from its parental variety.

2. We would have to learn whether each novel phenotype proceeds from a transient, purely physiological alteration or involves changes in the genetic apparatus of the cell and, further, to describe the nature of these changes. At present, there are three ways of doing this. One is by recombination analysis of matings between cells. Another is by nuclear transplants. Where these are impossible, one must infer the nature of the change by studying the rate of appearance and disappearance of the phenotype in relation to the growth of the total population, a practice employed with great precision in microbial genetics (13).

3. We would have to specify the cell interactions and other environmental factors which may induce many of the phenomic modifications and

which certainly must regulate the numbers of cells of each type to be found in the total population.

Clearly the complexity of the task demands that the total morphogenetic cycle be broken up into a serial array of smaller sequences during each of which the emergence of only a limited number of new phenotypes need be accounted for. Further, the system should be examined in a rigorously defined chemical and physical environment. The differential growth and death rates of the cell types must be calculable by growth of clones and concomitant viability determinations. The number of cells taking part in the development and their population density must be controlled.

Happily, for consistency's sake, we can report that cellular slime mold aggregation, as well as its other developmental stages, satisfies these criteria. At present only two cell types have been recognized to play a causal role during aggregation. The normal process can be carried out by myxamoebae free of exogenous nutrients and dispensed on washed agar. No detectable changes in cell number need occur during the process, and growth rates prior to it have been determined by clonal platings. The dependence upon cell number and population density has been extensively investigated. While the current description of the system is by no means complete, the broad outlines are, I think, now clear. The contributions to it that have emerged from our laboratory and that will be discussed in this paper were in large part due to the efforts of Drs. Raquel R. Sussman, H. L. Ennis, and S. G. Bradley, Mr. N. S. Kerr, Mrs. Frances Lee Fu, and Miss Elizabeth Noel.

The Position of Aggregation in the Developmental Cycle

The developmental cycle begins with spore germination. Myxamoebae emerge, feed on bacteria, and increase exponentially. With the onset of the stationary phase, morphogenesis begins. The randomly distributed cells elongate, orient radially, and move toward central collecting points, forming ramified streams as they do so. As the cells arrive at the center, a conical mound develops, and this is transformed into an organized, slug-shaped pseudoplasmodium. Ultimately, by a series of complex morphogenetic movements, the slug is transformed into a terminal fruiting body with a sorus or spore mass, a parenchymatous, cellulose-enclosed stalk, and a basal disk. In one genus this basic structure is modified by the appearance of whorled branches, each possessing an apical spore mass.

The developmental fate of the myxamoebae is determined by the order in which they entered the aggregate (15, 2). The first contingent constitutes the lower stalk of the fruit; the next arrivals become the upper stalk.

Cells arriving later comprise the spore assembly, and the last ones form the basal disk.

The Dependence of Center Formation on Population Density

The ability of population density to determine the number of aggregative centers was originally demonstrated with *Dictyostelium discoideum* wild type (24). Aliquots containing a constant number of washed myxamoebae were dispensed on washed agar at population densities between 80 and 750 cells/mm^2. Counts of aggregative centers were then made after suitable incubation. At very low density, no centers were formed. At very high density, the number of centers was depressed, presumably by competition between rival potential center-forming agencies for a common audience. At an intermediate value (200 cells/mm^2), center formation was maximal.

The dependence on population density thus revealed was found to hold true for 6 other stocks representing 3 species and 2 genera. As Table 1 shows, great differences were encountered in the values of threshold and optimal densities.

TABLE 1

Dependence of Center Formation on Population Density and Cell Number

Species	Strain	Threshold density	Optimal density	Center: Cell ratio
D. discoideum	wild type	80	200	1:2200
	Fruity(*Fty-1*)	40	200	1:24
	Fruity(*Fty-2*)	40	200	1:43
	Bushy(*Bu-1*)	70	350	1:1810
D. purpureum	wild type	20	100	1:330
	Bushy(*Bu-1*)	20	20	ca. 1:100
P. violaceum	wild type	50	250	ca. 1:180

Density values are given as no. cells/mm^2, determined by direct count and by calculation from total number of cells in sample and total area covered. Data for the first five strains were published previously (Sussman and Noel, 1952; Sussman, 1955). The results for the last two are from preliminary experiments and represent rough approximations.

The Dependence of Center Formation on Cell Number

The data also indicate that, at optimal density, the number of centers was proportional to the number of cells present. Thus, 10^5 *D. discoideum* wild type cells produced about 50 centers; 5×10^4 cells, about 25 centers; 2.5×10^4, about 12.5 centers. This corresponded to a distribution of one center among approximately 2000 cells. As the result of many such deter-

minations in the range between 5×10^3 and 10^5 cells, a value of 1:2200 for the center: cell ratio at optimal density was obtained.

The proportional relationship also held for the other six strains. However, as shown in the last column of Table 1, a wide variety of center : cell ratios was encountered. The lowest was that of *D. discoideum* wild type (1:2200) and the highest, that of the fruity mutant, *Fty-1,* of *D. discoideum* (1:24).

Apropos of the latter, *Fty-1* fruits illustrate some of the remarkable properties of this morphogenetic system. Consider that, at optimal density, the aggregates contain approximately 24 cells and in some cases as few as 10 to 12. The fruits which these cells construct are exquisite miniatures of the relatively enormous wild-type fruits such as emerge on growth plates at high population density. Photomicrographs of the mutant structures and considerations of the import that they bring to the problem of cellular interactions have been published elsewhere (33, 28).

Returning to the proportional relationship between centers and cells, this suggested that single myxamoebae were initiating the centers by inducing their neighbors to aggregate. This conclusion followed since, were more than one cell required, the relationship would have been exponential, not linear. The question remained, however, as to whether only special cells in the population could do this or, alternatively, whether any cell could ultimately attain initiative capacity. The latter would imply that the center : cell ratio reflected only the proportion of cells that had attained initiative capacity first.

The point was settled by examining the distribution of aggregates among very small, replicate population samples. Cell assemblies containing 250, 500, 900, 1025, and 2100 myxamoebae were dispensed on washed agar with a machined loop at densities high enough so that if they could have aggregated, they would have. Yet, as seen in Table 2, only a relatively small

TABLE 2

DISTRIBUTION OF AGGREGATES AMONG SMALL POPULATION SAMPLES
(Sussman and Noel, 1952; Ennis and Sussman, 1958b)

No. cells per sample	Total no. samples	Proportion of samples with: 0 centers	1 center	2 centers	3 centers	Center: Cell ratio
2100	85	0.42	0.50	0.07	0.012	1:2420
1025	91	0.63	0.32	0.044	0.011	1:2230
900	123	0.69	0.29	0.025	0.0	1:2430
500	99	0.80	0.19	0.01	0.0	1:2170
250	306	0.88	0.12	0.0	0.0	1:2020
					Mean	1:2250

proportion of the samples aggregated. Had a large number of the myxamoebae been capable of initiating centers, this result could not have been obtained. Instead, all of the samples would sooner or later have aggregated. This datum compelled acceptance of the conclusion that a small number of myxamoebae are uniquely constituted to be initiator cells and that these are distributed at random among their neighbors, the responder cells.

Confirmation was obtained by comparing the proportions of samples containing 0, 1, 2, and 3 aggregative centers with the Poisson distribution which holds only for systems in which the probability of an event is small and its distribution completely random. The general terms of this expansion are $P_k = \frac{m^k e^{-m}}{k'}$, where P_k is (in this case) the probability that a sample will contain k aggregates, and m is the average number of aggregates per sample. Comparison of the calculated and observed proportions of samples with 0, 1, 2, and 3 aggregates by Chi square test revealed a very good statistical agreement. Further, the Poisson expression was used to calculate the value of m from the observed P values. The term, m/no. cells per sample, yielded the center : cell ratio. The last column of Table 2 lists the calculated ratios, which agree closely with the ratio previously arrived at for *D. discoideum* wild type by examination of large populations.

The Identification of the Initiator Cell

The populational analysis of aggregation had provided a firm basis for belief in the existence of a specialized initiator cell. Therefore, in 1955, an attempt was begun in collaboration with Dr. Gaylen Bradley to determine if in *D. discoideum* wild type the initiator cell could be distinguished from its neighbors by morphological criteria prior to the onset of aggregation. A unique cell type (termed the I-cell) was indeed detected, and preliminary experiments encouraged the belief that it might be the initiator cell; but it was not until the past year, largely due to the efforts of Dr. Herbert Ennis, that micromanipulative and other techniques could be evolved to enable a crucial test of the possibility (8).

The I-cell is two to three-fold larger than the responder cells in diameter, three to ten-fold larger in area. It is much flatter, so as to acquire a bluish tint under appropriate illumination. It is highly motile in random directions before aggregation has begun. Enveloping lobopodia and great numbers of filopodia protrude constantly and explosively. Finally, it is more heavily granulated and vacuolated and its nucleus is considerably larger. Fig. 3 shows photomicrographs of I-cells and Fig. 4 presents histograms to illustrate the size difference between I-cells and responders.

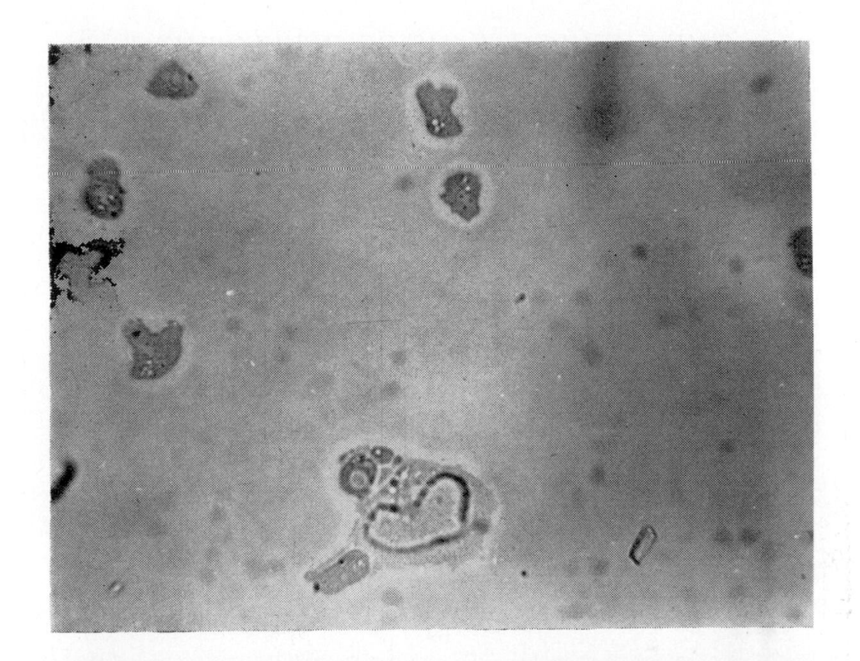

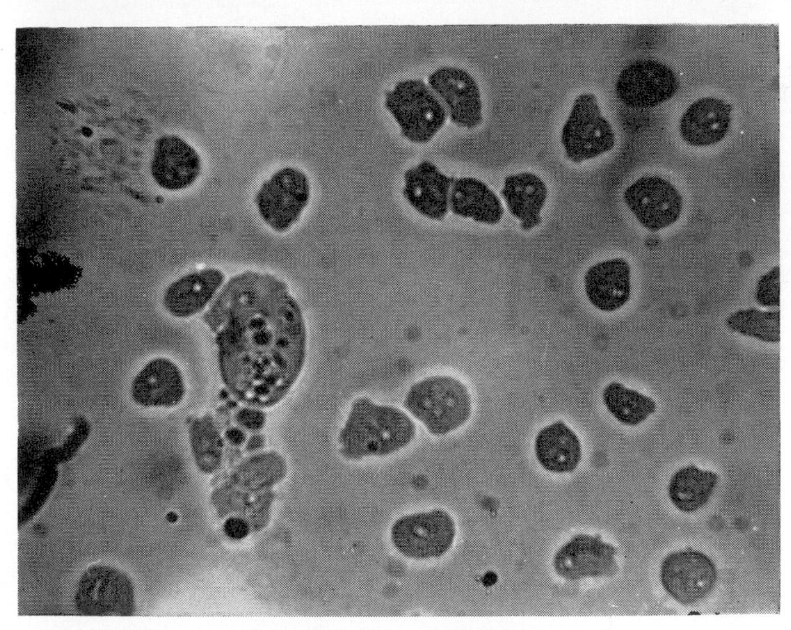

Fig. 3. Photomicrographs of two I-cells. 460 × magnification.
(Ennis and Sussman, 1958b).

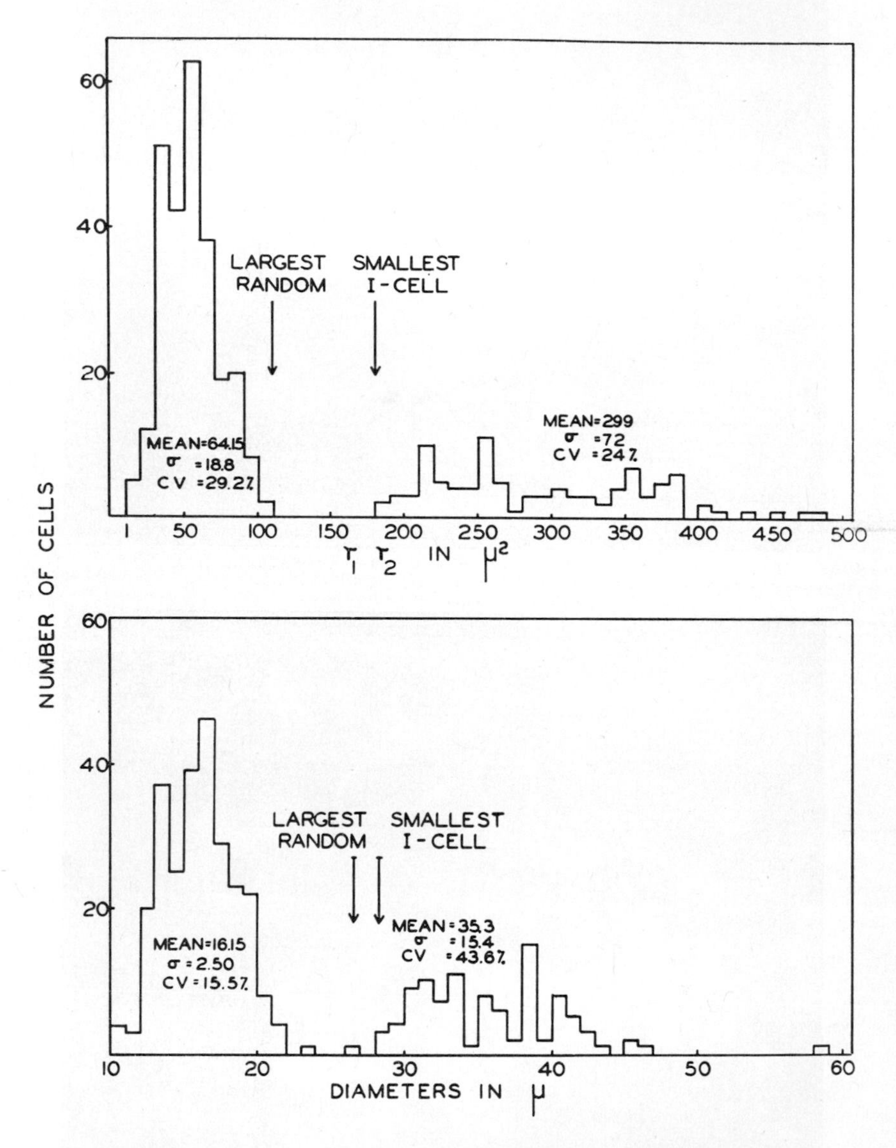

Fig. 4. Size differences between I-cells and randomly chosen cells after incubation on washed agar (Sussman et al., 1958).

terial. The solvent pair was n-butanol and 0.01 *N* NH_4OH. After 158 transfers, the activity peak was located in the tenth tube, indicating a partition coefficient of 0.06. The weight distribution and determinations of fluorescence and spectral absorption all agreed in suggesting that the active material was still grossly impure. At the moment, we have no information regarding the chemical nature of this component, but Dr. Barbara Wright-Kalckar will describe some exciting results that bear on this subject.

Having scarcely driven a wedge into the problem of the chemotactic complex, it would of course be premature to think seriously at present about the sensing apparatus of the myxamoebae or about the integrated actions of the cell assembly within this morphogenetic field. In this connection, Bonner has made the extremely important observation that not only the center but also the radial cell streams can produce the chemotactic agent (3, 4). His data suggest that a cell becomes sensitized to and excited by the incoming agent and then actively produces it (or perhaps some of its components).

2. *Cell Adhesion During Aggregation*

When one attempts to manipulate well-formed streams and centers, it is immediately obvious that the cells are no longer loosely massed but possess active, adhesive properties. Thus, segments of the aggregate can be removed intact from the substratum, and even prolonged trituration yields large cell clumps. In fact, the only way by which we have been able to prepare homogeneous, unclumped suspensions of cells in this stage for clonal plating, etc., has been treatment with trypsin at high *p*H, in accordance with procedures employed by embryologists for tissue dispersal (36).

Observations by many workers indicate that this adhesive property augments and complicates the chemotactic process (1, 16, 5, 23). For example, streams converging upon a center need not coalesce even though they are extremely close together. The streams often approach a center tangentially over a highly curved path, a response not easily interpretable as a purely chemotactic one. When the distal segment of a stream is separated from the proximal, it will often stop moving and form a satellite center, so as to suggest that chemotaxis and adhesion must operate in conjunction to maintain stream integrity.

Some of the adhesive properties may conceivably be explained in terms of the production of an extracellular cement. A precedent for this has been established by Raper and Fennell (18), who showed that the pseudoplasmodium of *D. discoideum* is held together by a slime envelope which is

spun out as a cylindrical ribbon behind the advancing slug. However, earlier observations of Raper and Thom (17) are not so easily explainable in these terms. They found that intergeneric mixtures of myxamoebae formed completely separate aggregative centers, the streams of which crossed each other and became intimately interlaced without disturbing the integrity of either. In mixtures of *D. discoideum* and *D. mucoroides,* common radiate aggregation patterns were formed and, by vital staining, it could be shown that both species were contributing to a common center. However, the cells were reshuffled upon reaching the center and two separate pseudoplasmodia appeared, each characteristic of one species. Chimeric hybrids were never encountered and replating of the spores provided no evidence that both types of cells had entered a single pseudoplasmodium. It is difficult to understand these actions without invoking some sort of specific adhesion.

To us, the most promising attempt at interpretation is that of J. H. Gregg (9, 10), who is proceeding upon the supposition that forces similar to those operating in antigen-antibody reactions can account for the specific adhesion. Gregg has followed the appearance of surface antigens by titration with rabbit antisera. His data indicate the presence of more than one kind of antigen and a regulated time sequence of appearance. He has also begun to study antigenic properties of a collection of mutants. The ultimate expectation is to correlate adhesive properties and morphogenetic potencies with antigenic topography. As Gregg has pointed out (9), this approach is predicated upon the hypotheses advanced by Tyler (37) and by Weiss (38) to explain the adhesion of metazoan and metaphytic tissues.

3. Interactions During Synergistic Aggregations by Wild Type and Mutant Cells

That the initiator cell must by its actions and its position affect the developmental fate of its neighbors is obvious, since whether they aggregate, and the order in which they enter the aggregate, determines their place in the terminal fruit (i.e. whether they are to become spores, stalk cells, or basal disk cells). That the responder cells might in turn affect the initiators is not immediately obvious but has been revealed through a study of mixed aggregations (7, 25, 26, 27).

The ability of potential initiator cells to induce their neighbors to aggregate has been found to depend in part upon the nature of the audience which they must excite (28). This was demonstrated by comparing the ability of potential initiator cells of the fruity mutant *Fty-1* to induce centers among a homologous audience, with their ability when faced with an

mixtures containing as many as 8000 to 9000 wild-type cells. This is remarkable, since all of the mixtures had been dispensed on washed agar in identical fluid volumes and consequently covered the same surface area. This means that while the lower numbers of wild type (500-6000) were present in the mixtures at population densities below optimal, the higher numbers (6000-9000) were at a density above optimal (200 cells/mm^2) and thus could have aggregated perfectly well, even had there been no aggregateless cells. Yet here too a multiplicity of centers was encountered, far more than the wild type alone could have produced. We were forced to conclude that the synergism can operate under two entirely different circumstances.

These were shown to be experimentally separable when the mutants and wild type were physically separated by a thin agar membrane. Excess mutant cells were dispensed on one side, and on the other side were placed wild-type cells either at a density below the threshold for any center formation or alternatively at a density above optimal, thereby simulating the circumstances alluded to above. At low density the wild type produced no centers at all, indicating that when the wild type is too sparse to aggregate alone, the mutant cells must contribute their physical presence if synergism is to operate. The mere supply of diffusible material is not enough.

In contrast, when the wild type was present at high density and was opposed by excess mutant cells, far more centers could be produced than in the absence of the latter. Table 10 gives the data for several pairings and

TABLE 10

Action of Aggregateless Cells Upon Wild Type Across Agar Membranes

Mutant	Center:wild-type cell ratio in mixtures	No. centers formed by 20,000 wild-type cells on agar membranes		
		Experimental	Control	Fold increase
Agg-204	1:76	34.2	3.6	9.5
Agg-70 (3 × 10^5 cells)	1:148	30.1	3.5	8.6
Agg-70 (1.5 × 10^5 cells)		19.1	3.5	5.4
Agg-53	1:980	5.3	3.2	1.7
Agg-72	1:00[1]	13.8	—	3.8

[1] The wild type can form no centers at all, even when mixed with small numbers of *Agg-72* cells and even when the wild type is at a density high enough for it to aggregate alone. This mutant actively inhibits the process, but, as seen in the data, only when physically present.

shows that the intensity of the effect depended on the number of mutant cells which had been placed on the membrane, and moreover that it was strain-specific.

This result forced the conclusion that, in mixtures where the wild

type is dense enough to aggregate alone, the mutants need only supply diffusible material to effect the synergistic multiplicity of centers and need not be physically present. Confirmation of this view was obtained in synergistic aggregations of wild type with *Agg-91,* a strain whose myxamoebae and (synergistically produced) spores are dwarf-sized and can be distinguished by inspection. In mixtures containing wild type at low density, the *Agg-91* cells comprised the major component of the fruit; but in mixtures containing wild type at optimal density or above, the *Agg-91* cells could not be found. Yet far more centers could be formed by the wild type in this circumstance than when alone.

The question arose as to whether cell-free preparations of mutant cells might not be active in affecting initiative capacity. As Table 11 indicates,

TABLE 11

EFFECT OF CELL-FREE EXTRACTS ON WILD-TYPE AGGREGATION AT OPTIMAL DENSITY

Source of extract	Fold activity[1]
Agg-70	2.6
Agg-72	2.5
Fty-1	11.4
Wild type	7.8

[1] Fold activity refers to the ratio of centers produced by 20,000 wild-type cells at optimal density on extract agar to that on control agar.

active preparations could be obtained not only from the aggregateless mutants but from the fruity (*Fty-1*) stock and from the wild type itself. This result becomes especially noteworthy when it is considered that no other treatment among trials of many kinds has ever succeeded in influencing initiative capacity.

To summarize, the foregoing indicates that aggregateless cells perform at least two functions in synergistic mixtures. First, they play an active role as responder cells, enter the aggregate, and become part of the fruit. As such, they can offset the lack of their wild-type counterparts where this is needed. Second, they produce diffusible material which can affect the initiative capacity of the wild type. This is the only function that is needed when adequate numbers of wild type are present and, in at least the case of *Agg-91,* it is the only function actually performed.

The implication of these findings for the relationship between wild-type initiator and responder cells is obvious, in view of the fact that cell-free material from the wild type can also affect initiative capacity. One may

ask why the mutant cells can exert the effect in mixtures when wild-type responders cannot. The answer is probably contained in the fact that the mutant cells could be packed around the wild type at densities as high as 20,000 cells/mm^2 in these mixtures. This cannot be done with exclusively wild-type populations because packing the cells more densely than 200 cells/mm^2 brings the initiator cells close enough together that they compete for a common audience and center formation is then depressed, as Fig. 3 shows.

The most interesting question at present concerns the bearing of these phenomena upon the I-cell. Unfortunately, the extract experiments were performed prior to the I-cell investigation. We mean to repeat the incubation of wild type on the extract agar and determine if the I-cell count rises in proportion to the increase in center formation.

A final and most interesting complex of interactions was uncovered in mixtures of wild type with *Agg-91*. When small numbers of the former (500-2000) were mixed with an excess of the latter, the ratio center : wild-type cells remained constant at 1:118. When larger numbers of wild type (2500-8000) were added, the ratio progressively decreased to 1:442. Because these mixtures had all been dispensed on washed agar in 0.01 ml. drops and consequently covered the same surface area, the increase in the wild-type contingent from 500 to 8000 meant a 16-fold increase in the density of the latter. When, however, the wild-type density was reduced by dispensing them on washed agar in larger-sized drops (while still maintaining an excess density of *Agg-91*), the larger numbers of wild type could induce proportionately as many centers as the smaller, and the ratio rose to 1:118.

This meant to us that the capacity of larger numbers of the wild type to induce centers in the presence of the mutant had originally been hampered by the wild type itself, since reducing the density of the wild type while maintaining a constant density of the mutant relieved the hindrance. The situation is analogous to that which obtains when wild type aggregates alone. That is, at densities greater than optimal the potential center-forming agencies are brought closer together, compete with each other, and thereby decrease the number of centers. The difference is that this depression is observed at densities greater than 200 cells/mm^2, whereas when excess *Agg-91* cells are present the depression in center formation becomes significant at 38 cells/mm^2!

Clearly the mutant cells must act upon the wild type in order to bring this about. But as mentioned before, the reduction in center formation ultimately involves interactions between the wild-type cells themselves. In

short, a hierarchical system operates in which one cell class acts upon another and causes the second to interact within itself. Coupled with these, it must be remembered, is the diffusible material contributed by the mutant, which at the very least permitted the wild type to induce many more centers (1:442) than they could when alone (1:2200). It would seem that the description of aggregation will not be complete unless the interactions cited above can be defined in chemical terms.

Environmental Effects

It is probable that the onset of aggregation is itself the direct result of an environmental influence, namely, the exhaustion of nutrients and the entrance of the population into the stationary phase. Raper (16) found that when aggregates or pseudoplasmodia were disrupted, the cells immediately reaggregated and completed the morphogenetic sequence. If, however, bacteria were added at this time, the myxamoebae reverted to the vegetative state until the fresh nutrient supply was exhausted. As mentioned previously, myxamoebae harvested from the lag and log phases and washed free of bacteria could aggregate normally (31). Yet left undisturbed, on the growth plate, these cells would have continued their vegetative state.

Hirschberg et al. (11, 12) have examined the effects of a wide variety of enzyme poisons, carcinogenic agents, and known cell constituents upon aggregation. Some of these were highly effective in inhibiting aggregation, but since viability determinations could not be performed at that time, it was not determined if the active compounds inhibited aggregation directly or did so only secondarily, as a consequence of having killed the cells. Hirschberg has since indicated the potentialities of this system as a screen for carcinogenic agents (12).

A subsequent examination was made of a large number of substances in which changes in the relation of center formation to cell number and density were employed as criteria of interference with aggregation or encouragement of it (6). Two interesting groups of compounds were encountered. The first of these consisted of adenine and guanine, which depressed center formation and greatly increased the threshold and optimal densities without killing the cells. The second included histidine and imidazole, which did not alter initiative capacity but which increased the sensitivity of the cells so that they could aggregate at phenomenally low densities. Studies of histidine uptake revealed that the cells became acutely sensitive simultaneously with entrance of histidine into the free amino acid pool, and that removal of exogenous histidine after that time did not

reduce the sensitivity. The free intracellular histidine was subsequently dissipated, some by entrance into protein, the rest by destruction and/or transformation of the imidazole nucleus.

REFERENCES

1. Arndt, A., *Wilhelm Roux' Arch. Entwicklungsmech. Organ.*, **136**, 681-747 (1937).
2. Bonner, J. T., *Am. J. Botan.*, **31**, 175-182 (1944).
3. ———, *J. Exptl. Zool.*, **106**, 1-26 (1947).
4. ———, *J. Exptl. Zool.*, **110**, 259-272 (1949).
5. ———, *Biol. Bull.*, **99**, 143-151 (1950).
6. Bradley, S. G., Sussman, M., and Ennis, H. L., *J. Protozool.*, **3**, 60-66 (1956).
7. Ennis, H. L., and Sussman, M., *J. Gen. Microbiol.*, **18**, 241-260 (1958).
8. ———, and ———, *Proc. Natl. Acad. Sci. U. S.*, (in press).
9. Gregg, J. H., *J. Gen. Physiol.*, **39**, 813-820 (1956).
10. ———, *Anat. Rec.*, **128**, 558 (1957).
11. Hirschberg, E., and Rusch, H. P., *J. Cellular Comp. Physiol.*, **37**, 323-336 (1951).
12. ———, *Bacteriol. Revs.*, **19**, 65-78 (1955).
13. Luria, S. E., and Delbrück, M., *Genetics*, **28**, 491-511 (1943).
14. Potts, G., *Flora* (Ger.), **91**, 291-307 (1902).
15. Raper, K. B., *J. Elisha Mitchell Scient. Soc.*, **56**, 241-282 (1940).
16. ———, *Growth* (3rd Symposium), **5**, 41-75 (1941).
17. ———, and Thom, C., *Am. J. Botan.*, **28**, 69-78 (1941).
18. ———, and Fennell, D., *Bull. Torrey Botan. Club*, **79**, 25-51.
19. Runyon, E. H., *Collecting Net, Woods Hole*, **17**, 88 (1942).
20. Shaffer, B. M., *Nature*, **17**, 975 (1953).
21. ———, *Science*, **123**, 1173 (1956).
22. ———, *J. Exptl. Biol.*, **33**, 645-657 (1956).
23. ———, *Quart. J. Microscop. Sci.*, **98**, 377-392 (1957).
24. Sussman, M., and Noel, E., *Biol. Bull.*, **103**, 259-268 (1952).
25. ———, *Biol. Bull.*, **103**, 446-457 (1952).
26. ———, and Sussman, R. R., *Ann. N. Y. Acad. Sci.*, **56**, 949-960 (1953).
27. ———, *J. Gen. Microbiol.*, **10**, 110-121 (1954).
28. ———, *J. Gen. Microbiol.*, **13**, 295-309 (1955).
29. ———, and Lee, F., *Proc. Natl. Acad. Sci. U. S.*, **41**, 70-78 (1955).
30. ———, *Ann. Rev. Microbiol.*, **10**, 21-50 (1956).
31. ———, *Biol. Bull.*, **110**, 91-95 (1956).
32. ———, Lee, F., and Kerr, N. S., *Science*, **123**, 1172 (1956).
33. ———, and Sussman, R. R., in *Cellular Mechanisms in Differentiation and Growth* (D. Rudnick, ed.), p. 125-153, Princeton Univ. Press, Princeton (1956).
34. Sussman, R. R., (unpub.).
35. ———, Ennis, H. L., and Sussman, M., (unpub.).
36. Trinkaus, J. P., and Groves, P. W., *Proc. Natl. Acad. Sci. U. S.*, **41**, 787-795 (1955).
37. Tyler, A., *Growth*, **10** (suppl.), 7-19 (1946).
38. Weiss, P. A., *Yale J. Biol. and Med.*, **19**, 235 (1947).
39. Wilson, C. M., *Am. J. Botan.*, **40**, 714-718 (1953).
40. ———, and Ross, I., *Am. J. Botan.*, **44**, 345-350 (1957).

ENZYME PATTERNS DURING DIFFERENTIATION IN THE SLIME MOLD

Barbara E. Wright and Minnie L. Anderson

Laboratory of Cellular Physiology and Metabolism, Enzyme Section, National Heart Institute, National Institutes of Health, Public Health Service, U. S. Department of Health, Education, and Welfare, Bethesda, Maryland.

Introduction

One of the simplest, and hence one of the most appealing model systems for a biochemical approach to differentiation is found in the slime molds. The unique life cycle of these microbes includes a vegetative, independent single cell as well as a multicellular stage. Multicellular differentiation involves only two cell types, and proceeds in the absence of growth. Thus any biochemical changes occurring during differentiation are neither confused by nor interdependent on biochemical changes accompanying growth.

Some hours after vegetative myxamoebae exhaust their food supply and have been washed free of any nutrient material (i.e., dead bacteria) and placed on purified agar, they aggregate in response to a diffusible, chemotactic substance called acrasin (25, 1) to form a multicellular pseudoplasmodium composed of about 150,000 cells. It should be emphasized that, although a multicellular unit is formed, the component cells do not arise as progeny from the growth of a single cell. The unit forms as a result of the aggregation of many single myxamoebae in the absence of cell division.

Once the pseudoplasmodium has formed, gradual specialization into two cell types begins (23, 2). The anterior third of the pseudoplasmodium contains the presumptive stalk cells of the eventual fruiting body, which is composed of a cellulose-rich stalk supporting a mass of spores. The presumptive stalk cells gradually acquire the ability to synthesize and deposit cellulose extracellularly; after so doing they are incorporated into the stalk, become highly vacuolated, and eventually die. They are the somatic cells of the organism. The presumptive spore cells in the posterior two-thirds of the pseudoplasmodium become transformed to spores by the

gradual accumulation of polysaccharides and the extracellular deposition of a cellulose husk (5, 24). In view of this very simple life cycle, it would not be surprising to find that the main biosynthetic activities during differentiation are associated with polysaccharide synthesis.

Gregg has shown that the dry weight of the slime mold drops only 6 per cent during differentiation, and that total reducing substances increase about 45 per cent based on dry weight (15, 16). A simultaneous decrease in total protein nitrogen occurs, accompanied by ammonia formation. These changes occur in the absence of external nutrients, and all the evidence supports the conclusion that endogenous protein is the major source of energy and building blocks for carbohydrate synthesis (16, 17).

Biochemically, how are these changes in metabolism brought about? This being an exclusively endogenous system, the new emphasis on carbohydrate synthesis must stem from internally induced stimulants and regulators of metabolism. By far the greatest protein utilization and carbohydrate synthesis occurs *after* the formation of the migrating pseudoplasmodium. Thus the new pattern of substrates, enzymes, and products must fully establish itself by the time that the pseudoplasmodium is formed.

Such a life cycle offers some rather unique experimental possibilities, and poses interesting questions about the metabolism of slime molds during differentiation.

A useful definition of differentiation is "the gradual production of differences between the descendents of the same ancestral type." This concept includes differentiation on a cellular level—phenomena such as enzyme induction in response to a substrate, as well as gradual changes in the metabolic pattern of a cell. The end product of "biochemical differentiation" in the slime mold is mainly represented by the accumulation of polysaccharide—predominantly cellulose. What is the gradual sequence of events by which the rate of carbohydrate synthesis is increased? Which specific biochemical pathways become activated, in what order, and how do they become activated? By the availability of essential cofactors? Or by the removal of specific inhibitors? Or by the sequential formation of substrates which induce the synthesis of their specific enzymes? It is clear that the answers to such questions depend upon a detailed knowledge of the particular metabolic characteristics of slime molds: the presence, concentration, and activity of relevant substrates, enzymes, and products. Even fragmentary information of this type about a critical biosynthetic pathway might supply some of the necessary keys for an understanding of the mechanisms controlling biochemical differentiation.

Methods

The myxamoebae of the slime mold *Dictyostelium discoideum* are grown on complex media with either live or dead bacteria (3, 7). They are then washed three times with cold distilled water and spread on washed agar plates, under conditions where no growth occurs (30). By freezing and thawing five times, cell-free preparations were made of cells harvested at succeeding stages of differentiation up to the migrating slug. With later stages, samples were also ground with alumina. The following enzymatic activities were followed spectrophotometrically at 340 mμ, by the increase or decrease in reduced pyridine nucleotide: isocitric dehydrogenase (TPN- and DPN-linked [1]), malic dehydrogenase (TPN and DPN), glucose-6-phosphate dehydrogenase (TPN), 6-phosphogluconic dehydrogenase (TPN), glutamic dehydrogenase (DPN), glyceraldehyde-3-phosphate dehydrogenase (DPN), and lactic acid dehydrogenase (DPN). G6P-phosphatase activity was followed by measuring orthophosphate liberation.

The enzyme forming uridine diphosphoglucose (UDPG) from uridine triphosphate (UTP) and glucose-1-phosphate is most conveniently followed by measuring glucose-1-phosphate (G1P), which is formed in the reaction: UDPG + PP → UTP + G1P (21). TPN, 1,6-phosphoglucomutase, and glucose-6-phosphate (G6P) dehydrogenase were present during the experiment in order to measure the G1P formed. To demonstrate the actual accumulation of G1P in the system, the incubation was carried out in the absence of added TPN, mutase, and G6P dehydrogenase. Following heat inactivation, these components were added to measure the G1P present. Glucose was determined in the hexokinase assay, and was further identified by analysis with glucose oxidase and glucose dehydrogenase. Routine quantitative determinations were made on deproteinized samples by means of the hexokinase assay (commercial zwischenferment was used as a source of both G6P dehydrogenase and hexokinase). A specific chemical test (20) was used to detect small amounts of fructose which might be present, since this compound was also active in the hexokinase assay. About 10-15 per cent of the hexose present was fructose.

The various enzymatic assays employed in these studies will be presented in greater detail elsewhere (33).

[1] Ammonium sulfate fractionation has demonstrated the separation of these two enzymes.

Experimental Results

Nature of the Chemotactic Substance

Shaffer developed a test system by which sensitive cells undergoing aggregation could be used to demonstrate the presence of the chemotactic agent (26). From the nature of its action, it appeared possible that acrasin might be a known hormone. Using the Shaffer test, crude hormone preparations were examined. The urine of a pregnant woman was extremely active, and consequently a number of steroids were tested for activity. Active compounds were: estradiol; estrone sulfate; 17(a)-methyl Δ^5 androstene-3(β), 17(β)-diol; Δ^4 androstene-3,17-dione; progesterone; testosterone; and 17-ethynyl-19-nor-testosterone. Inactive compounds included: cholesterol; androstane-diol, 3,17; Δ^1 androstene-3,17-dione; androstane-3,17-dione; diethyl stilbestrol; 17α methyl-19-nor-testosterone; pregnanediol; Δ^1 hydrocortisone; hydrocortisone; and somatotropin. With the exception of estrone sulfate, the exact potency of most of the active steroids could not be tested due to their extreme insolubility. However, three different preparations of estrone sulfate were found to be active at <0.05 γ/ml. Such activity is clearly in the range of physiological significance. Stability studies on acrasin are not incompatible with its being a steroid (27, 28, 29). However, the response of the amoebae to estrone sulfate is not as striking as to "pregnant urine" or to crude acrasin. Estrone sulfate may therefore be closely related to, but not identical with, acrasin (34).

The Acquisition of a More Aerobic Metabolism

Perhaps the most general and biochemically relevant description to be made of the slime molds is that their acquisition of a multicellular life is accompanied by the transition to a more aerobic metabolism. Gregg has shown that oxygen consumption increases strikingly from the amoeba stage until the stage of multicellular differentiation just prior to stalk formation; it then decreases, and is finally undetectable in the mature fruit (14). We have extended Gregg's data by showing that in fact the amoebae can grow as well "anaerobically" as aerobically, and have confirmed his observation that multicellular differentiation cannot proceed anaerobically. By growing the myxamoebae on dead bacteria, it could be shown that after 48 hours they had multiplied as rapidly under essentially anaerobic conditions (in an evacuated dessicator) as they had in the presence of air (Table 1). After removing a section of each plate to count the amoebae,

incubation was continued, with the results shown. The food supply was exhausted on both plates, and under aerobic conditions multicellular differentiation proceeded normally. It is quite possible that under completely anaerobic conditions the multicellular stages of differentiation would have been stopped altogether.

TABLE 1

OXYGEN REQUIREMENT OF DIFFERENTIATION

	Condition of plate		
Hours	48	72	96
Aerobic	2.5×10^7 amoebae	all slugs ca. 800	fruits
Limited O_2	2.0×10^7 amoebae	no slugs some aggreg.	10% slugs 90% aggreg.

A number of inhibitors have been found which, at a given concentration, do not interfere with amoebae growth but do not inhibit pseudoplasmodium formation to various degrees. These are listed in Table 2.[2] In the case of malonate and iodacetate, no pseudoplasmodia had formed by the time that fruiting had occurred on the control plate. The inhibition by malonate and dicoumerol is of particular interest, since it suggests a new importance for Krebs cycle enzymes and oxidative phosphorylation at this stage of differentiation. The inhibition by 8-azaguanine will be discussed below. Hirschberg has studied the effect of 2,4-dinitrophenol on aggregation of the myxamoebae, and has shown that at 10^{-4} M aggregation is reversibly inhibited (i.e., transferring the cells to agar without inhibitor allows aggregation to proceed). Furthermore, concomitantly with progressive weakening of the power of aggregation, the concentration of inorganic phosphate in the myxamoebae is increased; it reaches about 250 per cent of the initial value by the time the cells can no longer aggregate (19).

TABLE 2

INHIBITORS OF MULTICELLULAR DIFFERENTIATION

Inhibitor	Concentration (M)
8-azaguanine	2×10^{-3}
iodoacetate	2×10^{-3}
dicoumerol	2×10^{-3}
malonate	5×10^{-3}

[2] Had these inhibitors been in direct contact with the amoebae instead of being in the agar, their effective concentration would probably have been a good deal lower.

All of these data demonstrate that oxidative metabolism is required for multicellular differentiation in slime molds, and suggest that oxidative phosphorylation is also occurring and may be necessary for morphogenesis.

Enzymatic Changes During Differentiation

As an initial approach to understanding the over-all metabolism of slime molds during differentiation, a number of well-known, easily assayed enzymes were investigated. During the formation of the pseudoplasmodium, prior to migration, enzymes involved in aerobic metabolism, as well as an enzyme required for cellulose synthesis (uridine diphosphoglucose synthetase)[3] change from undetectable or very low activity in the amoebae to strikingly enhanced activity in the pseudoplasmodium during a period of a few hours at 25°C. Preliminary experiments consisted of preparing cell-free extracts from cells harvested at three stages during differentiation: the amoebae; the pseudoplasmodium (or "slug"); and the final fruit. The experiments shown in Figs. 1 and 2 were done with comparable amounts of protein from the three kinds of extracts.

It can be seen that amoebae extracts are very low in isocitric dehydrogenase and UDPG synthetase, whereas the pseudoplasmodium extracts are extremely active. In the absence of added TPN, mutase, and G6P dehydrogenase, G1P should accumulate from UDPG and PP. Such an accumulation occurred, and is illustrated by the data in Table 3.

TABLE 3

URIDINE DIPHOSPHOGLUCOSE SYNTHETASE

I. UDPG + PP → G1P + UTP.
II. Heat inactivate.
III. Measure G1P.

Enzyme source	Omitted	μM G1P accumulated
amoebae	—	0.004
slug	—	0.266
slug + amoebae	—	0.216
slug	UDPG	0.011
slug	PP	0.016

In the case of isocitric dehydrogenase and UDPG synthetase, as well as other enzymes to be described, no indication was found of (1) any inhibition of one extract by another, or of (2) any difference in relative activities of cell-free extracts as compared to homogenates (33). The increased enzymatic activities appear to be genuine, in the sense that they are not due

[3] Uridine diphosphoglucose has recently been implicated as the activated form of glucose for the synthesis of cellulose (13).

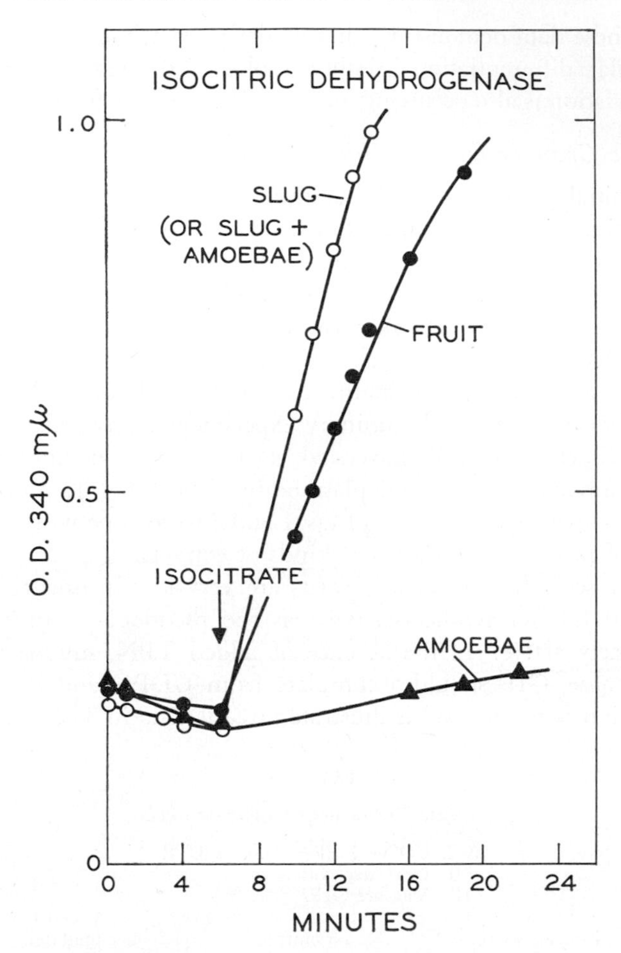

Fig. 1. Isocitric dehydrogenase activity measured in amoebae, slug, and fruit preparations. The amoebae were grown on dead bacteria; differentiation occurred at 20°C. Specific activities (μM TPNH per 10 min. per mg. protein) of the three preparations were: amoebae, 0.4; slug, 21.8; fruit, 15.1.

to the removal of a simple inhibitor or to differences in enzyme solubilities at various stages of differentiation. It has also been demonstrated that the changes in enzymatic activities are the same, whether the amoebae are grown on live or dead bacteria prior to washing them and allowing differentiation to proceed on washed agar (33).

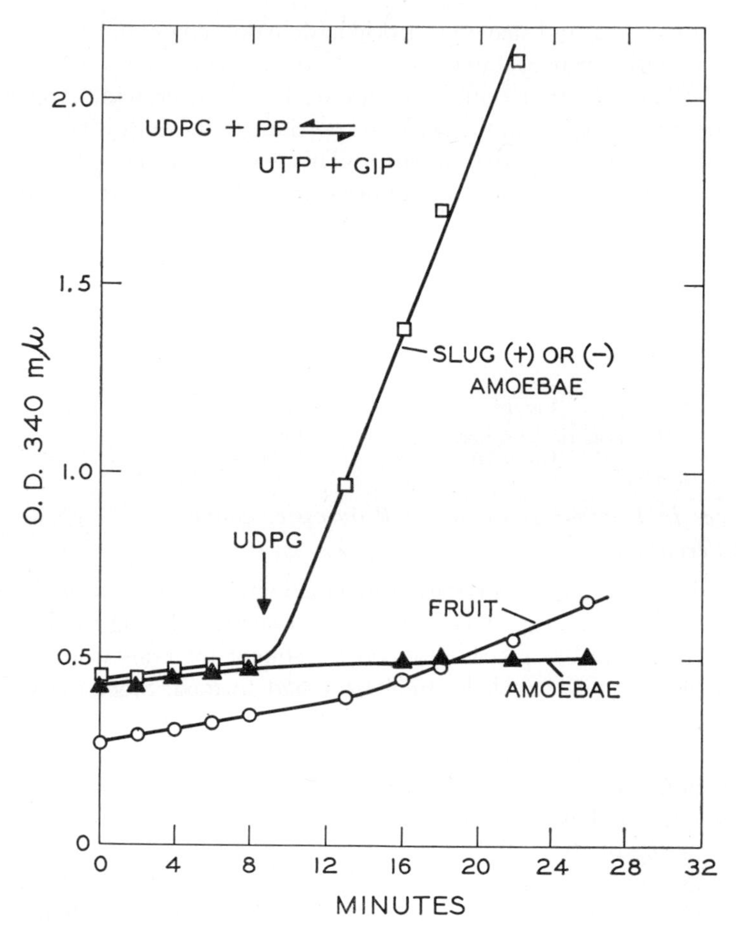

Fig. 2. UDPG synthetase activity. Conditions as for Fig. 1, except that the amoebae were grown on live bacteria. The specific activities were: amoebae, 0.00; slug, 33.2; fruit, 5.0.

Enzyme Localization

One essential characteristic of multicellular differentiation is localization of specific enzymatic activities. It is known that the chemotactic substance, acrasin, is produced predominantly by the presumptive stalk cells (4). Histochemically, studies have shown that these cells are also rich in an alkaline phosphatase activity, compared to the presumptive spore cells (5).

With a micropipette, about 50 migrating slugs were divided, their anterior and posterior portions pooled, and cell-free enzyme preparations were

made by freezing and thawing. Isocitric dehydrogenase and UDPG synthetase activities were examined in such extracts, with the results shown in Table 4. The relative specific activities are based on protein. Apparently the extract prepared from the posterior portion of the slugs is the most active with respect to these two enzymes. This was an unexpected result, and may represent an exception to Bonner's generalization that the anterior cells are enzymatically the most active.

TABLE 4

LOCALIZATION OF ENZYMES

Enzyme	Relative specific activity	
	Anteriors	Posteriors
Isocitric dehydrogenase	1.40	1.81
UDPG synthetase	1.21	1.73

Changes in Enzyme Activities at Progressive Stages of Differentiation

In order to attempt a correlation of enzymatic activities with the morphological changes (e.g., stalk formation) occurring during the life cycle, enzyme extracts were prepared at more frequent intervals from the time prior to aggregation until the final fruit had formed. Since the changes are extremely rapid at room temperature, most of these experiments were carried out at 20° or 13°C, in order to obtain more values at critical times. Fig. 3 shows the changes in relative specific activities of a number of enzymes, calculated on the basis of protein. The highest value obtained was given a figure of 100, and the others were calculated relative to this value. The enzymes examined in this experiment were UDPG synthetase, isocitric dehydrogenase (TPN- and DPN-specific), malic dehydrogenase (DPN), glucose-6-phosphate dehydrogenase (TPN), 6-phosphogluconic dehydrogenase (TPN), and glutamic dehydrogenase (DPN).

It can be seen that those enzymes which are involved in the Krebs cycle, the hexose monophosphate shunt, and UDPG synthesis increase strikingly in activity. The greatest increases in activity occur during the formation of the pseudoplasmodium. All of the enzymes examined thus far are listed in Table 5; they are grouped according to their maximum change in relative specific activity. It should be emphasized that these enzyme systems are being examined in crude extracts, and that the assays employed may not be definitive. Although it is clear that striking changes in enzymatic activities do occur, it is conceivable that some of these effects are secondary.

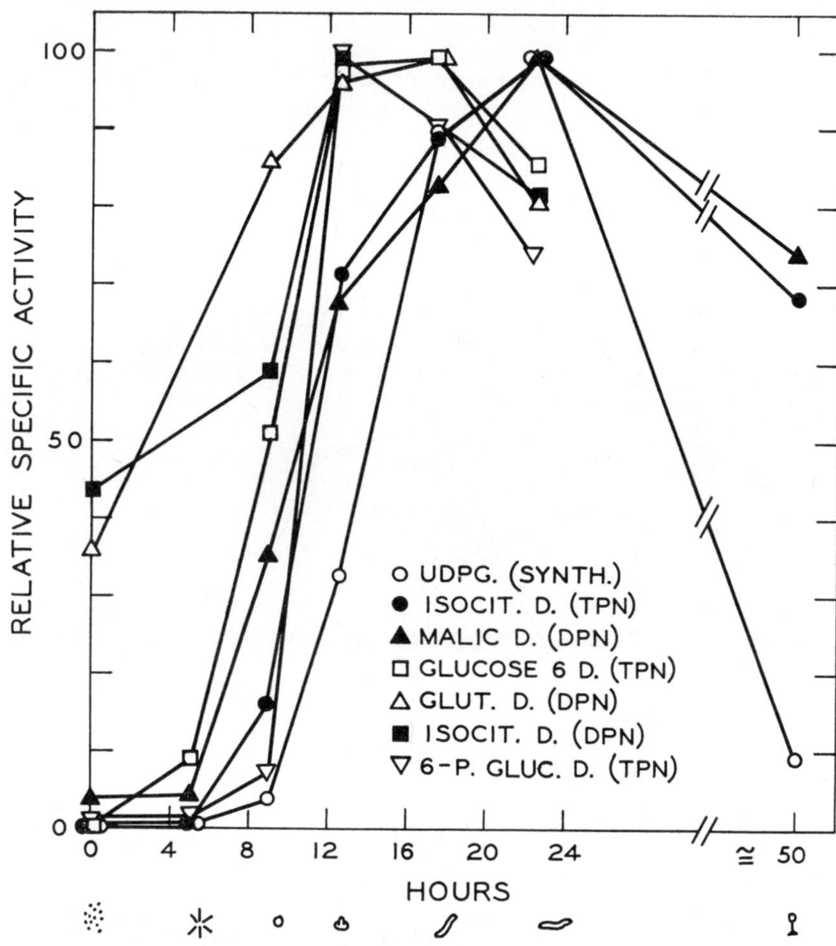

Fig. 3. Relative enzyme activities during differentiation on washed agar at 20°C; activities are based on protein. The amoebae were grown on dead bacteria. Zero time is arbitrary, and prior to aggregation. The enzymes examined and the stages of development at which samples are taken are indicated.

TABLE 5

ENZYME SUMMARY

1.5 to 3-fold increase	>10-fold increase
1. Lactic acid dehydrogenase	1. Glucose 6-PO_4 dehydrogenase
2. Glutamic dehydrogenase	2. 6-phosphogluconic dehydrogenase
3. Isocitric dehydrogenase (DPN)	3. UDPG synthetase
4. Malic dehydrogenase (TPN)	4. Isocitric dehydrogenase (TPN)
5. Glyceraldehyde phosphate dehydrogenase	5. Malic dehydrogenase (DPN)
6. Glucose-6-phosphatase	

Glucose Accumulation

During an attempt to assay for the presence of hexokinase in the slime mold extracts, an endogenous substrate was found there which required ATP and G6P dehydrogenase in order for TPN to be reduced. This endogenous material, which accumulated during differentiation, was identified as glucose. Fig. 4 gives the relative changes in glucose con-

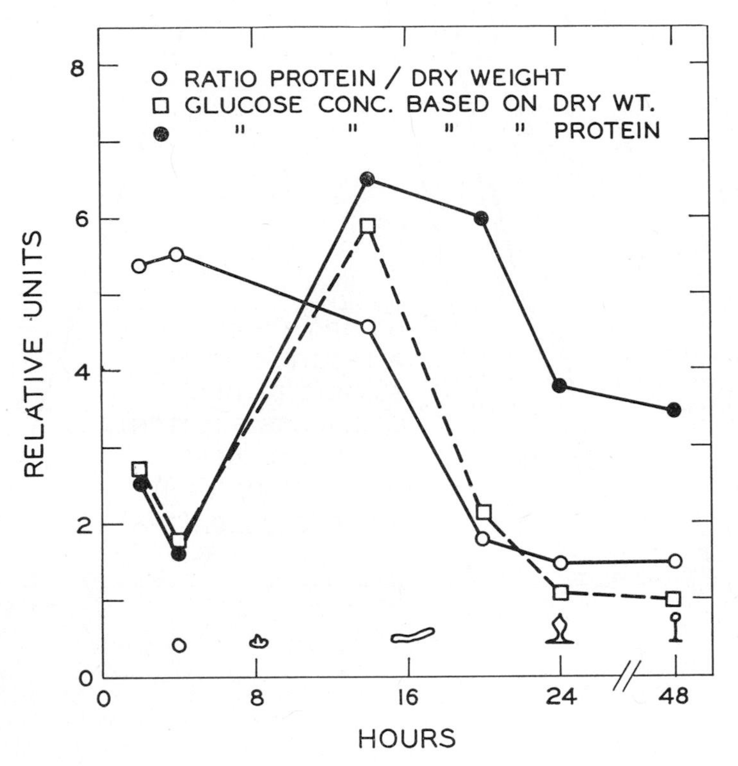

Fig. 4. Glucose concentration at various stages of differentiation in "starved" cells at 20°C. The amoebae were initially grown on live bacteria. The concentration is expressed on the basis of dry weight and of protein; the ratio of protein to dry weight during the experiment is also plotted. See text.

centration based on protein and on dry weight. Starved cells were used in this experiment, in the hope of observing maximum changes in endogenous glucose concentration during stalk formation. Starvation was encouraged by keeping the amoebae anaerobic for 48 hours at 13°C, so as to prevent multicellular differentiation. The experiment was initiated by

placing the plates aerobically at 20°C; within a few hours formation of the pseudoplasmodium began. It can be seen that the "metabolism of differentiation" in the absence of growth results in a net accumulation of glucose during formation of the slug. The glucose concentration then drops while the cellulose stalk is being formed. Polysaccharide synthesis is occurring prior to the stalk formation, in so far as the "slime sheath" is being deposited (24) and the presumptive spore cells in the posterior two-thirds of the slug are accumulating non-starch polysaccharides (5). Thus the accumulation of carbohydrate (glucose) represents the amount in excess of that necessary for husk formation. Only during more active polysaccharide synthesis (stalk formation) is there a net decrease in glucose concentration. Since protein is the main endogenous material used, and since the dry weight remains fairly constant, the concentration of glucose (as well as enzymatic activities) is best calculated on a dry weight basis. Based on protein, the concentration is abnormally high, particularly in the later stages of differentiation when the most striking decrease in protein occurs (15). The ratio of protein to dry weight is also shown in Fig. 4, and is a direct expression of the fact that the extractable protein drops relative to the dry weight during the fruiting process.

Fig. 5 shows the course of glucose accumulation and depletion in unstarved cells on the basis of dry weight. The relative activities of two enzymes are also indicated. As might be expected, the glucose level does not fall as far during stalk formation in unstarved cells as it did in the case of the starved cells. Although it is not plotted in this experiment, glutamic dehydrogenase again (see Fig. 3) increased two-fold; its decrease was very similar to that shown for isocitric dehydrogenase. Since the first experiment of this type was based on protein instead of dry weight (Fig. 3), the value for isocitric dehydrogenase in the final fruit was higher than in the present experiment, which based the relative activities on dry weight. Gregg's data on oxygen consumption at various stages of development have also been plotted (14). As with the enzymatic activities, the highest value (at preculmination) was taken as 100, and the others are given relative values.

Table 6 presents data for the absolute amounts of glucose and total reducing sugar present in slime molds. On a dry weight basis, the accumulation of free hexose is similar to that found in plants; this value is almost one hundred-fold higher than that for mammalian tissue. In relating Gregg's values for total reducing sugar to the amount of glucose accumulated in unstarved slime molds, it appears as though most of the reducing sugar in the pseudoplasmodium can be accounted for as free

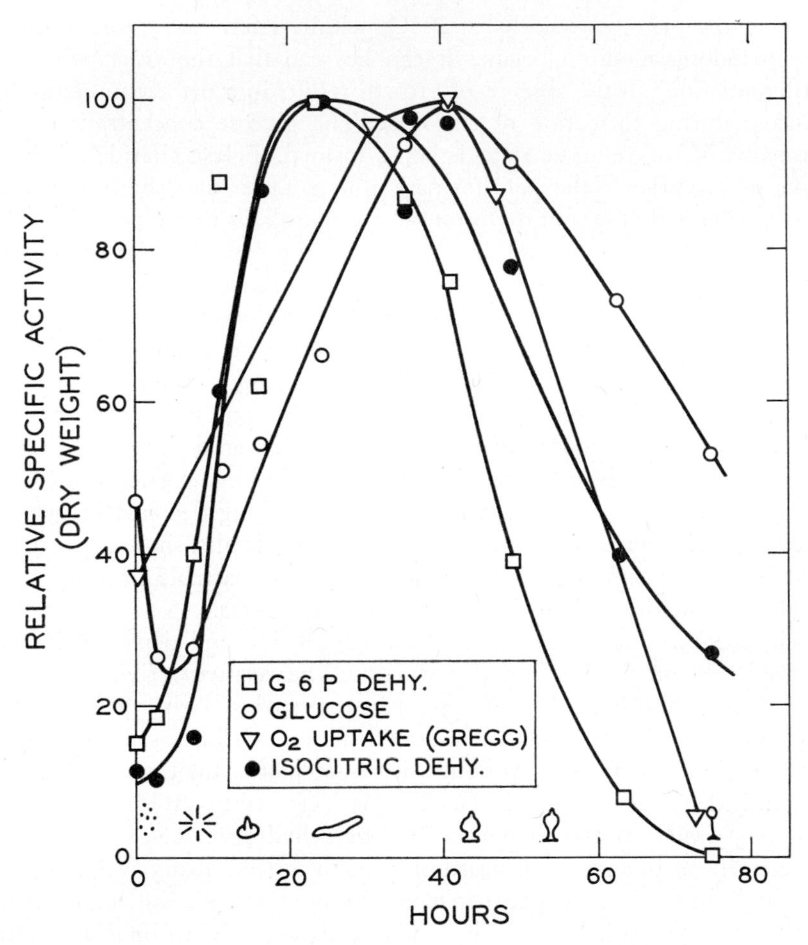

Fig. 5. Glucose concentration and enzyme activities in unstarved cells at 13°C; activities are based on dry weight. The amoebae were grown on live bacteria. Gregg's data on O_2 uptake during differentiation are plotted, as well as enzyme activities for glucose-6-phosphate dehydrogenase and isocitric dehydrogenase.

hexose. The amount of glucose found in the cells is the same whether or not they are washed once during their harvest; this suggests the presence of some permeability barrier in the cell membrane.

Fig. 6 presents more data on enzymatic changes during multicellular development. UDPG synthetase shows the usual pattern, followed also by the Krebs cycle and shunt enzymes. G6P-phosphatase was examined since it might be involved in the accumulation of glucose. Glyceraldehyde

TABLE 6

GLUCOSE AND TOTAL REDUCING SUGAR VALUES

Myxamoebae		mg. glucose / mg. dry wt.	mg. total[2] reducing sugar / mg. dry wt.
Starved	amoebae	0.016	—
	pseudopl.	0.058[1]	—
	fruit	0.010	—
Not starved	amoebae	0.025	0.085
	pseudopl.	0.088[1]	0.103
	fruit	0.046	0.125

[1] About 10-15% of the hexose accumulation is fructose.
[2] After Gregg (15).

phosphate dehydrogenase and lactic acid dehydrogenase increase relatively little in activity during pseudoplasmodium formation, although their decrease in activity is similar to that of UDPG synthetase. Apparently, G6P-phosphatase is unique among the enzymes tested thus far, in that no striking decrease in activity was observed during formation of the final fruit. Similarly, very little inhibition was observed for phosphatase action on 1,6-fructose diphosphate or β-glycerol phosphate. The ratio of protein to dry weight decreased by about 50 per cent during this experiment.

DISCUSSION

In a sense, the slime molds appear to be facultative aerobes, even though the multicellular stage of their life cycle cannot proceed anaerobically. There is a precedent, to be found in other facultative microbes, for the enzymatic changes observed in the slime molds. The investigations of Ephrussi and Slonimski (11), Hirsch (18), Chantrenne (8), and Englesberg and Levy (10) are all relevant to this discussion. The last-mentioned work is perhaps in best analogy to the situation in the slime molds. Englesberg and Levy examined a number of enzymes in extracts of *Pasteurella pestis* which had been (a) grown anaerobically, (b) grown aerobically, or (c) grown anaerobically, and then adapted to aerobic metabolism in the absence of growth. Glucose was present in all cases. Under conditions (b) and (c), they found enzymes involved in aerobic metabolism to be more active than in cells grown anaerobically. The most striking example was isocitric dehydrogenase (60-fold). Typical glycolytic enzymes, on the other hand, were as active or more active in anaerobically-grown cells.

In the slime molds, in contrast to *Pastuerella pestis,* it is the organism

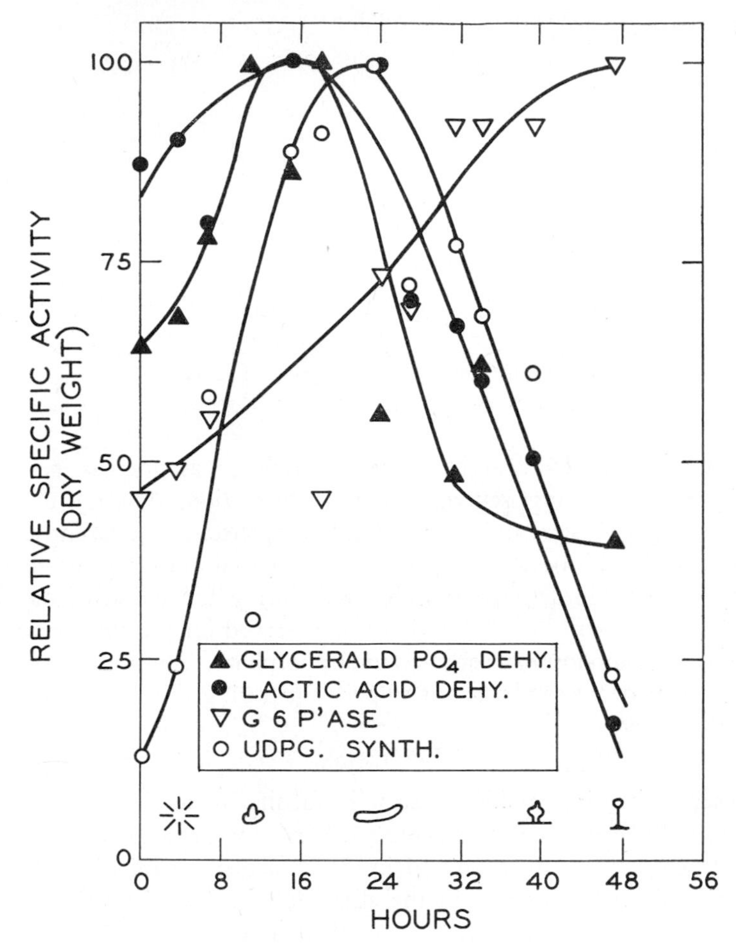

Fig. 6. Relative enzyme activities during morphogenesis in unstarved cells at 13°C; activities are expressed on a dry weight basis. Amoebae were grown on live bacteria. The enzymes examined are glyceraldehyde phosphate dehydrogenase, lactic acid dehydrogenase, glucose-6-phosphate phosphatase, and UDPG synthetase.

rather than the investigator which induces anaerobic or aerobic metabolism. The mechanism for this control is as yet completely unknown. It may be of general interest in understanding differentiating systems, since other cases are known in which more complex development is accompanied by a requirement for more aerobic metabolism (e.g., 6). In the slime molds, activity of the Krebs cycle may afford the energy necessary for migration and, in particular, polysaccharide synthesis.

One of the most immediate problems is to understand the mechanism underlying the observed enzymatic changes. Are we dealing with activation of already formed protein, or with substrate-induced synthesis of enzymes? The latter alternative is the most appealing one at the moment, although definitive experiments are not yet available. Preliminary results indicate that isocitrate can induce the formation of isocitric dehydrogenase, as well as some other enzymes to a lesser degree. If enzyme induction operates normally during differentiation, substrates inducing Krebs cycle enzymes might well arise via the amino acids liberated from protein breakdown.

Since there is a rise and fall of enzymatic activity in the absence of cell multiplication, it is possible that we are dealing with a dynamic state of enzyme synthesis and degradation. In other words, there may be a very high protein turnover, and a measured enzymatic activity at any time would represent the resultant of rapid synthetic and degradative reactions.[4] A number of factors could conceivably contribute to the general decrease in enzymatic activities observed. In view of the data on the inhibition of enzyme induction by glucose (9, 12, 22), it is tempting to attribute the decline in activity of various enzymes to an accumulation of glucose, which in turn could inhibit the continued induction of an enzyme by its substrate. In this connection, it is possibly significant that the initial drop in glucose concentration coincides with the time of the most rapid rise in enzymatic activities (Figs. 4 and 5). Although the data are not particularly good, it is clear that G6P-phosphatase does not decrease in activity during the later stages of differentiation (Fig. 6). This situation may be related to the hypothesis of Neidhardt and Magasanick, that hydrolytic types of enzymes are not inhibited by glucose, since their activity does not result in the accumulation of products similar to those formed by the metabolism of glucose (22).

The decline in enzymatic activities may also be a reflection of the general utilization and eventual depletion of protein material as a source of energy and building blocks for cellulose synthesis. Yet another factor to consider is the gradual exhaustion of substrates responsible for the presumed enzyme inductions. The observed pattern of decline in certain enzymatic activities may play a role in allowing the terminal steps of cellulose synthesis to proceed more rapidly. For example, the loss of G6P dehydrogenase would facilitate G1P accumulation (Fig. 5). One might expect to find many control mechanisms operating, interacting, and inter-

[4] The inhibition by 8-azaguanine referred to earlier might reflect a requirement for RNA synthesis during this period of active protein synthesis.

dependent in order to account for the stability and reproducibility of morphogenesis.

One of the most fascinating problems concerns the role of the chemotactic agent (acrasin) responsible for the initial aggregation of the myxamoebae into the multicellular unit. This is, after all, one of the more primary causes of differentiation, in that the amoebae are delegated at this time to the anterior or posterior region of the future pseudoplasmodium. Moreover, acrasin continues to be produced in the anterior portion of the pseudoplasmodium. Starvation of the amoebae apparently initiates a change in metabolism such that the cells produce the chemotactic hormone, become sensitized to it, or both. One appealing site of action for acrasin would be in the stimulation of endogenous protein breakdown during starvation. Activation of proteolytic enzymes could lead to the accumulation of critical substrates, and thus initiate a series of sequential enzyme inductions.

Evidence was presented earlier that acrasin may be a steroid-like hormone. Apparently there are a number of factors involved in the aggregation phenomenon, which is a very complicated process (31). The recent contribution of Talalay and Williams-Ashman (32) on the role of steroid hormones as coenzymes for transhydrogenase may be of particular interest in this connection. It remains to be seen whether acrasin may exert its effect on metabolism in some similar manner.

Summary

When the slime molds begin their multicellular life in the absence of external nutrition, aerobic metabolism is acquired. Closely correlated with an increase in oxygen uptake are striking increases in the activities of a number of enzymes involved in aerobic metabolism. An enzyme active in cellulose synthesis, UDPG synthetase, also increases markedly during pseudoplasmodium formation. These enzymatic changes occur *prior* to migration and cellulose synthesis. This observation is not incompatible with the hypothesis that the enhanced enzymatic activities are, in fact, necessary in order for these stages of differentiation to proceed. More specifically, these enzymes are at maximum activity prior to the period of major protein utilization and carbohydrate synthesis which occurs during morphogenesis. It is reasonable to assume that their activity may in part cause these gross metabolic changes.

Acknowledgment

We are grateful to Dr. E. R. Stadtman for stimulating criticism concerning this work. Drs. M. and R. Sussman introduced one of us (B.E.W.) to the slime molds, and we are

indebted to them for their continued helpfulness. We would like to thank Dr. W. Albers for generous aid and advice concerning microtechniques. Our thanks are also due to Drs. R. W. Bates, D. M. Bergenstal, and M. Horning for samples of various hormone and steroid preparations.

REFERENCES

1. Bonner, J. T., *J. Exptl. Zool.,* **106,** 1 (1947).
2. ———, *Amer. J. Bot.,* **31,** 175 (1944).
3. ———, *J. Exptl. Zool.,* **106,** 1 (1947).
4. ———, *J. Exptl. Zool.,* **110,** 259 (1949).
5. ———, Chiquoine, A. D., and Kolderie, M. Q., *J. Exptl. Zool.,* **130,** 133 (1955).
6. Brachet, J., *Arch. biol.* (Liége), **45,** 611 (1934).
7. Bradley, S. G., and Sussman, M., *Arch. Biochem. and Biophys.,* **39,** 462 (1952).
8. Chantrenne, H., and Courtais, C., *Biochim. et Biophys. Acta,* **14,** 397 (1954).
9. Cohn, M., in *Enzymes: Units of Biological Structure and Function* (Gaebler, O. H., ed.), p. 41, Academic Press, New York (1956).
10. Englesberg, E., and Levy, J. B., *J. Bact.,* **69,** 418 (1955).
11. Ephrussi, B., and Slonimski, P., *Biochim. et Biophys. Acta,* **6,** 256 (1950).
12. Gale, E. F., *Bacteriol. Revs.,* **7,** 139 (1943).
13. Glaser, L., *Biochim. et Biophys. Acta,* **25,** 436 (1957).
14. Gregg, J. H., *J. Exptl. Zool.,* **114,** 173 (1950).
15. ———, and Bronsweig, R. D., *J. Cellular Comp. Physiol.,* **48,** 293 (1956).
16. ———, and ———, *J. Cellular Comp. Physiol.,* **47,** 483 (1956).
17. ———, Hackney, A. L., and Krivanek, J. O., *Biol. Bull.,* **107,** 226 (1954).
18. Hirsch, H. M., *Biochim. et Biophys. Acta,* **9,** 674 (1952).
19. Hirschberg, E., and Rusch, H. P., *J. Cellular Comp. Physiol.,* **37,** 323 (1951).
20. *Methods in Enzymology,* (Colowick, S. P. and N. O. Kaplan, eds.), III, p. 76, Academic Press, New York (1957).
21. Munch-Petersen, A., Kalckar, H., Cutolo, E., and Smith, E. E. B., *Nature,* **172,** 1036 (1953).
22. Neidhardt, F. C., Magasanik, B., *Nature,* **178,** 801 (1956).
23. Raper, K. B., *J. Elisha Mitchell Scient. Soc.,* **56,** 241 (1940).
24. ———, and Fennell, D. I., *Bull. Torrey Botan. Club,* **79,** 25 (1952).
25. Runyan, E. H., *Collecting Net,* **17,** 88 (1942).
26. Shaffer, B. M., *Nature,* **171,** 957 (1953).
27. ———, *Science,* **123,** 1172 (1956).
28. ———, *J. Exptl. Biol.,* **33,** 645 (1956).
29. Sussman, M., et al., *Science,* **123,** 1171 (1956).
30. ———, pers. commun.
31. Sussman, R. R., Sussman, M., and Lee Fu, F., *Bacteriol. Proc.,* p. 32 (1958).
32. Talalay, P., and Williams-Ashman, H. G., *Proc. Natl. Acad. Sci. U. S.,* **44,** 15 (1958).
33. Wright, B. E., and Anderson, M. L., *Biochim. et Biophys. Acta,* (in press).
34. ———, *Bacteriol. Proc.,* p. 115 (1958).

DISCUSSION

DR. HADORN: I would like to ask Dr. Sussman what the nature of the mutants are with which he deals. Are these true so-called Mendelian mutants?

DR. SUSSMAN: Dr. Racquel Sussman has worked extremely hard trying to

demonstrate a Mendelian segregation of characteristics but we have been very much hampered by the fact that we can demonstrate no sexual process taking place here.

DR. HADORN: In your cultures which have mixed cell populations, that is, different mutants, do you obtain true chimaeric aggregates? And if you do obtain such aggregates, is the size a reflection of the genetic properties of the *I* or of the *R* cells.

DR. SUSSMAN: Yes, we do obtain chimaeric aggregates and we have looked at this situation by using a particular mutant called *Agg-91*. These cells are much smaller and give rise to small, non-viable spores in synergistic fruits. You will remember that there are two circumstances: if the wild type were present in low numbers a mutant had to contribute both cells and materials, but if the wild type were present in high numbers, then all that the mutant had to contribute was materials. Now in the system to which I am referring when the wild type was present in low numbers, the largest contingent in the aggregates and in the fruits, were the *Agg-91* cells but at the point where the concentration of wild type was high enough in the mixture so that they could aggregate alone, you found no mutant cells in the fruits. In this system the aggregateless mutant actually performs two functions with low concentrations of wild type and only the one with the high concentration of wild type.

DR. MARKERT: Is it true that *I* cells appear to be unresponsive to acrasin?

DR. SUSSMAN: I only know that in the great majority of cases when the center of the aggregate does not form exactly at the position of the *I* cell, the *I* cell is eventually left outside the aggregate.

DR. MARKERT: I wonder if one of the differences between the *I* and *R* cells might not be the inability of the *I* cells to destroy acrasin. If this were so, the *I* cell would fail to detect any differences in the concentration of acrasin, because it would be continuously surrounded by abundant acrasin produced by itself.

DR. SUSSMAN: Yes, of course the simplest hypothesis is that the *I* cell is the superior producer of acrasin and it is the initiator of the streaming process and that this is due to the lack of an enzyme which inactivates acrasin or some other similar phenomenon. I would hesitate at the moment to attribute the ability of the *I* cell to the production of a co-factor merely on the basis of economy.

DR. BROWN: What did you mean by a milliequivalent of crude powder?

DR. SUSSMAN: Well, a solution of crude powder could be diluted serially and have a minimal activity at about 0.8 mg./ml. Now we could chromatograph 10 milligrams of this crude extract on paper to get out a component, let's say the A component, which was then dissolved in 1 cc. This amount of a component was then called a 10 milliequivalent ml. solution.

DR. BROWN: I had the impression that you actually knew the molecular (or equivalent) weight of the compound when you used this expression.

DR. SUSSMAN: No, of course not, we were merely referring it to the total

activity of the original crude extract in order to standardize our procedures and see that we are not losing any large amount of activity in any one chemical step.

DR. PAPPENHEIMER: One thing was not clear to me. In these "starved" amoebae there seems to be a lot of protein synthesis going on because the organisms are synthesizing new enzymes. I was wondering where the nitrogen and the amino acids come from to serve this function.

DR. SUSSMAN: The word "starved" is an unfortunate one in this particular instance. In the normal sequence of events, even on a growth plate as Dr. Raper has shown, these cells stop growing, enter morphogenesis, and undergo their transformations. They are really not starved. I might mention, in addition, that we have obtained a defined medium for these organisms. A curious bacterial protein which is a specific growth factor is required and in addition one must add either proteose-peptone or gelatin or casein which can be used as a sole source of carbon and energy. Now these organisms have a tremendous endogenous supply of nutrient materials. You can blow them for 40 hours in a Warburg flask without substrate and they still continue to respire on their endogenous materials. Secondly, on washed agar they can go ahead and aggregate, form a fruit, the fruit will fall over and the spores hit the agar. The spores regerminate and produce amoebae which will then reaggregate and form another fruit. So they are not starved under any sense of the word.

DR. COHN: By growth do you mean division?

DR. SUSSMAN: No, by growth I mean growth. That is, an increase in cell mass. These cells are washed completely free of bacteria and put on agar which has been washed between 6 to 15 times depending upon the experiment and so there is nothing exogenous upon which they can increase their mass and all materials must come from within the cell.

DR. SPIEGELMAN: I am afraid I am confused now. Dr. Wright pointed out that these cells were breaking down their protein at a very high rate and therefore there was plenty of supply to form new enzymes from the catabolism taking place within the cells.

DR. COHN: Is this an experiment or a hypothesis?

DR. WRIGHT: No, these are the results as obtained by Gregg. The amount of endogenous protein goes down strikingly and the amount of total reducing sugar increases a great deal. On a dry weight basis, there is 10 times as much protein broken down as carbohydrate synthesized. Ammonia is also formed in very large quantities, so they are breaking down their protein into amino acids and these are the sources of energy and the building blocks for new specific proteins and for carbohydrate synthesis. There is a very high endogenous metabolism which goes on during differentiation.

DR. WILDE: I am a little confused about growth and differentiation in this system. As I understand it, the *I* and the *R* cells coexist during the logarithmic phase of growth. When are the *I* and *R* cells formed in the clone?

Dr. Sussman: Since they are present at all stages they must arise during the growth of the population. I think the confusion which exists here is one which exists in much of embryology. Namely, cellular differentiation does not refer to the differentiated state of the cell but refers to the process which gave rise to it. Aggregation is simply an expression or a scoring, if you will, of the two cell types. The problem of cellular differentiation in this organism, and certainly in any morphogenetic system, is before the expression of the differentiation.

Dr. Wilde: But then one can no longer maintain that, in the case of the cellular slime molds, growth is distinct and different from differentiation.

Dr. Sussman: I didn't say that. Growth is certainly separate from morphogenesis.

Dr. Wilde: Yes, that's so but certainly not from the origin of different cell types.

Dr. Weiss: It is very easy to disaggregate the slug and I wonder what happens when you do this. Do they revert to a former state?

Dr. Wright: Yes, you can take an early slug and disaggregate it. And the cells will sit down in the liquid and the enzyme activities will not increase. In fact, the enzyme activities will drop a little. However, if you add isocitrate then the level of isocitric dehydrogenase will increase as it would have if the cells had remained together in the slug. So by disrupting the cells they do dedifferentiate enzymatically at a particular stage when, had they remained together, the enzyme activity would have been rising rapidly.

Dr. Niu: I would like to ask you to comment about the alkaline phosphatase and the formation of the fruiting body.

Dr. Wright: The alkaline phosphatase activity was shown by Dr. Bonner to be localized in the pseudoplasmodium and it is predominantly in the presumptive stalk cells, that is, the anterior one-third of the slug. The enzyme was localized with the substrate beta-glycerol phosphate, and the presumptive spore cells did not have much activity. We studied a number of phosphatases, including alkaline phosphatase, in the whole homogenate, and found that they continued to rise in activity during slug and fruit formation and were not inhibited like the other enzymes. One might say then that if Dr. Magasanik's ideas on the glucose inhibition of the formation of enzymes is right, the phosphatases do not fall into the class of "synthetic type" enzymes which should be inhibited by glucose. Phosphatase activity would probably be necessary for glucose formation, for if glucose is formed from the breakdown of amino acid which then moved through the reversal of the Krebs cycle and up through the glycolytic pathway, then glucose-6-phosphate must be dephosphorylated by the phosphatase in order for glucose to accumulate.

Dr. Grant: I am just wondering if you considered the possible role of carbon dioxide in the differentiation of the plasmodium. I say this because of the work of Cantino on the effect of CO_2 on differentiation in the water mold. In

the slime mold, there might be extreme differences in the local concentration of CO_2 in the plasmodium which would not be evident in the amoeboid state.

DR. WRIGHT: No, I haven't considered that possibility. I only know that high concentrations of CO_2 will inhibit differentiation. Isn't that true, Dr. Sussman?

DR. SUSSMAN: Well, Cohn did this, but he used fantastic amounts of carbon dioxide. It was completely unphysiological.

DR. WRIGHT: CO_2 is produced along with ammonia during differentiation. However, I don't know any specific effect of it.

DR. SWIFT: What is the evidence for or against the *I* cells being polyploid and possibly arising by nondisjunction?

DR. SUSSMAN: There is really no evidence for this but there are several possibilities. Wilson has suggested from his cytological studies that zygote formation occurs during aggregation. In fact, he infers that it is a mandatory accompaniment of this process. From his pictures I suspect that what he has seen are *I* cells. He later amended his views and said that although it had no relationship to aggregation, that zygotes did occur. Now, these *I* cells are frequently much larger than these other cells, their nuclei are larger, and you often find them engulfing other myxamoebae. They might be zygotes by engulfment but I think I would prefer to call this cannibalism rather than mating. We hope to determine if the cells are polyploid by doing DNA determinations, but this has not been done as yet.

DR. GALL: It would be very interesting to try a low concentration of colchicine to see if an increase in tetraploid cells would lead to an increase in number of centers.

EXCHANGES BETWEEN CELLS

M. Abercrombie

Department of Anatomy and Embryology, University College,
Gower Street, London, W. C. 1.

Morphogenesis in both embryo and adult obviously involves a great deal of interaction between the parts of the developing system; though it is true, since many of the causal connections are trigger actions initiating complex responses, that limited aspects of the process for limited periods in limited regions are "self-differentiating." In analysing this pervasive nexus of interactions we can choose our units, the parts between which our hypotheses assert that interactions occur, from any of several levels of the hierarchy of separable parts making up the developing system. Classical transplantation embryology has for technical reasons worked with somewhat ill-defined multicellular regions of the embryo, and has been able to state many useful hypotheses, such as those concerned with induction, in terms of interactions between these units. There is a tendency now to jump a stage in the hierarchy, straight to the molecular level. It is not, however, possible to take full account of the organization of developing systems without pressing much further forward an intermediate level of analysis, the cellular. Metazoan organization is such that the cell is an indispensable unit for an important part of the analysis of growth (by mitosis), of spatial shifts of material (by cell locomotion), and of differentiation (by intracellular specialization). Much that the chemical level of analysis must ultimately deal with remains to be discovered by those who make cells their units of investigation.

Though the subject has been decisively put on the agenda by Holtfreter, Weiss, and others, what goes on between cells during morphogenesis is largely unknown. For that matter, what goes on between cells during the normal working of an adult is little known too. But interactions of two general kinds between adult cells are usually distinguished. One is by cell-to-cell contact, exemplified in the working of the nervous system. The other is by diffusion of substances (more or less assisted by flow of body fluids) through the tissues independently of mutual cell contacts, as exemplified in the activities of the endocrine glands. These two general kinds of

intercellular communication, highly specialized in their best known manifestations in the adult, are represented in the embryo in more primitive forms. No doubt one should not try to enforce a rigid segregation of the two types in morphogenesis, if only because "contact" will surely prove to be a relative term to the electron microscopist. But the distinction may be a useful approximation. As in the adult, very close cellular contact is likely to provide a refined and discriminating influence, and it might too ensure a more immediate "feed-back" of responding cell on stimulating cell; diffusion through the tissues is likely to be engaged in more generalized, less finely adjusted, responses.

Diffusion through the tissues naturally means the transfer of some substance from stimulating to reacting cells, though not necessarily to the inside of the reacting cells; it may act directly on their surfaces, for instance by blocking groups exposed there—the experiments of Spiegel (20) provide a model. An influence through cell contacts may on the contrary involve no material transfer, but merely a transfer of pattern. It was Needham (14) who first pointed out the possibility of such an effect, and the suggestion has been much developed by Weiss (26 and later). But contact action does not imply a mere pattern transfer. The necessity for intimate contact and the degree of localization of effect would for instance be almost the same if a stimulatory substance, but an unstable one, was produced by the stimulating cell.

Locomotion of Fibroblasts

The control of cell locomotion provides a clear instance of cellular interaction through mutual contact, which can best be considered by contrasting the behavior of normal and malignant fibroblasts in tissue culture. When cultured on a plane surface, normal fibroblasts show a kind of mutual behavior which we have called contact inhibition (5). Contact inhibition means that when a fibroblast travelling in a given direction makes contact with another fibroblast in its path its continued movement in that direction is obstructed. We are not here concerned with the results of this behavior; though it is worth mentioning that as they display themselves in a large population these results are probably not trivial. In fact, in conjunction with Weiss's contact guidance (25) perhaps all the directional aspects of the control of movement in a fibroblast colony in vitro can be explained. The radial nature of cell movement from an explant, the circular form taken up by fibroblast cultures, or the longitudinal migration on a cylindrical surface (Weiss) can for instance all be derived from contact inhibition alone. There has always been an inexplicable impulse amongst

tissue culturists to explain fibroblast behavior by first trying to make something else, a diffusion gradient or interfacial layer, take up by its internal interactions the required distribution and orientation, which it then imposes on the cells. But the cells by their direct interaction through contact inhibition can do all that is required.

The point for discussion here is not so much the results of contact inhibition as what exactly the interaction is. The following account of what happens when one fibroblast makes contact with another is chiefly based on an analysis of films of chick heart fibroblasts made with an interference microscope (2). Any moving fibroblast has its leading edge (if this is free from contact with other fibroblasts) in the form of a ruffled membrane extended over the substrate surface. There may also be other small undulating membranes elsewhere around the cell. When the leading membrane touches an obstructing fibroblast it appears to fuse with it. Although the junction is somewhat changeable and may partly break down and re-form with considerable rapidity, where the junction exists no border can be seen with a light microscope between the two cells. These are the adhesions described by Lewis (12) and investigated by Kredel (11) by means of microdissection, and found to require some force to break. This is also shown when adhering cells move away from each other. The point of adhesion then distorts the cells, and when it breaks the cells give the impression of snapping apart (4). The ruffling of the membrane that makes the contact is suppressed by the adhesion and with it the apparent pinocytosis that can often be seen to accompany the undulations. If the ruffled membrane was expanding in area at the time of the contact its expansion ceases. The general impression is in fact as if the membrane has become frozen into immobility. Sometimes it gives the impression of coming under tension. Soon after the adhesion has formed the inhibition of movement occurs. The fibroblast ceases to move in its original direction if it has run into a stationary cell, though this cessation may be preceded by a slight acceleration of movement as the contact is formed, perhaps connected with the apparent tension in the contacting membrane: such acceleration was detected statistically (4), but has not since been investigated. Exactly how the freezing of the membrane is related to the checking of the movement of the cell cannot profitably be discussed without more knowledge of the precise nature of the locomotory mechanism than is at present available.

When a contact inhibition has occurred in the way described there is a common but not invariable consequence. A new membrane, or more often a growth of an already existing minor membrane, starts up and, if

it can, leads the cell off in a new direction. We interpret the redirection of the cell's movement by a new membrane in terms of competition between membranes, a hypothesis already developed for behavior during contact guidance by Weiss and Garber (28). The new membrane cannot always redirect the cell, because it may immediately run into another obstructing cell and be itself inhibited. If a cell is completely surrounded by stationary cells it too must be stationary, apart from minor oscillations.

What is it possible to say about the transaction between the two cells which brings contact inhibition about? In the first place, it depends entirely on contact: there is no effect until the cells touch. It is not, however, the non-specific result of mere adhesion, since it must be remembered that the cell is adhering fairly firmly to its substrate. Adhesion is a prerequisite, but it is adhesion to a particular surface, that of another fibroblast, that counts. When such an adhesion occurs, it is hardly conceivable that no transfer of material between the cells happens. But it is also hardly conceivable that such a transfer of material is responsible for the events described. The contact is not only between two similar cells but may occur between similar parts of similar cells: two leading ruffled membranes can inhibit each other. There seems little possibility of one cell gaining something from the other that it has not already got. Nevertheless, there seems to be transmission of the effect within the inhibited cell. Events in other parts of the cell are altered by the contact of the membrane, in that the original movement is stopped, a new leading membrane is established, and locomotion in a new direction occurs. In perhaps an elementary way the events of contact inhibition seem to be a model of an entirely superficial interaction between cells, such as Weiss has so vigorously advocated in opposition to ideas of material transfer between cells.

This simple reaction between fibroblasts is not apparently highly specific. It can occur between fibroblasts from different organs and between fibroblasts from chick and mouse (6). Whether it is completely non-specific is not known, since only a limited range of the possible variants have been tested, and since most of them have not been tested in a way which would reveal small quantitative differences.

Even with contacts between similar cells the inhibition is not invariable. In a proportion of cases cells, which visible observation strongly suggests meet on a plane surface, nevertheless disregard each other, one cell moving over the other unobstructed by the contact. The impression that film shots of such an event give is that a cell momentarily loses some essential part of the contact inhibitory mechanism, perhaps its relevant surface properties, its "fibroblast surface markers," or perhaps a link in the chain connecting

specific adhesion with inhibition of movement; and this may last an appreciable time, since one cell may miss inhibition twice or more in successive encounters. It has proved possible to induce loss of the ability to undergo contact inhibition by applying very high concentrations of embryo juice to the cultures (Curtis, unpub.) and it is conceivable that this effect may represent a saturation of the surface markers, though there are several other possible hypotheses. Fibroblasts also seem to lose their surface markers when they enter mitosis since they then apparently cease to inhibit fibroblasts which run into them (Karthauser, unpub.).

Locomotion of Sarcoma Cells

A more striking case of loss of the properties responsible for contact inhibition occurs in malignant fibroblasts. So far as we have tested sarcomata (mouse sarcomata 37, 180, MC1M, Klein M2C), they at least contain many cells that are not inhibited by contact with normal fibroblasts (6) (Abercrombie and Karthauser, unpub.). Nor are fibroblasts inhibited by contact with S37 or S180 cells, though their reaction to fibrosarcoma cells is more complex. If the sarcoma is a solid form, that is to say is not one specially adapted to ascitic life, its cells in culture stick well to glass and to the surfaces of normal fibroblasts, on both of which they move. Malignancy therefore does not involve a completely non-specific loss of adhesiveness, though it may be true that some degree of diminution of general adhesiveness occurs.

A surface property which sarcoma cells have not lost is that responsible for contact guidance. In our experience sarcoma cells are highly susceptible to the classical situation of Weiss (25) where the cells are caused to move in or on orientated fibrin. They show Weiss's "two-center" phenomenon, when explants are placed near together, very strongly. It is perhaps stretching the topic of exchanges between cells unduly to include such behavior. But because of their deficient contact inhibition and strong propensity to be contact-guided, sarcoma cells become capable of a form of cell interaction that is forbidden to normal fibroblasts: they can be guided by orientated fibroblasts. This behavior proved at first very confusing. We found that sarcoma cells in vitro showed a remarkably direct movement towards a nearby fibroblast explant, travelling over the surface of the fibroblast outgrowth towards it, a direct movement performed by single sarcoma cells isolated from their kind, so that we at first interpreted it as chemotaxis. We soon found however that their movement was equally direct *away* from the fibroblast explant if that is where they were made to start from. It is one of the consequences of mutual contact inhibition that fibroblasts move

radially from an explant, in doing so tending to take up a polarized form; and it seems that this provides an effective contact guidance for sarcoma cells. Such a movement along cell surfaces is closely comparable to the movement of the amoeboid tips of nerve fibres along Schwann cells. In both cases the cells are so strongly polarized that they rarely turn back. It is a different transaction between cells from that involved in contact inhibition, but is again a surface relationship probably involving competition between pseudopodial membranes. In theory at least it may have high specificity (Weiss's *selective* contact guidance), but its main importance is probably between cell and extracellular structure rather than between cell and cell.

Aggregation

When cells in vitro are not moving actively their surface properties concerned with adhesion may come into play, with results somewhat different from the contact inhibition between fibroblasts I have discussed. It seems that their tendency to adhere to each other and to extend these mutual adhesions comes to exceed their ability to adhere to and move on the substrate. The result is aggregation. It has been perhaps most beautifully shown by Twitty (21) in amphibian melanoblasts. It does not occur in ordinary cultures of fibroblasts, which adhere well to the substrate, though it is probably expressed in the fusion of two fragments of chick heart (18) and of course in the reaggregation of disaggregated chick cells (13). Fibrosarcoma cells (mouse MC1M tumor) also become clumped late in the life of a culture, and the explant tends to become spherical. Numerous other examples of such aggregation can be found. The precise relation of the adhesion involved to that of contact inhibition is unknown, but the same argument can be applied, though with less assurance because there is less information: these are surface interactions between similar cells which seem hardly likely to be mediated by exchange of substances.

Cell Locomotion: Conclusions

Directed locomotion, and the groupings produced by adhesions and manifested in vitro by aggregation, are, it is now generally agreed, of great importance in establishing the pattern of cells in vertebrate morphogenesis, embryonic or adult. Contact reactions between cell and cell and between cell and extracellular structures are probably therefore a major source of the precise control of cell pattern. Contact inhibition between fibroblasts, for example, can provide a simple self-regulatory mechanism by which any space deprived of fibroblasts becomes exactly filled. It would be un-

wise, though, to dismiss diffused substances as an orientating influence on cell locomotion, particularly in view of the work of Twitty and Niu (22). The Weiss and Garber (28) hypothesis of pseudopodial competition in fibroblast movement makes it easy to see how chemotaxis could work in a fibroblast, by differential inhibition or encouragement of the pseudopodia at different parts of the cell surface exposed to different concentrations of some substance. We have indeed found a possible case of this, though an artificial one, in that chick fibroblasts are slowed in their movement towards cells of mouse sarcoma MC1M when several hundred micra away, and when very near turn aside. But the effectiveness of known contact reactions is potentially so considerable that we are justified at present in assuming that *directional* control of movement by diffusing substances, when it occurs, is either supplementary or a special case. Where substances diffusing independently of cell contacts have their main role in controlling cell movement is, I have recently argued (1), in influencing the general level of activation of the amoeboid mechanism. This influence on locomotion is closely connected with the control of mitotic rate.

Mitosis

In cultures of chick fibroblasts, where contact effects on locomotion are so striking, we have been unable to detect any relation between amount of cell contact and number of mitoses. The overwhelming influence on mitosis in such cultures seems to be one of inhibition in the neighborhood of the explant, an inhibition which is particularly extensive in the direction of another nearby explant. This suggests that a diffusing substance is concerned, and may well represent competition between the cells for some nutrient in the medium. These results reflect in miniature the wider picture of the control of mitosis. Contact effects, though they may be reasonably suspected in the embryonic central nervous system (see 10), are not yet demonstrated in vertebrates, as far as I am aware. Mitotic stimulation or inhibition by diffusing substances is on the other hand well known in adult morphogenesis, as in the thyroid-pituitary system (some instances are discussed in ref. 1). If such diffuse interactions exist in the embryo too, it is not surprising. Since the precise control of pattern is already provided by cell locomotion, exact location of mitosis is unnecessary.

Induction

I have considered in detail a contact reaction between cells, contact inhibition, that most probably involves no transfer of material; and I have mentioned the existence of interchanges controlling mitosis that operate by

diffusion of material through a distance. The other possible mechanism, by which material is transferred through cell contacts, is less easy to exemplify with confidence. But morphogenetic interaction by this means has long been accepted as the mechanism of many cases of induction in embryonic development. Neural induction, which normally involves close contact between the presumptive chorda-mesoderm and the overlying presumptive neural plate, is a suitable case for brief discussion. Thanks largely to the substantial measure of agreement reached between the schools of Toivonen, Yamada, and Nieuwkoop, there is now good foundation for supposing that in urodeles neural induction is due to two influences from the chorda-mesoderm, present in progressively different proportions along the cranio-caudal axis. One influence corresponds to the neural evocation long ago distinguished by Waddington (see 23) and produces complex archencephalic structures when acting alone. The other influence is the work of the mesodermal inductor, modifying the neural evocation in a more caudal sense. The nature of the neural evocation, now called the archencephalic inductor, is a notorious problem of many years standing, because the natural agent has so many successful imitators, while it appears itself to be highly labile (16). There is, however, so far no conclusive evidence that the mesodermal inductor is not a unique substance. It appears to be a protein, though it is found associated with pentose nucleic acid (29). It can be obtained in solution in saline, and Niu's results (15) suggest that it can induce mesoderm in such solution. There is therefore good evidence that a transferable substance *may* act in normal induction, at least by the mesodermal inductor; though it would still be legitimate to think that the inductor exerts its effects while remaining localized at the interface between chorda-mesoderm and ectoderm. Evidence as to whether the inductor leaves the chorda-mesoderm in vivo and whether it enters the ectoderm would be helpful. The former has been sought by interposing porous membranes, the latter chiefly by tracer experiments.

Induction has not yet been shown to traverse a gap separating chorda-mesoderm from ectoderm (7); but unfortunately while a positive result would be relatively unequivocal, a negative is not. Instability of the substance (at least in the interior of the embryo) might for instance make it impossible to transfer sufficient material across a gap; some such restriction on diffusion would of course improve the precision of the normal induction. The tracer experiments have not been much more helpful. Experimental juxtaposition of radioactively marked inducers and unmarked competent tissue (3, 8, 17, 19, 24) has merely indicated that there is no large-scale transfer of macromolecules. But sensitivity to drugs and hor-

mones suggests that a very small transfer might suffice for an induction. If on the contrary cells are reacting in exceedingly close contact, then even though the induction is a mere transfer of pattern, their surfaces are unlikely to be so stable that no passage of the surface macromolecular material of one into the cytoplasm of the other cell occurs. Some transfer of substance seems then to be compatible with hypotheses asserting that the inducing stimulus is either a pattern-transfer or a material-transfer, and further tracer studies of increased sensitivity seem unlikely to be decisive.

The problem of the exact transaction between inducing chorda–mesoderm and responding ectoderm is not therefore satisfactorily resolved, but the example must serve as the nearest we can get to interaction by transfer of material through contact, which at least is the general opinion of the process. Contact, with its accompanying precision of action, is certainly involved as it is in some other inductions. But yet others may be different. Grobstein (9) has shown how one inductor (though an "abnormal" one) can act across an extracellular space to produce metanephric tubules. Induction in such systems, perhaps even more so in the induction of the considerable mass of mesonephric tissue by the nearby Wolffian duct, may reasonably be by the shot-gun method of extracellular diffusion. The possibility should not be completely disregarded that such diffusion might be from induced to inductor, i.e., might be the consumption of an inhibitor.

Regulation

It would be idle to suppose that clear-cut induction, as exemplified by the neural reaction, is a very important form of cellular exchange during the process of determination in vertebrate embryos. The main problem, because it is commoner and so obscure in its mechanism, is the exchange that goes on during the development of a region capable of regulation. Although nothing precise can be said about the nature of this exchange, no opportunity should be lost of calling attention to the problem.

When a region capable of regulation, say a limb-field, is halved, or two are fused, and a single normally proportioned organ develops from the half or double region, then substantially all the cells do not develop as they would normally have done. Such a thorough reorganization of cellular presumptive fates precludes the possibility that there persists, undisturbed by the operation, some controlling group of cells. But something must in a sense persist. In some essential respect the new system must have the same spatial organization as the original, since the pattern of the

limb that emerges is the same. It might be thought that if the original pattern were a system of inherent axial gradients, half the region would possess the same pattern, and the problem of continuity of organization is solved. It is not solved, however, because the problem is not merely to keep the same crucial organization after the operation, but to reallocate the cells within the organization so that their individual presumptive fates are recast to fit the reduced or increased size of the organ-forming region. Persistent axial gradients are merely a secondary influence: they provide for persistent polarities, though they are not even the only way of doing that. It seems to me that there is only one form of relationship that will provide both continuity of pattern and reorganization of cellular presumptive fate. This is the inside-outside relation based on the difference between cells within the regulatory region (halved, double or single in origin) and cells outside it, which in turn means a difference between the peripheral and central parts of the region. Weiss (27) has considered how such a simple inside-outside relation in a mass of tissue can be translated into complex structure. The point in the present context is that it cannot be so translated, regardless (within limits) of differences in the size of the mass of tissue produced by operation, without extensive mutual influences between the cells. Directly or indirectly it seems that all cells must influence each other, so that each is informed of its relative position in the system. There is at present no indication of what form such interactions could take, and it may be that there is a role here for a so far unsuspected kind of conduction through cell contacts.

Conclusion

This discussion has been concerned with only a few of the large variety of cellular exchanges that take part in morphogenesis. I have concentrated on influences which trigger a complex response. The real task of the stimulus of complex cellular behavior, like that of a releaser in animal behavior, is simply to be potent and unequivocal: it is not required to contribute energy or material or organization to the ensuing response, though it may. The response goes its own way, once the stimulus threshold is past. Its complexity may be very great, as in neural induction, where the archencephalic inductor sets in train a further extensive set of interactions between ectodermal cells; or it may be relatively small, as in contact inhibition. It is of course precisely its repertoire of complex responses to simple stimuli that makes the cell an indispensable unit of interaction in the analysis of development.

REFERENCES

1. Abercrombie, M., *Symposia Soc. Exptl. Biol.*, **9**, 235-254 (1957).
2. ———, and Ambrose, E. J., *Exptl. Cell Research* (in press).
3. ———, and Causey, G., *Nature*, **166**, 229 (1950).
4. ———, and Heaysman, J. E. M., *Exptl. Cell Research*, **5**, 111-131 (1953).
5. ———, and ———, *Exptl. Cell Research*, **6**, 293-306 (1954).
6. ———, ———, and Karthauser, H. M., *Exptl. Cell Research*, **13**, 276-292 (1957).
7. Brachet, J., *Rev. Suisse Zool.*, **57**, 57-70 (1950).
8. Ficq, A., *J. Embryol. Exptl. Morphol.*, **2**, 204-215 (1954).
9. Grobstein, C., *Exptl. Cell Research*, **13**, 575-587 (1957).
10. Hamburger, V., in *Cellular Mechanisms in Differentiation and Growth* (D. Rudnick, ed.), p. 191-212, Princeton Univ. Press, Princeton (1956).
11. Kredel, F., *Bull. Johns Hopkins Hosp.*, **40**, 216-227 (1927).
12. Lewis, W. H., *Anat. Rec.*, **23**, 387-392 (1922).
13. Moscona, A., and Moscona, H., *J. Anat.*, **86**, 278-286 (1952).
14. Needham, J., *Biochemistry and Morphogenesis*, Cambridge, at the University Press (1956).
15. Niu, M. C., in *Cellular Mechanisms in Differentiation and Growth* (D. Rudnick, ed.), p. 155-172, Princeton Univ. Press, Princeton (1956).
16. Okazaki, R., *Exptl. Cell Research*, **9**, 579-582 (1955).
17. Pantelouris, E. M., and Mulherkar, L., *J. Embryol. Exptl. Morphol.*, **5**, 51-59 (1957).
18. Sigurdson, B., *Proc. Soc. Exptl. Biol. Med.*, **50**, 62-66 (1942).
19. Sirlin, J. L., Brahma, S. K., and Waddington, C. H., *J. Embryol. Exptl. Morphol.*, **4**, 248-253 (1956).
20. Spiegel, M., *Biol. Bull.*, **107**, 149-155 (1954).
21. Twitty, V. C., *J. Exptl. Zool.*, **100**, 141-178 (1945).
22. ———, and Niu, M. C., *J. Exptl. Zool.*, **125**, 541-574 (1954).
23. Waddington, C. H., *Principles of Embryology*, Allen & Unwin, London (1956).
24. ———, and Mulherkar, L., *Proc. Zool. Soc. Bengal*, Mookerjee Memor. Vol., 141-147 (1957).
25. Weiss, P., *J. Exptl. Zool.*, **68**, 392-448 (1934).
26. ———, *Yale J. Biol. and Med.*, **19**, 235-278 (1947).
27. ———, *J. Embryol. Exptl. Morphol.*, **1**, 181-211 (1953).
28. ———, and Garber, B., *Proc. Natl. Acad. Sci. U. S.*, **38**, 264-280 (1952).
29. Yamada, T., and Takata, K., *Embryologia*, **3**, 66-79 (1956).

SOME PROBLEMS OF PROTEIN FORMATION IN THE SCLERA AND CORNEA OF THE CHICK EMBRYO

HEINZ HERRMANN

FOR SOME TIME work has been in progress at our laboratory on protein formation in embryonic tissues, for the purpose of obtaining information about the properties of the protein-forming system in developing cells. This system may be regarded as the final target of nuclear and cytoplasmic factors which control the formation of proteins as chemically measurable indices of differentiation.

While continuing the exploration of protein formation in developing muscle tissue and in explanted chick embryos we have recently extended our analyses to the sclera and cornea of the developing chick. The consideration which led us to this line of work was the following. According to Laguesse (6) and Redslob (10) the corneal area of the chick eye contains only a few scattered mesenchymal cells up to the sixth day of development. Following this stage, mesodermal cells begin to migrate from the scleral portion of the head mesenchyme into the corneal area, and the divergent trends in the development of the corneal and scleral cells become apparent. The cells which remain in the sclera develop a cartilaginous matrix, whereas in the corneal area a non-cartilaginous material is formed which contributes to the transparency of the corneal stroma.

Characterizing the developments of these two tissues in chemical terms, both are found to produce collagen as the main protein component of their intercellular substance; but in the case of the sclera chondroitin sulfuric acid is formed as the intercellular mucopolysaccharide (MPS) constituent, while in the cornea keratosulfate appears as the additional MPS component (9). This must mean that before the sixth day of development the synthetic apparatus has not become stabilized in all scleral cells and that MPS synthesis in the cells which migrate into the corneal area is directed in the new environment toward synthesis of keratosulfate. Alternatively, one would have to assume that the scleral mesenchyme represents a heterogeneous population in respect to MPS synthetic capacities, and

that the cells which have the synthetic apparatus for corneal MPS production migrate selectively to the corneal area. According to Weiss and Amprino (12), the cartilage-forming capacity of the chick sclera becomes determined on the fourth day of development, and therefore synthetic functions must begin to become stabilized at least in a large number of scleral cells at that stage of development.

In approaching the question of the stabilization of synthetic capacities in scleral and corneal cells we compared first the formation of collagen, the protein component of the intercellular matrix of the sclera and the cornea. Thus far we have found that the analytically determined accumulation of collagen in the corneal area and in the sclera follow a similar course. However, a striking difference in the protein-forming system of the two cell types is indicated by tests in vitro which show that incorporation of tracer amino acids into the collagen fraction of the cornea is dependent to a large extent upon the presence of the ectodermal component of this tissue, while in the sclera the incorporation of the tracer into scleral collagen seems to be independent of other adjacent tissues (4). The experiments which led us to this conclusion are discussed in the following section of this paper.

Experimental Results

The first set of graphs shows the changes in the DNA content of the sclera and the cornea respectively (Fig. 1). This parameter is regarded as an index of the magnitude of the cell population in these tissues during the examined period of development (7). It can be seen that the increase in the DNA content of the sclera is a discontinuous process. During the periods from the 8th to 12th day, 16th to 18th day, and 22nd to 28th day, no statistically significant change in the DNA of this tissue could be observed, while the increases in the intervening periods were found to be statistically significant. This discontinuity may be indicative of alternating periods of proliferative activity and more stationary states, or it could suggest periodic phases of cell degeneration balancing continuous cell proliferation. In the cornea, periods of statistically significant increases of DNA were observed to continue up to the 16th day of development. After this period no statistically significant increase of the DNA content of the cornea could be established with 15, 14, and 9 determinations for the 16th to 18th day and the 22nd to 28th day periods, respectively. To what extent migration of scleral cells into the cornea or proliferation of the corneal cells themselves contribute to the rise in the corneal DNA content has not been determined.

The accumulation of collagen fractions in the cornea and in the sclera

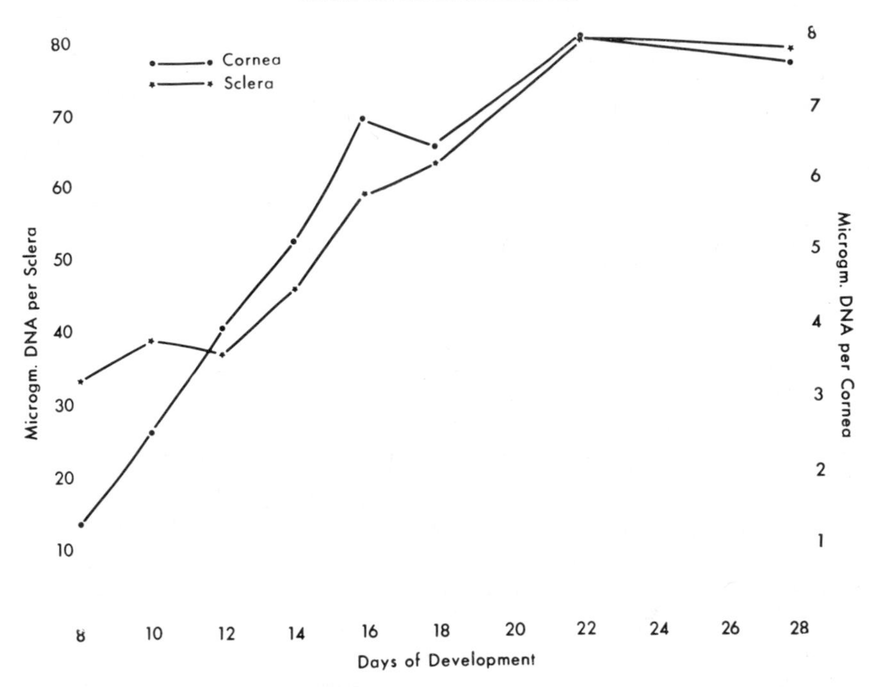

Fig. 1. Content of DNA in the sclera and cornea of the developing chick embryo.

is given in Fig. 2. Determined as hydroxyproline in hydrolysates of hot trichloroacetic acid extracts of the respective tissues, the curves for the collagen content of the sclera and of the cornea follow two similar, sigmoid curves with the inflection point at about the 18th day. In order to obtain comparable values for the protein-forming capacity for the scleral and corneal cells respectively, the ratios of total hydroxyproline/total DNA (HP/DNA) for the two tissues were calculated. The plots for these values give the collagen content in each tissue per unit of DNA (Fig. 3) or, for the equivalent, constant number of cells (7). These HP/DNA curves are also similar in respect to the overall acceleration as well as the total increase in the HP/DNA ratio. However, certain divergent aspects should be pointed out. It can be noticed that on the 8th day the HP/DNA ratio is markedly higher in the cornea (0.40) than in the sclera (0.076). Attempts to find determinable amounts of HP in the corneal area on the 6th day have failed so far, a result indicating that only negligible amounts of collagen can be present in the corneal area before arrival of mesenchymal cells. Another difference between the two tissues can be seen in compar-

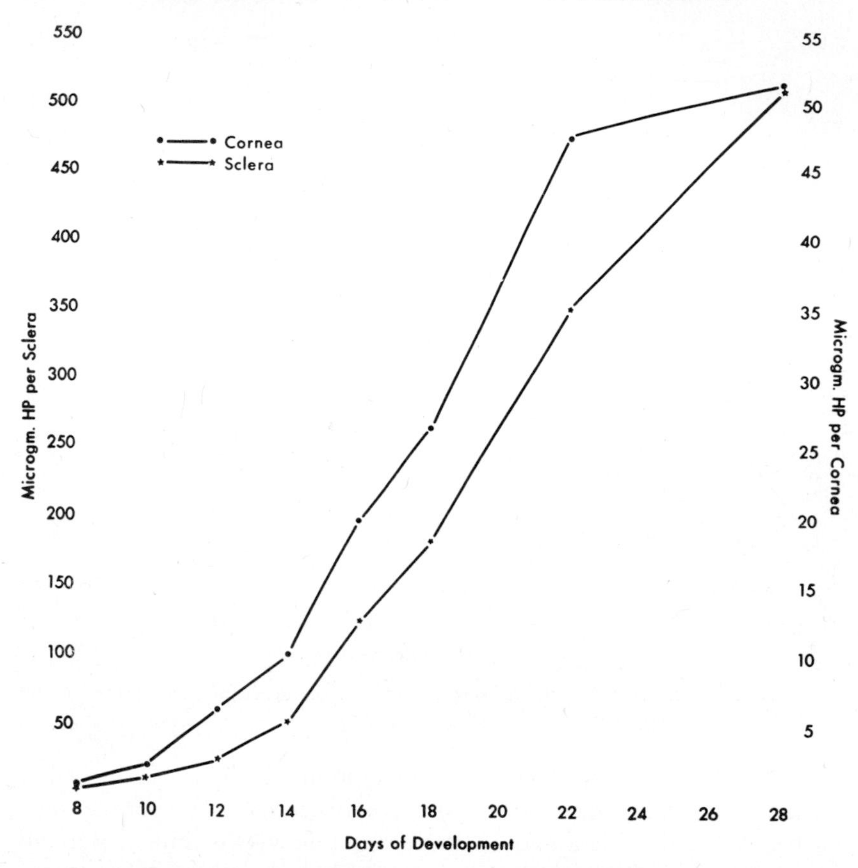

Fig. 2. Content of collagen, determined as hydroxyproline (HP), in the sclera and cornea of the developing chick embryo.

ing the curves for the HP/DNA ratios and for the ratio of non-collagenous proteins NCP/DNA (Fig. 3). In case of the cornea the HP/DNA values increase faster than the NCP/DNA values for the period examined except during the 14th-16th day interval, during which both parameters increase at the same rapid rate. In the case of the sclera, the two curves run parallel until the 22nd day, after which the HP/DNA curve maintains a steeper slope.

The above values for collagen accumulation were compared to the rates of tracer incorporation into the collagen fractions of the sclera and cornea. Using glycine-1-C^{14} the uptake of the tracer was observed for 1- to 4-hour incubation periods during which the tissues were suspended in two milli-

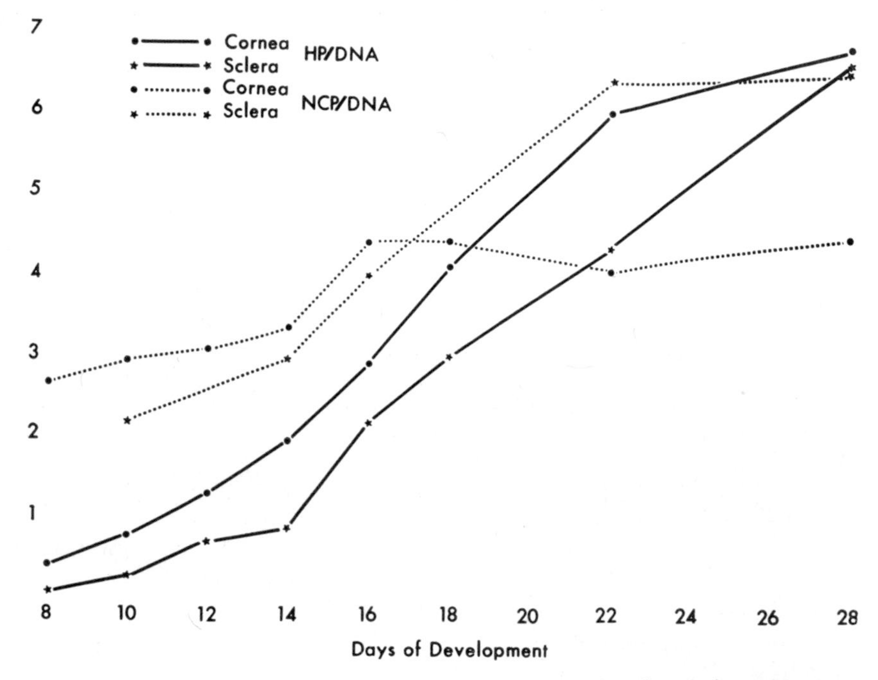

Fig. 3. Ratios of hydroxyproline (HP) per DNA in the sclera and cornea of the developing chick embryo.

liters of a nutrient solution to which was added 1 μc. of the labelled amino acid. To make these data comparable with the figures for accumulation, the tracer incorporation was expressed as cts./min./DNA of the respective tissues. Comparing the incorporation rates for the 9th-10th day period and for the 17th day of development (Table 1), a marked increase in the tracer uptake (cts./min./DNA) was observed which corresponds to the enhanced rate of increase of the HP/DNA ratio comparing the 8th-10th day period with the 16th-18th day period. The data show also that the values for incorporation of glycine-1-C^{14} into the collagen fraction of the two cell types are very similar on the 17th day of development. On the 10th day, however, the cornea shows a markedly higher incorporation rate under our experimental conditions than the sclera. This means, apparently, that on the ninth day of development collagen is formed more rapidly in the cornea than in the sclera, while the rates of collagen formation are of the same order of magnitude during later phases of development. These values were obtained for the collagen fraction formed in the stroma of the two tissues during incubation of the mesodermal portion together with the adjacent

TABLE 1

UPTAKE OF GLYCINE-1-C^{14} INTO COLLAGEN FRACTION OF SCLERA AND CORNEA AT DIFFERENT STAGES OF DEVELOPMENT

Age in days	cts./min./μg. DNA	
	Sclera	Cornea
9	5, 5, 9, 14 (1)	41, 41 (4)
9-10	14, 14, 18 (1)	66, 67, 70 (4)
17	193, 171, 216 175, 218, 218 (1)	231, 224 237, 157 (2)

The figures in parentheses indicate number of scleras or corneas, respectively, for each determination.

ectodermal components; with the retinal pigment epithelium or, if possible, with the entire retina in case of the sclera and with the epithelium in the case of the cornea. The ectodermal cells were removed after incubation, and the collagen fraction was prepared from the remaining mesodermal layer. Incubation of the tissues after removal of the ectodermal components did not lead to significant differences in the case of glycine incorporation into the collagen fraction from the scleral mesoderm. In the case of the cornea, however, a sharp drop in the incorporation was observed when the mesoderm was incubated in the absence of the corneal ectoderm (Table 2). The drop in incorporation was found to be proportional to the decrease in the stroma surface covered by the epithelium; metabolic inhibitors like dinitrophenol or iodoacetate markedly diminished the incorporation rate, and the presence of glucose in a salt solution enhanced the tracer uptake.

DISCUSSION

In introducing these experiments, it was suggested that differences in the chemical make-up of the mesodermal cells of the cornea and of the sclera may be due to a selective migration of one cell strain from a mixed cell population in the sclera, or that the cells derived from a relatively homogeneous population change their characteristics in their new environment. Although the first possibility cannot be ruled out, for the time being we are pursuing the alternative of a change in the scleral cells in the course of their interaction with the new corneal environment. This would mean that scleral cells, originally autonomous in respect to protein formation, become dependent for a rapid accumulation of the collagen fraction upon some factor contributed by the corneal epithelium. Since the corneal

TABLE 2

UPTAKE OF GLYCINE-1-C^{14} INTO A COLLAGEN FRACTION OF THE CORNEAL STROMA OF THE DEVELOPING CHICK (4)

The data are given as means of cts./sec./mg. N for the number of determinations indicated by the figures in parentheses.

10-day chick embryo			
		Stroma with epithelium	Stroma without epithelium
Complete medium			
Incubation time	1 hr.	453 (8)	77 (6) 17%[1]
Incubation time	2 hr.	1403 (2)	
Incubation time	4 hr.	3182 (4)	574 (2) 18%
Incubation time	6 hr.	5680 (2)	
3- to 8-day hatched chick			
Complete medium			
Incubation time	1 hr.	106 (16)	6 (12) 6%
Incubation time	4 hr.	386 (4)	15 (4) 4%
Incubation time	1 hr.		
½ epithelium removed		56 (4)	
¾ epithelium removed		36 (4)	
Complete medium			
Incubation time	1 hr.		
Dinitrophenol			
Final concentration	3×10^{-5} *M.*	84 (3)	
	1×10^{-4} *M.*	56 (3)	
	1×10^{-3} *M.*	25 (3)	
Iodoacetate			
Final concentration	1×10^{-3} *M.*	3 (2)	
P. C. solution			
Incubation time	1 hr.	75 (10)	
Incubation time	4 hr.	258 (2)	
P. C. solution with glucose			
Incubation time	1 hr.	99 (10)	
Incubation time	4 hr.	422 (2)	

[1] The percentage values refer to the fraction of tracer incorporated after removal of the epithelium.

stroma cells, especially in later stages of development, are at quite some distance from the epithelial layer, these factors would have to be assumed to be quite readily diffusible or readily propagated in some other fashion. At least in several tissues composed of an ectodermal and mesodermal component, the ectodermal layer seems to be the site of rather active oxidative metabolic reactions while the mesodermal component is poor in such oxidative enzymatic activity (2, 3). A similar situation seems to exist in the cornea at least of the fully developed beef eye (5). It is therefore suggested, as a tentative interpretation of our results, that in migrating to the corneal area the mesodermal cells become adapted to the utilization of the

oxidative energy produced in the epithelium for their own synthetic activities, in particular for the formation of proteins. This adaptation leads apparently to a more rapid initial production of collagen in the cornea, while the increase in the rate of protein formation in the sclera is somewhat slower and must be based on an energy supply provided by the scleral mesodermal cells themselves.

In this connection it must be remembered that other eye primordia (optic cup, lens) are held responsible for the induction of the cornea. To what extent these primordia participate in the control of the development of the corneal stroma remains to be investigated.

The interpretation of the different incorporation rates in the sclera and cornea has yet to be established conclusively by observations in vivo of the incorporation rates in the collagen fraction of the sclera and cornea, and by tests in vitro with a wider range of concentrations of the tracer, and a more detailed study of the time course of the incorporation in order to obtain information about the significance of the amino acid pool and possible collagen precursors in the final incorporation data. Also, it has to be demonstrated that the purified collagen contains the same amount of hydroxyproline at different stages of development. Finally, more evidence as to the metabolic pathways involved in this activation will be necessary to substantiate our hypothesis. These questions are being studied in our laboratory at the present time.

Whatever its mechanism may be, the fact of an ectoderm-dependent formation of protein in the corneal mesoderm has led us to approach experimentally the two following problems. First, it should be of interest to find out whether interaction of the corneal mesodermal cells with the corneal epithelium changes the rate of collagen production not only quantitatively but also gives rise to a qualitative change in the MPS-producing enzymes such as to form in the corneal stroma keratosulfate instead of chondroitin sulfuric acid, as in the sclera. Secondly, recent work by Saunders (10) and Zwilling (13) has shown that in the case of the limb bud the ectodermal component is essential for the normal development of the mesoderm of this primordium. In preliminary experiments with limb buds we have not yet been able to demonstrate an ectoderm-dependent incorporation of glycine into the protein moiety or into the nucleic-acid-containing trichloroacetic acid extract of the limb bud mesoderm. However, tests with a wider range of conditions in attempting to demonstrate such a dependence in the developing limb bud are in progress. It is hoped that observations in more numerous instances of a dependence of protein formation in one embryonic cell type upon the metabolic activities

or other processes in its cellular environment should prove to be useful in the investigation of mechanisms of cellular interactions and of their roles in embryonic development.

Materials and Methods Used

Fertilized eggs from Hi-Line hens were obtained from a commercial source and incubated at the laboratory at 38°C. For preparation of the sclera the eyes were dissected at the desired stages of development and the looser connective tissue was removed. The eyes were opened from the posterior pole with four meridional incisions to the rim of the cornea. The lens, vitreous body, cornea, and iris were discarded, to leave the four separate scleral sections with the retina attached. The corneas were excised from the eye remaining in situ, particular care being taken not to injure the epithelium. For incubation with the tracer, the scleras were used with or without attached whole retina or retinal pigment epithelium, and the corneas were also incubated with or without epithelium. The incubation was carried out in a Dubnoff shaker with nutrient solutions of 1 or 2 ml. volume and to which was added 1 μc. of tracer glycine-1-C^{14} (Nuclear, Chicago). If present during the incubation period, the epithelial components were removed after termination of the incubation. Preparation of the collagen fraction and counting procedure used in the tracer experiments were carried out as described previously (4). Collagen contents were determined using the methods of Fitch, Harkness and Harkness (1), and Martin and Axelrod (8). The quantities of collagen obtained by the two procedures used in the tracer experiments and in the content determinations respectively were in close agreement, and the ratios of hydroxyproline/total protein nitrogen were only slightly lower in case of the trichloroacetic acid extraction.

Acknowledgments

The author is indebted to Mr. R. D. Salerno and Mrs. M. Cooper for their competent technical assistance in carrying out the experiments reported in this paper.

The original work was supported by Grant B-549 from the National Institute of Neurological Diseases and Blindness of the National Institutes of Health, United States Public Health Service.

REFERENCES

1. Fitch, S. M., Harkness, M. L. M., and Harkness, R. D., *Nature,* **176,** 163-164 (1955).
2. Flexner, L. B., and Stiehler, R. D., *J. Biol. Chem.,* **126,** 619-626 (1938).
3. Friedenwald, J. S., Buschke, W., and Michel, H. O., *Arch. Ophthalmol.,* **29,** 535-570 (1943).

4. Herrmann, H., *Proc. Natl. Acad. Sci. U. S.,* **43,** 1007-1011 (1957).
5. ———, and Hickman, F. H., *Bull. Johns Hopkins Hosp.,* **82,** 225-250 (1948).
6. Laguesse, E., *Arch. anat. micros.,* **22,** 216-265 (1926).
7. Leslie, I., and Davidson, J. N., *Biochim. et Biophys. Acta,* **7,** 413-428 (1951).
8. Martin, C. J., and Axelrod, A. E., *Proc. Soc. Exptl. Biol. Med.,* **83,** 461-462 (1953).
9. Meyer, K., Linker, A., Davidson, E. A., and Weissmann, B., *J. Biol. Chem.,* **205,** 611-616 (1953).
10. Redslob, E., *Arch. anat. histol. embryol., Strasbourg,* **19,** 135-229 (1935).
11. Saunders, J. W., Cairns, J. M., and Gasseling, M. T., *J. Morphol.,* **101,** 57-87 (1957).
12. Weiss, P., and Amprino, R., *Growth,* **4,** 245-258 (1940).
13. Zwilling, E., *J. Exptl. Zool.,* **128,** 423-441 (1955).

blasts, and migrate over them with apparent ease. Abercrombie (2) has suggested that contact inhibition might play an important role in morphogenesis by providing a mechanism for the cessation of cell movements, and the restriction of such movements to noninhibited areas.

Orientation of Ameboid Cells

One possible source of direction for cell movements is to be found in the layer on which the cells are migrating. Weiss has postulated the theory of "selective contact guidance" (146, 148, 150) to account for the directed movements of mesenchyme and Schwann cells, and of axon outgrowths, from explanted tissue fragments. According to this theory, cells or cell processes follow lines of ultrastructural organization in the substratum, produced by stress or other orienting forces acting on the micellar components of the material. At least for some systems, both in vitro (147) and under certain circumstances in vivo (149), such a guiding mechanism can be shown to be operative. (For a recent review of this theory, especially as applied to neuron outgrowth, see ref. 151.) To account for the apparent fact that cells are capable of choosing "the right track" out of a multiply aligned system, Weiss suggests that the contact substrata have different specific properties which act as cues. He depicts such guide structures, situated in the intercellular matrix or in the surfaces of neighboring cells, as oriented lines of specific molecular groups, to which the cell can form temporary linkages by means of complementary groups in its own surface. A cell following such an oriented substratum would be exemplifying, according to Weiss's terminology, "selective conduction" (148). Extending these ideas to the movements of cells which are not guided by their substratum, "selective fixation" would account for any eventual pattern of localization. Cells would continue migrating until complementary groups in the substrate were encountered, at which time linkages would form and further movement cease. (This seems not unreasonable as a mechanism for Abercrombie's contact inhibition.) Conversely, cells might be stimulated to leave an area, or be destroyed there, a process termed "selective elimination."

Various other proposals have been made concerning the directive influences on single cells. Rosin (117) has suggested that propigment cells might be drawn ventrally toward an epidermal implant in response to a true chemotactic attraction exerted by the latter. Holtfreter has also described instances of pigment cell behavior indicative of their responsiveness to positive chemical attraction by lipoid substances (67). As mentioned above, an even less specific agent, carbon dioxide, has been tentatively

implicated by Twitty (137) and by Flickinger (40) in the direction of cell migration, and in a totally different system Harris (59) has provided clear evidence that mammalian granulocytes, in culture, respond to chemical gradients. Chemotaxis is also known to occur in the Myxomycetes or slime molds, a group which has been rigorously investigated by Bonner (17, 18) and by Sussman and associates (131 and this Symposium). Another orientative influence mediated by diffusible substances is to be seen in the direction of polarity in the egg of Fucus (153, 73). It should be noted, incidentally, that such chemical attractions "at a distance" between cells must be translated, operationally, into microgradients at the cell surface, which can affect the pseudopodial activity or adhesiveness of the plasma membrane.

Although Holtfreter has recognized the need for an "inside-outside chemical gradient" to understand fully the migratory regulation of amphibian cell masses, he has placed greatest emphasis, for many years, on the surface interactions of cells in explaining their movements (65, 66, 133). He has postulated a mechanism of cell guidance, which, like that of Weiss, is based on selective cell surface compatibilities. According to this theory, embryonic cells have specific positive affinities toward certain of their neighbors, while lacking such affinities toward others. Continued migration over the latter, and adhesion to the former, could eventually localize cells in their definitive positions. The control of movement of the propigment cells, for example, could be dependent upon their specific interactions or contact relationships with the cells of the epidermis. Holtfreter (65) has demonstrated such a positive affinity between chromatophores and epidermis, and Twitty and Niu (140) have confirmed and extended this observation. The latter authors were able to show that chromatophores in contact with epidermis migrate upon it whether or not a layer of mesoderm underlies it. On the other hand, chromatophores in contact only with somite mesoderm do not migrate. Finally, when epidermis is stripped from the underlying mesoderm subsequent to emigration of the propigment cells from the neural crest, all of the melanoblasts adhere to the epidermis instead of the mesoderm.

Further evidence in favor of selective association of cells of specific types was obtained by Weiss and Andres (152). They injected dissociated embryonic chick cells, including melanoblasts, from potentially pigmented donor strains, into the blood stream of host chick embryos of unpigmented breeds. These injected cells became scattered throughout the body of the host, but the donor melanoblasts proliferated and synthesized melanin only in locations in the host equivalent to those in which they normally

would have developed pigment in the donor. Never were donor melanocytes found in unusual cell associations. Caution must be employed however, in attributing such localization to properties of the cell surfaces alone. Ebert (34) has recently demonstrated that subcellular fractions (microsomal and supernatant) of spleen or kidney homogenates are differentially localized in the homologous host organ when injected into 9-day chick embryos.

In spite of the evidence that the adherence and migration of melanoblasts on different substrata are influenced by specific cell affinities, and that various chemotactic and chemotropic responses may be involved in the initiation and maintenance of such movements, it should be emphasized that there is no evidence of specific predetermined routes in the embryo, along which the chromatoblasts are unerringly guided. In normal development, pigment cells originate dorsally and descend in a ventrolateral direction. If, however, the crest is removed from its normal position along the neural tube, and reimplanted in a more ventral site, it has been shown by Twitty and Niu (140) that the chromatoblasts will migrate as readily in a dorsad direction as they normally do ventrally. In the words of these investigators, "We may best state the situation merely by saying that the cells spread from their source, wherever this may be situated on the embryo, and in so doing behave quite independently of any directional pulls or pathways associated with the axes of the organism" (p. 426). Control of the final position taken up by these cells would then represent an example of "selective fixation" rather than "selective conduction" (148).[1]

Mass Cell Movements

Much of the activity which constitutes true morphogenesis consists of the movements of interconnected masses or continuous layers of cells, rather than of cells as individuals. The invaginations and evaginations occurring during gastrulation, neurulation, and gut formation, or the migrations of organ primordia to their definitive sites of differentiation may be cited among the many examples of such mass movements. Whereas isolated cells can move only as a result of their own activity (excluding for the moment passive carriage by other tissues or along vascular routes), members of such layers or masses are clearly subject to other motive forces as well. Growth of a cell layer by mitotic division will cause peripheral areas of the layer to spread centrifugally, or, if these areas are anchored

[1] However, an interesting experimental study by W. M. Reams (*J. Morphol.*, **99**, 513-548, 1956), suggests that melanoblasts may indeed follow dorso-ventral lines of orientation in their invasion of the coelomic lining of the chick embryo.

firmly to the substrate, buckling, warping, or thickening of the layer must occur. Even without mitosis, if each member of a layer of cells alters its shape by an active process, as for example by flattening and expanding its area of contact with the substratum, the proportions of the entire layer will also change; in this case, again, expanding or buckling. This process is clearly exemplified in the blastodermal epiboly of fish embryos, in which expansion is caused by flattening and migration of the underlying syncytial periblast layer (90, 134, 135).

Another motive force influential in morphogenesis is that imparted to cells by the contraction of filopodial intercellular connections. The extent of such "filose" activity (9) of embryonic cells is apparently much greater than is generally recognized (101). Even before the turn of the century, intercellular connections were revealed between the cells of various invertebrate embryos (8, 9). These were considered not only as a means of cellular cohesion by which cells could be drawn together, but also as true "physiological connections" whereby the exchange of living protoplasm could take place.[2] Much more recently Dan and Okazaki (26) and Gustafson and Kinnander (56) have described the important role played by filopodial contraction during gastrulation in the sea urchin. Both primary and secondary mesenchyme cells spin out long thin pseudopodia, which attach to the ectoderm and draw the cell body, or the archenteron tip to which it adheres, toward the point of pseudopodial attachment.

In vertebrate tissues, similar intercellular connections have been reported. The contraction of chromatophore cell-processes in amphibia, as described by Twitty (138, 139), was noted above. In the chick embryo, Spratt (128) has seen fibers in living specimens, connecting adjacent and nonadjacent cells within and between germ layers. Many are elastic, and some appear to be spatially oriented in certain important growth regions such as the node area and neural plate. Even in the human embryo, extensive fibrillization between cells of the cardiogenic plate has been described in fixed material, although Davis (28) considers such structures largely artifactitious.

Most of the earlier references on intercellular connections are provided in Fisher's extensive discussion of the topic (38, especially chapters 2 and

[2] In 1897, Andrews (9) was able to make the following statement, which, I think, could well be taken as a standard for aesthetic and (in the light of modern knowledge) prophetic scientific prose: "If we look upon the cell wall as a part of the machinery of the embryo . . . , that is, as an organ of the mass of living substance, just as is the nuclear membrane, or any other local modification for psysiological purposes, we shall probably be nearer the truth than if we keep to an earlier conception, and hold that, for the living substance, cell walls a prison make" (p. 389).

3). He also takes up the question of whether such connections represent true protoplasmic bridges. Although opinions of workers in the field are divided, Fisher seems to conclude that in many tissues, and in cultured cells, cytoplasmic continuity can occur. On the other hand, Caesar, Edwards, and Ruska (22) have recently examined many adult tissues with the electron microscope, hoping to answer this question. They are able, in every case, to see continuous membranes between cells, even in tissues previously accepted as syncytial. They tentatively conclude that "continuity of protoplasm from cell to cell [does] not exist in vertebrate tissues, and perhaps not in any animal tissue" (p. 873). Whether or not such a generalization is valid, and whether or not it is equally applicable to embryonic cells, remains to be seen.

In spite of the evidence for such intercellular forces, there are many situations in which movements of cell masses are brought about by ameboid activity of individual cells or small groups of cells constituting the mass. Spratt (127, 129) has recently shown this to occur in the process of notochord elongation in chick embryos. He has found that in the head-process embryo there is a fairly well-defined group of cells, lying beneath the primitive pit and extending anteriorly to the edge of Hensen's node, which constitutes a single, median notochord center or "chorda bulb." Removal of the chorda center during regression of the primitive streak results in cessation of further notochord formation posterior to the site of operation, but has essentially no effect on continued formation of somites. Elongation of the notochord is accomplished partly by mitotic division of chordal cells, but to a greater extent by addition of cells originally posterior to the chorda bulb. Apparently most of the cells of the chorda center migrate actively in a posterior direction, at a rate which is much faster than the regression of the postnodal mesoderm. Since it is only if the chorda bulb cells accomplish this movement through the postnodal mesoderm that the latter are transformed into notochord, it is felt that chorda center cells exhibit an inductive influence upon the cells with which they come in contact during their migration.

What forces, it may be asked, maintain these wandering cells in their (literally) straight and narrow path down the middle of the embryonic area? Unfortunately, no experimental evidence is forthcoming from Spratt's studies which will shed light on this question, and we must thus look to analogous situations elsewhere in development. One of these is seen in the migration of myoblasts during the formation of discrete muscle bundles. It has been demonstrated in amphibian embryonic muscle cells in culture (68) and in chick myoblasts both in vitro and in freshly

teased preparations (70, 80) that motility is a function of pseudopodial activity concentrated mainly at the leading tip of the cell. Therefore, the selective contact guidance theory of Weiss and the specific cell affinity theory of Holtfreter may be applicable here. Hall (57) has studied myoblast movements in the forming head musculature of the urodele. He began his investigation with the working hypothesis that the pre-muscle masses elongate and migrate toward their points of origin and insertion in response to specific influences emanating from these points of attachment. At early stages of development, well before the muscle mesoderm had begun to segment, the prospective points of attachment or route of growth of the levator and depressor mandibulae muscles were modified by various operations. The results of these experiments emphasized the lack of importance, for differentiation and orientation of the muscles, of the structures which afford their origin and insertion. Excellent development was found in muscles lacking one or the other of these structures, and even in parts of muscles which lacked both. On the other hand, profound modifications of muscle structure, orientation, and position were obtained after neural crest extirpations had resulted in deficiencies in certain head cartilages. These modifications, it should be emphasized, often occurred in the presence of a well-developed origin and insertion. Hall concluded, therefore, that it is the mesectodermal elements which orient, and exert a trophic influence upon, the developing muscle primordia. He suggested that this might occur during elongation and differentiation of the muscles, at which time the neural crest cells have obtained their definitive positions and are differentiating into cartilages. It may also have occurred at earlier stages during which the neural crest material was migrating ventrally and surrounding the muscle mesoderm.

A similar directive influence of mesenchymal tissue has been described by Holtfreter in the development of the pronephric system (66). He was able to show that the caudal extension of the Wolffian duct is oriented by cells in the environment. The tendency of the duct to follow its normal course along the lower border of the somites seems to be due to a selective adhesion between the nephric cells and the endothelium of blood vessels, especially the posterior cardinal veins. In experimental animals in which accessory somites and blood vessels had been induced from implanted cells, the host duct was frequently seen to forsake its normal surroundings and follow, instead, the alternate route along the accessory structures. It is difficult to interpret these examples, as well as others which might be mentioned (see, e.g., 148) as representing anything other than an orientation of

movements resulting from characteristics of the cells or substratum on or through which the moving cells travel.

Townes and Holtfreter (133) have recently published an experimental analysis of this problem, the results of which add notably to our information regarding cell surface interactions. Tissues of known prospective fate were excised from amphibian embryos between gastrula and late neurula stages. The tissues were either explanted together in various combinations, or they were first disaggregated (with high *p*H), the individual cells of the tissues intermingled, and the "compound" tissues then allowed to reaggregate. Within a matter of hours the individual cells of such an aggregate begin to perform "directed movements" corresponding to those of the tissue fragments from which they were derived. Cells from the neural plate or mesoderm which had been combined with either epidermal or endodermal cells exhibited inward movements. (A clear example of "unipolar ingression," as claimed for the yolky endoderm cells of the early blastula, 122; but see 11.) The epidermal and, to a lesser extent, endodermal cells manifested a tendency to migrate centrifugally. Having reached the periphery of the aggregate, these cells spread out to form a flattened epithelium. As a consequence of these movements, the different cell types sort out into distinct homogeneous layers, corresponding to the normal germ-layer arrangement after gastrulation. The tissue segregation is then completed by an emergence of further selectivity of cell adhesion, homologous cells remaining in contact, nonhomologous cells being separated, either by continued migration, or by the formation of fluid-filled spaces between the cells.

Gregg and his associates (52, 53, 102) also have attempted to analyze the relation between tissue interaction and gastrulatory movements, using tissue combinations in vitro. A piece of presumptive head endoderm, notochord mesoderm, or ventral ectoderm from a stage 10 frog gastrula is explanted on a "base" of yolk endoderm in such a way that distinct types of cell movements can be observed separately. By applying various metabolic poisons and by using tissues from nongastrulating hybrid embryos, they have been able to demonstrate characteristic movements of specific cell masses, and to relate failure of these movements to developmental defects in intact embryos. Although their results to date are incomplete, much is to be expected from this type of attack.

The principle of specific cell affinities may also be applied in interpreting some of the observations on embryonic grafts in which donor tissue is found in contact only with homologous host tissues, often at sites distant

from the point of implantation. Such a situation has been described in endodermal implants in both amphibia (66) and fish (100); similarly, the histotypic development of organized tissues in chimeric aggregates can thus be depicted (95, 96, 97). Even those movements which cannot be accounted for wholly by autonomous activity of the cells, designated as "correlative movements" by Schechtman (123), are influenced by cellular adhesive properties, since traction forces set up in one area of an embryo would have to be transmitted to another part through cohesive chains or layers.

From the above examples it would appear that those movements of gastrulation, neurulation, and organ formation which involve active ameboid behavior of the individual cells of a mass are to a large extent controlled by the characteristics of the cell surfaces, and by the resultant "migration tendencies" (133) inherent in each cell type at a given stage in its differentiation and in response to a given contact surface. Changes in the membrane properties would result in alterations of both the migration tendencies and the specific contact affinities of cells.

Coordinated Movements of Cell Groups and Layers

Obviously, morphogenetic movements consist, not only of the motions of individual cells sliding past or over one another, but also of the movements of entire layers of cells in which each individual member maintains a relatively stable juxtaposition with its neighbors. A prime example of this is provided by the process of foregut development in the chick. By carefully marking the endoderm of early chicks with carbon particles, Bellairs (12, 12a) has determined the presumptive foregut areas and has followed the movements of the endodermal layer during development. She distinguishes "two-dimensional" and "three-dimensional" movements, the former occurring in the original plane of the endoderm, the latter folding certain regions medioventrally to form the floor of the foregut (Fig. 1). The anterior end of the gut is formed first as a pocket between two sets of opposing movements in the endoderm, a forward two-dimensional movement beneath the head process, and an obliquely mesiocaudad, three-dimensional movement on either side. These oblique movements result in a U-shaped ridge in the endoderm bordering the anterior intestinal portal. As the movements continue progressively backwards, the two limbs of the ridge are brought together in the mid-line, where they fuse and thus gradually close off the cavity of the foregut from that of the yolk-sac.

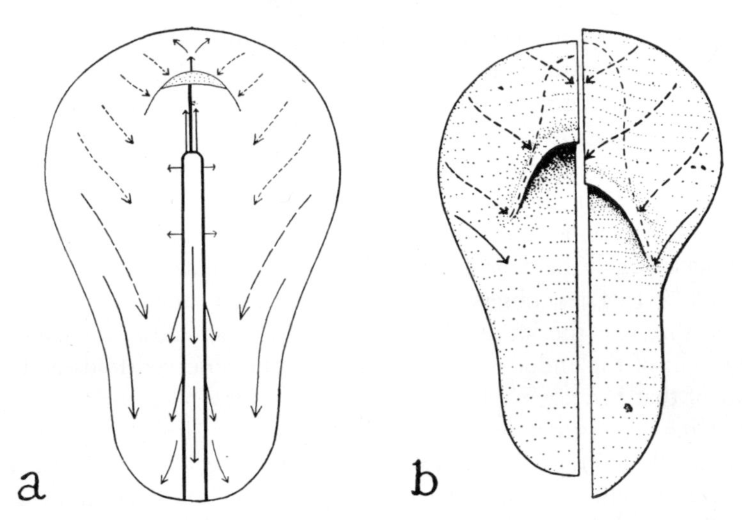

Fig. 1. Diagrams of the ventral aspect of the chick blastoderm during foregut formation and elongation. (After Bellairs, 12). Solid arrows show endodermal movements in the plane of the drawing. Broken arrows represent three-dimensional movements folding the endoderm medioventrally.
a. Initiation of head fold.
b. Stages in elongation of gut.

In seeking a mechanism for these mass movements, Bellairs has examined two possibilities. Spatially limited bursts of mitotic activity would be expected to cause locally variable changes in area and shape of the layer. Mitotic counts of the area pellucida endoderm, however, yielded no evidence suggesting that differences in mitotic rate were prerequisite for the observed morphogenetic movements (14). Furthermore, in a study of the anomalies produced by treatment of chicks with a mitotic inhibitor (menadiol diphosphate), it was concluded that failure of closure of the foregut, and other alterations of normal cell movements, were not attributable solely to interference with cell division (13). These findings are supported by the results of many recent studies, which largely eliminate cell division as a major causal factor in mass cell movements (133, 42, 144). Nonetheless, it is not to be concluded that mitosis plays no part whatsoever here, since both Bellairs (15) and Abercrombie (1) have recently suggested a secondary role of cell division in stimulating cell movement or ameboid activity.

A second candidate for the major motive force underlying the endodermal movements noted above is the phenomenon of change in shape of

individual cells of the layer. This is an idea which dates back to Rhumbler's studies of gastrulation on model systems (114). He conceived that the observed changes in cell shape might be causally, rather than consequentially, related to the invagination of the blastular wall. More recent workers have obtained much evidence supporting this concept (78, 79, 16, 21, 29, 42, 81, 144). Bellairs describes in detail such changes occurring in the cells of the endoderm: the thinning of the presumptive foregut roof, and thickening of the floor and lateral walls prior to and during gut formation (12, 12a). These observations and those in her more recent work (15) suggest that it is the locally varying patterns of spreading or contraction of the cells of the endoderm which produce the observed folds and movements of that layer.

Holtfreter has suggested that ameboid behavior similar to that seen in isolated cells (67) might be active in the folding of cell layers. Forces within each cell, probably related to some sol-gel transformation mechanism (61), and thus perhaps to a calcium-binding by cytoplasmic proteins (85, 88, 113, 116), could lead to autonomous cell shrinkage or extension. A mechanism early suggested to account for such shape-changes was the differential intake of water into cells. Glaser (44, 45) obtained evidence supporting this idea of differential imbibition, and Giersberg (41) and Hobson (64) were able to reverse the closure of the neural folds with strongly hypertonic media. Unfortunately for this hypothesis, however, Brown, Hamburger, and Schmitt (20) have been unable to demonstrate changes of density of more than five to ten per cent in the respective neural tissue of amphibia during gastrulation, indicating no large uptake of water. Moreover, the criticisms of Gillette (42), bringing into question the validity of the interpretation of experiments such as those of Giersberg and of Hobson, leave little support for any hypothesis demanding extensive cell swelling.

To account for such changes in shape without invoking water uptake, Waddington (144) has postulated the formation of fibrous structures in the internal cytoplasm. In the neck of the endodermal flask cells which form in the amphibian blastopore region, he has shown double refraction, indicating the presence of such fibrous structures. In most cells, however, there is little evidence that the bulk of the internal cytoplasm also contains oriented material of this kind (143). "It is therefore probable," admits Waddington, "that intracellular fibers play at best a very minor role in amphibian early morphogenesis" (144, p. 439).

Recent studies of morphogenetic mechanisms have attached great im-

portance to the properties of cell membranes. As cited above, Holtfreter has emphasized the importance of cell surface characteristics to his concept of specific cell affinities. Similarly, changes in cell adhesiveness could be postulated which would produce just those changes of cell shape observed in the endoderm and neural ectoderm. An increased tendency of a cell for adhesion to its neighbors would increase the area of contact, resulting in a transition from squamous to columnar forms, and decreasing the area of the layer constituted by these cells (20). Waddington (144) feels that it is quite probable that such forces arising from adhesiveness of the cell membranes play a part in the elongation and narrowing of the dorsal material, and the compensating expansion of the more ventral parts of the amphibian embryo during gastrulation and neurulation.

It has been demonstrated clearly by Gillette (42), in his detailed analysis of the size and shape of cells of the medullary plate during neurulation, that in the process of folding the cells become flask-shaped by shrinkage of that part of their surface facing the exterior, resulting in a shift of the nucleus and the bulk of the cytoplasm toward the internal side of the ectoderm. Lewis (81) attributes these form changes to contraction of the superficial gel layers of the cells. However, increased adhesiveness of the cells along their upper sides, resulting in a greater area of intercellular contact on that side, could bring about a similar effect. Sol-gel transformations involving calcium transfer within different parts of the cell (as mentioned above), coordinated with these surface changes, might also be involved.

Another process of development which has recently been examined from the point of view of changes in cell shape is the formation of the notochord in the mid-line of the invaginated amphibian mesoderm (93). It is quite clear here that the area of contact between cells does increase considerably as the notochord forms. Beginning as a group of loosely connected, rounded cells, the notochord grows progressively more compact, the cells taking on an arrangement comparable "to a pile of coins" (p. 402), each cell becoming a more or less flat disc with the maximum possible contact with other similar cells. Pending further evidence, we might conclude from these examples, as does Waddington (144), that "increase in cell contact is clearly one of the basic phenomena of morphogenesis, and it seems not unreasonable to accept it as a causal explanation of the events. Forces arising from the cell membranes may well be the prime cause of the changes of tissue configuration during the whole process of gastrulation and neurulation" (p. 451).

THE STRUCTURE OF THE CELL MEMBRANE AND THE MECHANISM OF ADHESION

We are brought back, then, to the first question asked in the introduction to this paper: what is the mechanism of cellular adhesiveness in the embryo? We must begin by considering first where such adhesiveness takes place. That is, we must recognize that a cell adheres to its neighbor or its substratum by means of its plasma membrane, and that it will be the properties and structure of this membrane, the properties and structure of the cell surface, to which we must look for mechanisms of cell adhesion. (For a recent discussion of specialized adhesive surface structures in adult cells, see 36.)

A detailed analysis of the various theories concerning the physico-chemical structure of the plasma membrane would be redundant, since several such reviews have been published in the last few years, examining the problem from one point of view or another (69, 91, 30, 60, 118, 106, 19). It is sufficient for our purpose here to note only that the protoplasmic membrane behaves, under numerous circumstances, like a highly condensed double phosphatide layer, complexed with proteins and probably with cholesterol (19, 30). Such lipo-protein membranes exhibit evidence of rather complex patterns of oriented molecules and even some suggestion of paracrystalline lattice structures (145, 124). The phosphatides most frequently noted are cephalin, lecithin, and possibly phosphatidic acid (19). At least in parts of the membrane, protein of both enzymic and antigenic nature is found at the surface (118, 125, 126), probably associated with nucleic acids (77, 119, 25).

As mentioned earlier, linkages formed between specific molecular groups in contact surfaces might be expected to bind the cells in a manner analogous to an enzyme-substrate or antigen-antibody system. Tyler has expanded upon this idea in elaborating his auto-antibody concept (see, e.g., 142). Weiss (146, 148, 150) has suggested a similar hypothesis wherein tissue affinities would be based on the presence in the contact surfaces of reciprocally identical, or complementary, protein configurations, interlocking and binding by "molecular attraction forces" (146, p. 188). Different degrees of adhesion might be explained by differences in the spacing of the molecules in each membrane.

These theories, based largely on analogy, are supported by three major classes of observation: (1) the marked specificity of cell adhesions, which can be accounted for readily in terms of the specificities of the postulated molecular groupings; (2) the disaggregation which is effected by prote-

olytic enzymes, such as trypsin or papain (152, 97, 37), indicating that peptide linkages are indeed involved somewhere in the adhesive mechanism; and (3) the inhibition of reaggregation of cells by antisera prepared against their surface antigens (125, 126).

As formidable as this evidence may appear, it must be pointed out that neither individually nor in the aggregate do the data form more than a suggestive basis for such a concept. Surface specificity can indeed be accounted for by any system incorporating patterned chemical bonding sites (see below), but, as suggested by Pauling (105), this might include configurations of ionic bonds, covalent, metallic, or hydrogen bonds, or London-van der Waals forces. Specific contact affinities might be provided by spatially patterned groups of any of these nonspecific interatomic forces, thus retaining none but the most general similarity to that observed in antigen-antibody reactions. Disaggregation by proteolytic enzymes, though practiced routinely in several laboratories, does not always produce a reversible separation. Feldman (36) disaggregated early amphibian neurula tissues with trypsin, papain, pepsin, or calcium-binding agents. Only with the last-named, in the absence of enzymes, was he able to get satisfactory reaggregation. Townes (132) has obtained similar findings. As to the inhibition of such reaggregation by antibodies to surface antigens, this would be expected whether or not those antigens represented the sites of cell binding. Indeed, Spiegel (125) recognizes the possibility that each of his antibody molecules simply "overhangs or somehow interferes with the activity of the adhesion site" (p. 144), while actually binding to an uninvolved antigen nearby. Finally, and perhaps crucially, the "lock and key" theory of cell adhesion does not take into consideration the voluminous evidence implicating divalent cations, especially calcium, in the adhesive mechanism.

As early as 1890, Ringer (115) was able to show that traces of calcium ions are required to prevent dispersion of the cells of mussel gills, and in the next few years the importance of calcium in maintaining tissue integrity was confirmed and extended by Herbst (62), Overton (103), and Lillie (82). Largely on the basis of the work of these authors, it was generally agreed that the cohesive material binding cells together was probably a reversible calcium salt of a weak acid (158). Other investigators have visualized an intercellular "cement substance" consisting of mucoprotein (50), calcium proteinate (158), histone (124), or other viscous material (see e.g. 23, 50). With the more recent use, not only of calcium-free solutions, but of various calcium-complexing agents, it has been possible to confirm that cells of many embryonic and adult tissues depend on the

presence of free divalent cations for their adherence to one another (although, see 63). Townes (132) and Feldman (37) have used citrate, oxalate, and glycine (an excellent calcium-binder) to produce reversible disaggregation of embryonic amphibian cells. Zwilling (159) introduced the use of a commercially available chelating agent, ethylene diamine tetraacetic acid ("Versene") for the dissociation of chick embryonic cells, and this same substance, along with other calcium complexers, has been found useful in separating the cells of adult rat liver (7). Furthermore, we know that calcium and other divalent cations are bound at the cell surface (77, 86, 92, 118, 6), and also would be expected to form an integral part of any mucoprotein matrix (76, 50, 55) if such exists in the embryo (see the discussion of intercellular matrices by Edds, in this Symposium).

In view of our present knowledge of the chemical composition of the cell membrane and its ability to bind ions, it seems most parsimonious to assume that the "weak acid" referred to by earlier workers, which was supposed, as a calcium salt, to form the intercellular adhesive material, actually is part of the membrane. The carboxyl groups of the membrane protein or—more likely—the orthophosphate or polyphosphate groups of phosphatides and nucleic acids would fill this role. Calcium ions might then form "bridges" between two cells, one valency of each ion binding to one of the contact surfaces. Enzymatic conversion between lecithin, cephalin, and phosphatidic acid, initiated from within the cell (19), could provide a means for altering the dissociation constant of the calcium complex, and thereby the degree of adhesiveness of any part of the cell membrane. A "zipper mechanism" analogous to that proposed by Schmitt (124) to account for changes in cell shape is thus made possible, utilizing only substances known to exist at the cell surface.

On the basis of observations on disaggregated amphibian cells, Steinberg (130) has reached a similar view. He has, in fact, devised a theory which accounts for both cell adhesiveness and specific cell affinities, in terms of a lattice array of calcium-binding sites on the cell surface. The degree of adhesiveness would be a function of the degree of congruency of such sites, and changes of cohesion during differentiation might be associated with alterations in the geometry of the lattice pattern.

Heretofore, very few workers (67, 150, 130) have recognized that a cell can adhere to its neighbor or to its substratum with more or less firmness, depending on the state of the membrane and the environment in which the cell finds itself. There has been a tendency on the part of most investigators in this field to treat cell dissociation as an all-or-none phenomenon. I should like to question this attitude, and emphasize that embryonic cells

can adhere to each other with varying strengths. Moreover, I propose not only that calcium is required for cell adhesion, but that it is an important factor in controlling the strength of that adhesion; i.e., that there is a correlation between the amount or "activity" (in the physical chemist's sense) of calcium in the surrounding medium, and the extent or firmness of cellular contact. Furthermore, it should be noted that the phenomenon of cell movement is in turn a function of cell adhesion. We have seen earlier how this is the case in cell layers. Although it has been said that "in morphogenesis the forces controlling directed movements must overcome those of cell adhesion" (133, p. 110), it is clear that migratory cells cannot move at all except in firm contact with a cellular or noncellular substrate (146, 151, 2).

In view of the above considerations, it should be possible, by means of limited removal of calcium from a developing embryo, to produce disturbances of intercellular or cell-substrate adhesion of just sufficient severity to cause abnormal morphogenetic movements, yet not yield disaggregation.

The Effects of Limited Cell Dissociation on Cardiac Development

In the normal development of the chick, heart-forming capacity can be traced back to a pair of mesodermal anlagen situated bilaterally on either side of Hensen's node in the head-process stage embryo (107). With the splitting of the mesoderm into somatic and splanchnic layers, the amniocardiac vesicles are formed. The presumptive cardiac cells remain in the splanchnic layer, closely applied to the endoderm (121). As the foregut is formed, the ventrocaudal folding of the endoderm (12a) carries the heart primordia toward the mid-line, where further mesiad migration brings the newly formed endocardial "gutters" together at their rostral ends to form the conus arteriosus. The familiar process of "zipping" together of the two sides over the regressing arch of the anterior intestinal portal then occurs, allowing progressive fusion of the bulbus cordis, the ventricle, the atrium, and finally the sinus venosus of the primitive tubular heart. This process has been described in detail in several vertebrates (28, 104, 120, 49, 155), and can readily be observed in the living chick embryo, explanted ventral side up, according to the method of New (99). Under these circumstances, with the embryo resting in its normal position on the vitelline membrane, development progresses satisfactorily for two to three days after explantation at the primitive streak stage. The heart and endodermal structures can be visualized clearly, especially during early phases, and ma-

nipulation or treatment of the chicks can be accomplished from the endodermal surface.

If a small crystal of acetylcholine (Ach) is allowed to dissolve on the endoderm of a primitive streak stage embryo, the folding of that layer and the migration of the presumptive cardiac mesoderm toward the mid-line will frequently be prevented or modified, producing a "cardia bifida" monster with two bilaterally situated beating hearts (31). An attempt to investigate the mechanism of this disruption of morphogenetic movements, and to relate the Ach effect with the hypothesis concerning cell adhesion and cell movements set forth above, will constitute the remainder of the present paper.

To confirm and extend the previous observations, a total of 250 embryos was divided into groups of about twenty, and each group was treated with 10 microliters of a solution of Ach in calcium-free Howard-Ringer (72). Control chicks were treated with 10 microliters of the same solution, lacking Ach, in which the *p*H had been adjusted to various levels with hydrochloric acid. Figs. 2-5 show a control and three treated embryos, fixed at 44-48 hours of incubation, the latter three having developed from the primitive streak stage in the presence of approximately molar Ach. This series demonstrates nicely the range of effects, from only a slight indentation in the anterior intestinal portal and improper fusion of the ventricles (Fig. 3), through complete separation of the right and left heart (Fig. 4), and finally to the stage having wide separation of the hearts, complete lack of a foregut, and open neural tube (Fig. 5). In each group treated with concentrations of 0.89 *M* Ach or greater, some of the embryos were completely disaggregated. Within a few minutes after addition of the Ach solution, separation of the two halves of the primitive streak occurred along the mid-line, the edges of the hole being drawn back toward the area opaca by tension in the blastoderm. Within 15-20 minutes, the space previously occupied by the area pellucida was empty except for a few isolated clumps of cells. By this time, usually, the area opaca had become reticular and "patchy," cells separating into strands, again migrating toward the periphery. By the next morning, each of these disaggregated embryos was represented only by a ring of vesicular tissue around the edge of the glass ring, the vitelline membrane being essentially empty.

In view of this continuum of effects, a system of grading was devised for the experimental embryos, using the following criteria:

Excellent—Heart, somites, and nervous system conform well with those of controls and the Hamburger-Hamilton normal stages (58); heart beating (if stage ten or older); tissues distinct and translucent.

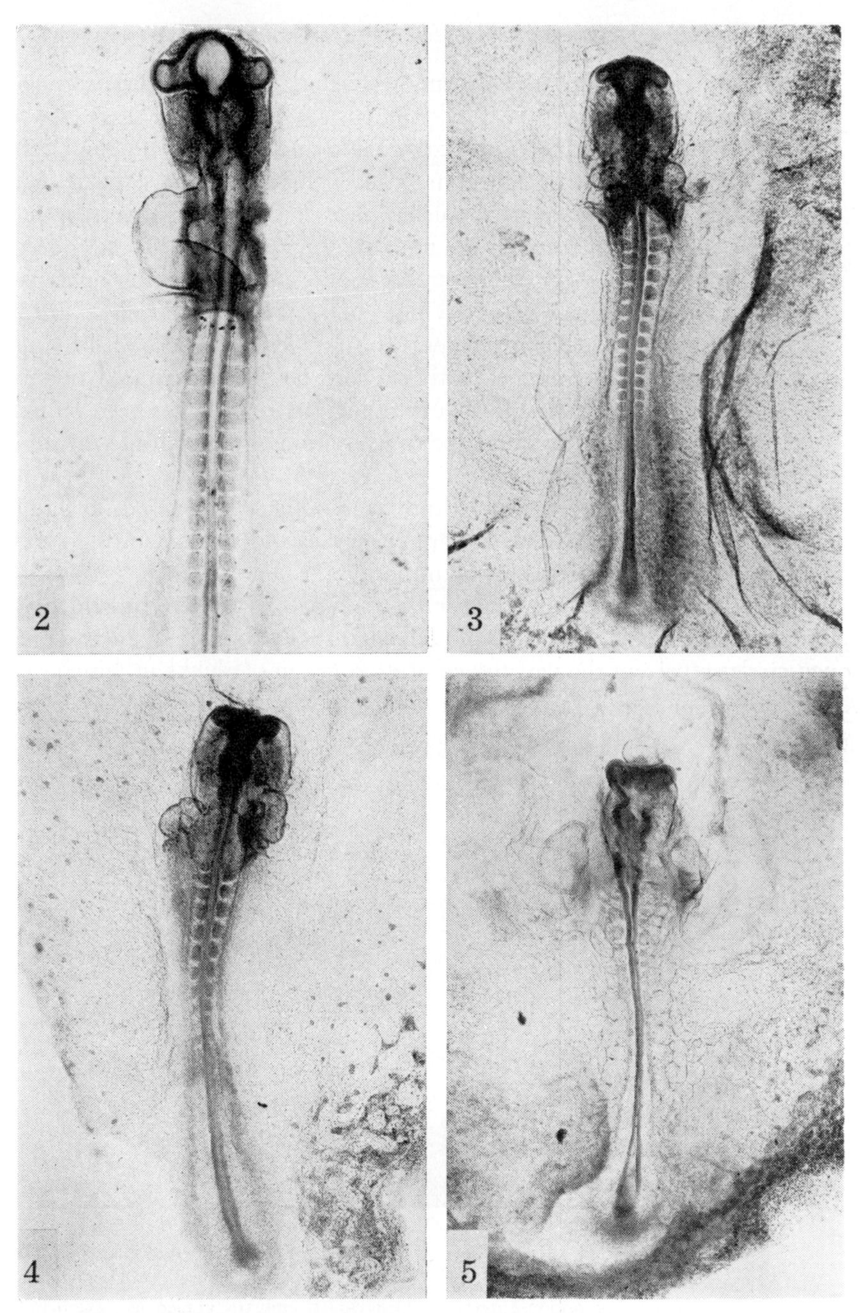

Fig. 2. Control chick, stage 11, explanted and treated at stage 4 with 10 microliters of calcium-free Howard-Ringer. Fixed in 10% neutral formalin. Stained in alcoholic cochineal. Photographed from ventral view. × 20.

Figs. 3-5. Cardia bifida (CB) embryos produced by treatment with acetylcholine (Ach) at stage 4. Mounted and photographed as with control.

Fig. 3. Stage 11, 1.0 *M* Ach, Partial CB.

Fig. 4. Stage 10+, 1.0 *M* Ach.

Fig. 5. Badly deformed stage 10+, 1.1 *M* Ach. Note indistinct somites and paired hearts; open, flattened neural tube, complete lack of foregut, and blistered appearance of blastoderm.

Good—Only minor variations from "excellent," e.g., no heart beat, abnormal flexures, etc.

Fair—Heart, brain, and foregut recognizable, and somites countable; permissible are stunted central nervous system structures, heart not beating, heart present in abnormal position as in situs inversus, but with normal structure; tissues more or less opaque.

Poor—Embryo noticeably disorganized, somites usually lacking or indistinct, tissues opaque; definitely not good enough to be called "fair."

Disaggregate—Area pellucida or entire blastoderm dissociated, leaving clear vitelline membrane (extreme care has been exercised not to confuse this situation with that in which the embryo has been pulled over to one side of the ring, due to separation of the blastoderm from the vitelline membrane).

Cardia bifida—Any of the first three grades (excellent, good, or fair) having double hearts, which are either beating spontaneously or respond to gentle mechanical stimulation.

The over-all concentration relations are shown in Fig. 6, in which is plotted increasing concentrations of Ach against developmental effect. The open circles represent the percentage of each group of chicks in which de-

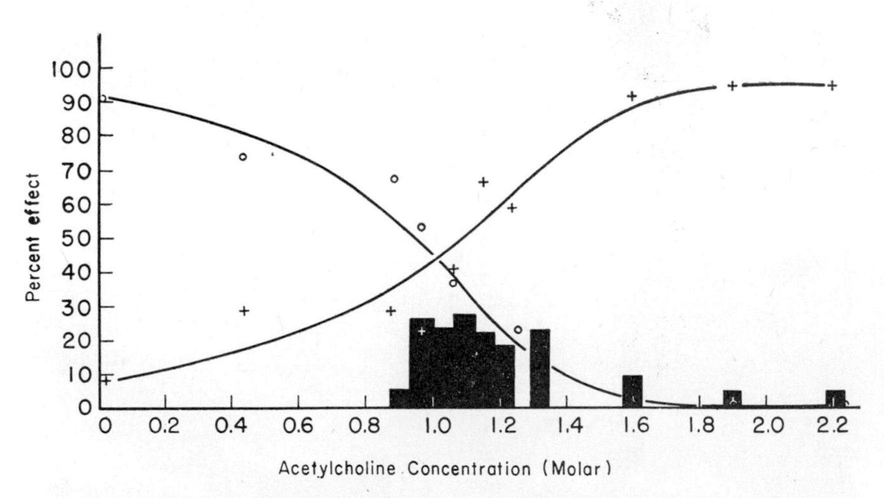

Fig. 6. Acetylcholine dose-response curves. Open circles, embryos graded as "excellent," "good," or "fair"; plus symbols, disaggregated or "poor"; histogram bars, percentage cardia bifida (CB).

velopment was normal (i.e. excellent, good, or fair). The plus symbols show the percentage which were disaggregated or poor; frequently these embryos were partly disaggregated and partly disorganized. The solid bars represent cardia bifida embryos, and have not been counted in either of the other two groups. It can be seen that at concentrations above 0.9 *M*, 20 to 30 per cent of the chicks form double hearts. Above 1.3 *M*, none of the chicks develop normally, most are disaggregated, and the small remainder are cardia bifida.

The anomalies of cardiac development produced in these experiments, if taken alone, would hardly suggest that poor cellular adhesion might be involved in their causation. However, the total range of effects, from partial inhibition of foregut fusion to complete cell dissociation, points more strongly in that direction.

At present there are only three known methods for chemically disaggregating tissues: (1) the use of proteolytic enzyme preparations; (2) the use of highly basic or acidic solutions; and (3) removal of divalent cations from the tissue. The question may be asked, then: does Ach, in the present circumstances, produce its effects by decreasing cellular adhesion, and if so, is its mode of action related to one of the above three possible mechanisms?

Acetylcholine bromide (Eastman Organic Chemicals), as used in these experiments, is a crystalline compound with strictly controlled, and very low, permissible limits of organic impurities, having no known activating or unmasking effect on proteolytic enzymes. A molar solution in Howard-Ringer (non-buffered) has a *p*H of about 5.4. Ten microliters of such a solution, added to a chick resting on a pool of about one milliliter of egg albumen (*p*H 7.8-8.2), a powerful buffer, can hardly be expected to shift the tissue *p*H markedly. To test this possibility, however, control chicks were treated with ten microliters of Howard-Ringer at *p*H levels of from eight to three. No adverse effects were seen. Thus, the first two possibilities mentioned above may be discarded.

Acetylcholine, as an organic cation, however, might be expected to have an effect on cell adhesion, if such adhesion is indeed dependent upon calcium-binding at the cell membrane. Because of its ion-binding capacities, referred to above, the cell surface, with its negative carboxyl and phosphoryl groups, has been analogized to an ion-exchange resin (61). It is well known that such resins will bind organic cations, and that these will be in equilibrium with metallic ions (154, 10). For example, choline, acting as a potent base, replaces some or most of the metal ions bound to the resin "Permutit" (154). Moreover, in unpublished experiments, it has been possible to show that Ach (or choline) will compete with Sr^{89} for binding

sites on a sulfonate resin IR-120 (Amberlite). The amount of Sr^{89} bound is in inverse proportion to the concentration of Ach, at the levels tested (0 to 0.5 *M*).[3]

In a related system, Gross (54) has suggested that competition for binding sites on cytoplasmic colloids, between organic cations and calcium, might be involved in the mechanism of sol-gel transformation. Moreover, a physiological cation-like effect of Ach has been recognized and traced to its charge reversal effects on phosphatides (19). In fact, Heilbrunn (61) has put forth the idea that the neuronal effects of Ach, and other "stimulants," may be explained in terms of calcium displacement. Thus, it seems not unreasonable to propose that Ach might produce its effects on chick embryos by displacing calcium-ion bridges from their sites of binding between two cell surfaces.

It should be emphasized here that these experiments should not necessarily be taken as support for the theory that Ach acts as a neurohumor simply through its ability to substitute for metallic ions. The concentrations required in the present work make it unlikely that the effects were within the "physiological" range.

In view of this high concentration needed to produce cardia bifida and disaggregation, the possibility that sheer hypertonicity might have played an important role cannot be completely ruled out. Furthermore, observations such as those of Hobson (64) that hypertonic solutions of sodium chloride or glycerol can prevent or reverse fusion of the neural folds in chick embryos tend to support this view. Several points about Hobson's work should be noted, however: (1) the solutions used were much more concentrated than those in the present experiments, being 20% (3.45 *M*) NaCl and 50% or 100% (6.8 or 13.7 *M*) glycerol; (2) blastoderms were completely immersed in a relatively large volume of one of these solutions; (3) with 20% NaCl some degree of cell dissociation is not surprising, since one would expect that high enough concentrations of any univalent cation might tend to displace calcium from the cell surface; and (4) Hobson clearly demonstrated (p. 126) that only osmotic balance, and not cellular cohesion, was affected by his glycerol solutions.

To test further the effects of hypertonicity on chicks under experimental conditions comparable to those in which cellular dissociation was produced, forty-one embryos were explanted as before and treated with 10 microliters each of 1.0 or 1.5 *M* sucrose. It was assumed that this substance would have no tendency to displace calcium ions from the cell surface. Most of

[3] I wish to thank Dr. Laurence S. Maynard, of the Department of Anatomy, Johns Hopkins School of Medicine, for performing these experiments with radiostrontium.

these animals developed quite normally, not differing from saline controls. Development in six of them was affected to the extent that spatial relations were distorted, nervous structures stunted, and tissues were more or less opaque. None developed double hearts, although one did have a heart the two halves of which had fused improperly over the anterior intestinal portal, but which were beating synchronously (one of the several hundred untreated or saline control embryos also developed such an improperly fused heart). Ten of these embryos, however, exhibited degenerative changes similar to disaggregation, in which the area pellucida was empty upon examination after 24 hours of culture.

Accepting that this destruction of the embryos with sucrose was the same as the disaggregation noted above when organic cations were used, one must conclude either that the degree of osmotic imbalance imposed by any 1 *M* solution is sufficiently deleterious to disperse 20-25 per cent of the embryos, or that sucrose itself has physico-chemical actions other than its influence on tissue osmolarity. In view of the known effects of monohydric alcohols on condensed phosphatide layers, as to their ion-binding properties and state of coacervation (19), it seems not unreasonable that a polyhydric alcohol (sucrose) would have related effects. For the present, all that can be said is that no substance applied to chick embryos in concentrations of 1 *M* or higher was without deleterious effect. It does not appear, however, that this is sufficient to account for the specific anomalies produced with Ach. Moreover, we shall see that other substances can yield effects similar to those of Ach, in concentrations far too low to influence tissue osmolarity. Hypertonicity, then, cannot be excluded from involvement, but it is clearly neither necessary nor sufficient as an agent in producing limited cell dissociation.

If the foregoing ideas are at all valid, one might generalize that removal of divalent cations from between cells, by displacement with univalent ions or by any other means, should decrease cellular adhesiveness, producing a spectrum of morphogenetic anomalies and disaggregation. In my first report of the production of cardia bifida with Ach (31), I noted that crystals of sodium acetate had a similar effect, and that this substance also produced much disaggregation in the embryos. It was this observation and the knowledge that acetate can form weak complexes with polyvalent cations (43) which, in fact, suggested the entire hypothesis outlined above. As pointed out by Martell and Calvin (84, p. 477), however, the stability constants for metal complexes with acetate are exceedingly low. Thus, this argument, alone, is relatively weak. More significant evidence was provided by a limited number of chicks treated with sodium citrate, in

which a few cardia bifida embryos and several disaggregates were found. The effective concentration of this substance was less than 0.1 *M*.

Therefore, a series of experiments was set up to determine whether a powerful chelating agent, at carefully controlled concentrations, would produce effects similar to those of Ach, presumably by removal rather than displacement of calcium from between cells.

A total of 545 chicks was explanted as before, in groups generally of 20 to 30 each. Each chick was treated with 10 microliters of Versene[4] at concentrations of 0-10 m*M*, in Howard-Ringer. The droplet of solution was placed on the endoderm with a constriction pipette, and was generally sufficient to flood the area pellucida and some of the area opaca. The chicks were treated in a warm box, under the dissecting microscope, and then removed to a 38°C incubator overnight.

Figs. 7 and 8 show Versene-produced cardia bifida embryos. Their similarity to those formed in the presence of Ach is apparent. It should be noted that these effects could not have resulted from an osmotic imbalance, since the concentration of Versene used was only 5-6 m*M*. The chicks shown in Figs. 9 and 10, treated with 4.8 and 6.5 m*M* Versene, respectively, are relatively unusual examples of partial dissociation. In these embryos, the primitive streak split and separated when Versene was applied. Instead of leading to total disaggregation, however, the process stopped before Hensen's node was damaged, and development could continue. The more anterior structures, apparently being more resistant, were disturbed only enough to cause cardia bifida and abnormalities of the nervous system.

The dose-response curves of Versene in calcium-free solution are given in Fig. 11. Cardia bifida was produced in the critical concentration range of 4.5-5.4 m*M*, and the concentration at which 50 per cent of the embryos were damaged ("D_{50}") is 4.3 m*M*. Below that range, little damage was done, and above it essentially all of the chicks were disaggregated or totally disorganized. To test whether calcium is actually the ion which was involved in these effects, a second dose-response curve was obtained (Fig. 12) with Versene dissolved in Howard-Ringer containing 1.52 m*M* calcium chloride. Under these circumstances the cardia bifida range is seen to be 5.3-6.7 m*M* and the D_{50} is 5.8 m*M*. Thus a close agreement is noted between the amount of calcium available and the concentration of Versene required to produce its effects. Moreover, concentrations of Versene as high as eight millimolar (which yield 100 per cent disaggregation in calcium-free solution) have no effect whatsoever when added to embryos in solutions containing excess calcium (15 m*M*). Of greater significance is

[4] Disodium salt of ethylenediamine tetraacetic acid, Bersworth Company.

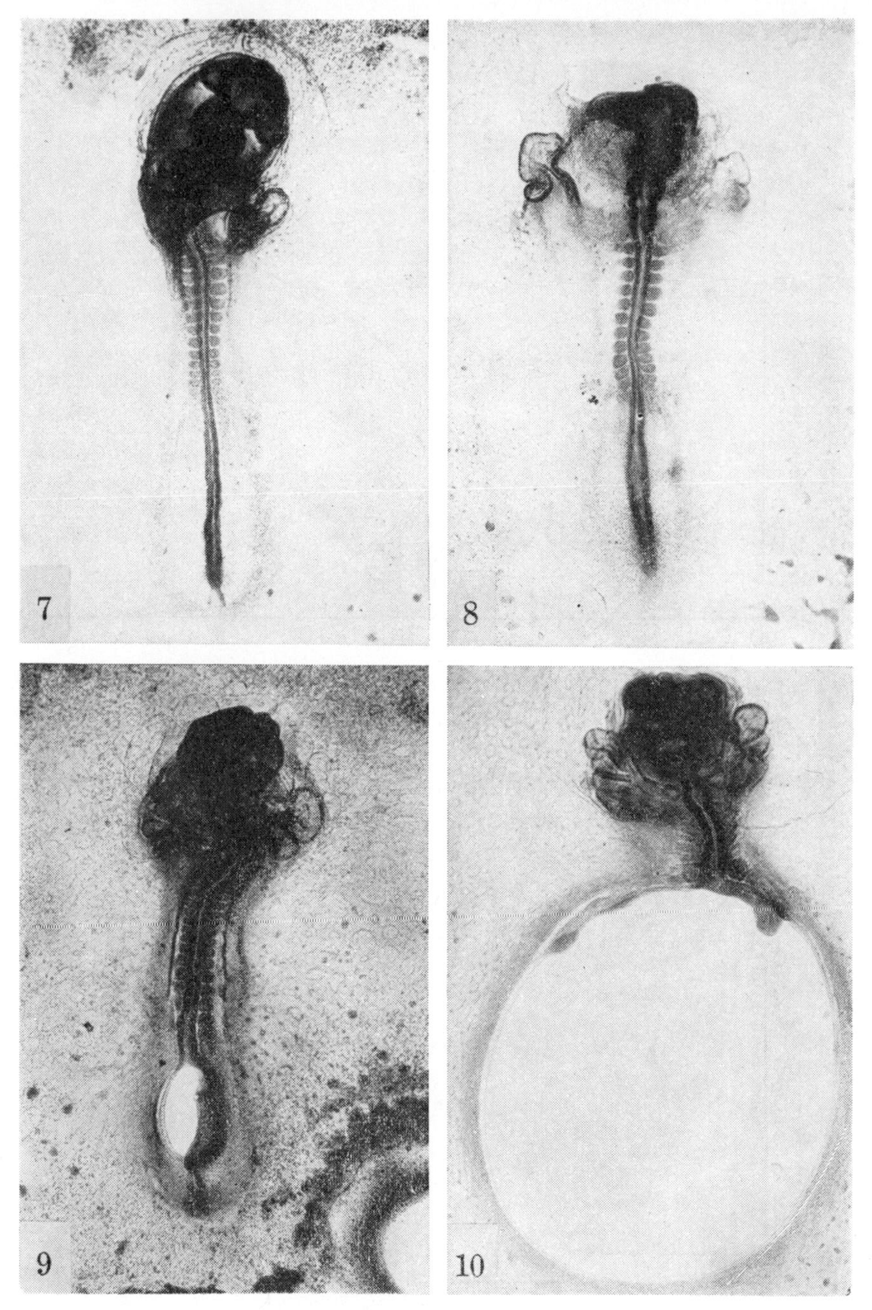

Figs. 7-10. Cardia bifida embryos produced by treatment with Versene. Compare with Figs. 2-5. × 20.

Fig. 7. Stage 11+, 6.2 m*M* Versene in Howard-Ringer.

Fig. 8. Stage 10, 5.65 m*M* Versene in Howard-Ringer.

Fig. 9. Stage 12, 4.8 m*M* Versene in calcium-free Howard-Ringer. Note opacity of tissues and arrested disaggregation which began in early primitive streak and extra-embryonic areas in the blastoderm.

Fig. 10. Approx. stage 11, 6.5 m*M* Versene in Howard-Ringer. Arrested disaggregation.

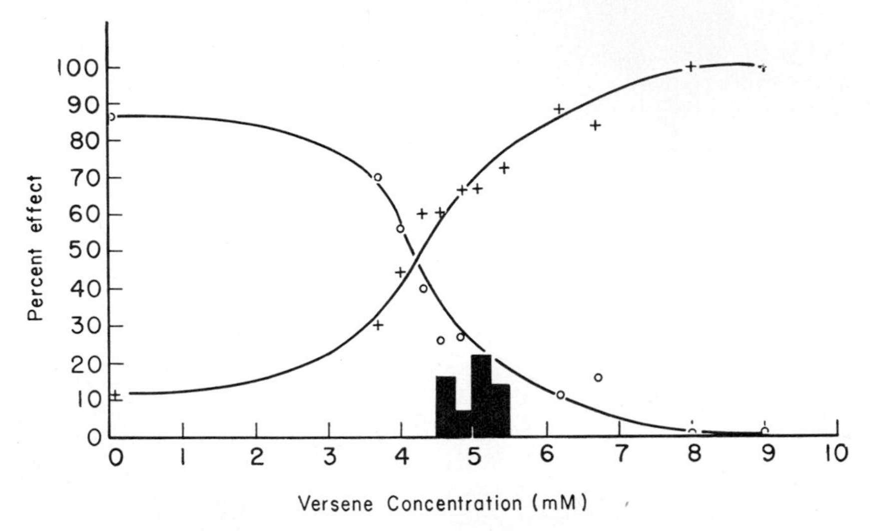

Fig. 11. Dose-response curve of Versene in calcium-free Howard-Ringer Symbols as in Fig. 6.

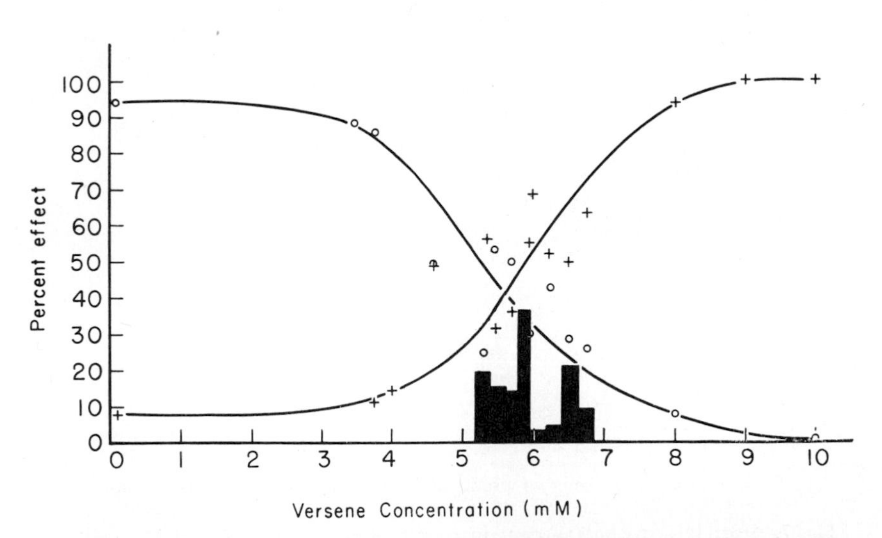

Fig. 12. Dose-response curve of Versene in Howard-Ringer containing 1.52 m*M* calcium chloride. Compare with Fig. 11. Note that critical responses, i.e., range of CB and D_{50}, are displaced about 1.5 units to the right along the abscissa.

the finding that equimolar concentrations of Versene and calcium chloride (4.5 m*M*), when added to chicks together, have no deleterious effects. Magnesium also will prevent Versene dissociation of chick tissues; however, it is less potent in this protective role than is calcium. In a group of chicks treated with 4.5 m*M* Versene in calcium-free Ringer containing 4.5 m*M* magnesium chloride, 22 per cent were cardia bifida and an equal number were disaggregated or disorganized. Versene (4.5 m*M*) in the presence of a ten-fold excess (45.0 m*M*) of magnesium produces no cardia bifida or disaggregation. However, neither the experimental animals nor the controls (treated with 45 m*M* magnesium but no Versene) develop quite normally, probably due to the high concentration of the metal.

The combination of Versene and the alkaline earth metals is low on the scale of stability constants when compared with other di- and tri-valent cations. Calcium is bound somewhat more strongly than magnesium, but manganese, iron, cobalt, etc., are much more tightly chelated (84). Thus, if Versene were producing its effects by removing one of these heavy metals from the cell (thereby perhaps disturbing an enzymatic function), neither calcium nor magnesium should offset the effect. If removal of magnesium by the chelating agent were the primary cause of cell dissociation, addition of Versene and calcium in equimolar concentrations should have a protective effect, but the amount of magnesium required to prevent cardia bifida and disaggregation should be equal to or less than that of calcium. This, as we have seen, is not the case, and we must conclude, therefore, that calcium is, in fact, the ion involved.

These experiments tend to support the hypothesis set forth earlier, stating that morphogenetic movements are dependent upon proper cellular adhesion, and that cell adhesiveness is in turn dependent upon calcium bound at cell surfaces. There are other possible interpretations of this work, however. One is that the developmental anomalies produced resulted from more general toxic effects of the agents used. It is difficult to predict the influences of molar concentrations of a quaternary ammonium compound on various aspects of cell physiology or structure. However, we have already seen that Ach markedly alters the colloidal behavior of phosphatides (19), and it has also been suggested that this substance can modify the configuration of proteins (98, 32). Its effect on enzyme systems is unknown. Versene, too, is known to have effects on cells, unrelated to the chelation of surface-bound calcium ions. Fabiny and Hamilton (35) have reported an inactivation of phosphatase by this compound, resulting in decreased synthesis of ribonucleic acids, and Mazia (87), Kaufmann, and co-workers (74, 89) and Kihlman (75) have described chromo-

somal aberrations in animal and plant cells resulting from treatment with Versene.

Another idea to account for the anomalies observed above stems from the report of Dornfeld and Owczarzak (33) that Versene causes marked surface "bubbling" and ameboid activity of chick heart fibroblast cells. Holtfreter (69) has described a similar response of amphibian cells to calcium-free or highly alkaline solutions. Thus, as Steinberg suggests, under circumstances of markedly increased cell surface activity and bleb-formation, a fabric of cells would tend to dissociate simply because the cell membranes were irregularly deformed (130). Irrespective of whether one envisions cell adhesion as involving calcium bridges or complementary protein configurations, some stable pattern is required for its maintenance.

Still a third possible mechanism hinges on a disturbance of normal inductive processes. Flickinger (40a) has reported inhibition of melanoblast differentiation with amino acids, and suggests that normal development of these cells is dependent upon factors contributed by solubilized yolk proteins. This solubilization normally requires calcium, and, therefore, is prevented when calcium is chelated by the amino acids. Bellairs (15) has recently suggested that the folding of the foregut results from induction by the splanchnic mesoderm. Thus, it is conceivable that normal folding of the endoderm is dependent upon the availability of some substance requiring divalent cations for its solubilization or entry into the cells. The action of complexing agents such as Versene or citrate would thus be predicted. The effects of Ach, however, would have to be accounted for in some other manner.

Since none of these last interpretations of the experimental results has more than suggestive evidence supporting it, further discussion would seem unprofitable for the present.

Recapitulation and Conclusions

I might conclude by reiterating briefly those factors which, at the present time, seem most likely to be involved in the initiation and organization of morphogenetic movements, in cases of directed movements of single ameboid cells, such as those derived from the neural crest. (1) these cells are probably dispersed from their site of origin by a chemically mediated mutual cell repulsion, each cell migrating away from its fellows: (2) there is as yet no evidence that this migration, in vivo, is limited to predetermined routes or directions dictated by chemical attraction to distant sites or organs, or by specific pathways built into the substratum upon which the cells are migrating. There is, however, suggestive evidence of

influences by apparently nonspecific chemical gradients such as CO_2, oxygen, or lipids. (3) Some crest derivatives, though probably not directionally oriented by their substrate, do indeed choose a given cell-type upon which to migrate. Thus, the importance of the cell-to-substrate relationship is reaffirmed. (4) The final pattern of cell locations is evidently determined by specific cell affinities and disaffinities. Secondary localizing factors such as contraction of originally dispersed cell groups into dense areas, or destruction of cells in noncompatible sites, also occurs.

In the case of mass cell movements, in which groups or aggregates of cells move by means of their own pseudopodial or gliding activity, two factors have been implicated: (a) relatively nonspecific chemical gradients; and (b) specific cell affinities and disaffinities. Evidence that embryonic cells (other than neural crest derivatives) may be influenced in their movements by chemical gradients stems from a limited number of in vitro or abnormal circumstances. Whether such gradients play a role in normal embryogenesis is not clear at the moment. On the other hand, observations are plentiful supporting the idea that cell masses are guided in their movements by the neighboring cells and structures over which they migrate. Moreover, the fact that cells can "recognize" and adhere, or fail to adhere, to their neighbors, depending on specific surface characteristics of the latter, is well substantiated. It seems reasonable to assume that such surface recognition would be mediated through patterned molecular groupings in the cell membrane. It must be assumed here that embryonic cells continue to migrate until a sufficient number or a special type of group is encountered at the contact surface so that firm linkages may be formed and further movement inhibited.

In epithelial layers, where each cell maintains a more or less fixed position in relation to its adjacent neighbors, the folding, invagination, spreading, or thickening that is seen must be explained in different (though related) terms. Alterations in adhesiveness of different parts of the cell surface, and the resultant change in area of cell contact, seem sufficient in general to account for such movements. Increased cell cohesion of one side of a layer would tend to cause the cells to contract or taper on that side, and shift the main mass of cytoplasm toward the other side, thus buckling or evaginating the stratum. Shortening of intercellular connections of various sorts, which can often be observed in embryos, is recognized as a probable contributing factor. It should be noted that when a filopodial process makes contact with, and sticks to, another cell, this represents merely a special case of the general problem of cell adhesion.

Of the three major hypotheses put forth as a mechanism for cellular ad-

hesiveness (viz., complementary protein linkages, viscous intercellular cement, and calcium bridges), evidence has been marshalled favoring that invoking the binding of calcium ions between cell surfaces. The production of limited cell dissociation with high concentrations of organic cations or with calcium-complexing agents, resulting in a range of effects from minor disturbances of neural or cardiac fusion to disaggregation, lends support to this idea, although other interpretations are not ruled out.

Such an hypothesis immediately suggests several lines of experimental investigation to test its validity further. For example, is it possible to demonstrate differential adsorption of calcium at the surface of cells which appear to be increasing in adhesiveness during differentiation? Such a question might well be answered by histological studies of embryological material, using refined histochemical or biophysical techniques for ions (46, 83, 157). What is the effect of limited dissociation of cells, when studied under circumstances such as those employed by Twitty and Niu (141) or by Gregg and associates (52, 53, 102)? What is its effect on "contact inhibition" or on "contact guidance"? The abolition by Versene of Fetuin-induced adhesiveness of cells cultured on glass has been described recently (39). Further analysis of this phenomenon with carefully controlled removal of divalent cations might prove fruitful. An especially interesting question arises as to the effects of limited dissociation on a system such as that used by Chiakulas (24) to demonstrate specificity of cell adhesion. Are the adhesive sites identical with those providing specificity, as implied by Steinberg's lattice hypothesis (130), or is this latter property indeed provided by large molecular configurations, leaving cohesion, but not the specificity thereof, to be a function of calcium?

Professor B. H. Willier has, over the years, ended his graduate seminars with a statement to the effect that the value of any investigation or discussion is to be measured less by the number of answers it provides than by the number of new questions, and lines of experimental attack on these questions, that it stimulates. Perhaps, in this sense, the present discussion may represent a small contribution.

Acknowledgments

I wish to acknowledge my debt to Dr. James D. Ebert and Prof. Johannes Holtfreter for their critical reading of my manuscript, and to Drs. Malcolm S. Steinberg and Mary E. Rawles for several stimulating discussions of various aspects of this paper. I would also like to thank Mrs. Nancy C. Fait for her superb technical assistance with the original work described herein.

REFERENCES

1. Abercrombie, M., *Symposia Soc. Exptl. Biol.*, **11**, 235-254 (1957).
2. ———, *Proc. Zool. Soc. Bengal,* Mookerjee Memor. Vol., 129-140 (1957).
3. ———, and Heaysman, J. E. M., *Exptl. Cell Research,* **5**, 111-131 (1953).
4. ———, and ———, *Exptl. Cell Research,* **6**, 293-306 (1954).
5. ———, ———, and Karthauser, H. M., *Exptl. Cell Research,* **13**, 276-291 (1957).
6. Alexander, A. E., Teorell, T., and Aborg, C. G., *Trans. Faraday Soc.,* **35**, 1200-1205 (1939).
7. Anderson, N. G., *Science,* **117**, 627-628 (1953).
8. Andrews, E. A., *Zool. Bull.,* **2**, 1-13 (1898).
9. Andrews, G. F., *J. Morphol.,* **12**, 367-389 (1897).
10. Applezweig, N., *Ann. N. Y. Acad. Sci.,* **49**, 295-314 (1947).
11. Ballard, W. W., *J. Exptl. Zool.,* **129**, 77-98 (1955).
12. Bellairs, R., *J. Embryol. Exptl. Morphol.,* **1**, 115-124 (1953).
12a. ———, *J. Embryol. Exptl. Morphol.,* **1**, 369-385 (1953).
13. ———, *Brit. J. Cancer,* **8**, 685-692 (1954).
14. ———, *J. Embryol. Exptl. Morphol.,* **3**, 242-250 (1955).
15. ———, *J. Embryol. Exptl. Morphol.,* **5**, 340-350 (1957).
16. Boerema, I., *Wilhelm Roux' Arch. Entwicklungsmech. Organ.,* **115**, 601-615 (1929).
17. Bonner, J. T., *J. Exptl. Zool.,* **106**, 1-26 (1947).
18. ———, *J. Exptl. Zool.,* **110**, 259-272 (1949).
19. Booij, H. L., and Bungenberg de Jong, H. G., *Protoplasmatologia,* **1**, 1-162 (1956).
20. Brown, M. G., Hamburger, V., and Schmitt, F. O., *J. Exptl. Zool.,* **88**, 353-372 (1941).
21. Burt, A. S., *Biol. Bull.,* **85**, 103-115 (1943).
22. Caesar, R., Edwards, G. A., and Ruska, H., *J. Biophys. Biochem. Cytol.,* **3**, 867-878 (1957).
23. Chambers, R., *Cold Spring Harbor Symposia Quant. Biol.,* **8**, 144-153 (1940).
24. Chiakulas, J. J., *J. Exptl. Zool.,* **121**, 383-417 (1952).
25. Curtis, A. S. G., *Nature,* **181**, 185 (1958).
26. Dan, K., and Okazaki, K., *Biol. Bull.,* **110**, 29-42 (1956).
27. Danforth, C. H., and Foster, F., *J. Exptl. Zool.,* **52**, 443-470 (1929).
28. Davis, C. L., *Contribs. Embryol. Carnegie Inst.,* **19**, 245-284, #107 (1927).
29. Davis, J. O., *Biol. Bull.,* **87**, 73-95 (1944).
30. Davson, H., and Danielli, J. F., *The Permeability of Natural Membranes,* Cambridge, at the Univ. Press (1952).
31. DeHaan, R. L., *Proc. Natl. Acad. Sci. U. S.,* **44**, 32-37 (1958).
32. Demin, N. N., *Biokhimiya,* **20**, 317-327 (1955).
33. Dornfeld, E. J., and Owczarzak, A., *Anat. Rec.,* **128**, 541 (1957).
34. Ebert, J. D., *Carnegie Inst. Wash. Year Book,* 327-329 (1957).
35. Fabiny, R. J., and Hamilton, H. L., *Anat. Rec.,* **128**, 545 (1957).
36. Fawcett, D. W., and Selby, C. C., *J. Biophys. Biochem. Cytol.,* **4**, 63-72 (1958).
37. Feldman, M., *J. Embryol. Exptl. Morphol.,* **3**, 251-255 (1955).
38. Fisher, A., *Biology of Tissue Cells,* Gyldendalske Boghandel, Copenhagen (1946).
39. Fisher, H. W., Puck, T. T., and Sato, G., *Proc. Natl. Acad. Sci. U. S.,* **44**, 4-10 (1958).
40. Flickinger, R. A., *J. Exptl. Zool.,* **119**, 1-22 (1952).
40a. ———, *Am. Naturalist,* **41**, 373-380 (1957).
41. Giersberg, H., *Wilhelm Roux' Arch. Entwicklungsmech. Organ.,* **103**, 387-424 (1924).
42. Gillette, R., *J. Exptl. Zool.,* **96**, 201-222 (1944).
43. Gilman, H., and Jones, R. G., *Chem. Revs.,* **54**, 835-890 (1954).

44. Glaser, O. C., *Anat. Rec.*, **8**, 525-551 (1914).
45. ———, *Science*, **44**, 505-509 (1916).
46. Gomori, G., *Microscopic Histochemistry*, Univ. Chicago Press, Chicago (1952).
47. Goodrich, H. B., Hines, R. L., and Reynolds, J., *J. Exptl. Zool.*, **114**, 603-626 (1950).
48. ———, Marzullo, C. M., and Bronson, W. R., *J. Exptl. Zool.*, **125**, 487-506 (1954).
49. Goss, C. M., *Amer. J. Physiol.*, **137**, 146-152 (1942).
50. Gray, J., *Brit. J. Exptl. Biol.*, **3**, 167-187 (1926).
51. ———, *Experimental Cytology*, Cambridge, at the Univ. Press (1931).
52. Gregg, J. R., and Klein, D., *Biol. Bull.*, **109**, 265-270 (1955).
53. ———, and Ornstein, N., *Biol. Bull.*, **105**, 466-476 (1953).
54. Gross, P. R., *Trans. N. Y. Acad. Sci.*, **20**, (ser. II), 154-172 (1957).
55. Grossfeld, H., Meyer, K., Godman, G., and Linker, A., *J. Biophys. Biochem. Cytol.*, **3**, 391-396 (1957).
56. Gustafson, T., and Kinnander, H., *Exptl. Cell Research*, **11**, 36-51 (1956).
57. Hall, E. K., *J. Exptl. Zool.*, **113**, 355-378 (1950).
58. Hamburger, V., and Hamilton, H. L., *J. Morphol.*, **88**, 49-92 (1951).
59. Harris, H., *J. Pathol. Bacteriol.*, **66**, 135-146 (1953).
60. Harvey, E. N., *Protoplasmatologia*, **2**, 1-30 (1954).
61. Heilbrunn, L. V., *Dynamics of Living Protoplasm*, Academic Press, New York (1956).
62. Herbst, C., *Wilhelm Roux' Arch. Entwicklungsmech. Organ.*, **9**, 424-463 (1900).
63. Herrman, H., and Hickman, F. H., *Bull. Johns Hopkins Hosp.*, **82**, 182-207 (1948).
64. Hobson, L. B., *J. Exptl. Zool.*, **88**, 107-134 (1941).
65. Holtfreter, J., *Arch. exptl. Zellforsch. Gewebezücht.*, **23**, 169-209 (1939).
66. ———, *Rev. Can. biol.*, **3**, 220-250 (1944).
67. ———, *J. Morphol.*, **80**, 25-55 (1947).
68. ———, *J. Morphol.*, **80**, 57-91 (1947).
69. ———, *Ann. N. Y. Acad. Sci.*, **49**, 709-760 (1948).
70. Holtzer, H., Marshall, J. M., and Fink, H., *J. Biophys. Biochem. Cytol.*, **3**, 705-724 (1957).
71. Hörstadius, S., *The Neural Crest*, Oxford Univ. Press, Oxford (1950).
72. Howard, E., *J. Cellular Comp. Physiol.*, **41**, 237-260 (1953).
73. Jaffe, L., *Proc. Natl. Acad. Sci. U. S.*, **41**, 267-270 (1955).
74. Kaufman, B. P., and McDonald, M. R., *Proc. Natl. Acad. Sci. U. S.*, **43**, 262-270 (1957).
75. Kihlman, B. A., *J. Biophys. Biochem. Cytol.*, **3**, 363-380 (1957) .
76. Kwart, H., and Shashoua, V. E., *Trans. N. Y. Acad. Sci.*, **19**, 595-612 (1957).
77. Lansing, A. I., and Rosenthal, T. B., *J. Cellular Comp. Physiol.*, **40**, 337-345 (1952).
78. Lehmann, F. E., *Wilhelm Roux' Arch. Entwicklungsmech. Organ.*, **108**, 243-282 (1926).
79. ———, *Wilhelm Roux' Arch. Entwicklungsmech. Organ.*, **113**, 123-171 (1928).
80. Lewis, W. H., *Contribs. Embryol. Carnegie Inst.*, **18**, 1-22 (1926).
81. ———, *Anat. Rec.*, **97**, 139-156 (1947).
82. Lillie, R. S., *Am. J. Physiol.*, **17**, 89-141 (1906).
83. Lindstrom, B., *Acta Radiol.* (Suppl.), **125**, 1-206 (1955).
84. Martell, A. E., and Calvin, M., *Chemistry of the Metal Chelate Compounds*, Prentice-Hall, New York (1952).
85. Mast, S. O., and Fowler, C., *Biol. Bull.*, **74**, 297-305 (1938).
86. Mazia, D., *Cold Spring Harbor Symposia Quant. Biol.*, **8**, 195-203 (1940).
87. ———, *Proc. Natl. Acad. Sci. U. S.*, **40**, 521-527 (1954).
88. McCutcheon, M., and Lucké, B., *J. Gen. Physiol.*, **12**, 129-138 (1928).
89. McDonald, M. R., and Kaufman, B. P., *Exptl. Cell Research*, **12**, 415-417 (1957).
90. Milkman, R., and Trinkaus, J. P., *Anat. Rec.*, **117**, 558-559 (1953).
91. Mitchison, J. M., *Symposia Soc. Exptl. Biol.*, **6**, 105-127 (1952).

92. Monné, L., *Experientia,* **2,** 153-196 (1946).
93. Mookerjee, S., Deuchar, E. M., and Waddington, C. H., *J. Embryol. Exptl. Morphol.,* **1,** 399-409 (1953).
94. Moore, A. R., *J. Exptl. Zool.,* **87,** 101-111 (1941).
95. Moscona, A., *Proc. Soc. Exptl. Biol. Med.,* **92,** 410-416 (1956).
96. ———, *Proc. Natl. Acad. Sci. U. S.,* **43,** 184-194 (1957).
97. ———, and Moscona, H., *J. Anat.,* **86,** 287-301 (1952).
98. Nachmansohn, D., and Wilson, I. B., in *Electrochemistry in Biology and Medicine,* (T. Shedlovsky, ed.), p. 167-186, John Wiley & Sons, New York (1955).
99. New, D. A. T., *J. Embryol. Exptl. Morphol.,* **3,** 326-331 (1955).
100. Oppenheimer, J. M., *J. Exptl. Zool.,* **128,** 525-560 (1955).
101. ———, *Surv. Biol. Progr.,* **3,** 1-46 (1957).
102. Ornstein, N., and Gregg, J. R., *Biol. Bull.,* **103,** 407-420 (1952).
103. Overton, E., *Arch. ges. Physiol., Pflüger's,* **105,** 176-290 (1904).
104. Patten, B. M., *Physiol. Revs.,* **29,** 31-47 (1949).
105. Pauling, L., in *Specificity of Serological Reactions* (K. Landsteiner), rev. ed., p. 275-293, Harvard Univ. Press, Cambridge (1945).
106. Ponder, E., *Protoplasmatologia,* **10,** 1-123 (1955).
107. Rawles, M. E., *Physiol. Zool.,* **16,** 22-45 (1943).
108. ———, *Physiol. Zool.,* **17,** 167-183 (1944).
109. ———, *Physiol. Zool.,* **18,** 1-16 (1945).
110. ———, *Physiol. Revs.,* **28,** 383-408 (1948).
111. ———, *Am. J. Anat.,* **97,** 79-128 (1955).
112. ———, in *Analysis of Development* (B. H. Willier, P. Weiss, and V. Hamburger, eds.), p. 499-519, W. B. Saunders Co., Philadelphia (1955).
113. Reid, M. E., *Physiol. Revs.,* **23,** 76-99 (1943).
114. Rhumbler, L., in *Handbuch der biologischen Arbeitsmethoden* (E. Abderhalden, ed.), **5** (3A), 219-440, Berlin (1923).
115. Ringer, S., *J. Physiol.,* **11,** 79-84 (1890).
116. Robertson, J. D., *Biol. Revs. Cambridge Phil. Soc.,* **16,** 106-133 (1941).
117. Rosin, S., *Rev. Suisse Zool.,* **50,** 485-578 (1943).
118. Rothstein, A., *Protoplasmatologia,* **2,** 1-86 (1954).
119. ———, and Meier, R., *J. Cellular Comp. Physiol.,* **38,** 245-270 (1951).
120. Sabin, F. R., *Contribs. Embryol. Carnegie Inst.,* **6,** 63-124 (1917).
121. ———, *Contribs. Embryol. Carnegie Inst.,* **9,** 213-262, (1920).
122. Schechtman, A. M., *Univ. Calif. Publ. Zool.,* **39,** 303-310 (1934).
123. ———, *Univ. Calif. Publ. Zool.,* **51,** 1-40 (1942).
124. Schmitt, F. O., *Growth,* **5** (Suppl.), 1-20 (1941).
125. Spiegel, M., *Biol. Bull.,* **107,** 130-148 (1954).
126. ———, *Biol. Bull.,* **107,** 149-155 (1954).
127. Spratt, N. T., *J. Exptl. Zool.,* **128,** 121-164 (1955).
128. ———, *Anat. Rec.,* **124,** 364 (1956).
129. ———, *J. Exptl. Zool.,* **134,** 577-612 (1957).
130. Steinberg, M. S., *Am. Naturalist,* **92,** 65-82 (1958).
131. Sussman, M., and Sussman, R. R., in *Cellular Mechanisms in Differentiation and Growth* (D. Rudnick, ed.) p. 125-154, Princeton Univ. Press, Princeton (1956).
132. Townes, P. L., *Exptl. Cell Research,* **4,** 96-101 (1953).
133. ———, and Holtfreter, J., *J. Exptl. Zool.,* **128,** 53-120 (1955).
134. Trinkaus, J. P., *J. Exptl. Zool.,* **118,** 269-319 (1951).
135. ———, and Drake, J. W., *J. Exptl. Zool.,* **132,** 311-348 (1956).
136. ———, and Groves, W., *Proc. Natl. Acad. Sci. U. S.,* **41,** 787-795 (1955).
137. Twitty, V. C., *J. Exptl. Zool.,* **95,** 259-290 (1944).

138. ———, *J. Exptl. Zool.,* **100,** 141-178 (1945).
139. ———, *Growth,* **13** (Suppl.), 133-161 (1949).
140. ———, and Niu, M. C., *J. Exptl. Zool.,* **108,** 405-438 (1948).
141. ———, and ———, *J. Exptl. Zool.,* **125,** 541-574 (1954).
142. Tyler, A., *Growth,* **10** (Suppl.), 7-19 (1946).
143. Waddington, C. H., *J. Exptl. Biol.,* **19,** 284-293 (1942).
144. ———, *Principles of Embryology,* Macmillan Co., New York (1956).
145. Waugh, D. F., and Schmitt, F. O., *Cold Spring Harbor Symposia Quant. Biol.,* **8,** 233-241 (1940).
146. Weiss, P., *Growth,* **5** (Suppl.), 163-203 (1941).
147. ———, *J. Exptl. Zool.,* **100,** 353-386 (1945).
148. ———, *Yale J. Biol. and Med.,* **19,** 235-278 (1947).
149. ———, *J. Exptl. Zool.,* **113,** 397-461 (1950).
150. ———, *Quart. Rev. Biol.,* **25,** 177-198 (1950).
151. ———, in *Analysis of Development* (B. H. Willier, P. Weiss, and V. Hamburger, eds.), p. 346-401, W. B. Saunders Co., Philadelphia (1955).
152. ———, and Andres, G., *J. Exptl. Zool.,* **121,** 449-487 (1952).
153. Whitaker, D. M., *Growth* (Suppl., Second Symposium), 75-90 (1940).
154. Whitehorn, J. C., *J. Biol. Chem.,* **56,** 751-764 (1923).
155. Wilens, S., *J. Exptl. Zool.,* **129,** 579-606 (1955).
156. Willier, B. H., *Bios,* **23,** 109-125 (1952).
157. Zeitz, L., and Baez, A. V., *X-ray Microscopy and Microradiography* (V. E. Cosslett, A. Engström, and H. H. Pattee, Jr. eds.) p. 417-434, Academic Press, New York (1957).
158. Zweifach, B. W., *Cold Spring Harbor Symposia Quant. Biol.,* **8,** 216-223 (1940).
159. Zwilling, E., *Science,* **120,** 219 (1954).

DISCUSSION

DR. HOLTFRETER: I wonder to what extent your observations on the chick embryo can be related with the general topic of your paper. The method of disaggregating embryonic tissues by various means, of mixing the isolated cells together in different permutation and allowing them to reshuffle themselves so as to form well-segregated tissues, has become quite fashionable. You did not do this sort of experiment. You applied some chemicals to the prospective heart region of the chick embryo. The result was anatomic malformation, especially of the heart.

There are several ways of connecting causally the intervening chemical agent with the final morphological manifestation. At face value it seems that the heart malformations observed cannot be readily connected with the principles of cellular locomotion or cell affinity which are your general topic. The chemicals you used may have simply acted as toxic or semi-toxic agents. Some of your results, such as two lateral hearts can be achieved by surgical interferences.

All that matters here is to prevent a junction of the lateral heart primordia in the ventral midline. It might be expected that by killing or damaging the midventral juncture heart region by chemical means would produce such an obstacle. We know that embryonic cells can be killed by an excess of oxalate,

citrate, Versene; what high concentrations of acetylcholine would do to the cells I don't know. Have you studied microscopically the immediate and successive reactions of the individual cells subjected to your treatments? My suspicion is that the treatments either killed the area affected outrightly or incapacitated it in such a way that it became a barrier to the fusion of the heart primordia.

Dr. DeHaan: Yes, I have checked these preparations under the high powered microscope. I don't know that I haven't killed cells but I can say that most of the cells appear to be alive. I say this not only on the basis of their appearance under the microscope, but I also wish to refer you to the appearance of the partial disaggregates which I referred to during my discussion. In these cases disaggregation apparently occurred and then the reaggregation occurred around the periphery of the glass circle after 24 hours time.

Dr. Zwilling: Have you tried a solution of acetylcholine on early chick embryos to see if it will disaggregate their tissues?

Dr. DeHaan: No, as a matter of fact I have not checked this with isolated tissues.

Dr. Zwilling: This happens very readily with Versene. The other thing is whether you have considered another possibility. As you know in our laboratory a great deal of evidence has been accumulated by Dr. Landauer indicating that various metabolites are involved in teratology. In these systems the coenzymes seem to be implicated very strongly. We know that many of the coenzymes need metal activation to perform their functions, say with iron or magnesium for instance. Virtually all of the work which you have presented could be explained on the basis of the inhibition of coenzyme function which has resulted from the chelation of metal-activating agents.

Dr. DeHaan: I think you have a good point there and it is one that I have considered. I can only say that all of the agents which do produce the effect are, in some way, related to calcium. They can either displace it from a surface, or bind it. Of course, these agents can do this to other ions as well. It is just that when you talk about coenzymes it seems rather unlikely that acetylcholine would be displacing magnesium or iron from an enzyme site in the cell. This is especially so since Nachmansohn and others have pointed out that acetylcholine does not penetrate into cells very well. Of course the one molar concentration which we have used here might indeed get into cells. Another point is that I am basing a large part of this hypothesis on the continuum idea, that is, that we see a gradation of effects which merge imperceptibly into one another when we increase the concentration of the agent in the medium, culminating in disaggregation. It seems to me rather unlikely that such a continuum would be caused by displacement of increasing amounts of an ion from a coenzyme, since I know of no evidence linking coenzyme function and cell adhesion. Also, I would refer you to my discussion of the stability constants of the chelate compounds formed between Versene and various polyvalent

metals, suggesting that calcium is indeed the ion involved in these effects, and not those metals known to act as coenzymes such as iron, magnesium, manganese, cobalt, etc.

DR. ZWILLING: But here I think the point which Dr. Holtfreter made is very important. The role of cell death has to be evaluated carefully in this situation. Cell separation of some sort is a frequent symptom of early moribundity.

DR. DEHAAN: I would certainly agree with you that this may be an important factor.

DR. BOELL: I should like to ask if you observe abnormalities in the nervous system. You would expect that the neural folds would not fuse if your explanation is a valid one.

DR. DEHAAN: Indeed you do observe this effect. In two of the slides which I presented this morning, even though seen through the ventral side of the embryo it is quite apparent that the folds of the neural tube have not fused completely. This again can occur in varying degrees of severity. I think that one of the reasons why we get the teratogenic effects on the ventral side of the embryo more frequently than on the dorsal side is simply because that is where I am directly adding the agent. Therefore the agent has to diffuse through three layers of cells before it can get to the nervous system in the dorsal side of the embryo.

DR. BOELL: But aren't these hearts themselves tubular?

DR. DEHAAN: Yes, that too is a very good point, but I just don't know what happens there. I do get beautiful tubular structures in the double hearts in the case of *cardia bifida.* In some cases, if I let them go long enough, circulation is established so that I know the tubular vascular system is intact. I am afraid I just can't explain that. I can only suggest that since the original tubules of the heart form from vaso-formative mesenchymal tissue as it is folding under with the endoderm possibly we have two different mechanisms; one for the folding of epithelial sheets or tissues which is dependent upon calcium, as I have suggested, and another mechanism which is involved in the hollowing out of mesenchymal tissues. I just don't know.

DR. TRINKAUS: In our work on *Fundulus* gastrulation we have found support for the hypothesis that coordinated movements of masses of cells may be due in part to a change in the character of the individual constituent cells. In this study we dissociated blastoderms of *Fundulus heteroclitus* in late cleavage, blastula and early gastrula stages with Versene and cultured suspensions of individual cells in standing drops on a glass substratum. The medium consisted of 0.2% proteose peptone and 0.5% glucose in double strength Holtfreter's solution buffered with phosphate and bicarbonate to *p*H 7.4. Under these conditions cells from late cleavage stages and from blastulae (up to stage 10) are semispherical and actively protrude lobopodia during the first few hours in culture. In contrast, cells from eggs in which epiboly has already begun (stage 11 to 12) become attached to and actively spread over the substratum during the

first 30 minutes after culturing. In this fashion they rapidly achieve a fibroblast-like shape with abundant filopodia and contact each other to form a flattened lacework of cells. Cells from advanced blastulae (just prior to the onset of epiboly, i.e. stage 10½) are typically spherical with lobopodia during the first hour in culture, but during the next hour they spread on the substratum. At this time intact control eggs have commenced epiboly (stage 11½).

We conclude from these observations that the spreading of the whole blastoderm in epiboly is due in part to the acquisition by individual cells of the capacity to spread over the substratum. Moreover, this spreading character is relatively stable under conditions in vitro.

Part III

PROBLEMS OF SPECIFICITY IN GROWTH AND DEVELOPMENT

COMPARATIVE CYTOCHEMISTRY OF THE FERTILIZED EGG

J. J. Pasteels

Embryological Laboratories of the Faculty of Medicine, Université libre de Bruxelles, Belgium

Introduction

The time is past when the relations between the morphologists and the biochemists consisted only of a "dialogue between deaf men." Refinements of techniques have brought them both to the same level of ultrastructure, where spatial organization and enzymatic mechanisms are necessarily complementary. The different methods of study are now often employed in the same laboratory, often by the same man, to achieve the essential goal of the Biologist: the integration of the structure and the function of the cytoplasm.

The correlation between structure and biochemical mechanisms has been studied mainly in adult cells, particularly the hepatic cells of mammals. We propose to examine the way in which this correlation may be considered in the case of the egg, limiting ourselves to the fertilized, unsegmented egg. There is no doubt that more problems will be proposed than will be solved. The fact that a problem is presented is nevertheless of considerable interest, and its subsequent study can be of importance in helping solve the main problem under consideration.

The egg should be considered from two points of view. (1) The egg as a cell: this presents a paradox, since the egg is undifferentiated on the one hand, and highly specialized on the other. The question arises as to whether this particular case of the egg-cell also has particularities of structure and chemistry. (2) The egg as a future embryo: one can forget too easily that the principal function of an egg is to form an embryo. This ultimate morphogenesis must essentially be preenvisaged by structural particularities. Thus, it is important to be familiar with the relationship between chronology and topography. The correlation between the structure and function of the egg will only be considered as definitely established when the results obtained by different techniques agree. This agreement has been obtained only rarely in the particular case of the egg. It is im-

portant to consider the value of these various methods, always keeping in mind limitations in order not to overestimate the results.

Before attempting to get at the base of these two problems, it might therefore be a good idea to review briefly the methods of study:

(a) *The isolation of cytoplasmic particles by fractional centrifugation of cellular homogenates.* This method is to a large extent responsible for the recent rapid development of cytology. Nevertheless, there does exist a great danger of misinterpretation due to artifacts. Fortunately, the source of the artifacts produced by this method is known today. Thus, it appears that the microsomes formerly considered as fundamental organelles of the cytoplasm and controlling protein synthesis, have no real value as such but are the result of an artifact consisting of a fragmentation of the ergastoplasm (11). The method of homogenization in electrolytic media has been criticized (61) on the basis that it can provoke elutions, contamination, or agglomeration of the particles. Thus, most of the results of studies made on eggs have been obtained by this method, and the current improvements in the technique, such as the homogenization of the material in solutions containing glucose, have been utilized only in very recent studies (90, 91, 101, 149).

(b) *The analysis of enzymatic or respiratory activity of fragments of eggs obtained by centrifugation of eggs in the living state* (57). This method permits consideration of these activities with respect to the presence or absence of specific cytoplasmic particles (62, 64, 65). It should be pointed out that although the danger of an artifact is much more limited in this than in the preceding technique, it is not totally excluded, since the sedimentation of the particulates in an area can modify their enzymatic and respiratory activities (17, 155). The results obtained by this method can be justly evaluated only after a correlation with the results obtained by cytochemical and microscopical investigation, particularly with the electron microscope. Indeed, we shall see that the presence or absence of mitochondria can be confirmed only after a study of the ultrastructure made with ultrathin sections (cf. pp. 386-387).

(c) *The study of the respiratory or enzymatic activities of isolated blastomeres or egg fragments without previous centrifugation* (8, 9, 10, 67). This method gives us information on the subsequent linkage between these activities and the morphogenetic tendencies of the territories. The application of this method is, for reasons easy to understand, rather limited. In addition to this, the method is not exempt from artifacts: the activity of an isolated fragment can be different, following a morphogenetic regulation, from that of the corresponding territory in an intact egg.

(d) *Cytochemical studies of sections.* One disadvantage of this technique is that it can only be applied to a limited number of substances. This method gives us important topographical information and has an advantage over the others in that it permits us to establish more easily the relationship between morphology and chemistry, although it is very rarely quantitative. The field of cytochemistry is constantly growing. Even at the present time it is possible to study the cytochemistry of the living egg by using metachromatic stains (34, 35, 39, 122). Another recent aspect of cytochemical study gives promise of a bright future. This involves the use of radioactive tracers in sections (1, 18, 49, 158). Up to now, however, these particular methods have practically not been used for the study of the first stages of development. It would seem that a combination of these techniques with microsurgical techniques might greatly increase the scope of their application (1).

(e) *Studies with the electron microscope.* The analysis of the fine structure of the egg with the electron microscope is still in its infancy. This method seems indispensable in permitting the determination of the nature of the constituents, as revealed by the other techniques. The weakness of this method lies in the difficulty of choosing an adequate fixative. It cannot be overemphasized that the osmic fixatives which are excellent for the preservation of all lipoproteic structures preserve the other structures very poorly or not at all (86, 87).

The Egg as a Cell

A. The Cytoplasm

1. *Ribonucleic acid.* It is because of its decisive role in protein synthesis, in embryonic cells as well as in adult cells, that the RNA is considered to be a fundamental constituent of the egg. Cytochemical tests have provided valuable information on its topographical localization. It is paradoxical to state, however, that its structural localization (that is, its relationship with the ultrastructure of the cytoplasm) has been until recently entirely ignored. It is generally accepted that the RNA is more loosely combined in the egg than in the adult cell; that is, it is associated with much smaller particles, possibly even as isolated molecules. The technique of high-speed, fractional centrifugation of homogenates shows that in amphibians (14, 19) and sea urchins (53, 170), the RNA is found in the supernatant. In *Arbacia* eggs, it has been shown that the RNA is found in the particles of which only 25 per cent sediment at a centrifugal force of 25,000 g, the remainder sedimenting at 100,000 g. The latter have been estimated to

have a diameter of 3×10^{-6} cm. (300 Å), corresponding to a molecular weight of 10,000,000 (170). It should be pointed out, however, that these conclusions result from experiments with homogenates in solutions containing KCl. The authors have observed that the solubilization of RNA increases with the concentration of KCl. A more recent study has confirmed these conclusions by showing that the sedimentation of these granules is accelerated in the presence of Ca^{++} ions (53).

These conclusions seem to be corroborated by the results of cytochemical studies. In *adult cells* centrifuged in the living state, the ergastoplasm is displaced toward the centrifugal pole (11, 134), whereas in the case of the centrifuged *eggs,* the RNA is more often found centripetally, in the hyaloplasm just beneath the lipid pole (19).

Several remarks can be made in regard to this point. (1) It is very difficult to compare the relative sedimentation conditions of an adult cell and of an egg which is very rich in heavy vitelline platelets. (2) In addition to the RNA in the hyaloplasm, it has been possible to demonstrate the presence of RNA in heavy particles which are displaced toward the centrifugal pole. This has been shown in *Limnaea* eggs (134), and, as we will show later, in *Paracentrotus* eggs. (3) Interesting observations made with *Cyclops* show that during the phases of the approach of the pronuclei and of the first mitotic divisions, there is a cyclic evolution of RNA, sometimes dispersed in the hyaloplasm, sometimes accumulating in large and heavy granules which sediment more rapidly. (4) Finally, studies made with invertebrates such as *Ascaris, Acanthoscelides* (a bruchid beetle), and *Cyclops* (117, 103, 164) have shown that a relationship exists between the richness of the granular system of RNA and the origin of the gonocytes, a relation explaining also the basophilia which is so unique in genital determinants. It thus seems that RNA can be linked to these different cytoplasmic organites and is modified during the cellular cycle.

The study of the ultrastructure of the cytoplasm of the ovule, particularly its relationship with its basophilia, is much less advanced than that of adult cells. The few studies which have appeared up to now concern the polar plasm of *Tubifex* eggs (86, 87, 173), the unfertilized egg of *Psammechinus* (2), and oocytes of the mollusks *Otala* and *Spisula* (138, 139, 168).

Although the cytochemistry of the oocyte will not be considered here, some space will be devoted to the unexpected discovery of the new concept of the ergastoplasm as consisting of annulate membranes (membranae fenestratae, periodic lamellae). These have a structure which is typical of that of a nuclear membrane, with its double lamella. This can be shown

cytoplasmic particles at the beginning of the egg's development is certainly exaggerated and is based at least partly on errors in technique.

As for the localization of RNA, the results obtained by homogenization in media containing electrolytes should be considered with suspicion, since recent studies (90, 91, 101, 149), whereby a sucrose solution was utilized for the homogenates, have led to different conclusions. Proteases acting in the same *p*H range have been displaced in the supernatant as well as in the mitochondrial layer of *Paracentrotus* material. The respective activities of these two enzymatic fractions vary in a different manner after fertilization. The activity increases in the supernatant and diminishes in the mitochondrial fraction (90). ATPase has been shown to be fixed to the mitochondria of the unfertilized or recently fertilized egg of the same sea urchin (101). It has been shown that there are two levels of ATPase activity, which are activated by Mg^{++} ions, but at different *p*H optima, and which are linked to two kinds of particles, both probably mitochondrial, but sedimenting differently and differently pigmented (149). The cytochrome system has been localized in one of these mitochondrial fractions, the most pigmented one (91). These new studies point out the diversity of the granular enzyme-carrying systems in the egg. This point seems to be one of the present concerns of cytologists studying the adult cell.

Recent works (3, 4, 46, 47, 51, 107, 108) have shown the existence in hepatic cells of a new cytoplasmic particle smaller than the mitochondria and containing enzymes such as acid phosphatase, ribonuclease, deoxyribonuclease, cathepsin, and β-glycuronidase. These "lysosomes" have peculiar properties, in that they are surrounded by a membrane isolating the enzymes from their substrates.

It is difficult to decide at the present time if particles analogous to the lysosomes exist in the cystoplasm of the egg. It is possible, however, to confirm that acid phosphatase is localized in particular systems different from the mitochondria and that the linkage of the acid phosphatase to mucopolysaccharides can be demonstrated by vital metachromatic staining.

The significance of the metachromasia of the toluidin blue reaction in vivo has been linked to the presence of mucopolysaccharides in the eggs of mammals (33-37, 41). Later, it was shown that the production of these granules is linked to nucleolar activity and that they are incorporated in an area close to the nucleus and rich in plasmalogen. The histochemical reactions in these same rat eggs show a progressive activity of acid phosphatase beginning at fertilization, progressing during the stages of the

pronuclei, and accentuating during the first phases of segmentation (104). This enzymatic activity appears in two systems: (1) in the large metachromatic perinuclear granules, and (2) in small, diffuse granules. The appearance of the latter coincides with a high acid phosphatase activity in the nucleolar region of the pronuclei. The author of these observations (104) has tried to assimilate the large juxtanuclear granules to the mitochondria, whereas the small diffuse granules would be analogous to the lysosomes. It is hoped that these hypotheses will be tested with the electron microscope.

However that may be, the linking of acid phosphatase to granules rich in mucopolysaccharides and staining metachromatically with dyes such as toluidin blue, brilliant cresyl blue, and azure B is considered to be a general phenomenon, since it has been demonstrated in the eggs of two mollusks (122), three sea urchins (105, 119, 120), one annelid (120), and one ascidian (39). In the eggs of invertebrates studied thus far, the metachromatic stains are fixed selectively on the "α granules" which could not be distinguished from the vitelline platelets except by their particular density after centrifugation and their selective staining by alcian blue at a *p*H of 0.2 after oxidation with permanganate (120). Ultimately, and parallel with the spreading of the asters (spermaster or asters of segmentation), the stain leaves the α-granules to become fixed to a new type of granule, β, which is lighter and more strongly metachromatic. Future studies should try to define or clarify the structure of these granules, and the conditions which determine their affinity for toluidin blue. It is no less true that the β granules always show a strong acid phosphatase activity, and observations made with *Paracentrotus* discredit their mitochondrial nature. In centrifuged eggs of this species these β granules separate in the superior vitelline layer. It is precisely in this zone that there appear (1) the alcian blue reaction at *p*H 0.2, demonstrable without preoxidation (hence indicating very acid mucopolysaccharides); and (2) the very strong acid phosphatase activity, which can already be demonstrated after 10 to 20 minutes incubation. No definite structure has been able to be demonstrated in this zone with the electron microscope, unless a great number of Golgi vesicles. Future studies will show whether or not this is only a coincidence.

In *Arbacia* and *Chaetopterus* these granules sediment in the hyaline layer. They give a positive acid phosphatase reaction and a reaction with alcian blue (105). Thus, in all of the kinds of eggs which have been examined up till now (sea urchin, mollusk, annelid, ascidian, and rodent) the phosphatase activity appears on the particles which are rich in muco-

polysaccharides and which are metachromatic in vivo. This result thus indicates the existence of a new cellular organelle of unknown function, but presumably important because of its general properties. Its relationship to the lysosomes of the hepatic cells should be considered.

In summation: (1) it is at least exaggerated to pretend that the ovular enzymes are not linked to the cytoplasmic particles, and become linked only during the course of development; (2) enzymes such as cytochrome oxidase, succinic dehydrogenase, ATPase, and acidic phosphatase have been localized on organelles in the ovular cytoplasm; and (3) certain cytoplasmic particles other than mitochondria can be considered as "platforms" for enzymes.

B. The Nucleus

In the egg, where the nucleus is considerably enlarged, the measurement of DNA, which is diluted, presents many difficulties. The illusion that the nucleus of the unfertilized egg contains no DNA is due to this very dilution (95, 96). However, the Feulgen technique has shown the presence of DNA in the form of a thin crust just within the nuclear membrane (18, 21). Aside from certain divergent opinions (89, 121), the majority of authors agree that from the beginning the nuclei of the two gametes contain an equal amount of DNA, equivalent to half that of the diploid adult cells (98, 167, 169). Without attempting to discuss this point here, it seems that the idea of an absolute constancy of nuclear DNA, expressed in all its rigidity, is excessive.

Apart from such reservations, two facts seem well established. (1) The quantity of DNA doubles in each of the pronuclei during its swelling (42). (2) In the first mitoses of segmentation, the synthesis of DNA is brought about at the very beginning of interkinesis, whether this stage be short, as in the egg of the sea urchin (98), or whether it be exceptionally prolonged, as in the case of rodents (42).

The mitotic apparatus during the first stages is characterized by its great richness in RNA. The results of a study made on the segmentation of *Cyclops* (165) show that the spindle RNA originates from the nuclear sap. The same author has also shown (166) that the interkinetic nuclei and the mitotic apparatus of segmenting eggs in various organisms (*Sabellaria, Cyclops, Clupea harengus,* and *Gadus morrhua*) are very rich in polysaccharides, as demonstrated by the periodic acid Schiff (PAS) reaction, whereas this reaction is negative in the nuclei of cells which have a low mitotic activity. The nuclei of sea urchin eggs are also rich in polysaccharides (99) and cytochemical observations have shown a cyclic varia-

tion during the first division (74) of these substances on the asters as well as on the chromosomes.

The fixation of polysaccharides can present real difficulties, and these observations should be verified. Furthermore, these observations have only a descriptive value, and their relationship with the mitotic mechanism does not yet seem clear. On the other hand, the great richness of the spindles in —SH groups (132) has been correlated with the structure of a specific protein extracted from the achromatic apparatus of the egg of the sea urchin (97).

In most of the eggs which have very short interkinesis phases, the nucleolar activity is easily passed unnoticed. In the case of the eggs of mammals, however, and particularly of rodents, the very long interkinesis phase has permitted the observation of a cyclic activity in the nucleus with active intervention by the nucleolar mechanism, by means of cytochemical methods (31, 36-38). It also appears that the number of nucleoli and their content of RNA and of polysaccharides vary during the phases of swelling of the pronuclei and the first interkinesis. This activity has been correlated with the elaboration of juxtanucleic cytoplasmic bodies, particularly those complexes which are rich in mucopolysaccharides and in plasmalogene (38).

Finally, the cytochemical studies made with *Ascaris* eggs have shown the formation of an appreciable quantity of RNA at the area of contact with the male pronucleus (109-111, 117). The chemical reactions in the nucleus during the first stages of development are still not very well understood. The results so far obtained indicate that a continuation of the work would be well worthwhile.

The Egg as a Future Embryo

The length of this paper prohibits any complete examination of all of the relationships between structure and morphogenesis of the unsegmented egg. Such an analysis would require the scope of a full-length book. The present purpose is only to examine certain key problems. Can we show that in the unsegmented egg there is a cytochemical pattern capable of explaining, completely or in part, its ultimate morphogenesis? In what way are the morphogenetic properties of the diverse ovular territories linked to this kind of pattern?

With the actual techniques available today one cannot demonstrate that in the egg of the sea urchin there is any certain pattern related to its morphogenetic properties. RNA, platelets rich in polysaccharides, lipids, and mitochondria are dispersed in a rather uniform manner. The only topographical differentiation which appears in such an egg is a perinuclear

area containing fewer platelets and more ergastoplasm. However, there doesn't seem to be any indication of ***bilateral symmetry*** or ***polarity***. It is in later phases of development that there appear some cytochemical manifestations in relationship with the gradients shown by experimental analysis. The results of studies of differential reduction with *r*H indicator dyes can be cited here (68, 69, 70); also, modifications of the nucleus appear after the reaction of Hale once the eggs have been placed in sea water without sulfate (73). An unequal distribution of mitochondria along the animal-vegetal axis has also been described. The latter observations have however been the object of serious criticism (156, 157).

In numerous other cases, however, it has been possible to show a direct relationship between a morphogenetic activity and a cytochemical peculiarity in a certain region of the unsegmented egg.

Certain authors are tempted to believe that the first case involves "regulative" eggs, and the second case "mosaic" eggs. Such a distinction does not seem too likely, however (29). It implies too easily, and wrongly, an eventual qualitative difference between two types of development. In effect, all transitions can be found from eggs which display partial development following merogony or a separation of the first blastomeres to those which give evidence of a widespread aptitude toward regulation. Moreover, eggs which are very regulative, such as those of amphibians, show a direct relationship between a cytochemical pattern and morphogenesis.

Polarity

The cytochemistry of the egg in relationship to its polarity has been the object of numerous studies. Particularly, it has been shown with annelids, mollusks, and fishes that the polarity can be only faintly demonstrated in the unfertilized egg and that it is defined and accentuated during maturation, especially at the moment when the two pronuclei fuse. It is this which has previously been referred to as "bipolar differentiation" (133, 150, 151, 160-162), or "ooplasmic segregation" (27, 28).

There is a question as to whether there is a cause and effect relationship between this cytochemical polarity of the fertilized egg and the polarity of the future organism. This relationship has often been denied, since in many cases the distribution of inclusions and cytoplasmic particles has been altered by centrifugation without changing the future embryo. One should not attempt to overgeneralize this idea, since in at least one case, that of the amphibians, a direct cause and effect relationship could be shown between the distribution of particles and inclusions according to the polarity of the egg, and the polarity of the adult organism.

In the unsegmented amphibian egg, there exists a gradient in the distribution of RNA with a maximum at the animal pole (13, 15, 16). On the other hand, there is a decreasing gradient both in dimension and number of vitelline platelets from the marginal zone to the animal pole (118). This distribution of cytoplasmic particles can be modified by gravity. Turning an egg down and centrifuging it lightly can invert the orientation of the gradients of RNA and vitellus. Such an egg will give a larva with an inverted cephalo-caudal polarity. The head will always form in the area which is richest in RNA, whether that be at the animal pole in the normal egg, or at the vegetal pole in the inverted egg.

Maintaining the egg in this inverted position but without centrifugation will produce partial alterations in the distribution of the inclusions. Double, and even triple, embryos can be formed from the "marginal zones," that is, from the territories situated at the limit of the vitelline mass (114, 125-127). Cytochemical analysis always shows a mixture of granules rich in RNA and abundant vitelline platelets, analogous to the distribution found in the normal marginal zone (118).

Finally, by centrifuging the unsegmented egg in the normal position, it is possible to dissociate the ribonucleic granules from the vitelline platelets. The former accumulate in the centripetal or animal pole, while the latter accumulate at the centrifugal or vegetal pole (19, 118). Such a manipulation leads to hypomorphic embryos which, in spite of a sufficient gastrulean invagination, are incapable of differentiation in the middle layer (115), with a correlative lack of induction of the outer layer.

This series of experiments tends to imply that, in the case of amphibians, the differentiation of the chordomesoblast and its cephalo-caudal polarization depend directly on the gradient between the animal and vegetal poles of cytoplasmic particles in the unsegmented egg.

Bilateral Symmetry

In many cases, cytochemical studies have revealed a bilateral symmetry in the fertilized egg, sometimes even in the unfertilized egg. We will cite only the two best examples of such a bilateral pattern: rodent eggs and ascidian eggs.

In the oocyte and in the fertilized egg of the rat (30, 36, 37, 43), two kinds of granules rich in RNA can be observed: small granules forming a "cloud" in the center of the cytoplasm, and large granules distributed under the cortex. These two categories of particles clearly visible with the light microscope are rich in phospholipids and have been considered provisionally as mitochondria. Their exact nature is being studied at present

(40). The cortical "mitochondria" are clearly dominant on one side of the egg, whether it be fertilized or unfertilized, while the cytoplasm on the opposite side has an alveolar structure. The ultimate evolution is clearly different in these two ovular territories. The side which is rich in cortical RNA granules leads to blastomeres which are smaller, but which, beginning with the 8- or 16-cell stages, become intensely basophilic following the secondary appearance of fine granules surrounding the nucleus. These are the blastomeres which are destined to form the ectophyll (ectoblast + chordomesoblast) of the embryo. The other side of the egg gives larger blastomeres which are characterized by the appearance of granules which are rich in mucopolysaccharides and acid phosphatase (cf. pp. 386, 387), and which stain metachromatically in vivo. These large blastomeres envelop the smaller blastomeres and form the trophoblast as well as the endophyll.

It is not excluded that the bilateral symmetry of mammalian eggs, like those of other vertebrates, might be modified at the moment of fertilization. However, no indication of such an alternative has appeared up to now. Certain observations made on cheiropteran eggs give strong indication of a continuity between the bilateral symmetry of the oocyte and that of the fertilized egg (159).

The evolution of the cytochemical pattern of the mammalian egg thus shows a primary bilateral symmetry in the oocyte which, after fertilization, seems to maintain a continual relationship with the diversification of the embryonic and extra-embryonic parts of the germ.

With the present techniques for the cultivation of mammalian eggs, it has not been possible to determine whether an experimental modification in the distribution of the cytoplasmic particles would provoke an alteration of the ultimate morphogenesis.

Such an investigation has been made in the case of ascidian eggs (142, 143, 146, 152, 171). The classical observations of Conklin have elucidated the signification of the ventral "yellow crescent," that is, the manner in which the crescent organizes after fertilization, and the fact that centrifugation of this egg, contrary to most cases, provokes a profound disturbance in the morphogenesis, particularly in the formation of the myoblasts. It has been shown (142, 143, 146, 152, 171): (1) that the "yellow crescent" contains an accumulation of mitochondria rich in cytochrome oxidase and in benzidine peroxidase; (2) that the mitochondria are found in the myoblast; and (3) that the ectopic differentiation of the myoblast in the embryos deriving from centrifuged eggs can be related to the displacement of the mitochondria.

In the particular case of ascidian eggs, a mitochondrial pattern with its specific enzymatic components has been able to be directly related to an important differentiation of the embryo.

Signification of Mitochondrial Patterns

The Nadi reaction and the Janus green B reaction have permitted the study of mitochondrial patterns in numerous marine eggs. Accumulations of mitochondria with their respiratory enzymes thus appear in the cortical plasm of ctenophores (129, 130, 144). They have also been followed from the unsegmented egg stage through the cell linkage which is so particular in annelids and mollusks (5, 6, 83, 84, 85, 130, 131, 147). The results of all of these works indicate that a mitochondrial mass selectively prepares the differentiation of locomotor organs such as muscles, in the case of ascidians, ciliated bands in the case of ctenophores, or in the larva of mollusks. It has been concluded (144) that the mitochondria could be considered as "organ-forming substances," in the sense that they afford a "supply of energy." If in effect this is so, the accumulation of respiratory enzymes in a selective territory of the unsegmented egg does not necessarily have an actual signification, that is, they do not necessarily alter the metabolism in that territory of the unsegmented egg (see p. 387).

Parallel observations made with ascidians show that such a position is well founded. Microchemical methods have confirmed the results of cytochemical studies. After homogenization of the ventral blastomeres, it has been possible to show a cytochrome oxidase activity 2.7 times greater than that of the dorsal blastomeres (9). However, the consumption of oxygen by the isolated dorsal and ventral blastomeres has been shown to be identical (67).

The cytochemical localizations of the unsegmented egg are thus not necessarily linked to the actual life of this unsegmented egg. Such a conception can explain the contradictions which seem to arise too frequently between the study of the cytochemistry of the egg and its relation with morphogenesis.

The Case of the Polar Lobe of Spiralia

The preceding observations made on the eggs of amphibians, mammals, and ascidians tend toward an optimistic view: there exists an easily explainable relationship between these patterns and morphogenesis. This relationship seems to be so direct that at first hand one would be tempted to consider the mitochondrial mass as the true "germinal localizations." It is to be noted, however, that such a situation is really exceptional. In many

cases, a comparative study of different species having the same type of morphogenesis makes the existence of a common cytochemical pattern difficult to conceive. The polar lobe and the polar plasma of annelids and mollusks can be cited as examples of this.

We know that these plasms, which are eventually united in a polar lobe, have essential morphogenetic properties corresponding to the formation of the somatoblast (*2d* and *4d*). The cytoplasm of the polar lobe of the mollusk *Ilyanassa* (102), and the annelid *Sabellaria* (137) does not show any apparent difference from the rest of the vegetative portion of the egg. The polar plasmas of *Tubifex* (86, 172) are characterized by a great abundance of Nadi-positive mitochondria and a vesiculated ergastoplasm. In the aberrant annelid *Myzostoma,* one also finds in the polar lobe a "green plasma" which has been shown to be an accumulation of Nadi-positive mitochondria (130). This "plasma" is found at the vegetative pole from the time when the egg is laid. In these forms, displacement by centrifugation does not affect segmentation, especially the formation of the lobe and the inequality of the first two blastomeres (113). Similarly, in *Ilyanassa* the polar lobe forms normally regardless of the abnormal stratification produced by centrifugation (102). In the mollusk lamellibranch *Gryphaea,* one finds in the polar lobe (and in the corresponding vegetative territories of the egg from the beginning of maturation) an accumulation of RNA, while the vitelline platelets are much less abundant (122). In another lamellibranch, *Mytilus,* cytological examination does not show any notable particularity in the lobe (8). Once the latter has been isolated, it is characterized by a consumption of oxygen which is 25 per cent less (per unit volume) than that of the rest of the egg. In addition to this, the respiration of the blastomere *CD* (which contains the polar lobe) is less than that of *AB* (10). The authors of these experiments insist on the fact that this last notation shows that the decreased respiration of the polar lobe is in fact real and is not due to the fact that the isolated polar lobe is an anuclear fragment. However, it has been demonstrated that the incorporation of labeled amino acids is less in a polar lobe that has been isolated than in one which has been left in situ (1).

Discussion

The results of the experiments performed using the usual cytochemical techniques thus tend to lead to conclusions which are contradictory. In certain cases (polarity of the amphibians; bilateral symmetry of the ascidians) a direct link can be established between a cytochemical pattern and development, and a topographical alteration of this pattern produces a dis-

turbance which can be correlated with development. In other cases, however, one cannot define a general pattern for all forms having the same type of morphogenesis. What is even more striking is that an alteration of pattern has no effect on the ultimate morphogenesis.

Two remarks can be made at this point. The first concerns the significance of centrifugation experiments. It is practically a classical statement to say that one can easily centrifuge an egg without altering its morphogenesis and by consequence state that the "inclusions," taken in the broadest sense of the word, do not play an essential role in this morphogenesis. In that form, such a conclusion is certainly false. We have already seen two examples where centrifugation of an unsegmented egg, although moderate, can cause profound disturbances in development, and it would be easy to find other examples (112). On the other hand, the real effects of centrifugation on a living egg, especially if negative, should be most carefully scrutinized before one can derive valuable conclusions, as has already been pointed out (136). The sedimentation caused by centrifugal force can return to the normal position more rapidly than had been formerly perceived. The presence of intercellular membranes does not always present an obstruction to such rearrangement (136). Finally, as we have seen previously (p. 386), the exact distribution of sedimented materials cannot be considered as being known until after a profound examination, including one with the electron microscope. Each experiment concerning centrifugation of the egg should be studied minutely and systematically before coming to formal conclusions.

The second remark concerns the methods used up to now for the study of these patterns. In such studies as those which have a topographical nature, only cytochemical methods could be utilized up to now. What has been demonstrated consists of a limited number of enzymes (cytochrome oxidase and phosphatases), ribonucleic acid, and polysaccharides. In other words, we are better informed on the tools than on the skilled worker. These "tools" can be put into place earlier or later according to the different types of eggs, but sometimes even according to the species having the same type of development, as in the case of the polar lobe. A disturbance of the topography can lead to irreversible consequences, as after the centrifugation of eggs of ascidians, amphibians, and annelids (*Tubifex*). Very often, however, the fundamental structure of the egg can possess sufficient resources to repair the disturbed mechanism before it is too late.

Besides morphogenetic regulation, one should consider structural regulation, the study of which could present one of the most fascinating of all embryological problems. Thus, by studying the mechanisms and methods

of repair of the machinery, one will get to know the engineer. But this engineer should be studied also by direct means.

The main problem remains open: to study the protein organization of the fundamental cytoplasm, particularly in the ovular cortex. This could be done by applying on a topographical plan the most refined cytochemical studies such as the incorporation of labelled isotopes or immunological methods. We are convinced that a complete cytochemical study of the protein structure, as well as the energy-producing mechanisms, seems to be the best future plan of organization for the study of development in direct correlation with the structure of the unsegmented egg.

Conclusion

The comparative cytochemical study of the unsegmented egg has been considered under two aspects. The first consists of a comparison of an ovular structure to that of the adult cell. It seems that the differences in organization between these two types of cells have been overestimated. In particular, the most recent studies made with reliable techniques show that the enzymes which are linked to cytoplasmic particles in the adult cell are likewise so linked in the egg. As in the adult cells, there appears to be a number of enzyme-carrying systems in the egg. The question regarding the eventual association of non-mitochondrial acid-phosphatase-carrying granules with the lysosomes in hepatic cells is still open. Although the RNA is linked, in part at least, to the ergastoplasmic systems, the latter can, however, be of very atypical structure, as in certain tumor cells.

The second aspect consists of a correlation between the cytochemical pattern and the morphogenetic properties of an unsegmented egg. A synthetic view appears here more difficult, and a comparison made with different animal types has led to contradictory conclusions. It is reasonable here to refer to our insufficient information on this subject. The topographical cytochemistry, with the methods utilized used up to now, informs us more about the "machinery" than regarding the "direction" of the morphogenetic undertaking. It is hoped that a topographical cytochemistry of the proteins will soon fill this gap. It is no less true that the direct intervention of localized accumulations of mitochondria or of ergastoplasm have been very nicely demonstrated in certain types of morphogenesis.

REFERENCES

1. Abd-El-Wahab, A., and Pantelouris, M., *Exptl. Cell Research,* **13,** 78-82 (1957).
2. Afzelius, B. A., *Z. Zellforsch u mikroskop. Anat.,* **45,** 660-675 (1957).

3. Appelmans, F., and Duve, C. de, *Biochem. J. (London)*, **59,** 426-433 (1955).
4. ———, Wattiaux, R., and Duve, C. de, *Biochem. J. (London)*, **59,** 438-455 (1955).
5. Attardo, C., *Ricerca sci.*, **25,** 2797-2800 (1955).
6. ———, *Acta embryol. et morphol. exptl.*, **1,** 65-70 (1957).
7. Ballentine, R., *Biol. Bull.*, **77,** 328 (1939).
8. Berg, W. E., *Cell Biology* (Proc. 15th Ann. Biol. Colloq., Oregon State Coll., Corvallis) 30-34 (1954).
9. ———, *Biol. Bull.*, **110,** 1-7 (1956).
10. ———, and Kutsky, Ph. B., *Biol. Bull.*, **101,** 47-61 (1951).
11. Bernhard, W., Gauthier, A., and Roullier, C., *Arch. anat. microscop. morphol. exptl.*, **43,** 236-275 (1954).
12. Boell, E. J., in *Analysis of Development* (Willier, B. H., Weiss, P. A., and Hamburger, V., eds.), p. 520-555. W. B. Saunders, Philadelphia (1955).
13. Brachet, J., *Embryologie chimique*. Desoer, Liége; Masson & Cie., Paris (1944).
14. ———, *Experientia*, **3,** 329 (1947).
15. ———, *Compt. rend. Soc. Biol.*, **142,** 1241-1254 (1948).
16. ———, *Chemical Embryology*, Interscience, New York (1950).
17. ———, *Biochemical Cytology*, Academic Press, New York (1957).
18. ———, and Ficq, A., *Arch biol. (Liége)*, **67,** 431-446 (1956).
19. ———, and Pasteels, J., unpub., cited in 17.
20. ———, and Shaver, J. R., *Experientia*, **5,** 204-205 (1949).
21. Burgos, M. H., *Exptl. Cell Research*, **9,** 360-363 (1955).
22. Carrano, F., *Ricerca sci.*, **25,** 3049-3052 (1955).
23. ———, *Atti accad. nazl. Lincei, Rend., Classe sci. fis. mat. e nat.* [8] **22,** 216-219 (1957).
24. ———, *Ricerca sci.*, **27,** 1121-1124 (1957).
25. ———, and Palazzo, F., *Riv. biol. (Perugia)*, n. s., **47,** 193-201 (1954).
26. Clement, A. C., and Lehmann, F. E., *Naturwiss.*, **43,** 478-479 (1956).
27. Costello, D. P., *J. Elisha Mitchell Sci. Soc.*, **61,** 277-289 (1945).
28. ———, *Ann. N. Y. Acad. Sci.*, **49,** 663-684 (1948).
29. Dalcq, A., *L'oeuf et son dynamisme organisateur*. Albin Michel, Paris (1941).
30. ———, *Koninkl. Ned. Akad. Wetenschap., Proc., Ser. C*, **54,** 351-372; 469-477 (1951).
31. ———, *Compt. rend. assoc. anat.*, **38e** *Réun. (Nancy)*, 345-361 (1951).
32. ———, *Arch. anat. et embryol. (Vol. Jub. Prof. Dubreuil)*, **34,** 157-169 (1951).
33. ———, *Biol. Jaarboek (Gand)*, **19,** 52-59 (1952).
34. ———, *Compt. rend. soc. biol.*, **146,** 1408-1411 (1952).
35. ———, *Compt. rend. assoc. anat.*, **39e,** *Réun. (Nancy)*, 513-516 (1952).
36. ———, *Compt. rend. soc. biol.*, **148,** 1332-1373 (1954).
37. ———, *Stud. on Fertility* (Blackwell Scientific Publications, Oxford) **7,** 113-122 (1955).
38. ———, *Exptl. Cell Research*, **10,** 99-119 (1956).
39. ———, *Bull. soc. zool. franc.*, **82,** 296-316 (1957).
40. ———, pers. commun.
41. ———, and Massart, L., *Compt. rend. soc. biol.*, **146,** 1436-1439 (1952).
42. ———, and Pasteels, J., *Exptl. Cell Research*, suppl. **3,** 72-97 (1955).
43. ———, and Seaton-Jones, A., *Compt. rend. assoc. anat.*, **36e** *Réun. (Nancy)*, 170-175 (1949).
44. Dalton, A. J., and Felix, M. D., *Symposia Soc. Exptl. Biol.*, **10,** 148-156 (1957).
45. Deutsch, H., and Gustafson, T., *Arkiv Kemi*, **4,** 221-231 (1952).
46. Duve, C. de, *J. de physiol. (Paris)*, **49,** 113-115 (1957).
47. ———, *Symposia Soc. exptl. Biol.*, **10,** 50-61 (1957).
48. Evola-Maltese, C., *Acta embryol. et morphol. exptl.*, **1,** 99-104 (1957).

49. Ficq, A., *Exptl. Cell Research,* **9,** 286-293 (1955).
50. Gersch, M., *Arch. exptl. Zellforsch.,* **22,** 549-564 (1939).
51. Gianetto, R., and Duve, C. de, *Biochem. J. (London),* **59,** 433-438 (1955).
52. Green, D. E., *Symposia Soc. exptl. Biol.,* **10,** 30-49 (1957).
53. Gross, P. R., *J. Cellular Comp. Physiol.,* **47,** 429-447 (1956).
54. Gustafson, T., and Hasselberg, I., *Exptl. Cell Research,* **2,** 642-672 (1951).
55. ———, and Lenicque, P., *Exptl. Cell Research,* **2,** 642-672 (1952).
56. ———, and ———, *Exptl. Cell Research,* **8,** 114-117 (1955).
57. Harvey, E. B., *Biol. Bull.,* **64,** 125-148 (1933).
58. ———, *Biol. Bull.,* **81,** 114-118 (1941).
59. Harvey, E. N., *Arch. exptl. Zellforsch.,* **22,** 463-476 (1939).
60. ———, and Lavin, G. L., *Biol. Bull.,* **86,** 163-168 (1944).
61. Hogeboom, G. H., Schneider, W. C., and Palade, G. E., *Proc. Soc. Exptl. Biol. Med.,* **65,** 320-322 (1947).
62. Holter, H., *Arch. exptl. Zellforsch.,* **19,** 232-237 (1937).
63. ———, *Advances in Enzymol.,* **13,** 1-19 (1952).
64. ———, *J. Cellular Comp. Physiol.,* **8,** 179-200 (1936).
65. ———, Lanz, H., Jr., Linderstrøm-Lang, K., *J. Cellular Comp. Physiol.,* **12,** 112-127 (1938).
66. ———, Lehmann, F. E., and Linderstrøm-Lang, K., *Compt. rend. trav. lab. Carlsberg (Ser. chim.),* **21,** 259-262 (1938).
67. ———, and Zeuthen, E., *Compt. rend. trav. lab. Carlsberg, (Ser. chim.),* **25,** 33-65 (1944).
68. Hörstadius, S., *J. exptl. Zool.,* **120,** 421-436 (1952).
69. ———, *J. Embryol. exptl. Morphol.,* **1,** 257-259 (1953).
70. ———, *J. exptl. Zool.,* **129,** 249-256 (1955).
71. Howatson, A. F., and Ham, A. W., *Cancer Research,* **15,** 62, 69 (1955).
72. Hutchens, J. O., Kopac, M. J., and Krahl, M. E., *J. Cellular Comp. Physiol.,* **20,** 113-118 (1942).
73. Immers, J., *Exptl. Cell Research,* **10,** 546-548 (1956).
74. ———, *Exptl. Cell Research,* **12,** 145-153 (1957).
75. Keltch, A. K., Strittmatter, C. F., Walters, C. P., Clowes, G. F., *J. Gen. Physiol.,* **33,** 547-553 (1949).
76. Krahl, M. E., *Biol. Bull.,* **98,** 175-217 (1950).
77. ———, *Biochim. et Biophys. Acta,* **20,** 27-32 (1956).
78. ———, Keltch, A. K., Neubeck, C. E., Clowes, G. H. A., *J. Gen. Physiol.,* **24,** 597-617 (1941).
79. Krugelis, E. J., *Biol. Bull.,* **93,** 209 (1947).
80. Lansing, A. I., *J. Histochem. Cytochem.,* **1,** 266 (1953).
81. Lazarow, A., and Cooperstein, S. J., *J. Histochem. Cytochem.,* **1,** 234-241 (1953).
82. Lehmann, F. E., *Naturwiss.,* **29,** 101 (1941).
83. ———, *Naturwiss.,* **29,** 101 (1941).
84. ———, *Folia. Biotheor.,* **3,** 7-24 (1948).
85. ———, *Rev. suisse zool.,* **55,** 1-43 (1948).
86. ———, *Naturwiss.,* 289-296 (1956).
87. ———, and Wahli, H. R., *Z. Zellforsch.,* **39,** 618-629 (1954).
88. Lindahl, P. E., and Holter, H., *Compt. rend. lab. Carlsberg, (Ser. chim.),* **23,** 249-255 (1940).
89. Lison, L., and Pasteels, J., *Arch. biol. (Liége),* **62,** 1-43 (1951).
90. Maggio, R., *J. Cellular Comp. Physiol.,* (in press).
91. ———, and Ghiretti, A., *Exptl. Cell Research,* (in press, quoted by personal communication, courtesy A. Monroy).
92. Mancuso, V., *Ricerca sci.,* **24,** 1886-1888 (1954).

93. ———, *Atti Accad. nazl. Lincei, Rend., (Classe sci. fis. mat. e nat.)* [8] **21,** 504-506 (1956).
94. ———, *Ricerca sci.,* **26,** 2756-2760 (1956).
95. Marshak, A., and Marshak, C., *Exptl. Cell Research,* **5,** 288-300 (1953).
96. ———, and ———, *Exptl. Cell Research,* **8,** 126-146 (1955).
97. Mazia, D., and Dan, K., *Proc. Natl. Acad. Sci. U. S.,* **38,** 826-838 (1952).
98. McMaster, R., *J. Exptl. Zool.,* **130,** 1-23 (1955).
99. Monné, L., and Slautterbach, D. B., *Exptl. Cell Research,* **1,** 477-491 (1950).
100. ———, and ———, *Arkiv. Zool.* (ser. 2), **3,** 349-356 (1952).
101. Monroy, A., *J. Cellular Comp. Physiol.* (in press).
102. Morgan, T. H., *J. Exptl. Zool.,* **64,** 433-467 (1933).
103. Mulnard, J., *Bull. classe sci., Acad. roy. Belg.,* **36,** 767-778 (1950).
104. ———, *Arch. biol. (Liége),* **66,** 525-685 (1955).
105. ———, pers. commun.
106. ———, and Dalcq, A., *Compt. rend. Soc. Biol.,* **149,** 536-839 (1955).
107. Novikoff, A. B., *Symposia Soc. Exptl. Biol.,* **10,** 92-109 (1957).
108. ———, Beaufay, H., Duve, C. de, *J. Biophys. Biochem. Cytol.,* suppl. **2,** 179-184 (1956).
109. Panijel, J., *Bull. soc. chim. biol.,* **29,** 1098-1106 (1947).
110. ———, Thèses Fac. Sci. Univ. Paris (Ser. A 2326), n°3198, 1-331 (1951).
111. ———, and Pasteels, J., *Arch. biol. (Liége),* **62,** 354-369 (1951).
112. Parseval, M. von, *Roux' Arch. Entwicklungsmech. Organ.,* **51,** 468-497 (1922).
113. Pasteels, J., *Arch. Anat. microscop.,* **30,** 161-197 (1934).
114. ———, *Arch. biol. (Liége),* **49,** 629-667 (1938).
115. ———, *Arch. biol. (Liége),* **51,** 335-386 (1940).
116. ———, *Arch. biol. (Liége),* **52,** 321-339 (1941).
117. ———, *Arch. biol. (Liége),* **59,** 405-446 (1948).
118. ———, *Bull. Soc. zool. Fr.,* **76,** 231-270 (1953).
119. ———, *Bull. classe sci. Acad. roy. Belg.* (5e série), **41,** 760-768 (1955).
120. ———, *Arch. biol. (Liége)* (in press).
121. ———, and Lison, L., *Nature,* **167,** 948 (1951).
122. ———, and Mulnard, J., *Arch. biol. (Liége),* **68,** 115-163 (1957).
123. ———, Castiaux, P., and Vandermeerssche, G., *J. Biophys. Biochem. Cytol.* (in press).
124. Peltrera, A., *Pubbl. staz. zool. Napoli,* **18,** 20-49 (1940).
125. Penners, A., *Z. wiss. Zoöl.,* **148,** 189-220 (1936).
126. ———, and Schleip, W., *Z. wiss. Zoöl.,* **130,** 365-454 (1928).
127. ———, and ———, *Z. wiss. Zoöl.,* **131,** 1-156 (1928).
128. Petrucci, D., *Acta embryol. et morphol. exptl.* **1,** 105-117 (1957).
129. Pittoti, M., *Pubbl. staz. zool. Napoli,* **18,** 250-272 (1940).
130. ———, *Pubbl. staz. zool. Napoli,* **21,** 93-100 (1947).
131. Pollicita, M., *Ricerca sci.,* **25,** 3114-3115 (1955).
132. Rapkine, L., *Ann. physiol. physicochim. biol.,* **7,** 382-405 (1931).
133. Raven, Chr. P., *Acta Neerl. Morphol. norm. pathol.,* **1,** 337-357 (1938).
134. ———, *Arch. néerl. zool.,* **7,** 91-119 (1945).
135. ———, *Biol. Revs. Cambridge Phil. Soc.,* **23,** 333-368 (1948).
136. ———, and Bretschneider, L. H., *Arch. néerl. zool.,* **6,** 255-278 (1942).
137. Raven, P., Van Brink, J. M., Van de Kamer, J. C., *Verhandel. Koninkl. Ned. Akad. Wetenschap., Afdel. Natuurk.* (Sect. II), **47,** 1-48 (1950).
138. Rebhun, L. I., *J. Biophys. Biochem. Cytol.,* **2,** 93-104 (1956).
139. ———, *J. Biophys. Biochem. Cytol.,* **2,** 159-170 (1956).
140. Recknagel, R. O., *J. Cellular Comp. Physiol.,* **35,** 111-129 (1950).
141. Reverberi, G., *Pubbl. staz. zool. Napoli,* **18,** 129-139 (1940).

142. ———, *Experientia,* **12,** 55-61 (1956).
143. ———, *Pubbl. staz. zool. Napoli,* **29,** 187-212 (1957).
144. ———, *Arch. embryol. morphol. exptl.,* **1,** 134-142 (1957).
145. ———, *Scientia (Milan),* (ser. 6), **51,** 1-6 (1957).
146. ———, and Pittoti, M., *Comment. pontif. Acad. Sci.,* **3,** 469-488 (1939).
147. ———, and ———, *Pubbl. staz. zool. Napoli,* **18,** 256-263 (1940).
148. ———, and ———, *Pubbl. staz. zool. Napoli,* **21,** 237-258 (1947).
149. Ricotta, C. M. B., *Experientia,* **13,** 491-2 (1957).
150. Ries, E., *Pubbl. staz. zool. Napoli,* **16,** 364-399 (1937).
151. ———, *Arch. exp. Zellforsch. Gewebezücht.,* **22,** 569-584 (1939).
152. ———, *Arch. exp. Zellforsch. Gewebezücht.,* **23,** 95-119 (1939).
153. Schleip, W., *Die Determination der Primitiventwicklung.* Akademische Verlagsgesellschaft, Leipzig (1929).
154. Schultz, H., *Oncologia,* **10,** 307-329 (1957).
155. Shapiro, H., *J. Cellular Comp. Physiol.,* **6,** 101-116 (1935).
156. Shaver, J. R., *Exptl. Cell Research,* **11,** 548-559 (1956).
157. ———, in *The Beginnings of Embryonic Development* (A. Tyler, R. C. von Borstel, and C. B. Metz, eds.), p. 263-290, Am. Assoc. Advance. of Sci., Washington, D. C. (1957).
158. Sirlin, J. L., *Experientia,* **11,** 112 (1955).
159. Skreb, S., *Arch. biol. (Liége),* **68,** 381-428 (1957).
160. Spek, J., *Protoplasma,* **18,** 497-545 (1933).
161. ———, *Roux' Arch. Entwicklungsmech. Organ.,* **131,** 362-372 (1934).
162. ———, *Protoplasma,* **21,** 394-405 (1934).
163. Steinbach, H. B., and Moog, F., in *Analysis of Development* (B. H. Willier, P. A. Weiss, and V. Hamburger, eds.), p. 70-90. W. B. Saunders, Philadelphia (1955).
164. Stich, H., *Roux' Arch. Entwicklungsmech. Organ.,* **144,** 364-380 (1950).
165. ———, *Z. Naturforsch.,* Pt. b., **6,** 259-261 (1951).
166. ———, *Chromosoma,* **4,** 429-438 (1951).
167. Swift, H. H., *Physiol. Zoöl.,* **23,** 169-198 (1950).
168. ———, *J. Biophys. Biochem. Cytol.,* **2** (suppl.), 415-418 (1956).
169. ———, and Kleinfeld, R., *Physiol. Zoöl.,* **26,** 301-311 (1953).
170. Tsuboi, K. K., De Terra, N., and Hudson, P. B., *Exptl. Cell Research,* **7,** 32-43 (1954).
171. Urbani, E., and Urbani, Mistruzzi L., *Pubbl. staz. zool. Napoli,* **21,** 69-82 (1947).
172. Weber, R., *Rev. suisse zool.,* **63,** 277-288 (1956).
173. ———, and Boell, E. J., *Rev. suisse zool.,* **62,** 260-268 (1956).
174. Wessel, W., and Bernhard, W., *Z. Krebsforsch.,* **62,** 140-162 (1957).
175. Wicklund, E., *Nature,* **161,** 556 (1948).
176. Woodward, A. A., *Biol. Bull.,* **99,** 367 (1950).
177. Yčas, M., *J. exptl. Biol.,* **31,** 208-217 (1954).

A CYTOCHEMICAL STUDY OF THE GROWTH OF THE SLUG OOCYTE

RONALD R. COWDEN[1, 2]

Biology Division, Oak Ridge National Laboratory[3]
Oak Ridge, Tennessee

INTRODUCTION

The development of the germ cells of gastropods has been the subject of a number of classical cytological studies. The main object of this investigation, however, was to consider the changes in the morphological relationships of a number of the intracellular substances, as demonstrated by cytochemical methods, during the growth of the slug oocyte. In an earlier study, Bridgeford and Pelluet (6) described some of the chemical relations between the primary nucleolus and the one or more secondary nucleoli that appear during development of the slug oocyte. In view of the general relation considered to exist between the nucleolus and protein and ribonucleic acid (RNA) synthesis (7), an investigation of the unusual nucleolar system found in the slugs is of particular interest and is the focal point of this investigation.

The slugs used in this investigation were collected on the grounds of the Biology Division of the Oak Ridge National Laboratory and were subsequently classified as *Deroceras reticulatum*. Some other unclassified species of the genus *Deroceras* were also used. The animals were decapitated, the viscera exposed, and the ovotestes quickly removed. These were fixed in one of three fixatives: acetic-acid–alcohol (1:3), 10 per cent buffered formalin, or Baker's calcium formal. These were embedded in Tissuemat and sectioned at 15 μ.

For the study of each class of nucleic acid, a number of methods were employed. For deoxyribonucleic acid (DNA) the Feulgen reaction and Einarson's (11) gallocyanin-chromalum after ribonuclease (RNAase) di-

[1] This work was performed while the author was a U. S. Public Health Postdoctoral Fellow (HF-6176).

[2] Present address: Department of Biology, The Johns Hopkins University, Baltimore 18, Maryland.

[3] Operated by the Union Carbide Corporation for the U. S. Atomic Energy Commission.

gestion were used. For RNA, Kurnick's (13) modification of the methyl-green-pyronin method, the azure B bromide method of Flax and Himes (12), and the previously mentioned gallocyanin-chromalum method of Einarson (11) were used. The material stained for RNA received prior incubation in deoxyribonuclease (DNAase). Both DNAase and RNAase, Worthington products, were used as suggested by Swift (17). Acetic-acid-alcohol (1:3) fixed material was used for all studies on nucleic acids.

Two procedures were used for the demonstration of proteins: the fast green method of Alfert and Geschwind (1) for basic nucleoproteins (histones) and the naphthol yellow S method of Deitch (9) for the dibasic amino acid residues of lysine, arginine, and histidine. The latter was coupled with the Feulgen reaction as suggested by Deitch (10). When used in this manner, the stain is still qualitatively specific, but there is some reduction in the intensity of naphthol yellow S binding resulting from the hydrolysis in 1 *N* HCl.

The mucopolysaccharides were demonstrated by the periodic acid Schiff (PAS) reaction, in some cases preceded by incubation in 1 per cent malt diastase at 37°C for 4 hours to remove glycogen. Lison's alcian blue method (15) was used to stain mucin and other acid mucopolysaccharides. Prior incubation at 37°C in 1 per cent bovine testis hyaluronidase had no effect on the staining in this material. Both formalin-fixed and acetic-acid–alcohol-fixed material were used for this purpose.

Phospholipids were demonstrated by the alcoholic alcian blue method of Pearse (16), and control sections were extracted in pyridine at 60°C for 8 hours. Bradley's method (5), which involves squashing in acetocarmine and then in 45 per cent acetic acid saturated with Sudan black B, was used for the demonstration of lipids in general.

An ocular micrometer was used to measure the diameters of the two classes of nucleoli in all the uncut nucleoli of two sets of serial sections stained by the azure B bromide method.

Observations

The Chromosomes

In young oocytes, the chromosomes at leptotene were observed as distinct elongated threads filling the space around the nucleolus (Fig. 1). At pachytene (Fig. 2) their "lamp-brush" nature could be discerned. Likewise, the diplotene stage was distinctly observable (Fig. 3), in which the much shortened and thickened chromosomes stained deeply with gallocyanin-chromalum. The nucleolus persisted throughout this development, but diakinesis

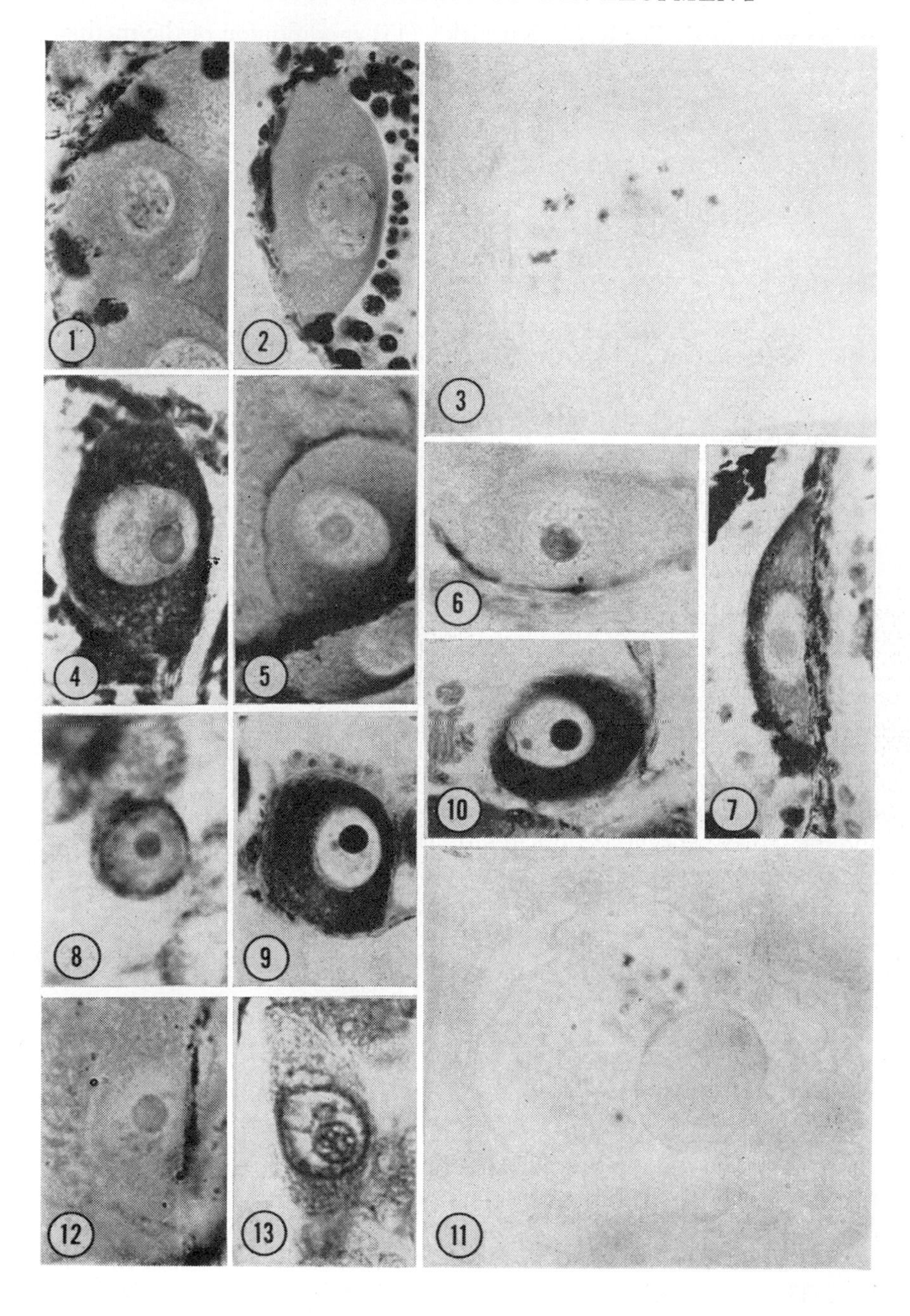
1
2
3
4
5
6
7
8
9
10
11
12
13

seemed to be the latest stage of meiosis reached in the ovotestis. The chromosomes appeared to be stained much more readily by gallocyanin-chromalum after RNAase digestion than by the Feulgen reaction. Some metachromatic binding of azure B bromide was noted in the chromosomes of the oocytes after DNAase treatment. Fast green was also faintly bound by the chromosomes of the oocytes—so faintly that it was not possible to make adequate photographs. In other types of nuclei, e.g., nurse cells, spermatocytes, the specific binding of fast green in only the chromosomes and nuclei was evident.

The Cytoplasm

The cytoplasm of all sizes of oocytes contained a demonstrably large amount of RNA. In the smaller cells, the binding of various stains was more intense than in the larger ones; this could be caused by a greater increase in the volume of the cell than of new RNA. The same relation held for the dibasic amino acid residues of lysine, arginine, or histidine, and for phospholipids. The cytoplasmic glycogen also appeared to be more intensely concentrated in the cytoplasm of the smaller oocytes. Alcian blue

---

Fig. 1. The leptotene chromosomes stained with gallocyanin-chromalum after RNAase treatment. 450 ×.

Fig. 2. Pachytene chromosomes stained with gallocyanin-chromalum after RNAase treatment. 450 ×.

Fig. 3. Diakinesis chromosomes stained with gallocyanin-chromalum after RNAase treatment. 970 ×.

Fig. 4. Oocyte stained for phospholipids by Pearse's method, nucleolus counterstained with aqueous neutral red. 450 ×.

Fig. 5. Oocyte stained by the PAS reaction. 450 ×.

Fig. 6. Oocyte stained by the PAS reaction after digestion in malt diastase. 450 ×.

Fig. 7. Oocyte stained in 0.1 per cent fast green after 5 per cent TCA extraction at 90°C for 15 min. 450 ×.

Fig. 8. Youngest oocyte stained with azure B bromide after DNAase treatment showing a single nucleolus. 970 ×.

Fig. 9. A later oocyte, stained as in Fig. 8, and showing a small secondary nucleolus lying next to the primary nucleolus. 450 ×.

Fig. 10. A fully developed oocyte with a primary and secondary nucleolus, stained as in Fig. 8. 450 ×.

Fig. 11. The nucleolar membrane shows some binding of gallocyanin-chromalum after treatment with RNAase, probably representing nucleolus-associated chromatin in the diplotene oocyte. 970 ×.

Fig. 12. Oocyte stained with alcian blue for acid mucopolysaccharides; the nucleolar membrane binds this dye. 450 ×.

Fig. 13. Oocyte stained with naphthol yellow S for dibasic amino acid residues; both classes of nucleoli bind this dye. 450 ×.

(Photomicrographs by Mr. John Spurbeck, Illustration Division, Johns Hopkins University).

did not stain the cytoplasm to any degree, but some sudanophilia was observed. Fast green at *p*H 8.0 stained the cytoplasm of the oocytes to a considerable degree, but not that of any other cell types. An example of the distribution of the above-mentioned materials in the largest class of oocytes is given in Figs. 4-7.

The Nucleoli

As mentioned earlier, the unusual nucleolar system in slugs, previously described by Bridgeford and Pelluet (6), was the object of principal interest in this investigation. According to their description the primary nucleolus, which was present in the youngest and smallest oocytes, underwent cyclical changes from acidophilic to basophilic and back to acidophilic; the secondary nucleoli were never basophilic, and seemed to arise from the primary nucleoli during growth and development. Although no direct evidence of the origin of secondary nucleoli from the primary nucleolus was observed, the fact that the secondary nucleolus is always seen in direct contact with the primary nucleolus during the early part of its growth would tend to support their interpretation. In Figs. 8-10, the origin of the secondary nucleolus and the separation of the nucleoli in young oocytes are shown. In these pictures, the disparity in azure B bromide binding is also apparent between the two classes of nucleoli. The differences in volume do not seem great enough to account for the differences observed in the intensity of staining. Just as the cytoplasm appears to have a higher concentration of RNA in the smaller oocytes, there are some changes in intensity of staining in the very large primary nucleoli that suggest once more that the volume has increased at a higher rate than RNA. In the large nucleoli, some inhomogeneity in the distribution of RNA was observed. In most instances, the secondary nucleoli were less intensely stained, indicating a generally lower concentration of RNA; there was a greater variability in the intensity of basophilia in secondary nucleoli of a given size class than in primary nucleoli of the same size class. In material stained with the Feulgen reaction or with gallocyanin-chromalum after RNAase treatment, there was a perinucleolar binding of dye (Fig. 11) that was removable by prior incubation in DNAase. The periphery of the primary nucleolus also stained with fast green at *p*H 8.0, indicating the presence of histones (Fig. 7). The secondary nucleoli gave no evidence of such binding. Furthermore, only the primary nucleoli appeared to possess a mucopolysaccaride-containing envelope that stained with either the PAS reaction or alcian blue, and which was not removable with either 1 per cent malt diastase or 1 per cent hyaluronidase at 37°C for 4 hours (Figs. 6, 12). Both the

classes of nucleoli stained with the naphthol yellow S method of Deitch (10) for basic amino acids, and with apparently equal intensity (Fig. 13).

The primary nucleolus has a ring of DNA around it that may be chromatin associated with the nucleolus. The secondary nucleoli do not, since they are unable to bind dyes specific for DNA and histones. Furthermore, it is possible that the primary nucleoli possess some form of nucleolar membrane containing mucopolysaccharides that is not found in the secondary nucleoli. In view of the disparity in the concentration of RNA between the two types of nucleoli, it is particularly interesting that both seem to bind naphthol yellow S equally, so as to indicate the presence of dibasic amino acids, i.e. lysine, arginine, or histidine.

The cytochemical data gathered from these investigations are summarized in Table 1.

The diameters of all the nucleoli of both classes that were undamaged by sectioning were measured and the volumes of the two classes of nucleoli were compared in two ways. In Fig. 14 the volumes of the secondary

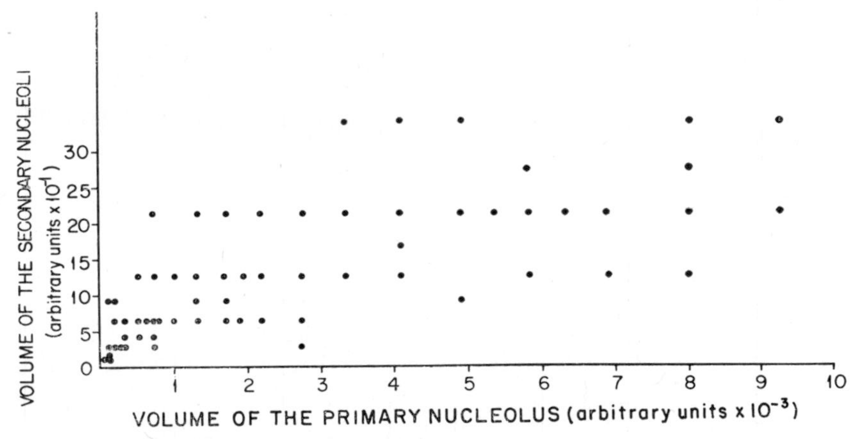

Fig. 14. A scatter diagram of the nucleolar volumes in single cells.

nucleoli were compared with the volumes of the primary nucleoli in each individual cell. The resulting scatter diagram indicated that there probably is no linear relationship between the sizes of the two classes of nucleoli. In Fig. 15 a frequency distribution is given of the ratio of volumes of primary to secondary nucleoli. Although the most common ratio observed was eight, i.e., the diameter of the secondary nucleolus is one-half that of the primary nucleolus, there was enough variation to invalidate any general statement about the parallel growth of the two classes of nucleoli.

TABLE 1

A SUMMARY OF THE CYTOCHEMICAL FINDINGS ON SLUG OOCYTES

Staining procedure	Stains	Oocyte cytoplasm	Oocyte chromosomes	Primary nucleolus	Secondary nucleolus
Feulgen	DNA	−	+	Periphery only	−
after DNAase	Removes DNA	Pink	−	Pink	−
Gallocyanin-chromalum					
after RNAase	DNA	−	+	Periphery only	−
after DNAase	RNA	+	−	+	+
Azure B bromide					
after RNAase	DNA	−	+	−	−
after DNAase	RNA	+	+ light	+	+ light
PAS	Mucopolysaccharides	+	−	+	−
after malt diastase	Removes glycogen	−	−	+	−
Alcian blue	Acid mucopolysaccharides	−	−	+	−
after hyaluronidase	Removes some ground substance	−	−	+	−
Naphthol yellow S	Basic proteins: dibasic amino acid residues of lysine, arginine, and histidine	+	−	+	+
Fast green	Histones	+	+	Periphery only	−
Pearse phospholipid	Phospholipids	+	−	Nucleolus stained red	−
after pyridine	Removes phospholipids	−	−	Nucleolus stained red	−
Sudan black B	Neutral fats	+	−	−	−

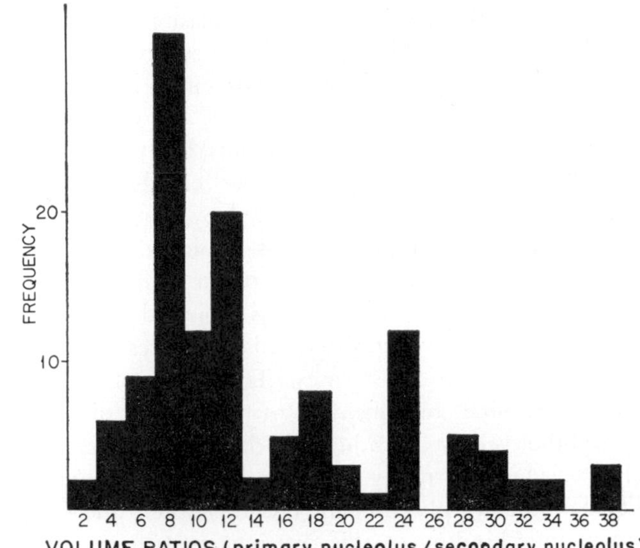

Fig. 15. The frequency distribution of classes of volume ratios between the primary and secondary nucleoli in the same cell.

Discussion

The chromosomes do not represent an unusual situation in any respect in this slug material. Characteristic of oogenesis, the "lamp-brush" stage was clearly observed, particularly in the material stained by gallocyanin-chromalum after incubation in RNAase. By diplotene the chromosomes had undergone considerable contraction, occupying only a small fraction of the nucleus.

The employment of gallocyanin-chromalum as a stain for DNA has vastly improved the quality of the staining of the chromosomes in oocyte material over that generally found in Feulgen-stained material. Although the Feulgen method has given excellent results in other types of tissues where the chromosomes were more condensed, in oocyte material it has left a great deal to be desired. This is particularly interesting since both these methods are supposedly qualitatively and quantitatively specific for DNA. Perhaps Wood's report (19) that the acid hydrolysis, which is an integral part of the Feulgen reaction, tends to remove a portion of the DNA accounts for this difference in intensity of staining. The difference in stain intensity may lie in the different mechanisms by which the two dyes attach to DNA.

The data concerning the distribution of cytoplasmic materials are about what one would expect from the previous descriptions of Brachet (4) and his school. The lack of nuclear phospholipids might be explained by the recent evidence introduced by Chayen, LaCour, and Gahan (8) that calcium formal does not fix nuclear phospholipids, but that Lewitsky's fixative (equal parts 10 per cent formalin and 1 per cent chromic acid) will fix this material so that it may be demonstrated by Berg's (3) benzpyrine-caffeine method. Otherwise the data are as would be expected, including the observed decrease in staining intensity of the cytoplasm of the larger oocytes. None of these staining methods was subjected to semiquantitation with a microphotometer; however, the visual differences were great enough to make this unnecessary in most cases. The most notable exception to this is the lysine, arginine, and histidine method where differences in the intensity of naphthol yellow S binding are difficult to assess visually. Fast green at *p*H 8.0, which normally stains basic nucleoproteins exclusively, was found to stain the cytoplasm of the oocytes. Alfert and Goldstein (2) observed cytoplasmic binding of this dye in a protozoan. In a personal communication, Alfert suggested that such cytoplasmic binding *might* be caused by accumulations of oxidative enzymes of the proper isoelectric point to bind fast green at *p*H 8.0. This possibility underlines the ease with which erroneous interpretations may be drawn from supposedly specific cytochemical reactions that depend on only the interaction of a basic or acidic dye at a particular *p*H with the material in question.

Most cytologists today accept the general conclusions of Caspersson (7), that the nucleolus is the principal site of RNA and protein synthesis, and that the function of the nucleolus is in some way influenced by the "nucleolus-associated chromatin" or nucleolar organizer. Recent evidence to support this has come from Lin (14), who found a linear increase in RNA per nucleolus in maize microsporocytes with each extra nucleolus organizer inserted in the genome. Taylor, McMaster, and Caluya (18) found that P^{32} was incorporated first into the nucleolar organizer, next into the nucleolus, and last into the chromosomes of *Drosophila* salivary gland cells. In the present investigation, the most obvious differences between the two classes of nucleoli concern the lack of DNA or histone associated with the secondary nucleoli. Since the secondary nucleolus seems to arise during the course of development from the primary nucleolus, it follows that the initial synthesis of RNA and protein probably was regulated by the primary nucleolus, and possibly under the control of the DNA and histone associated with the primary nucleolus. Since the secondary nucleoli seem to grow independently of primary nucleoli, and since the rate of growth

does not seem to be specifically controlled with respect to the rate of growth of the primary nucleolus, it is possible that the secondary nucleoli represent an independent center of RNA and protein synthesis.

Summary

1. The growth of the slug oocyte was studied cytochemically with respect to DNA, RNA, histones, basic proteins, mucopolysaccharides, and phospholipids.

2. It was discovered that the two classes of nucleoli found in the oocyte nuclei of some slug species are of different chemical composition.

3. A primary nucleolus is present from the beginning of oocyte growth throughout the life of the cell in the ovotestis. It is characterized by perinucleolar DNA, histone, and a mucopolysaccharide-containing nucleolar envelope; in common with the secondary nucleolus, it contains RNA and dibasic amino acid residues of lysine, arginine, and histidine.

4. Secondary nucleoli do not appear until later in the development of the oocyte and appear to arise from the primary nucleoli; while these nucleoli contain both RNA and the basic amino acids, lysine, arginine, and histidine, the concentration of the former is lower and much more variable in secondary nucleoli as compared to primary nucleoli of the same size class.

5. No consistent volume ratio relationship was observed to exist between the two classes of nucleoli.

6. From these observations, it is suggested that secondary nucleoli may represent independent centers of protein and RNA synthesis produced during the course of oocyte growth.

REFERENCES

1. Alfert, M., and Geschwind, I. I., *Proc. Natl. Acad. Sci. U. S.,* **39,** 991 (1953).
2. ———, and Goldstein, N. O., *J. Exptl. Zool.,* **130,** 403 (1955).
3. Berg, N. O., *Acta Pathol. Microbiol. Scand.,* Suppl., **90** (1951).
4. Brachet, J., *Chemical Embryology.* Interscience Publishers, New York (1950).
5. Bradley, M. V., *Stain Technol.,* **32,** 85 (1957).
6. Bridgeford, H. B., and Pelluet, D., *Can. J. Zool.,* **30,** 323 (1952).
7. Caspersson, T., *Cell Growth and Cell Function,* Van Nostrand, New York (1950).
8. Chayen, J., La Cour, L. F., and Gahan, P. B., *Nature,* **180,** 652 (1957).
9. Deitch, A., *Lab. Invest.,* **4,** 324 (1955).
10. ———, *Anat. Record,* **117,** 583 (1953).
11. Einarson, L., *Acta Pathol. Microbiol. Scand.,* **28,** 82 (1951).
12. Flax, M. H., and Himes, M. H., *Physiol. Zool.,* **25,** 297 (1951).
13. Kurnick, N. B., *Stain Technol.,* **30,** 213 (1955).
14. Lin, M., *Chromosoma,* **7,** 340 (1955).

15. Lison, L., *Stain Technol.*, **29**, 131 (1954).
16. Pearse, A. G. E., *J. Pathol. Bacteriol.*, **70**, 554 (1955).
17. Swift, H., in *The Nucleic Acids*, Vol. II (E. Chargaff, ed.), p. 51. Academic Press, New York (1955).
18. Taylor, J. H., McMasters, R. D., and Caluya, M. F., *Exptl. Cell Research*, **9**, 460 (1955).
19. Woods, P. S., *J. Biophys. Biochem. Cytol.*, **3**, 71 (1957).

DISCUSSION

DR. ALLEN: I would like to introduce a word of warning about the interpretation of staining properties underneath the fat cap of centrifuged eggs. It is seen that in the electron microscope studies, many of the heavy particles which it seems ought to be centrifuged down, simply don't move down in this area. So, if yolk granules are in this area, and you felt yolk granules give you artifactual results, they might give you false staining reactions.

DR. PASTEELS: Yes, but in the case of *Paracentrotus* you can see that there is no collection of granules under the oil cap. A very peculiar fact is that there is a correlation between the different zones of stratification of different eggs.

DR. WEBER: It bothers me a little bit that the localization of acid phosphatase differs in *Paracentrotus* and *Arbacia*. Did you try to detect the activity of this enzyme in particle fractions, isolated from homogenates?

DR. PASTEELS: No, we haven't done that. It will be done later, of course. We have only studied the Gomori reaction.

DR. SWIFT: I wondered about the localization of the metachromatic granules under the electron microscope and also where the annulate lamellae are in your scheme of things.

DR. PASTEELS: As for the annulate lamellae, in the case of *Arbacia*, they are probably just above the yolk region. Sometime ago there was some work done with the electron microscope by McCullough that showed lamellae in this region. However, I did not see anything of the metachromatic granules under the electron microscope. Perhaps they are too easily confused with the yolk platelets, or possibly they are not fixed with osmic acid. In the case of *Arbacia* these metachromatic granules are above the yolk and could be distinguished from the yolk. Dr. Mulnard has already made fixations for detecting these granules and I hope in a few weeks we will have the results of his studies.

DR. NOVIKOFF: Where is the Golgi material located in the striated egg?

DR. PASTEELS: The Golgi material is in the upper part of the yolk layer.

DR. NOVIKOFF: It is interesting that Golgi material and acid phosphatase activity are found in the same zone.

Our electron microscopic study, with Dr. de Duve, of the "lysosome" fraction isolated by him from liver led us to suggest the possibility that acid phosphatase (and the other hydrolytic enzymes) were localized in the peribiliary "dense bodies." In attempting to test this suggestion by the staining method for acid phosphatase, we have been impressed with the similar locations of acid phos-

phatase-rich granules and Golgi apparatus. In three experimental situations we have studied, when the granules move away from the bile canaliculus region so does the Golgi apparatus.

I wonder, Dr. Pasteels, if you would comment on the fact that in your photographs the stain for acid phosphatase activity seemed diffuse, whereas in liver (and kidney, too) we always find it associated with particles about the size of small mitochondria.

Dr. Pasteels: Yes, but perhaps this is a matter of fixation techniques. We fix these in cold calcium saline formol.

Dr. Novikoff: We fix them in the same medium.

Dr. Flexner: I wonder if Dr. Pasteels wouldn't like to add the fluorescent antibody technique to his array of cytochemical techniques. You gave us a very adequate coverage of the pitfalls and advantages of cytochemical techniques, Dr. Pasteels, and I wondered if you would not like to add the fluorescent antibody technique to your arsenal.

Dr. Pasteels: Yes, we certainly would like to try this technique in the future.

CHANGES IN ENZYMATIC PATTERNS DURING DEVELOPMENT

S. C. SHEN *

Osborn Zoological Laboratory, Yale University
New Haven, Connecticut

THE CONCEPT of a chemical basis of embryonic development derives, though not its very origin, a major source of inspiration from the discovery of the phenomenon of embryonic induction. For over thirty years, a vigorous search has been sustained for some chemically identifiable substance or substances that might act as a causal agent in initiating early embryogenesis. The implication was that the chemical nature of such an agent, if and when discovered and understood, would provide a powerful clue to the chain of events it initiates or catalyzes, first in chemical terms, then translated into biological terms. The outcome of many years' extensive investigation with this objective in mind, unfortunately, has not thus far yielded information as illuminating as it was optimistically anticipated. In the light of our newer knowledge of protein synthesis, and aided by technical advances in chemistry and physical optics, the problem of embryonic induction is being investigated with renewed vigor and sophistication in the hands of some particularly valiant and capable embryologists. Rewarding results are beginning to emerge from these investigations (29). Encouraged by these and perhaps more significantly by the enviably successful work of the geneticists, particularly the microbial geneticists, there has been a phenomenal trend in the past decade toward a mass transformation of experimental embryologists into what are now known as molecular biologists. This extraordinarily rapid advance of the frontier of embryology from study of the whole embryo to one of submicroscopic dimensions of life inevitably leaves behind it a vast territory in which a prodigious number of mopping up operations remain to be carried out if some sort of tangible communication between the front and the rear echelons is to be established.

It is this scarcely explored land that is assigned to the cytochemists as their base of operation. Their task is a challenging one: to reorient the

* Present address: Department of Anatomy, College of Physicians and Surgeons, Columbia University, New York, N. Y.

extracted macromolecules in their proper perspective or, conversely, to identify their orientation in vivo. It is surely too elementary a thought to suggest that a particular species of macromolecule, were it to give rise to a specific biological structure or function, must not only be present in quantitative adequacy but also with spatial specificity at a given time of the developmental processes. Enzymes, as species of specific protein molecules, must also conform to such requirements whether they act as causative agents or are present merely as end-products of protein synthesis. Evidences from contemporary enzymology strongly suggest that most, if not all, intracellular enzymes are structurally bound in the living system. It is a moot question whether such enzymes may be regarded as structural proteins even if they can be solubilized or crystallized by very drastic means.

The present discussion therefore attempts to focus our attention on the change of enzyme patterns not as patterns of abstract curves of enzyme content or because of their metabolic implications, but rather as structural patterns formed on a histological or cytological level during embryogenesis. There are a number of recent reviews summarizing and evaluating a considerable body of observations on changes in the enzyme content of embryo or tissue homogenates (1, 20).

Distribution of Enzymes

In recent years, embryologists interested in developmental enzymology have become increasingly aware of the possibility that an unequal distribution of enzymes among different cell types, or within a given cell at different stages of development, may illuminate the chemical basis of cellular differentiation. With sufficient refinement, techniques for enzyme assays applicable to embryo or tissue homogenates can also be applied, with comparable quantitative precision in some instances, to a single cell. The chief difficulty is, however, in the isolation of a single cell from a multicellular system without radically altering its structure and physiological properties. Spratt (28) has shown that an isolated piece of chick blastoderm exhibits a very different cytochemical behavior from that of the same piece in situ. It is quite apparent that practically all the inherent weaknesses in enzyme assay techniques of homogenates are present in cytochemical staining of tissue sections. The chief advantage of the latter technique is that it does preserve to a large extent structural orientations of individual cells as well as cell-to-cell relations. Under suitable conditions, enzyme localization may be resolved to subcellular dimensions. It thus enables one to see, as it were, both the topography of a forest and the characteristics of individual trees. Such information would provide, in part, a useful background for conceiv-

ing the process of embryogenesis basically as one of cellular and ultimately molecular ecology.

The major criticism against the present-day techniques of enzyme cytochemistry is their lack of quantitative precision as compared with direct chemical analysis. No one would wish to contest such a criticism; there is however no need for undue pessimism that available techniques cannot be so improved upon as to yield meaningful quantitative data. Indeed, one should be much encouraged by the successful photometric measurement of cytochemical reactions of nucleotides in the cell nucleus. To discredit the contributions of cytochemistry because of the present inadequacy in quantitative precision is like discrediting the anatomical and cytological descriptions upon which rest the validity of experimental biologists. At present, enzyme cytochemists are more preoccupied with the following problems: (1) to devise methods for detecting and localizing enzymes that have hitherto eluded cytochemical procedures; (2) to minimize structural and chemical damage to cells by cytochemical manipulations; and (3) to increase the resolution of enzyme localization by minimizing diffusion artifacts and by reducing the dimensions of the visualized products. To determine the precise distributional patterns of enzyme molecules on biological fine structures must surely be among the fondest hopes of cytochemists, electron-microscopists and, possibly, molecular embryologists.

Mitochondrial Enzymes in Embryogenesis

The cell nucleus is generally regarded as the exclusive domain of the geneticists. Embryologists who are interested in cellular differentiation must content themselves with the remainder of the cell: the cytoplasm and the cell membrane. Fortunately, the cytoplasm alone appears to be sufficiently complex and intriguing to divert the embryologists. Within the resolving power of the optical microscope, mitochondrial particles are perhaps the most unique among cytoplasmic inclusions. Embryologists have long suspected that mitochondria have an important role in cytodifferentiation and embryogenesis. For example, mitochondria in myoblasts were believed to be the actual precursors of myofibrils (11). Independently, chemical embryologists, not particularly impressed by the fine points of cytology, were largely concerned with cellular respiration and the oxidative enzymes as clues to developmental processes. The postulation of an oxidation-reduction gradient or field in developing embryos has long dominated the thinking in causal embryology. The remarkable discovery in recent years of the fact that mitochondria are virtually the exclusive loci of oxidative and phosphorylating enzymes, among others, has profoundly